BIBLIOTHECA MYCOLOGICA

HERAUSGEGEBEN VON

J. CRAMER

BAND 4a

BRITISH
STEM- AND LEAF-FUNGI
(COELOMYCETES)

by

W. B. GROVE

VOLUME I

REPRINT 1967

3301 LEHRE

VERLAG VON J. CRAMER

WHELDON & WESLEY, LTD. AND STECHERT-HAFNER SERVICE AGENCY, INC.

CODICOTE, HERTS.   NEW YORK, N.Y.

REPRINTED 1967

BY PERMISSION
OF THE ORIGINAL PUBLISHER
BY

VERLAG VON J. CRAMER · 3301 LEHRE

PRINTED IN GERMANY

THE BRITISH COELOMYCETES

BRITISH
STEM- AND LEAF-FUNGI
(COELOMYCETES)

*A Contribution to
Our Knowledge of the Fungi Imperfecti
Belonging to the Sphaeropsidales
and the Melanconiales*

BY

W. B. GROVE, M.A.

VOLUME I

SPHAEROPSIDALES

To the end of the Sphaerioideae which
have colourless or nearly
colourless spores

CAMBRIDGE
AT THE UNIVERSITY PRESS
1935

TO THE

Professor of Botany
in the University of Manitoba

A. H. REGINALD BULLER, F.R.S.
Author of *Researches on Fungi*,

Whose long-continued friendship with me,
founded securely upon a common love of the study of plants,
has been one of the brightest episodes
of my life

"The world is so full of a number of things."

R. L. S.

PREFACE

Of all the vast hosts of Fungi that beautify and diversify the vegetation of the world, there are two groups that stand high above the others in their great economic importance.

The first of these is the Rust Fungi (Uredinales), represented in Britain by about 260 species which work mischief in our gardens and the countryside; of these I treated in my *British Rust Fungi*, published more than twenty years ago. The second is the group to which in 1919[1] I gave the name Coelomycetes (the Sphaeropsidales and Melanconiales), a group belonging to what are called "Imperfect Fungi", but infesting leaves and stems just as the Uredinales do, and probably no less effective than the Uredinales in causing loss and disfigurement. It is true that, in books, their ravages are usually credited to what are called their "Perfect" stages, but it remains, nevertheless, a fact that the greater part of the harm which is done by them is done during their "Imperfect" stages. The Coelomycetous section of the "Imperfect Fungi" to be treated of in these volumes numbers more than 2000 reputed British species, and many of these are well-known despoilers of our field-crops, our orchards, and our woods.

It is now sixty-three years since the famous mycologist, M. C. Cooke, in his *Handbook of British Fungi* (1871) devoted 62 pages to the Coelomycetes (which he reckoned as a part of the Coniomycetes), and in those pages he enumerated just over 200 species. Since that time no comprehensive account of the subject has appeared in this country, and the present work is an attempt to fill the gap.

All the species here described have been seen and microscopically examined, except where the contrary is indicated. The specimens of Coelomycetes collected by the revered forefathers of the study of Fungi—Fries, Corda, Persoon, Léveillé, Desmazières and their disciples—and now counted among the treasures of the great Herbaria at Kew and at the British Museum, have been carefully compared with those collected in this country by Berkeley, Broome, Plowright, Cooke,

---

[1] *Journal of Botany*, 1919, p. 208.

Massee, and many others. In addition, there are preserved in my own herbarium over 3000 specimens of the British Coelomycetes. Many of these I have gathered in the field during the past half-century, but many have been kindly sent to me by my excellent co-workers of more recent times—the late D. A. Boyd of Saltcoats and J. W. Ellis of Liverpool, as well as one who, unhappily, has been quite recently torn from us by a tragical and early death, the Rev. P. G. M. Rhodes, D.D., of Oscott and Evesham, to whose uncanny skill in detecting microfungi in the field I am especially indebted. There are many other correspondents, like Professor J. W. H. Trail of Aberdeen, Dr Jessie S. Bayliss Elliott, Mr W. G. Travis, and Mr F. Rilstone, who have contributed fewer but still occasionally rare and valuable species and whose names are mentioned in their places.

My thanks are due to Professor A. H. R. Buller for his great aid in furtherance of the work, and to Mr C. G. C. Chesters for his help in completing the illustrations. I wish also to put on record my acknowledgment of the kindness of the authorities of the Royal Botanic Gardens at Kew and of the British Museum at South Kensington for placing at my disposal all needful facilities.

The present volume includes all the British Sphaeropsidales to the end of the SCOLECOSPORAE; the remainder of them and the Melanconiales, which embrace species of greater beauty and complexity, will form a second volume of about the same size.

The account given of each species is in the main purely morphological; few pathological or cultural details are included, except very briefly. This is intentional. The two departments of Mycology, as experience many times has shown, are best treated by specialists, but working in happy conjunction. Even if the author had wished to combine the two rôles—from the Elysian Fields the poet of Venusia (brought up to date) might have wisely whispered:

Non cuivis homini contingeret esse Klebahno.

BIRMINGHAM.   W. B. G.
December 1934

CONTENTS

VOLUME I

ABBREVIATIONS

Wk.   = Warwicks. = Warwickshire ⎫
Ws.   = Worcs.   = Worcestershire ⎬ The three counties sur-
St.   = Staffs.   = Staffordshire ⎭ rounding Birmingham.

p.p.   = in part only.

q.v.   = which see (singular), in the text.

qq.v.   = which see (plural).

n.v.   = *non vidi* (I have not seen a British specimen).

n.ex.   = specimen seen, but not examined microscopically.

T.B.M.S. = Transactions of the British Mycological Society.

All.   = Rabenhorst's Kryptogamen-Flora: vol. i, Die Pilze, Abth. vi (1901) and Abth. vii (1903), by A. Allescher.

Died.   = Kryptogamen-Flora der Mark Brandenburg, Pilze, vii (1915), by H. Diedicke.

Mig.   = Kryptogamen-Flora von Deutschland, Deutsch-Oesterreich, und der Schweiz (1921), by W. Migula.

Trav.   = Flora Italica Cryptogama. Pars i, Fungi, vol. ii, fasc. 1 (1906), by J. B. Traverso.

Volume and page of a serial publication are cited thus: ix. 114 = vol. 9, p. 114.

In all other citations the letter p. (page) is usually omitted only when no other Arabic numeral occurs besides the page number.

Square brackets are used to enclose the particulars of any species which has been wrongly reported as British, as well as of a few which (though likely to grow here) have not yet been found.

FUNGI IMPERFECTI

INTRODUCTION

Those fungi which do not bear their spores on typical basidia (Basidiomycetes) or in asci (Ascomycetes), but nevertheless have septate mycelium like those two groups, are called Imperfect Fungi. It is believed that most of these, perhaps all, are not autonomous, i.e. are not self-subsistent species, independent of other fungi, but are merely stages in the growth and development of the Perfect Fungi, i.e. of Basidiomycetes or of Ascomycetes, and chiefly of the latter group. On this account Saccardo called them Deuteromycetes.

They may be divided into two large classes: (1) those which bear their spores *within some cavity* of the matrix on which they grow: to these I have given the name COELOMYCETES;[1] and (2) those which bear their spores *outside* the matrix, although of course the mycelium may often be, for the most part, hidden within that matrix; these have long been known as HYPHOMYCETES.[2] It is the former class that is treated of in this work.

The COELOMYCETES may be further subdivided into two sections or orders: (1) those which have the spore-bearing cavity surrounded by a special structure formed of mycelial hyphae and extending more or less above, below, and around the cavity; this structure is called a *pycnidium*, and the order is known as the SPHAEROPSIDALES; and (2) those in which the layer of hyphae producing the spores lies mainly or solely at the bottom of the cavity, the rest of the cavity being surrounded by the tissues of the host-matrix alone; these are called MELANCONIALES, the basal stratum being known as the proliferous layer and the mass of spores as a *pustule*.

---

[1] Greek κοῖλος, *hollow*.
[2] It need not be said at this time of day that such verbal distinctions cannot be perfect. It passes the wit of man to elaborate for natural objects a definition to which there will be no exception.

The distinction formerly drawn between these two orders cannot logically be made absolute. There are numerous cases where the peridium, though present, is scanty or hardly perceptible, and moreover the same fungus may have no peridium at one period of its growth and yet a well-developed peridium at another period, as is shown by many species of *Phomopsis* and *Phleospora*. Hence the invention of the term COELOMYCETES, the only term which includes both these orders under a common title. The separation into two sections, however, is still helpful for systematic clearness and will be retained for that purpose.

Each of these orders may be divided into subordinate groups and finally into genera, according to certain differences which they exhibit, e.g. whether a stroma is present or not, what is the form and character of the sporophores on which the spores are borne, and, finally and most importantly, what is the shape and colour of the spores themselves. This classification does not indicate to the same degree as in the higher plants the genetic relationships of genera and species among themselves; some authors, therefore, prefer to use the designations *form*-genera and so on. But, if the fact is once admitted, the prefix may with advantage be dropped in practice.

The definition of the species in a genus is often extremely difficult, or even quite impossible, on mere morphological grounds, and may therefore be compelled for the present to rest upon a difference of the host. In the genera *Cytospora*, *Phomopsis*, *Septoria*, and the like, the list of presumed species cannot be considered as anything but an interim catalogue of the known and described forms. Yet even here, on the whole, the evidence available in the field tends to show that two allied fungi growing upon two different hosts may themselves be equally different. Therefore, generally, in these pages the host will be made the supreme test.

In this work the species in the larger genera, such as *Phyllosticta* and *Phoma*, are arranged on the basis of the host-genera in alphabetical order, with certain useful modifications which are stated in each case; in the small genera this modification is not needed. Described species have not been united, unless

convincing evidence was available; in other cases mere suggestions are made, or the opinions of other authors are quoted.

After the name adopted for each species, the second one, if with another generic but the same specific appellation, is that conferred upon it by the original discoverer or describer. The rest are considered to be synonyms. I have ventured to correct the spelling of the names whenever the rules of etymology seemed to require it.

One result of the re-examination of a large number of the British type-specimens of Berkeley and Cooke has been the correction of certain errors and oversights which crept into the third volume of Saccardo's *Sylloge*. Corrections of a similar character regarding non-British species have been already published in the *Kew Bulletin*: Part I in 1919, pp. 177–201; Part II in 1919, pp. 425–45; and Part III in 1921, pp. 136–57.

The short Latin diagnoses of the new species described for the first time in the present volume are placed in an Appendix at the end. In addition, I have many specimens to which, as yet, no name can be assigned. In fact, so numerous are these Imperfect Fungi, so pullulating is the race, that it would be only a slight exaggeration to say that, at any time of the year, in any suitable locality, an ardent coelomycetologist might without difficulty collect a number of forms which no one as yet has ever seen in this country.

COELOMYCETES

Spores produced on simple or branched sporophores within a cavity of the matrix.

The group comprises two Orders:

I. SPHAEROPSIDALES

In these the cavity is more or less surrounded by one or more layers of fungal cells which form a peridium, the whole structure being called a pycnidium.

A. Pycnidia complete all round, usually opening when mature by a mouth (pore or ostiole).

    a. Pycnidia membranaceous, coriaceous, or carbonaceous, more or less dark-coloured . . . . SPHAERIOIDEAE

    b. Pycnidia soft, fleshy, clear-coloured (whitish, yellow, or red) . . . . NECTRIOIDEAE

B. Pycnidia not complete all round, always dark-coloured.

    a. Pycnidia at first closed, then losing the upper part and becoming ± saucer-shaped . . . . EXCIPULACEAE

    b. Pycnidia more or less dimidiate, i.e. shield-shaped and composed as it were of the upper part only of a pycnidium
                                           LEPTOSTROMATACEAE

II. MELANCONIALES

In these a peridium is nearly or completely wanting, the mass of spores being called a pustule.

SPHAERIOIDEAE

A. Spores colourless or very faintly coloured.

    a. Spores not more than a few times longer than broad.

        1. Spores continuous . . . . HYALOSPORAE

        2. Spores uniseptate . . . . HYALODIDYMAE

    b. Spores more elongated.

        1. Spores oblong or ± fusoid, mostly with two or more transverse septa . . . . HYALOPHRAGMIAE

        2. Spores filiform, septate or not . . . SCOLECOSPORAE

B. Spores more or less strongly coloured.

    a. Spores short or with not more than one septum.

        1. Spores continuous . . . . PHAEOSPORAE

        2. Spores uniseptate . . . . PHAEODIDYMAE

    b. Spores elongated; two or more septa.

        1. Spores transversely septate only . . PHAEOPHRAGMIAE

        2. Spores muriform . . . . DICTYOSPORAE

HYALOSPORAE

Spores eseptate, unicellular, colourless or nearly so.

SECTION I. *Pycnidia without any stroma*

I. Pycnidia obtuse or shortly papillate, tending to be thin-walled, parenchymatous or prosenchymatous, cells not sclerotioid.
- A. Pycnidia glabrous.
  - *a.* Without or with little hyphal subiculum . . **Phomeae**
  - *b.* With an extensive hyphal subiculum . . . *Asteroma*
  - *c.* In or on Erysipheae . . . . *Cicinnobolus*
- B. Pycnidia with external bristles . . . . *Pyrenochaeta*

II. Pycnidia often with very thick walls, cells ± sclerotioid except when young.
- A. No distinct sporophores visible at maturity.
  - *a.* Pycnidia almost superficial . . . . . *Plenodomus*
  - *b.* Pycnidia immersed, then erumpent . . *Sclerophoma*
- B. Sporophores at maturity quite distinct . . *Phomopsis* [1]

III. Pycnidia beaked . . . . *Sphaeronaema*

SECTION II. *Pycnidia provided with a stroma*

I. Stroma not valsoid.
- A. Pycnidia botryosely aggregated on the stroma . *Dothiorella*
- B. Pycnidia immersed in the stroma.
  - *a.* Stroma flat, thin; spores cylindric or ovoid *Placosphaeria*
  - *b.* Stroma convex, thick; spores ellipsoid . . *Rabenhorstia*

II. Stroma valsoid.
- A. Spores large, ellipsoid or subfusoid . . . . *Fusicoccum*
- B. Spores small, allantoid; sporophores long, linear or subulate . . . . *Cytospora*
- C. Spores cylindrical . . . . *Ceuthospora*

[1] The pycnidia of *Phomopsis* on herbaceous stems are, when young, very like those of *Phoma*, but usually have fusoid spores on long and persistent sporophores, and very often each pycnidium is surrounded by a little blackish area or halo.

PHOMEAE

A. Pycnidia not at first superficial, ± erumpent.

    a. Spores simple, without appendages.

        1. Sporophores imperceptible or short.

            α. Pycnidia not within anthers.

                * Pycnidia thin-walled, mostly on leaves . *Phyllosticta*

              ** Pycnidia thicker-walled, mostly on stems.

                    † Spores rarely more than 15μ long . .   *Phoma*

                    †† Spores more than 15μ long . . . *Macrophoma*

            β. Pycnidia within anthers .   .   .   . *Hapalosphaeria*

        2. Sporophores longer.

            α. Sporophores simple .   .   .   .   . *Clinterium*

            β. Sporophores branched .   .   .   . *Dendrophoma*

    b. Spores simple, furnished with mucoid appendages at the apex. .   .   .   . *Neottiospora*

    c. Spores concatenate .   .   .   . *Sirococcus*

B. Pycnidia superficial from the first.

    a. Spores small.

        1. Pycnidia on wood .   .   .   . *Aposphaeria*

        2. Pycnidia on needles of Conifers .   .   . *Rhizosphaera*

    b. Spores large and round .   . [*Mycogala* and *Pleosporopsis*]

For the rejected genus *Polyopeus*, see p. 162.

PHYLLOSTICTA "Pers." Fr. Syst. Myc. ii. 527.

Pycnidia globose, lens-shaped, hemispherical, or subconical, immersed in the host-tissue, at first covered by the epidermis, afterwards erumpent and more or less projecting, typically completely enclosed by an all-round thin parenchymatous or plectenchymatous wall (peridium), furnished with a distinct ostiole. Spores always small, continuous, oval, oblong, or sub-cylindric, hyaline or very faintly coloured, mostly biguttulate; sporophores simple, short, always inconspicuous. (Figs. 1 and 2.)

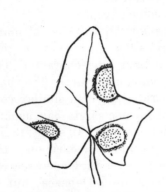

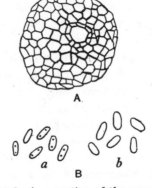

Fig. 1. *Phyllosticta hedericola* on Ivy leaf, showing three "spots" produced on the leaf by the fungus. The pycnidia are seen as black dots scattered over the spots; reduced.

Fig. 2. A, a portion of the pycnidial wall of *Phyllosticta prunicola*, including the ostiole, as seen under the micro-scope. B, spores of *a*, *Ph. brassicicola*, and of *b*, *Ph. hedericola*, both × 750.

Almost all the species occur on leaves, in which they produce a distinct "spot", i.e. a more or less rounded area which is killed by the mycelium and consequently becomes discoloured. This spot is at first usually dark in colour, becoming paler from the centre outwards and sometimes even nearly white; but it generally remains darker at the margin, and is often surrounded, while fresh, by a differently coloured zone of leaf-tissue which is not yet killed. The dead portion may drop out, leaving a "shot-hole", such as can also be produced by other leaf-fungi.

The best distinction between Phoma and Phyllosticta has been much disputed. Allescher adopted the strict rule: "*Phyllosticta* upon leaves (except those of Conifers), *Phoma* upon any other part of the plant*"*. This is quite meaningless, for many Phyllostictas attack leaves and stems of a plant, indiscriminately. The true distinction is rather a biological one—*Phyllosticta* is usually a parasite (holoparasite); *Phoma* is a saprophyte or a facultative parasite (generally, if not always, a wound-parasite); therefore Phyllosticta is mostly confined to the "spot", which it kills. Also usually, perhaps always, the peridium of a Phyllosticta is thin and translucent, not composed of dark firm-walled (pseudo)parenchymatous cells like that of a typical Phoma. But no distinction can be made to which there will not be some exceptions.

In Coniothyrium the spores are similar to those of many Phyllostictas, and remain colourless for so long a time that only persistent search will reveal their true character. The spores of Ascochyta also, when young, are exactly like those of Phyllosticta, and since the peridia are also similar confusion is easy, but the septum of an Ascochyta can usually be seen on looking for it in the older pycnidia. In some species of these two genera only empty pycnidia or even only the "spot" may be discoverable, except after prolonged search; such were placed by Fries in the section Depazea, but in many of these spores have since been found. A curious, and as yet unexplained, phenomenon is that some species of Phyllosticta, e.g. *Ph. Ruborum* Sacc., *Ph. Ericae* All., frequently have Cytospora-like spores intermingled in large numbers with the normal ones. It is also notable that in many species a Phyllosticta is accompanied or followed by a Septoria on the same plant, presumably as a part of the same life-cycle.

The species of Phyllosticta that follow are arranged in the alphabetic order of the genera of the hosts, except that those living on the Rose family (being numerous) are for better comparison listed together under the title ROSACEAE, and that the monocotyledonous and cryptogamic hosts are placed after the others. A similar plan will be followed in most of the other large genera of the Coelomycetes. For the sake of

definiteness, in quoting the shortened form of the names belonging to *Phyllosticta* and *Phoma, Ph.* will always be used for the former and *P.* for the latter.

Acer

Phyllosticta Aceris Sacc. Syll. iii. 14. All. vi. 16. Died. 16. Mig. 5. *Ascochyta Aceris* Sacc. Myc. Ven. 194.

Spots subcircular, up to 5–10 mm. across or more, on drying becoming ochraceous or ochraceous-brown, with a faint darker border line. Pycnidia clustered in the middle of the spot and forming a hard lump there, epiphyllous or rarely hypophyllous, punctiform, globose or lens-shaped, just perforating the epidermis, black, pierced by a pore. Spores ovoid or ovoid-oblong, often biguttulate, $5-7 \times 2 \cdot 5-3 \mu$.

On living leaves of *Acer campestre.* Kent; Sussex; Surrey; Warwicks.; Worcs.; etc. Jul.–Sept.

There were slight indications in the spores of the Sussex and Warwickshire specimens that they might ultimately develop into an Ascochyta.

Fr. Germ. Denm. Ital.

Phyllosticta campestris Pass. *in litt. apud* Brun. in Rev. Mycol. 1886, p. 139. Sacc. Syll. x. 108. All. vi. 17. Died. 15.

Spots visible on both sides, bounded by the veins, angular, fuscous, then paler in the middle, often confluent and spreading widely. Pycnidia amphigenous, scattered, lenticular, somewhat projecting, $60-100\mu$ diam., parenchymatous, brown. Spores oblong, eguttulate, $2-3 \times 1\mu$.

On seedlings of *Acer campestre.* Woodstock, Oxon. (Rhodes). Oct.

Very probably nothing but a younger state of the preceding species.

Phyllosticta Platanoidis Sacc. Syll. iii. 13. All. vi. 16. Died. 17. Mig. 227.

Spots none or rather indistinct. Pycnidia hypophyllous, densely gregarious and collected here and there into little groups, immersed, globose, blackish, $60-100\mu$ diam., pierced by a pore; texture very pale brown, thin and translucent, pseudopycnidial. Spores cylindrical, straight, $4-6 \times 0 \cdot 5-1\mu$, rounded at both ends each of which has usually an indistinct guttule, and for that reason often appearing subconstricted in the middle.

On fading cotyledons of *Acer Pseudoplatanus*, West Kilbride, Ayrshire (Boyd), June. On leaves of the same, Epsom,
Sept. On seedlings of *Acer Pseudoplatanus*, Gower peninsula
(Ellis). On fading leaves of young seedling plants of *Acer
platanoides*, Heythrop Park, Oxon., in November, the affected
parts remaining green longer than the other parts (Grove and
Rhodes); Himley Park, St.

Accompanied by *Phleospora Pseudoplatani* Bubák, of which it
appears to be the forerunner. They can both be found on the same
spot; these spots, which are roundish and about 4–5 mm. broad, seem
to be caused chiefly by the Phleospora; the pustules of the latter are
amphigenous, while the pycnidia of the Phyllosticta are entirely
hypophyllous and frequently make a dense border around the spot.
On the mature leaves these spots closely resemble those of *Leptothyrium Platanoidis* Pass., which doubtless belongs to the same life-
cycle; in fact the two forms (*Phyllosticta* and *Leptothyrium*) may often
be found on the same leaf.
Germ. N. Amer.

Aegopodium

Phyllosticta Aegopodii All. in Hedwig. 1895, xxxiv. 256; Rab.
Kr. Flor. vi. 100. Died. 18. Mig. 38. T.B.M.S. 1912, iv. 173. *Sphaeria
Aegopodii* Curr. Simpl. Sphaer. 332.

Spots not distinct at first, but gradually becoming dingy-
brown and spreading over the whole leaf. Pycnidia mostly
hypophyllous, scattered or congregate, lens-shaped, immersed,
then free, 80–100μ diam., with an indistinct plectenchymatous texture, dark-brown. Spores numerous, cylindrical,
straight, obtuse at both ends, 5–7 × 0·5–1μ.

On living or fading leaves of *Aegopodium Podagraria* often
in company with *Phleospora Aegopodii* = *Septoria Podagrariae*.
Renfrewshire; Ayrshire; Lanarkshire (Boyd).   Jun. Jul.

In these specimens the spores were rather ellipsoid, 3–5 × 1–2μ, and
the pycnidia were smaller, 65–75μ. It is an early stage of the Phleospora, and both, as proved by Potebnia (Ann. Myc. viii. 59), are the
pycnidia of *Mycosphaerella Aegopodii* Pot.
Germ.

Aesculus

Phyllosticta Paviae Desm. in Ann. Sci. Nat. 1847, viii. 32. Sacc.
Syll. iii. 4. All. vi. 62. Duggar, 345.

Spots rufous, irregular, beginning at the tip and along the
margin, extending irregularly inwards, with a broad yellow
border. Pycnidia small, epiphyllous, scattered or crowded,

occupying only portions of the spots, convex, then depressed, becoming black. Spores cylindric-ellipsoid, biguttulate, 10–12μ long.

On leaves of *Aesculus parviflora* (*Pavia macrostachya*). Kew Gardens. Autumn.

"The leaf-blotch caused by this fungus is probably the most important malady of the Horse-chestnut. The irregular spots develop rapidly as the season advances, and the larger part of the leaf may become involved, from the margin to the midrib, as if sunburned" (Duggar, of the American disease).

Fr. Belg. Austr. U.S.A.

Ajuga

Phyllosticta Ajugae Sacc. & Sp. Syll. iii. 50. All. vi. 100. Died. 19.

Spots various, 2–6 mm. broad, numerous, pale ochraceous when dry, with a fuscous border. Pycnidia few, scattered, globose, rather prominent, 90–100μ diam., pierced at the summit; texture loosely parenchymatous, smoky-brown. Spores ovate-ellipsoid, straight or curvulous, occasionally biguttulate, 7–8 × 2·5–3μ.

On living leaves of *Ajuga reptans*. Lyndhurst; Aberdeen; Ayrshire; Argyllshire; Co. Mayo, Ireland. Autumn.

Sometimes associated with *Ramularia Ajugae* Niessl. The spots are much like those of *Ph. Glechomae*, but larger.

Fr. Ital. ? Germ.

Anemone

Phyllosticta Hepaticae Brun. in Act. Soc. Linn. Bord. 1890, p. 33. Sacc. Syll. xi. 477. All. vi. 101. Died. 58. Mig. 47.

Spots marginal, thence spreading all over the leaf, sharply margined with a blood-red border, becoming cinereous within. Pycnidia scattered over the paler part, epiphyllous, subglobose, not protruding, opening with a round pore, 100–150μ diam.; texture parenchymatous, fuliginous. Spores ovoid, 7–8 × 2·5–3μ.

On fading leaves of *Anemone Hepatica* (*Hepatica triloba*). West Kilbride, Ayrshire (Boyd). Sept.

Fr. Germ.

Angelica

Phyllosticta Angelicae Sacc. Syll. iii. 46. All. vi. 102. Died. 23. Mig. 38.

Spots grey, indeterminate. Pycnidia hypophyllous, aggregated in little groups which are bounded by the venules,

lens-shaped, 80–90μ in diam., pierced at the summit; texture
loosely parenchymatous. "Spores oblong, 4–5 × 1μ."

On living or fading leaves of *Angelica silvestris*. Highgate
(Cooke). Ayrshire (Boyd).   Nov.

Said to be the pycnidium of *Phyllachora Angelicae* Fckl. All the
specimens that I have seen were barren.
Fr. Germ. Ital.

Antirrhinum
Phyllosticta Antirrhini Syd. in Hedwig. 1899, xxxviii. (134).
Gard. Chron. 1924, p. 150. Mig. 38. ? *Phoma oleracea* var. *Antirrhini*
Sacc. Syll. iii. 135. *Phoma poolensis* Taubenh. Dis.Greenhouse Crops,
1919, p. 203.

Spots visible on both sides of the leaf, pallid above, green
beneath, mostly on the margin or at the tip, up to 1 cm.
across, bordered, sometimes subzonate. Pycnidia epiphyllous,
roundish, scattered or somewhat gregarious, blackish-brown,
100–180μ diam. Spores oblong, colourless, eguttulate, 4–6 ×
1·5–2μ.

On living stems (near the base), seed-capsules, and leaves
of cultivated *Antirrhinum*. Surrey; Middlesex; Bucks.; Norfolk; Berks.; Herts.; Warwicks.; etc.

Sometimes listed as *Phoma Antirrhini* when it occurs on stems, in
which it causes a stem-rot and can survive the winter.
Germ. U.S.A. (on *Pentstemon* also).

Apium
Phyllosticta Apii Halsted, in Rep. New Jers. Agric. St. 1891,
p. 253, with fig. Sacc. Syll. xi. 478. All. vi. 102. Massee, Dis. Cult.
Pl. ed. II, p. 567.

Spots brown, large. Pycnidia numerous, punctiform, globose, black, pierced at the summit by an impressed pore.
Spores ovoid-oblong, not guttulate, 5–7 × 3–4μ.

On leaves of *Apium graveolens*. Recorded as British by
Massee, but I have seen no specimens. Cf. *Phoma apiicola*.

North Amer.

Arbutus
Phyllosticta Arbuti Sacc. Syll. iii. 23. All. vi. 21. *Cheilaria*
Arbuti Desm. in Ann. Sci. Nat. 1846, vi. 68. Cooke, Handb. 454.

Spots minute, dark coloured. Pycnidia epiphyllous,
crowded, erumpent, very minute, roundish-oblong, black,
shining, dehiscing by a longitudinal fissure or a pore. "Spores
ovoid, biguttulate, 5μ long."

On dead leaves of *Arbutus Unedo*. Kew Gardens; Highgate; Swanscombe; Shrewsbury; Kemerton. Nov.–Jan.

It is found nearly always (in *all* British specimens) in the sporeless (Depazea) state, and is probably only an immature pyrenomycete, possibly a Mycosphaerella (though Saccardo, Syll. iii. 648, suggests that it is a Labrella); if so, *Macrophoma cylindrospora* (*q.v.*) may be its pycnidium, *p.p.*

Arctium

Phyllosticta Lappae Sacc. Syll. iii. 44. All. vi. 128. Died. 63. Mig. 48.

Spots numerous, roundish or sinuous, up to 6 mm. diam., when dry greyish-brown, with a darker margin. Pycnidia few, epiphyllous, remotely scattered, sometimes more numerous and crowded, punctiform, lens-shaped, about 70μ diam.; texture thin, yellowish. Spores ovoid-oblong or somewhat reniform, 5–$6 \times 3\mu$.

On leaves of *Arctium Lappa*. Shropshire; Yorkshire. Sept.

In Germany it is often found in company with an Ascochyta. Germ. Ital. U.S.A.

Asperula

Phyllosticta Asperulae Grove in Journ. Bot. 1922, p. 14. *Depazea Asperulae* Lasch, Sacc. Syll. iii. 63. (Not *Ph. Asperulae* Sacc. & Fautr. Syll. xvi. 840, quae *Sporonema punctiforme* Petrak, in Hedwig. 1921, p. 299.)

Pycnidia hypophyllous, round, globose or lens-shaped, 60–75μ diam., black, immersed, at length somewhat superficial, opening by a central pore; texture brownish, plectenchymatous, darker round the pore. Spores oblong, biguttulate, 3–4×0.75–1μ; no sporophores visible.

On fading or dead leaves of *Asperula odorata*. Dalry, Ayrshire (Boyd). Jan.

Pycnidia on irregular spots which are indistinct, withered, and pale, but not bleached white. Most of the pycnidia were immature, and contained no spores; see Klotzsch, Herb. Myc. no. 1867. The spores were found only in pycnidia on dead leaflets. Germ.

Aucuba

Phyllosticta aucubicola Sacc. Syll. iii. 30. All. vi. 22, 344. Died. 26. Mig. 8.

On fading leaves of *Aucuba*. Kew Gardens (Cooke). Mar.

These specimens ("spores $6 \times 2\mu$", Cooke) are certainly not *Ph. aucubicola*, but may be *Ph. Aucubae* S. & S. Germ. Holl. Denm. Ital.

Berberis

Phyllosticta Berberidis Raben. in Herb. Myc. no. 1865. Sacc.
Syll. iii. 26. All. vi. 23. Died. 28. Mig. 9. (*Non* Westd.)

Spots round or sinuous, grey when dry, then becoming
whitish, sometimes with a purplish border. Pycnidia epiphyllous, scattered, punctiform, lens-shaped, brown, 75–100μ
diam. Spores ovoid, 4–5 × 2–3μ.

On living leaves of *Berberis vulgaris*. Darenth, Kent (labelled
Septoria); Cheshire; Scarborough.   Apr.

Occurs abroad on other species of *Berberis*, and has been given
several names. *Ph. Westendorpii* Thüm. is probably one of these forms.
Europe generally, Canada.

Phyllosticta asiatica Cooke, in Grevill. xiii. 91. Sacc. Syll. x. 100.

Spots orbicular or irregular, mostly marginal, tawny, surrounded by a dark purplish-brown border which passes into
crimson as it spreads into the leaf. Pycnidia few, mostly
epiphyllous, gregarious, very minute, punctiform, black.
Spores 4 × 1·5μ; sporophores rather longer.

On fading leaves of *Berberis asiatica*. Kew Gardens.

Mar. Apr.

Seems to be a doubtful species.

Betula

Phyllosticta betulina Sacc. Syll. iii. 82. All. vi. 23. Died. 29.
Mig. 229. Grove, in Journ. Bot. 1885, p. 162.

Spots none. Pycnidia widely scattered over parts of the
leaf (which may become withered and brown), mostly epiphyllous, here and there densely aggregated in little clusters,
immersed, then piercing the epidermis by the minute pore,
globose or lens-shaped, black. Spores sausage-shaped, rather
curved, 4–6 × 1–1·25μ (Sacc.), 5–7 × 1·5–2μ (Allesch.), but
occasionally reaching up to even 10 × 2·5μ.

On living leaves of *Betula*. Not uncommon in England.

Aug.–Nov.

Apparently the pycnidial stage of *Mycosphaerella maculiformis*,
f. *Betulae*, in company with which it is often found. It can be easily
overlooked. Frequently the epidermis over the pycnidium becomes
loosened so as to form a minute circular whitish patch surrounding the
ostiole.
Fr. Germ. Ital. Latvia.

Brassica

Phyllosticta brassicicola McAlp. in Bull. Victoria Agr. Dept. 1901, p. 27. Grove, in Journ. Roy. Hort. Soc. 1914, xl. 76. *Asteroma Brassicae* Chev. Flor. par. i. 449. Berk. in Ann. Nat. Hist. 1841, vi. 365. Sacc. Syll. iii. 209. All. vi. 455. Died. 217. Mig. 135. *Sphaeria Brassicae* B. & Br. in Ann. Nat. Hist. 1852, ix. 384, pl. 12, f. 42.

Spots very numerous, small or large, up to 5–10 mm. diam., roundish, often spreading over the whole leaf, pallid in centre, at length fuscous and surrounded by a greenish border. Pycnidia very numerous, subepidermal, not projecting, minute, black, arranged in dense concentric circles, globose, thin-walled, under the microscope translucent-olivaceous, opening by a minute pore. Spores cylindrical, occasionally slightly curved, obtuse at both ends, frequently biguttulate, 4–5 × 1–1·5μ. (Fig. 2a.)

On leaves of Cabbage, Broccoli, Cauliflower. Not uncommon in Wales and S.W. England. Autumn and spring. The pycnidial stage of *Mycosphaerella brassicicola* Lindau.

The "Ring-spot of Cauliflower" can be a destructive disease, but in most cases does little injury. The ascophorous stage is later in occurrence and is more rarely seen, but is on similar spots. As usual, it is the imperfect stage which does the harm, though it is presumably the ascospores that tide over the dead period.

Depazea Brassicae Curr. Simpl. Sphaer. p. 334, no. 392 (on fading leaves of *Brassica*) is this species, but *Phyllosticta Brassicae* Westd. in Bull. Acad. Brux. 1851, xiii. 397 (Sacc. Syll. iii. 38. All. vi. 106) can hardly be the same, unless Westendorp made a mistake in describing the spores as "oval, 2–3-guttulate, issuing in rosy tendrils". Some authors would make *Ph. brassicicola* a stage in the development of *Phoma Lingam* (Tode), but wrongly. *Phyllosticta Napi* Sacc. (Syll. iii. 38) is evidently very closely allied, probably identical. *Ascochyta Brassicae* Thüm. (Contr. Myc. Lusit. no. 602) might be the Mycosphaerella with the asci overlooked.

Europe, U.S.A., Australia, New Zealand.

Buxus

Phyllosticta buxina Sacc. Syll. iii. 24. All. vi. 25. Grove, in Journ. Bot. 1922, p. 15.

Spots variable in form, becoming pallid when dry, with a distinct narrow dark-purple border. Pycnidia epiphyllous, rather densely scattered, punctiform, black, about 100μ diam., subglobose with a projecting papilla and a pale spot in the centre. Spores numerous, oblong-ellipsoid, hyaline, eguttulate, 4–5 × 1·5–2μ.

On living leaves of *Buxus sempervirens*. Box Hill, Surrey.
Aug.

Distinguished from *Ph. limbalis* Pers. by the colour and the character of the spot, the minute pycnidia, and the abundant spores. It is
probably an early state of *Ascochyta buxina* Sacc. *l.c.* p. 393.
Holl. Ital.

Phyllosticta limbalis Pers. Champ. Comest. 148. Sacc. Syll. iii.
24. Cooke, Handb. 453. All. vi. 24. Died. 30. Mig. 9. *Ph. Auerswaldii* All. vi. 25. *Depazea buxicola* Fr. Syst. Myc. ii. 528.

Spots oval or oblong, ivory-white with a distinct but very
narrow brownish border, usually on the lateral edges of the
leaves. Pycnidia few, amphigenous, scattered or grouped,
sometimes confluent, subglobose, blackish-brown. Spores
"rather large, oblong, with three or four guttules", $6 \times 8\mu$
(Sacc. Syll. x. 113).

On living leaves of *Buxus sempervirens*. Shere (Capron).
Forden (Vize). Ovenly Hill (Phillips). Box Hill (Cooke).

I have found no spores in these specimens; the conspicuous dead-
white spots are often well developed without any signs of pycnidia,
and even when the pycnidia are fully formed they seem usually to be
without spores, though they may contain roundish cells, uniguttulate,
$3-4\mu$ diam. *Ph. Auerswaldii* All. is the same species with more mature
spores, $5-7 \times 3-4\mu$.
Fr. Belg. Germ. Ital. Port.

Caltha

Depazea calthicola Sacc. Syll. iii. 62. *Sphaeria lichenoides, calthae-
cola,* DC. Flor. fr. vi. 149. Duby, Bot. Gall. ii. 713.

"Spots white, scarcely bordered. Pycnidia minute, scattered, flat, black." Spores undescribed, not seen.

On leaves of *Caltha palustris*. Colney Hatch (Cooke).
Cheshire (Ellis). Apr.–Jun.

"Spots 2 mm. broad, numerous, roundish, oval, or confluent, frequently sterile" (DC.).
Fr.

Camellia

Phyllosticta Camelliae Westd. in Kickx, Flor. Crypt. i. 416.
Sacc. Syll. iii. 25. All. vi. 26. Died. 31. Mig. 10. *Ph. camelliaecola*
Brun. Misc. Mycol. p. 13. Sacc. Syll. x. 101.

Spots large, roundish or oblong, up to 25 mm. wide,
whitish-grey, with a narrow thickened blood-red border,

visible on both sides of the leaf. Pycnidia epiphyllous, immersed, globose, papillate, black, 150–300μ diam., piercing and at length bursting the epidermis. Spores ovoid-oblong, biguttulate, 4–5 × 2–2·5μ.

On living leaves of *Camellia japonica*. Ward End Hall, near Birmingham. Dec.

It is obvious, on comparing the descriptions of the two supposed species with these specimens, that they are one and the same; large and small pycnidia, closely intermixed, occur on the same spot.

Fr. Belg. Holl. Germ.

Campanula

Phyllosticta carpathica All. & Syd. in Hedwig. 1897, xxxvi, p. (157). Sacc. Syll. xiv. 854. All. vi. 109. T.B.M.S. iv. 173. Died. 32. Mig. 41.

Spots small, about 5 mm. wide, somewhat irregular, visible on both sides of the leaf, whitish, with a dark brown margin. Pycnidia amphigenous, small, scattered, black. Spores cylindrical-oblong, obtuse at both ends, very rarely provided with a single septum, 5–12 × 2–2·5μ.

On living leaves of *Campanula persicifolia*. Ayrshire (Boyd). Aug.–Oct.

Probably an early state of an *Ascochyta* (*carpathica*). In the Ayrshire specimens the spots are up to 7–8 mm. wide, greyish-brown, and surrounded by a broad purplish border. See p. 297.

Germ.

Castanea

Phyllosticta maculiformis Sacc. Syll. iii. 35. All. vi. 29. Died. 34. Mig. 10. *Sphaeria maculiformis* Pers. Syn. 90, *p.p.* Fr. Syst. Myc. ii. 524, *p.p.* Curr. Simpl. Sphaer. 332.

Pycnidia hypophyllous, clustered here and there into little black spot-like groups, depressed-globose, 80–100μ diam., pierced at the summit; texture parenchymatous, blackish-olive. Spores cylindrical, straight or curvulous, 4–6 × 1–1·5μ.

On fading or dead leaves of *Castanea vesca* and *Quercus Robur*. England, Scotland. The pycnidial stage of *Mycosphaerella maculiformis* (or of one of its allies) which it constantly accompanies. The spores can best be found, on fallen leaves, in May.

The texture of the pycnidium is more like that of a Phoma. It is sometimes also associated with *Septoria castaneicola* Desm., of which

the Phyllosticta may be a forerunner. There is a variety recorded on *Fraxinus*.

Europe, N. Africa, U.S.A.

Circaea

Phyllosticta lutetiana Sacc. Syll. iii. 56. All. vi. 112. Died. 38. Mig. 42.

Spots somewhat circular, up to 8 mm. across, dark at first, pale ochraceous when dry, with a narrow chestnut-brown border. Pycnidia scattered, punctiform, pierced. Spores ovoid, hyaline, then olivaceous, $5 \times 4\mu$.

On leaves of *Circaea lutetiana*. Kew Gardens; Dinmore. Aug. Usually barren.

Fr. Germ. Ital.

Cirsium

Phyllosticta Cirsii Desm. in Ann. Sci. Nat. 1847, viii. 31. Sacc. Syll. iii. 44. Cooke, Handb. 452. All. vi. 113. Died. 38. Mig. 42.

Spots various, but mostly small (3 mm. diam.), somewhat roundish, numerous, whitish, when dry cinereous, with a fuscous border. Pycnidia epiphyllous, scattered, immersed, black. Spores oblong-ovoid, biguttulate, $5-7 \times 2\cdot5-3\mu$.

On leaves of *Cirsium arvense*. Bungay (Cooke). Surrey.

Sept.

Fr. Belg. Germ. Ital.

Cornus

Phyllosticta cornicola Raben. in Klotzsch, Herb. Myc. no. 454. Sacc. Syll. iii. 21. All. vi. 33. Died. 40. Mig. 13. *Depazea cornicola* DC. *Ph. Corni* Westd. in Kickx, Crypt. Fl. i. 419. Sacc. Syll. iii. 21.

Spots rather large (6–8 mm. diam. or even larger), roundish, scattered all over the leaf, dark blood-red, then becoming paler in the centre. Pycnidia epiphyllous, few, punctiform, lens-shaped, $150-200\mu$ diam., pierced at the summit. Spores ellipsoid-oblong, rather acute at the ends, $7-9 \times 3-4\mu$.

On leaves of *Cornus alba, C. sanguinea*. King's Cliffe; Darenth; Dartford; Chichester; Audley End; Ayrshire; etc.

Aug.–Oct.

The spores are sometimes slightly larger. This species is often accompanied in Germany by *Septoria cornicola*. It occurs also on other species of *Cornus*.

Europe, Siberia, N. Amer.

Corylus
Phyllosticta Coryli Westd. in Bull. Acad. Roy. Belg. xix, no. 9.
Sacc. Syll. iii. 31. Died. 41. All. vi. 34. Mig. 14.

Spots scattered over the leaf, rather large, fuscous-
ochraceous, then dingy-whitish. Pycnidia lens-shaped, 100–
150μ diam., pierced by a pore; texture smoky-yellow. Spores
ellipsoid, rounded at both ends, biguttulate, 7–8 × 2–3μ.

On living leaves of *Corylus Avellana*. West Kilbride,
Ayrshire (Boyd). Rous Lench, Worcs.; Wyre Forest.

July.

Accompanied on the same spots by *Labrella Coryli* Sacc., of which
it seems to be an early state, for all possible sizes and shapes of spores
could be found between those of the Phyllosticta and the typical
spores of the Labrella.
Belg. Holl. Ital. U.S.A.

Cotyledon
Phyllosticta Umbilici Brun. in Act. Soc. Linn. Bord. 1891, xliv.
242. Sacc. Syll. xi. 478. T.B.M.S. iv. 174.

Spots without a definite border, becoming pale. Pycnidia
loosely gregarious, numerous, globose-lens-shaped, smoky-
brown, about 150–180μ diam., pierced by a pore; texture
minutely parenchymatous. Spores ellipsoid, biguttulate,
5–6 × 2·5μ.

On fading and dead leaves and stalks of *Cotyledon Umbilicus*.
Ayrshire (Boyd).   July.

Fr.

Crepis
Phyllosticta eximia Bubák, Pilzfl. Montenegr. 1903, p. 11. Sacc.
Syll. xviii. 238. T.B.M.S. iv. 174.

Spots on both sides of the leaves, angular, limited by the
veins, dark-brown or blackish. Pycnidia amphigenous,
numerous, crowded, hemispherical, 60–120μ diam., dark-
brown or blackish, shining. Spores oblong, 4–6·5 × 0·5–1μ.

On fading leaves of *Crepis paludosa*, on spots previously
attacked by *Ramularia eximia* Bub. Ayrshire; Renfrewshire
(Boyd).   Jul. Aug.

The pycnidia of the British specimens are paler in colour (? younger)
than those of Bubák.
Montenegro.

Cucumis

Phyllosticta Cucurbitacearum Sacc. Syll. iii. 52. All. vi. 114. Died. 42. Mig. 42.

Spots epiphyllous or on both sides, variable, when dry dingy-whitish. Pycnidia punctiform, lens-shaped, 80–100μ diam., pierced by a pore. Spores oblong, rather obtuse at both ends, curvulous, biguttulate, hyaline, 5–6 × 2·5μ.

On leaves of *Cucumis sativus*. Cheshunt. *n.v.* Recorded abroad on *Cucurbita Pepo* also.

Fr. Ital.

Cytisus

Phyllosticta Cytisi Desm. in Ann. Sci. Nat. 1847, viii. 34. Cooke, Handb. 453. Sacc. Syll. iii. 10. All. vi. 37. Died. 44. Mig. 15.

Spots often few, of various sizes, round or irregular, greyish-brown when dry, with a narrow brown border which is sometimes hardly perceptible. Pycnidia epiphyllous, scattered, punctiform, black, about 150μ diam. Spores ovoid-oblong, rounded at both ends, often curvulous, biguttulate, 5–6 × 3–4μ.

On fading leaves of *Cytisus Laburnum*. Kew Gardens; Highgate; Shere; Hampton-in-Arden; Rous Lench; etc. But see *Ascochyta Laburni*, p. 300.   Aug.–Nov.

Fr. Belg. Germ. Austr. Denm. Ital.

Dahlia

Phyllosticta dahliicola Brun. Champ. Saint. 1887, p. 429. Sacc. Syll. x. 129. All. vi. 116. Died. 45. Mig. 43.

Spots suborbicular, large, brown, becoming pale. Pycnidia lens shaped, immersed, black. Spores ovoid or ovoid-oblong, hyaline, 8–9 × 2·5μ.

On fading leaves of cultivated *Dahlia*. East Malling, Kent (Wormald); etc. On dead stems and peduncles of *Dahlia*, Saltcoats, Ayrshire (Boyd).   Oct.–Dec.

Doubtless an early state of *Ascochyta dahliicola* Petr. in Ann. Mycol. xxv. 201.

Fr. Germ.

Dianthus

Phyllosticta Dianthi Westd. in Bull. Acad. Roy. Belg. xviii. 397. Sacc. Syll. iii. 43. All. vi. 117.

Spots whitish, round or oval, often confluent. Pycnidia epiphyllous, very minute, numerous, fuscous, situated in the

centre of the spot. Spores ellipsoid, triguttulate, issuing in white tendrils.

On fading leaves of *Dianthus barbatus*. In gardens.

This is the young state of *Ascochyta Dianthi* Berk. (*q.v.*) p. 298. Allescher found in a French specimen fusoid spores 10–18 × 3–4μ, 3- or 4-guttulate.

Fr. Belg. Holl. Germ. Ital.

Digitalis

Phyllosticta Digitalis Bell. in Westd. Exs. no. 1053. Sacc. Syll. iii. 47. All. vi. 117.

Spots somewhat circular or irregular, small, scattered, confluent, becoming grey, with a purplish border. Pycnidia epiphyllous, few, semi-immersed, pierced by a pore. Spores ovoid, biguttulate, 7 × 2·5μ.

On leaves of *Digitalis purpurea*. Shere; Lyndhurst. Aug.

Fr. Belg. Germ. Bohem. U.S.A.

Elaeagnus

Phyllosticta argyrea Speg. Fung. Arg. ii. no. 121. Sacc. Syll. iii. 29; xiii. 421.

Spots epiphyllous, broad, orbicular or irregular, white. Pycnidia densely scattered, punctiform, black, 90–100μ diam. Spores ellipsoid, hyaline, 3–5 × 1–2μ.

On leaves of *Elaeagnus pungens variegata*. Hayling Island (Wormald). Kent. Nov.

The spots on other species of *Elaeagnus* vary much in colour and size. There is a *Septoria argyraea* Sacc. on the same plant found in Latvia and Italy.

Germ. Argentina.

Epimedium

Phyllosticta Epimedii Sacc. Syll. iii. 39. All. vi. 119.

Spots rather large, irregular, ochraceous, with a rufous border. Pycnidia scattered, punctiform, pierced. Spores oblong-ellipsoid, biguttulate, 6 × 1·5–2μ.

On leaves of *Epimedium alpinum*. Kew Gardens. *n.v.*

Ital.

Erica

Phyllosticta Ericae All. vi. 119. Syd. Beitr. z. Kennt. Pilzfl. Brand. in Hedwig. xxxvi, p. (158), *p.p.* Sacc. Syll. xiv. 857. Died. 49. *Ph. ericicola* Died. *ibid.*

Pycnidia scattered, few on each leaf, epiphyllous, covered by the epidermis, then erumpent and nearly superficial,

depressed-globose, black, 100–150μ diam.; texture variable,
sometimes Phyllosticta-like, sometimes thicker and darker.
Spores oblong or shortly cylindric, rounded at both ends,
often biguttulate, 4–5 × 1·5–2μ, when older eguttulate, 7–10 ×
2–2·5μ.

On dead leaves of *Erica Tetralix*. West Kilbride, Ayrshire
(Boyd).   Jan.

The dead leaves are reddish-brown. Sydow considered this fungus
to be a dangerous parasite on *Erica carnea* in a nursery in Berlin,
gradually discolouring and killing the leaves. The British specimens
differ but slightly. The curious minute spores found in the fungus by
Allescher (Cytospora-like) occur also in many other Coelomycetes,
mixed with the normal spores.

Germ.

Erysimum
Phyllosticta Erysimi Westd. in Bull. Soc. Bot. Belg. ii. 245.
Sacc. Syll. iii. 39. Cooke, Handb. 454. All. vi. 120.

Spots rounded, whitish, 1–4 mm. diam., with a broad
thickened dark-fuscous border. Pycnidia numerous, scattered
about the centre of the spot, conspicuous, immersed, blackish,
opening by a pore. Spores ovoid, biguttulate, about 10 × 8μ.

On leaves of *Sisymbrium* (*Erysimum*) *Alliaria*. Shere
(Cooke). Perthshire (Boyd).   Sept.–Dec.

Fr. Belg.

Euonymus
Phyllosticta Bolleana Sacc. Syll. iii. 15. All. vi. 41. *Ph. Euonymi*
Thüm. Contr. Fung. Lit. no. 220, f. 20 (*non* Sacc.).

Spots irregular, dry, whitish-cinereous, with a narrow
fuscous border. Pycnidia scattered, epiphyllous, 140–200μ
diam., globose, half-emerging, black. Spores ellipsoid, rounded
at both ends, faintly coloured, 4–5 × 2–2·5μ.

On leaves of *Euonymus japonicus latifolius*. Polperro
(Rilstone). Wisley, Surrey. Probably the same as the following species, after all.

Ital.

Phyllosticta Euonymi Sacc. Syll. iii. 15. All. vi. 40.

Spots small, angular, white when dry, bordered with
brown. Pycnidia scattered, punctiform, lens-shaped, about
100μ diam., pierced. Spores oblong, often inequilateral, ob-

tuse at the ends, indistinctly biguttulate, with a greenish tinge, $4-5 \times 3 \cdot 5-4\mu$.

On leaves of *Euonymus japonicus*, *E. europaeus*. Ayrshire (Boyd) on *E. japonicus*. Kew Gardens (Cooke). Sept.

Phyllosticta euonymella, which is very similar, is said often to occur with it on the Continent, but has cylindrical straight spores, rounded at both ends, about $4 \times 0 \cdot 75\mu$ when mature, i.e. Cytospora-like; texture of pycnidium rather solid. Boyd's specimen belongs rather to this form of the species.
Fr. Holl. Germ. Denm. Ital. U.S.A.

Phyllosticta subnervisequa All. vi. 42. Sacc. Syll. xiii. 468. *Phoma subnervisequum* Desm. in Ann. Sci. Nat. 1853, xx. 219. Sacc. Syll. iii. 113.

Spots amphigenous, without definite border, whitish or yellowish-brown. Pycnidia rather large, $200-250\mu$ diam., sometimes oblong and then 500μ long, following the course of the nerves, convex, prominent, black, somewhat shining, greyish-yellow within; ostiole distinct, papillate, at length circumscissile and falling off. Spores ovoid-oblong, $10-15\mu$ long.

On dry leaves of *Euonymus latifolius*, Polperro. Causing damage to hedges of *Euonymus* in the Scilly Isles in 1923.

Eupatorium
Phyllosticta Eupatorii All. in Ber. Bay. Bot. Ges. 1896, p. 3; Kr. Flor. vi. 121. Sacc. Syll. xiv. 855. Died. 50. Mig. 45. T.B.M.S. iv. 174. *Asteroma Eupatorii* All. in Hedwig. 1895, p. 264.

Spots small, almost circular, 2-4 mm. diam., dark-grey, with an indistinct purple margin, often confluent and covering large areas of the leaf. Pycnidia epiphyllous, scattered, small, globose, black. Spores subcylindrical, rounded at both ends, biguttulate, $10-15 \times 3-4\mu$.

On fading leaves of *Eupatorium cannabinum*. Ayrshire (Boyd). Aug.

In the German specimens it was accompanied by *Septoria Eupatorii* R. & D. (spores $25-35 \times 1 \cdot 5\mu$), of which it may be merely an early stage.
Germ.

Forsythia

Phyllosticta Forsythiae Sacc. Syll. iii. 27; Fung. Ital. pl. 87. All. vi. 43. Died. 52. Mig. 17. T.B.M.S. iii. 117.

Spots suborbicular, becoming ochraceous, scarcely bordered. Pycnidia epiphyllous, rarely amphigenous, often concentrically arranged, lens-shaped, at first immersed, yellowish, 150–180μ diam., opening by a pore. Spores ovoid or cylindric-ovoid, biguttulate, 5–7 × 2·5–3μ.

On leaves of *Forsythia suspensa*. Ayrshire (Boyd). *n.ex.* Aug.

Holl. Germ. Denm. Ital.

Fraxinus

Phyllosticta fraxinicola Sacc. Syll. iii. 21. All. vi. 44. Died. 53. Mig. 17. *Depazea fraxinicola* Curr. Simpl. Sphaer. no. 388, f. 148.

"Spots roundish or irregular, fuscous-brown, margined with a narrow darker line. Pycnidia very minute, black. Spores variable, irregular, ellipsoid or somewhat turbinate or boat-shaped, averaging 5–7·5 × 1·5–2μ, but both smaller and larger ones occur."

On leaflets of *Fraxinus excelsior*. Argyllshire (Boyd)! Herb. Currey; Keswick; Cheshire; Yorkshire; etc. Common in the barren state. Jul.–Sept.

Spots roundish or irregular-oval, one or two on each leaflet, up to 1 cm. diam., ochraceous-brown with a reddish-brown margin. Pycnidia few, chiefly in centre of the spot, epiphyllous, black, rather prominent, pierced. Spores very variable in size, mostly ellipsoid, 4–6 × 1·5μ.

Mr Boyd's Argyllshire specimens agreed very well with the description, having a truly phyllostictoid pycnidium, with ellipsoid spores; but these spores were borne on Phomopsis-like sporophores (about 15 × 1μ), rising from a thin dusky proliferous stratum, like that of a real Phomopsis; moreover, these sporophores were permanent—a thing not known in any other Phyllosticta. Could these be the spores of *Phomopsis scobina*, which is recorded in Yorkshire Fungus Flora, p. 319, on "Ash-leaves"? Could not the records of this species refer, in fact, mainly to this Phomopsis, which might well often fail to bear fruit on the leaves?

Fr. Germ. U.S.A.

Fuchsia

Phyllosticta fuchsiicola Speg. Fung. Chil. 1910, p. 138. Sacc. Syll. xxii. 839. T.B.M.S. vi. 48.

Spots whitish, orbicular, visible on both sides of the leaf, 1–5 mm. across, determinate and bounded by a wide purple

line. Pycnidia few, immersed, lens-shaped, 75–90μ diam., membranaceous, ostiolate. Spores subcylindrical or ellipsoid, 4–6 × 1·5–2μ.

On the dead bark of stems of *Fuchsia*. West Kilbride, Ayrshire (Boyd). Differs from the type described above (which was on living leaves of *Fuchsia coccinea*) in having no specialised spots, but otherwise similar.

Chili.

Galeopsis

Phyllosticta Galeopsidis Sacc. Syll. iii. 50. All. vi. 122. Died. p. 54, p. 22, ii, f. 7.

Spots of various forms, pale-ochraceous when dry, without a distinct border. Pycnidia epiphyllous, lens-shaped, covered by the epidermis, 60–90μ diam., pierced. Spores oblong, often inequilateral, rounded at the ends, 4–6 × 2–3μ.

On leaves of *Galeopsis Tetrahit*. Aberdeen (Trail).

Said by Saccardo to be associated with *Mycosphaerella umbrosa*, but the latter has not yet been found in this country. "Spots often very numerous on a leaf, rounded or irregular, dry, pale-ochraceous. Pycnidia 50–70μ diam.; spores 4–5 × 2·5–3μ" (Trail).

Ital. Germ.

Garrya

Phyllosticta Garryae Cooke & Hark. in Grevill. ix. 84. Sacc. Syll. iii. 24.

Spots elliptical or irregular, large, grey, with a purple border. Pycnidia epiphyllous, conspicuous, convex, rather prominent, black, somewhat shining. Spores narrowly ellipsoid, 10–12 × 2–2·5μ.

On leaves of *Garrya elliptica*. Kew Gardens.   Oct.

U.S.A.

Hedera

Phyllosticta hederacea All. vi. 46. Died. 55. Mig. 18. *Phoma hederacea* Arc. Erb. Critt. Ital. ser. 2, no. 840. Sacc. Syll. x. 156.

Spots circular, sharply margined with a thick clear-brown narrow line, but without a broad darker border, whitish above, more or less ochraceous below. Pycnidia scattered, fuscous, subglobose, piercing the epidermis, 60–120μ (or even 180μ) diam.; texture of dense small cells. Spores roundish or oblong, hyaline, 4–5 × 2μ (Died.).

On dead parts of the leaves of *Hedera Helix*. No certain
British locality known.

Diedicke (Centralbl. f. Bakt. part II, xix. 168) says that this species
is a saprophyte and not, like the two others on Ivy here mentioned,
parasitic. It may occur on the spots which have been previously
killed by *Ph. hedericola*, throughout the year.

Phyllosticta Hederae Sacc. & Roum. in Mich. ii. 620. Sacc. Syll.
iii. 20. All. vi. 46. Died. 56. Mig. 18.

Spots roundish or none, indistinct, dull-brown. Pycnidia
epiphyllous, widely and densely gregarious, lens-shaped,
fuscous, 130–180μ diam., pierced by a pore; texture very
thin and pale, darker round the pore. Spores oblong, 4–4·5 ×
1–1·5μ, often biguttulate.

On dead spots in living leaves of *Hedera Helix*. Aberdeen
(Trail). Ayrshire (Boyd). Fowey; Elmdon, Wk., etc. July.

"Spots dry, circular, except where broken by the leaf-margin, pale
in the middle, with a darker border; pycnidia numerous, lenticular;
spores very small, 3–4 × 1–1·25μ" (Trail).

Possibly only a younger state of *Ph. hedericola*, but in its most pro-
nounced form with amphigenous widely spread pycnidia, with no
spots, it looks very different. Cf. *Ph. decipiens* Ell. & Ev.

Fr. Belg. Germ. Ital.

Phyllosticta hedericola Dur. & Mont. Syll. Crypt. 1856, p. 279.
Sacc. Syll. iii. 20. Grove, in Journ. Bot. 1912, p. 50. Grevillea, xiv.
71. All. vi. 45. Died. p. 56, p. 22, II, f. 2. Mig. 18.

Spots large, conspicuous, roundish or irregular, whitish-
brown, surrounded by a very broad brown border. Pycnidia
epiphyllous, numerous, gregarious, globose, but sometimes
rather flattened, black, piercing the epidermis by the short
ostiole, 125–200μ diam.; texture thin, pale-fuscous, often
darker around the ostiole. Spores oblong, faintly biguttulate,
involved in mucus, 5–7 × 2–2·5μ. (Figs. 1 and 2*b*.)

On living leaves of *Hedera Helix*. Very common in England
and Wales.   Jan.–Dec.

Sometimes the margin of the spot is marked by several concentric
brown borders, with narrow intermediate bands of whitish-brown,
like successive waves on a beach.

This species is probably only a more developed state of *Ph. Hederae*;
Ph. concentrica Sacc. (Syll. iii. 21) lies between the two in the character
of the spots, but in that the pycnidia are distinctly arranged in con-

centric circles, and the spores are much larger ($10 \times 8-9\mu$). *Ph. hederi-cola* seems in some way to be a forerunner of the equally common *Septoria Hederae, q.v.*, but the two species do not appear to accompany one another. It is worthy of notice that *Ph. Hederae* stands to *Ph. hedericola* as *Sept. insularis* does to *Sept. Hederae*. Does the Phyllosticta change gradually into the Septoria, the *concentrica* spores being one of the passage-forms?

Europe, N. Africa, U.S.A.

Helianthemum

Phyllosticta Helianthemi Roum. in Rev. Mycol. iv. 217. Sacc. Syll. iii. 38. All. vi. 125.

Spots somewhat circular, minute, whitish, with a purplish border. Pycnidia epiphyllous, punctiform, black. Spores oblong, $3 \cdot 5 \times 1\mu$.

On leaves of *Helianthemum vulgare*. Lyndhurst; Dunottar; Aberdeen.   Autumn.

"Spots nearly circular or confluent, small, pale with a red-brown border. Pycnidia epiphyllous, few, dark. Spores very small, oblong, $3-4 \times 1\mu$, sometimes biguttulate" (Trail).

This and *Ph. helianthemicola* with its accompanying Septoria spores constitute a group of forms closely resembling those just described on *Hedera*, and carrying the same suggestion of fundamental unity.

Fr.

Phyllosticta helianthemicola All. in Ber. Bayer. Bot. Gesell. 1895, p. 31. Raben. Kr. Flor. vi. 125; see also *ibid.* vii. 767. Grove, in Journ. Bot. 1922, p. 15. Died. 57. Mig. 46. Sacc. Syll. xiv. 846.

Spots indefinite, ochraceous, or none. Pycnidia roundish or angular, lens-shaped, blackish, densely scattered, often occupying the whole leaf, $80-100\mu$ diam., furnished with a pore; texture thin, pale-brown, indistinctly prosenchymatous. Spores oblong-cylindrical, $\pm$ rounded at each end, faintly biguttulate, $6-8 \times 1 \cdot 5-2\mu$, but varying much.

On dead leaves, sepals, and petals of *Helianthemum*. Perceton, Ayrshire (Boyd).   Aug.

Most of the pycnidia contained only the spores described above, but here and there were also found, *in the same pycnidia*, many Septoria spores, cylindric-filiform, eguttulate, $25-60 \times 1-2\mu$; these could hardly be anything else than *Septoria Helianthemi* (Vest.) Allesch. The pycnidia were exactly as Vestergren describes, except that none was found quite so large. Sydow met with a form (*marginata*) with distinctly bordered spots; see Hedwig. 1899, p. (135).

Germ.

Helleborus

Phyllosticta helleborella Sacc. Syll. iii. 37. All. vi. 124.
Var. **nigra** Cooke, in Journ. Roy. Hort. Soc. 1902–3, p. 9, pl. 1,
f. 1; Grevill. xiv. 73.

"Spots usually epiphyllous, large, irregular or angular,
without a border, blackish, when older whitish and margined
with black. Pycnidia minute, punctiform, lens-shaped,
± immersed, blackish, opening by a wide pore. Spores
oblong-ovoid, rather acute at the ends, biguttulate, $7 \times 3\mu$."
On leaves of *Helleborus niger*. Kew Gardens (Cooke).
n.ex. Aug.

The typical form is found in Italy on *H. foetidus* and *H. viridis*,
often in company with *Mycosphaerella Hermione*, of which it is said
to be the pycnidium. Cf. *Coniothyrium Hellebori*, of which Cooke's
above variety *nigra* is probably a mere form, having no connection
with Saccardo's Phyllosticta.
Ital.

Heuchera

Phyllosticta Heucherae Brun. in Act. Soc. Linn. Bord. 1890,
p. 57 (extr.). Sacc. Syll. xiv. 853. All. vii. 768.
Forma **sanguineae** Grove, in Journ. Bot. 1922, p. 16.

Spots brown, irregular-roundish, without a definite border.
Pycnidia scattered, globose, punctiform, black. Spores ellip-
soid, somewhat curved, apiculate below, $7–9 \times 2–2 \cdot 5\mu$.
On fading leaves of *Heuchera sanguinea*. West Kilbride,
Ayrshire (Boyd). Aug.

This variety differs from the type in the size and colour of the spots
(brown instead of grey), and in longer, narrower, and curved spores
(spores of the type oval, $5–7 \times 3\mu$).
Fr.

Hoya

Phyllosticta Hoyae All. vi. 48. *Phoma Bolleana* Thüm. Contr.
Fung. Lit. no. 168, pl. 1, f. 18. Sacc. Syll. iii. 104. (Not *Phyllosticta
Bolleana* Sacc. Syll. iii. 15.)

Spots large, dry, irregular, at length torn away, white
with a pale fuscous margin. Pycnidia densely gregarious,
somewhat prominent, $200–300\mu$ diam., globose, black, ostiolate, mostly epiphyllous, but at length also hypophyllous.
Spores globose-ovoid, $1 \cdot 5–2 \times 1–1 \cdot 6\mu$.

On living leaves of *Hoya carnosa*. Neatishead. *n.ex.* Aug.

The epidermis of the spots becomes free, and looks, when dry, like a thin waxy parchment membrane, stretched like a drum over the affected area and studded with dark dots.
Austr.

Humulus

Phyllosticta Humuli Sacc. & Speg. in Mich. i. 144. Sacc. Syll. iii. 53. All. vi. 126. Died. 59. Mig. 47.

Spots various, up to 1 cm. wide, fuscous, becoming bleached. Pycnidia amphigenous, scattered, punctiform, lens-shaped, 80–100μ diam., thin, membranaceous, smoky-yellow, pierced by a narrow pore. Spores oblong, rounded at the ends, straight or curvulous, 6–9 × 4–5μ, with 1–3 guttules.

On fading leaves of *Humulus Lupulus*. Swanscombe.

Germ. Ital. U.S.A.

Hydrocotyle

Phyllosticta Hydrocotyles A. L. Smith, in T.B.M.S. 1919, vi. 153.

Spots amphigenous, irregular, large. Pycnidia hypophyllous, scattered, immersed, yellowish-brown, about 250μ broad, with a round pore. Spores oblong, biguttulate, 5 × 2μ.

On leaves of *Hydrocotyle vulgaris*. West Kilbride, Ayrshire (Boyd).   Aug. Sept.

Ilex

Phyllosticta aquifolina Grove, nov. nom. *Phoma Aquifolii* Cooke, in Herb.

Spots at first small and round, then irregular, 1–3 mm. across, greyish-fuscous, with a dark-brown border. Pycnidia gregarious, 300–400μ diam., black, covered by the epidermis which is conically elevated and white over each. Spores oblong-ellipsoid, often acute at the ends, straight, biguttulate, 6–7 × 2–2·5μ; sporophores filiform, often curved, 15–20μ long.

On living leaves of *Ilex Aquifolium*. Kew Gardens.   Apr.

This might pass externally for *Phoma leucostigma* (*q.v.*) if it were not on living leaves. Cf. *Ph. Haynaldi*; also *Ph. Aquifolii* All. vi. 57, and the species of Phomopsis which occur on Holly.

Phyllosticta Haynaldi R. & S. in Mich. ii. 342. Sacc. Syll. iii. 25. All. vi. 49. Died. 59. Mig. 19.

Spots various, the smaller ones circular, the larger ones sinuous, up to 10 mm. across, purplish, then cinereous, with a fuscous-brown border. Pycnidia scattered or gregarious, lenticular, covered by the epidermis, with a round pore, 100–130μ diam.; texture dark-fuscous. Spores ovoid, biguttulate, 3–5 × 2–3μ, sometimes smaller.

On leaves of *Ilex Aquifolium*. Hereford; Sutton Park, Wk.; Whitby.   Jan.–May.

Very similar to *Ph. Ilicis* Oud. (Sacc. Syll. xvi. 832), which is said to differ in having pycnidia mainly hypophyllous and spores 5–7μ long, equably filled with protoplasm and not guttulate. But see p. 304. Fr. Germ. Denm.

"Phyllosticta ilicicola Fr." in Kew Bull. Add. Ser. 5, p. 171, "on leaves of Holly".

There is, on *Ilex*, a *Phyllosticta ilicicola* Pers. *in litt. apud* Moug. =*Depazea ilicicola* Fr. but without known spores. There is also *Phyllosticta ilicicola* Pass. (Sacc. Syll. x. 118) on *Quercus Ilex*; see also *Phoma Ilicis* Desm. which is equally confused, *infra*, and *Phoma ilicicola* Sacc. Syll. iii. 106, with spores 10–12 × 5–6μ, which was called *Sphaeropsis ilicicola* by Cooke & Ellis in Grevill. vi. 3, pl. 96, f. 28, and afterwards *Phyllo. ilicicola* by Ellis & Everhart, in Fung. Col. no. 70. But which was the Kew fungus it is impossible to decide.

Impatiens

Phyllosticta Impatientis Fautr. in Rev. Mycol. xx. 109. *Depazea Impatientis* Kirchn. in Lotos, 1856, p. 184. Sacc. Syll. iii. 62.

Spots roundish, varying in size, ochraceous, with an ill-defined brown border. Pycnidia epiphyllous, minute, erumpent, brown. Spores roundish or ovoid, 3–5 × 3μ.

On living and fading leaves of *Impatiens parviflora*, Kew Gardens. On *I. noli-tangere*, Ayrshire (Boyd).   Aug. Sept.

The pycnidia are usually imperfect and without spores, but the Ayrshire specimens, on the dying leaves, yielded a few pycnidia with spores as described, which oozed out and formed a little globule at the mouth. Germ. Austr. Siber.

Lamium

Phyllosticta Lamii Sacc. Syll. iii. 49. All. vi. 127. Died. 61.

Spots visible on both sides, olivaceous, then whitish, with a broad brown border which at length fades, often confluent and

up to 1 cm. wide. Pycnidia epiphyllous, few, not protruding; texture yellowish-brown. Spores oblong to cylindric, rounded at both ends, biguttulate, $7 \times 3\mu$; sporophores filiform, $5 \times 3\mu$.

On fading leaves of *Lamium album*. Stevenston, Ayrshire (Boyd).   Autumn.

These specimens incline towards *Ascochyta Lamiorum* Sacc.

Laurus

Phyllosticta Lauri Westd. Exs. no. 650. Sacc. Syll. iii. 17. All. vi. 51.

Spots sinuous, fuscous, then $\pm$ bleached and with a distinct dark-brown border. Pycnidia scattered, epiphyllous, punctiform, lens-shaped. Spores oblong-ovoid, biguttulate, $10 \times 3\mu$.

On leaves of *Laurus nobilis*. Swanscombe; Highgate; Scarborough.   Nov. Dec.

Fr. Belg. Germ. Ital. Port.

Ligustrum

Phyllosticta Ligustri Sacc. Syll. iii. 21. All. vi. 52. Died. 64. Mig. 19.

Spots brown, then becoming paler, varying in form and size, with a brown or reddish border. Pycnidia few, epiphyllous, lens-shaped, pierced by a pore, brown, $60-80\mu$ diam. Spores ovoid-oblong, biguttulate, $5-7 \times 2 \cdot 5-3\mu$; sporophores of about the same length.

On living leaves of *Ligustrum vulgare*. Kew; Highgate; Shere; Cheshire; Inveraray; Aberdeen; etc. Autumn and spring. The pycnidium of *Mycosphaerella Ligustri* (Fckl.).

See also *Septoria Ligustri*. *Ph. ligustrina* Sacc., with spores $4 \times 1\mu$, is recorded for Heswall, but is probably merely a young state of this species.

Germ. Denm. Ital. Port.

Lonicera

Phyllosticta Lonicerae Westd. in Bull. Acad. Brux. 1851, p. 399. *Ph. vulgaris* Desm. in Ann. Sci. Nat. 1849, xi. 350, *p.p.* Cooke, Handb. 454. Sacc. Syll. iii. 18. All. vi. 53. Died. 65, 390. Mig. 20.

Spots amphigenous, scattered, roundish or irregular, reddish-olivaceous, becoming pale and, when old, altogether brown, with a brown border. Pycnidia epiphyllous, immersed, but rather prominent, globose-depressed, $40-50\mu$ diam., at first amber-coloured, then fuscous, finally black, pierced by

a pore. Spores cylindric-ovoid, obtuse at both ends, biguttulate, $8-14 \times 2 \cdot 5-3 \cdot 5\mu$ ($5-9\mu$, Trail), issuing in whitish tendrils. On leaves of *Lonicera Periclymenum*. Common everywhere.   Jun.–Nov.

It is sometimes accompanied by *Leptothyrium Periclymeni*; it is often misnamed *Septoria Lonicerae* in herbaria. Bubák and Kabát consider it to be identical with their *Ascochyta vulgaris* (*q.v.*). Varieties of *Ph. vulgaris* (which is a collective species) are recorded on *Philadelphus coronarius* and *Symphoricarpus racemosus* (both at Kew, in August), and Diedicke gives a variety on *Viburnum Opulus*, having larger spores than *Ph. Opuli* Sacc. (*q.v.*).
Europe, U.S.A.

Lychnis
Phyllosticta lychnidina Grove, in Journ. Bot. 1918, lvi. 288.

Spots large, marginal, 10–25 mm. diam., dusky-ochraceous, then paler in the centre, with an indistinct margin. Pycnidia amphigenous, numerous, scattered, round, lens-shaped, immersed, blackish, $100-120\mu$ diam., the pore slightly piercing the epidermis; texture pallid-fuscous, darker round the pore. Spores oblong, rounded at each end, $4-5 \times 2\mu$.

On living leaves of *Lychnis dioica*. West Kilbride, Ayrshire (Boyd).   Jul.–Aug.

The texture of the pycnidium is that of a true Phyllosticta, but the fungus is evidently not a more developed state of *Depazea Lychnidis* Fr., though it might be an early state of *Ascochyta Lychnidis* Lasch, of which nothing is known but the name.

Phyllosticta punctiformis All. vi. 129. Grove, in Journ. Bot. 1918, p. 289. *Phoma punctiformis* Desm. in Ann. Sci. Nat. 1849, xi. 283. Sacc. Syll. iii. 145. *Sclerophoma punctiformis* v. Höhn., in Hedwig. 1918, p. 135.

Pycnidia amphigenous, but chiefly epiphyllous, numerous, scattered, without any distinct spots, subglobose, papillate, covered by the epidermis, which is at length penetrated by the pierced ostiole, blackish-brown, $125-200\mu$ diam.; texture pale-brown, thin, darker round the pore. Spores narrow-oblong, $4-7 \times 1 \cdot 5\mu$, but variable.

On fading leaves of *Lychnis dioica*. Largs, Ayrshire (Boyd).
                                                       Sept.

The pycnidia are visible to the naked eye as black dots spread pretty uniformly all over the leaf, and not confined to the faded parts. The

texture of the pycnidium supplies the reason why this species should
be placed in Phyllosticta.
Fr. Germ. Austr.

Magnolia

Phyllosticta Magnoliae Sacc. Syll. iii. 25. All. vi. 55, with fig.
Died. 67. Cooke, in Grevill. ix. 94. Mig. p. 21, pl. 1, f. 4, 5. *Ph.
Cookei* Sacc. *l.c.*

Spots usually epiphyllous, variable in shape, bleached
when dry, indistinctly bordered. Pycnidia few, scattered,
punctiform, lens-shaped, covered by the epidermis, then projecting, 180μ diam. Spores oblong, rounded at the ends,
8–12 × 3–4·5μ.

On living leaves of *Magnolia grandiflora*. Kew Gardens
(Cooke). Hadzor Hall, Ws. (Rhodes).   Feb. Aug.

Spots rounded or irregular, fairly large, cinereous when dry, mostly
with a brownish border. Saccardo gave the size of the spores as
4 × 1·5–2μ; Briosi and Cavara found them 6–10 × 2–4μ. The fact is that
the spores increase in size as the fungus matures.
Fr. Germ. Ital. U.S.A.

Mahonia

Phyllosticta Mahoniae Sacc. & Speg. in Mich. i. 153. Sacc. Syll.
iii. 25. All. vi. 57. Died. 67. Mig. 21.

Spots indistinct. Pycnidia scattered, punctiform, lens-
shaped, smoky-ochraceous, pierced by a narrow pore, about
200μ diam. Spores roundish-ellipsoid, rather obtuse at both
ends, 4–6 × 3–4μ.

On fading leaves of *Mahonia Aquifolium*, *M. japonica*.
Kew Gardens; Shere; Swanscombe; Worcs.; Aberdeen; etc.

Sept.–Mar.

The spots vary considerably; the pycnidia are often barren.
Diedicke describes the spots as resembling those which I have assigned to *Ph. mahoniana*; it appears to me as if the two species are the
same, with Passerini's as an intermediate form.
Fr. Germ. Ital. Denm.

Phyllosticta mahoniana All. vi. 57. Died. 67. T.B.M.S. iii. 118,
367. Mig. 230. *Phoma mahoniana* Sacc. Syll. iii. 117. *Phyllosticta
mahoniaecola* Pass. *in litt. apud* Brun. in Rev. Mycol. 1886, p. 140
(on *M. japonica*).

Pycnidia on large irregular cinereous-brown dried parts
of the leaf, especially round the edges, scattered or loosely
gregarious, globose-depressed, about 150μ diam.; texture

densely parenchymatous. Spores oblong or $\pm$ ellipsoid, 8–10 × 2–3μ; sporophores rod-shaped, 10–12 × 1μ.

On fading leaves of *Mahonia Aquifolium*. Inverness-shire; Kirkcudbrightshire; Ayrshire (Boyd). Aberdeen (Trail). Flintshire; Cheshire; Lancashire (Ellis). Derbyshire; Surrey; Worcestershire. Sept.–May.

Saccardo records (Syll. xvi. 851) a variety, *sicula*, differing in its larger scattered pycnidia, with ellipsoid biguttulate spores on longer (13–15μ) sporophores. Passerini's species (*supra*) had smaller spores, 7·5–8 × 2·5, with two distinct guttules.

Fr. Germ. Ital.

Phyllosticta japonica Thüm. Contr. Myc. Lusit. (1890), *ex* Sacc. Syll. iii. 25. Grove, in Journ. Bot. 1912, p. 50. (*Non* Fautr. 1891; see Sacc. Syll. x. 133.)

Spots large, arid, greyish or whitish, distinctly margined with brown, dingy-ochraceous below. Pycnidia epiphyllous, numerous, gregarious, minute, punctiform, long covered by the epidermis, then conical, emerging. Spores numerous, ellipsoid, rounded at both ends, with a large guttule, 4–5 × 2–3μ.

On fading leaves of *Mahonia japonica*. Studley Castle; Sussex; Worcestershire; Flintshire; etc. May–Oct.

Port.

Malva

Phyllosticta destructiva Desm. in Ann. Sci. Nat. 1847, viii. 29. Sacc. Syll. iii. 40. All. vi. 55. Died. 50, 68. *Ph. sidicola* Cooke, in Grevill. xiv. 39. Sacc. Syll. x. 103.

Spots numerous, somewhat circular, tending to assume an ochraceous colour, margined with fuscous. Pycnidia epiphyllous, $\pm$ concentrically arranged, yellowish or olive, at length black. Spores ovoid or oblong, subhyaline, biguttulate, 6–9 × 3–4μ (Died.), issuing as a pinkish tendril.

On living leaves of *Malva silvestris*. Kew Gardens; Dartford; Lyndhurst. On fading leaves of *Sida Napaea*, Kew Gardens. Jul. Aug.

Var. **Menyanthis** Rabenh. in Winter, Fung. Eur. no. 3092 (as *Menyanthidis*). Died. 69.

On *Menyanthes trifoliata*. Ayrshire (Boyd). But see p. 307.

A confused species. No spores were found in any of these specimens. It has been recorded also on *Althaea, Crataegus, Euonymus, Fraxinus, Hedera, Lycium, Prunus, Syringa,* and *Ulmus,* in other countries, but in most cases incorrectly. *Ph. Syringae* certainly belongs to Ascochyta, and so does Boyd's Ayrshire fungus (*supra*). *Ph. destructiva* var. *Hederae* Desm. (Pl. Crypt. Fr. 1859, no. 680) is very like *Ph. hedericola* D. & M., but has smaller spores (? younger). *Ph. sidicola* Cooke (*l.c.*) was stated to have ellipsoid spores, $4 \times 2\mu$.

Europe, U.S.A.

Medicago

Phyllosticta Medicaginis Sacc. Syll. iii. 42. All. vi. 130. Died. 69. Mig. 49. *Ascochyta Medicaginis* Fckl. Symb. Myc. 388.

Spots yellowish. Pycnidia immersed, black, pierced by a pore at the vertex. Spores cylindrical, more or less curved, $5–6 \times 1\mu$, issuing to form a hyaline globule at the mouth.

On living leaves of *Medicago sativa.* Dartford, etc.

The spots on the leaves are far more common than the pycnidia. Recorded abroad on *M. falcata* also. It is likely that it is merely a stage of *Pseudopeziza Medicaginis* Rehm.

Germ. Austr. Ital.

Menyanthes, see **Malva**

Mercurialis

Phyllosticta Mercurialis Desm. in Ann. Sci. Nat. 1849, xi. 351. Sacc. Syll. iii. 53. All. vi. 132. Cf. *Ascochyta Mercurialis, infra.*

"Spots minute, white, dry, without a distinct border, sometimes confluent. Pycnidia amphigenous, immersed, pale amber-coloured, then becoming fuscous-black, opening by a pore. Spores oblong, hyaline, straight, obtuse at both ends, 1-septate or having three or four guttules, $20–25\mu$ long" ($40–50\mu$, Sacc.). The description is that of Desmazières (*l.c.*).

On fading leaves of *Mercurialis perennis.* Darenth; Dinmore; Bungay; Fife; Forth; Forres; etc. Jun.–Oct.

A very dubious species which I have never met with; the spots are far more common than the spores. The size of the spores given by Desmazières makes it more mysterious, but it is of course not a Phyllosticta.

It is possibly a state of *Ascochyta Mercurialis* Bres., but there has been also some confusion between it and *Cercospore Mercurialis* Pass. (which is not uncommon and makes similar spots), and the spores attributed to it by Saccardo (*l.c.*) are no doubt those of the smaller-spored variety of that Cercospora (var. *fructicola* Sacc. Fung. Ital. pl. 674) which has spores $35–50 \times 5\mu$.

W. Europe, N. Africa.

Myrtus

Phyllosticta nuptialis Thüm. Contr. Myc. Lusit. no. 585. Sacc.
Syll. iii. 9. All. vi. 60. Mig. 22. Sm. & Ramsb. in T.B.M.S. v. 424.

Leaf-spots roundish, becoming ochraceous-whitish when
dry, surrounded by a purple zone (blackish on the underside?). Pycnidia mostly epiphyllous, scattered or sometimes
in groups, conical, black, at first covered by the epidermis,
then free and soon dropping out. Spores subglobose or ovoid,
eguttulate, 2–2·5 × 1·5μ.

On living leaves of *Myrtus communis*. Torquay (Gepp).
Foxcote, near Ilmington.

Port. Bosn.

Nasturtium

Phyllosticta anceps Sacc. Syll. iii. 39. All. vi. 132. Died. 71.
Forma **noxiosa** Grove, in Journ. Bot. 1922, p. 14.

Spots scattered, small, roundish, pale ochraceous-yellow
(not greenish at first), visible on both sides, 1–2 mm. across,
but the leaf-tissue round the spots is yellowed for a considerable distance. Pycnidia crowded, frequently circinate,
70–80μ diam., amphigenous, black, globose-lens-shaped,
pierced by a pore or faintly papillate; texture very thin,
parenchymatous, darker round the pore. Spores oblong or
elliptic, rounded at both ends, often slightly curved, mostly
with a rather large guttule at each end, 4–5 × 1·5–2μ.

On young radical leaves of *Nasturtium amphibium*, which
it nearly destroys. River Cole, Yardley Wood, Birmingham.

Apr.

Spots most abundant on the narrowed leaf-bases, crowded, confluent and killing the tissues for some distance. On the lamina the
spots are more distinct, bordered by a narrow brown line, and each
containing few pycnidia. Saccardo's species was a less virulent
parasite.

Fr.

Nepeta

Phyllosticta Glechomae Sacc. Syll. iii. 50. All. vi. 123. Died. 55.
Mig. 46.

Spots variable, sinuous, brown when dry, without a distinct
border. Pycnidia epiphyllous, scattered, punctiform, lens-
shaped, 120–140μ diam., pierced by a pore. Spores oblong,

rounded at both ends, straight or curvulous, biguttulate, $7 \times 3-3\cdot5\mu$.

On living leaves of *Nepeta Glechoma*. Kew Gardens; Lyndhurst; Scotland. Aug.–Oct.

Spots roundish or somewhat sinuous, few on each leaf, brownish, becoming pale in the centre, with a broad brown border, at length dropping out and leaving a roundish hole in the leaf.
Fr. Germ. Ital.

Nymphaea
Phyllosticta hydrophila Speg. Nov. Add. no. 152. Sacc. Syll. iii. 56. All. vi. 133.

Spots indefinite, rather round, brownish. Pycnidia seated on the spots, at first immersed in the mesophyll, then rather prominent, globose-lens-shaped, $150-180\mu$ diam.; texture rather close, parenchymatous, smoky-brown. Spores cylindric-fusoid, curved like a bow, rather acute at the ends, $5-7 \times 1\cdot5-2\mu$.

On fading leaves of *Nymphaea alba*. Kew Gardens. Aug.

The specimens appear to be somewhat doubtful.
Ital. Germ.

Oxalis
Phyllosticta Oxalidis Sacc. Syll. iii. 39. All. vi. 134. Grove, in Journ. Bot. 1922, p. 16.

Spots various, chiefly marginal, whitish-pallid, with a golden-tawny border. Pycnidia few, epiphyllous, scattered, lens-shaped, brown, pierced by a pore; texture very thin and translucent. Spores oval to ovoid, tapering slightly below, about $5 \times 2\cdot5\mu$.

On leaves of *Oxalis Acetosella*. Beith, Dalry, and West Kilbride, Ayrshire (Boyd). Jul. Aug.

The spots in all cases remind one strongly of those of *Stagonospora hygrophila* (*q.v.*). Saccardo suggests that the Phyllosticta is the pycnidial stage of *Mycosphaerella Selene*.
Ital. U.S.A.

Paulownia
Phyllosticta Paulowniae Sacc. Syll. iii. 27. All. vi. 62. Mig. 22.

Spots variable, sinuous and confluent, when dry ochraceous, with a darker margin. Pycnidia epiphyllous, gregarious, punctiform, lens-shaped. Spores oblong, $3-7 \times 1\cdot5-3\mu$.

On leaves of *Paulownia imperialis*. Kew Gardens.   Aug.

Spots rather large, ochraceous, roundish with a sinuous margin and a very narrow brown border.
Fr. Germ. Ital.

Pentstemon

Phyllosticta Pentstemonis Cooke, in Grevill. xiv. 90. Sacc. Syll. x. 130. All. vi. 135. Died. 73. Mig. 50.

Spots irregular, brown, up to 3 cm. broad, indistinctly margined. Pycnidia subimmersed, often concentrically arranged, at times scattered, punctiform, black. Spores ovoid-oblong or subellipsoid, about $5 \times 3\mu$.

On living leaves of *Pentstemon grandiflorus*. Kew Gardens. *n.ex.*   Oct.

Forms of this, on other species of *Pentstemon*, have occurred in Germany, in which the spores were more mature, measuring 7–10 $\times 3$–$3\cdot5\mu$, sometimes biguttulate. As in many other Phyllostictas, the spots are more abundant than the pycnidia or the spores.
Germ.

Philadelphus, see **Lonicera**

Phillyrea

Phyllosticta Phillyreae Sacc. Syll. iii. 23. All. vi. 64. Mig. 23.

"Spots epiphyllous, variable in form, greyish-ochre, with a rufous border. Pycnidia punctiform, hemispherical, 80–100μ diam., pierced at the summit. Spores oblong-fusoid, biguttulate, 6–$7 \times 3\mu$."

On leaves of *Phillyrea*. Kew Gardens. *n.v.*

Fr. Germ. Ital.

Plantago

Phyllosticta Plantaginis Sacc. Syll. iii. 53. All. vi. 139. Died. 78. Mig. 51.

Spots nearly circular, 1–3 mm. diam., ochraceous or whitish, with a narrow brown border. Pycnidia scattered, depressed-globose, covered, 60–80μ diam., pierced by a pore; wall thin, clear-brown. Spores oblong or ovoid, hyaline, about $5 \times 2\mu$; a few more elongated, subcylindric, rounded at both ends, 10μ long, with an indistinct septum.

On living leaves of *Plantago major*. Cheshire (Ellis). Aug.

Merely the early state of *Ascochyta Plantaginis* Sacc. & Speg. (*q.v.*).

Podophyllum

Phyllosticta Podophylli Wint. in Sacc. Syll. iii. 55. *Ascospora Podophylli* Curt. in Peck, 23rd Rep. N.Y. State Mus. p. 65 (1872).

Spots amphigenous, angular and irregular, determinate, up to 12 mm. or more broad, sometimes confluent, fuscous. Pycnidia amphigenous, gregarious, usually arranged along the nerves, globose, 100–120μ diam., black. Spores subglobose or ellipsoid, 8–9 × 5–6μ, with a large oil-guttule.

On living leaves of *Podophyllum peltatum*. Kew Gardens.

Sept.

U.S.A.

Polemonium

Phyllosticta Polemonii Sm. & Ramsb. in T.B.M.S. 1916, v. 244.

Spots irregular, expanded and often occupying the whole of a leaflet, brown, then grey. Pycnidia amphigenous, loosely gregarious, immersed, covered by the epidermis, pallid-brown, 60–90μ diam. Spores cylindric-ellipsoid, obtusely rounded at the end, 5–7 × 2μ.

On fading leaves of *Polemonium*. Ayrshire (Boyd).

Jul. Aug.

Polygonum

Phyllosticta Polygonorum Sacc. Syll. iii. 54. All. vi. 140. Died. 79. Mig. 52.

Spots roundish or sinuous, varying in size, whitish-ochraceous, with a narrow blood-red or red-brown border. Pycnidia rather few and distant, punctiform. Spores globose, then ovoid, 4 × 2–2·5μ.

On leaves of *Polygonum Persicaria*. Irstead (Cooke).

Germ. Ital. Denm. U.S.A.

Populus

Phyllosticta populina Sacc. Syll. iii. 33. All. vi. 68. Died. 81. Mig. 24.

Spots at first small, roundish, 2–3 mm. diam., with a yellow border, at length larger, confluent and angular or sinuous, brown or grey with a darker margin. Pycnidia epiphyllous, punctiform, about 150μ broad, pierced at the

summit. Spores ellipsoid or ovoid, $6-8 \times 2\cdot5-3\cdot5\mu$ (at first hyaline, then olivaceous, Died.).

On living or fallen leaves of *Populus nigra*, *P. serotina*. Holloway (Cooke). Cheshire (Ellis).

In Germany and Italy it is usually accompanied by *Septoria Populi* Desm. (*q.v.*). The spores are described as being at first hyaline, then olivaceous, but in the specimens examined (Ellis) the olive-coloured spores seemed to be accidental intruders (? Cladosporium).
Holl. Germ. Austr. Denm. Ital. U.S.A.

Phyllosticta Populi-nigrae All. in Rab. Krypt. Fl. vi. 68. Mig. 24. *Phoma Populi-nigrae* All. in Allg. Bot. Zeitschr. ii. 26. Sacc. Syll. xi. 486.

Spots "visible on both sides of the living leaf, irregular or subcircular, indistinctly margined, brown". Pycnidia very minute, loosely gregarious, black, up to 100μ diam., globose, projecting through the burst epidermis, convex, then collapsed. Spores cylindrical, nearly but rarely quite straight, rounded at both ends, $12-15 \times 2\mu$, faintly guttulate, colourless.

On the upper side of a dead leaf of *Populus Tacamahaca*, lying on the ground. Ainsdale, S. Lancs. (Travis). Aug.

In this leaf the spots were still faintly perceptible, but were grey, not brown. The original find was on a living leaf of *P. nigra*.
Germ.

Primula
Phyllosticta primulicola Desm. in Ann. Sci. Nat. 1847, viii. 30. Sacc. Syll. iii. 56. Cooke, Handb. 453. All. vi. 142. Died. 83. Mig. 52.

Spots visible on both surfaces, 1–2 cm. across, bleached, dry, greyish, sometimes surrounded by a yellow border. Pycnidia numerous, epiphyllous, rather prominent, globose, black, shining. Spores "oblong, biguttulate, $3-4 \times 1-1\cdot5\mu$, Allesch." ($4-5 \times 2-3\mu$, Massee.)

On fading leaves of *Primula acaulis*, and on a garden hybrid Primula. Spring and autumn. Very common, but the pycnidia are nearly always empty. It has been recorded also on *P. veris* and *P. elatior*, abroad.

Europe generally.

Quercus, see Castanea

Ranunculus
Phyllosticta Ranunculorum Sacc. & Speg. in Mich. i. 150. Sacc.
Syll. iii. 37. All. vi. 142. Died. 86. Mig. 53.

Spots scattered over the leaf, smoky-brown. Pycnidia
between semiglobose and lens-shaped, somewhat prominent,
pierced by a pore. Spores ovoid, 5–6 × 3–3·5μ.

On living leaves of *Ranunculus repens*, Abridge (Cooke).
On fading leaves of *R. aconitifolius*, Ayrshire (Boyd). Sept.

Saccardo says that in the Italian specimens the pycnidia appeared
upon the same spots which had been previously occupied by *Didy-
maria Ungeri* Corda. Allescher says the same. Mr Boyd's specimens
had pycnidia about 300μ diam., translucent-brownish under the
microscope and with ovoid spores about 5 × 2·5μ.

Germ. Ital.

Rhamnus
Phyllosticta Rhamni Westd. in Bull. Acad. Roy. Belg. 1857, ii.
26. Sacc. Syll. iii. 14. All. vi. 76. Died. 87. Mig. 28.

Spots scattered irregularly over the leaf, roundish or
angular, ochraceous or brown, with a darker border. Pycnidia
epiphyllous, scattered or gregarious towards the centre of
the spot, minute, blackish, pierced at the summit. Spores
oblong or ovoid, hyaline, "then appearing olivaceous in
mass", often biguttulate, 5–6 × 3–3·5μ, Sacc. (5–7 × 2–4μ,
Allesch.)

On living leaves of *Rhamnus Frangula*. Lyndhurst (Cooke).
Aug.

In Germany it is said to be accompanied by *Septoria Frangulae*.
I have not seen any tinge of olive in the spores. The only specimen of
Westendorp's exsiccatum which I have seen showed nothing but the
spermogonia of *Aecidium Rhamni*.

Western Europe.

Phyllosticta rhamnicola Desm. in Ann. Sci. Nat. 1847, viii. 32.
Sacc. Syll. iii. 14. All. vi. 77. Died. 87. Mig. 29. *Depazea rhamnicola*
Lasch.

Spots visible on both surfaces, nearly circular or irregular,
brownish-grey, cinereous, or whitish, scattered, often confluent. Pycnidia numerous, hypophyllous, subglobose, prominent, then collapsing and concave, black, shining. "Spores
very slender, subcylindrical, obtuse at both ends, mostly
straight, 5–6 × 1μ" (All.).

On leaves of *Rhamnus catharticus*. Darenth, Kent (Cooke).

These specimens yielded no spores, the particulars of which are taken from Allescher. According to him this species is accompanied in Germany by *Ph. rhamnigena* on the upper side of the same leaves and spots. The difference is said to be in the spores, which in the latter are ovoid-oblong, $4\cdot5-5\times2\cdot5-3\mu$, and brownish-olive in colour; is this latter not therefore a Coniothyrium?
Fr. Belg. Germ.

Rhododendron

Phyllosticta Rhododendri Westd. in Bull. Acad. Brux. 1851, p. 399. Sacc. Syll. iii. 23. All. vi. 79. Mig. 29. ? *Ph. Saccardoi* Thüm. Contr. Myc. Lusit. no. 600, *p.p.*

Spots rusty-fuscous, mostly on the margin of the leaf. Pycnidia epiphyllous, somewhat projecting, black. Spores cylindric-ovoid, $9\times2\mu$, with three or four guttules, issuing in flesh-coloured tendrils.

On leaves of cultivated *Rhododendron*. Haverfordwest, Pemb. (Rhodes). Cheshire (Ellis). Kew Gardens; Shrewsbury.
May–Dec.

The Kew specimens are named *Ph. Saccardoi*, but do not agree with Sydow's specimen of that species (*ex* Berlin), for in that each pycnidium is surrounded by a distinct minute brown patch on the grey spots. The Kew specimens have no brown patch. The eight or more Phyllostictas recorded on Rhododendron are much confused.
Belg. Holl. Germ. Ital. Port.

Phyllosticta Saccardoi Thüm. Contr. Myc. Lus. iii. 48. Sacc. Syll. iii. 23. All. vi. 80. Died. 90. Mig. 30. *Ph. Rhododendri* Sacc. in Mich. i. 531 (*non* Westd.).

Spots beginning usually at the tip of the leaf and spreading widely, especially along the edges of the leaf, at length becoming grey, with a sharply defined boundary, which is margined by a broad dark-brown line. Pycnidia epiphyllous, scattered, covered, then erumpent, lens-shaped, pierced by a pore, brownish-black, about 60μ diam. Spores somewhat linear, not always straight, hyaline, $4\times1\mu$.

On fading leaves of *Rhododendron*. Haverfordwest (Rhodes). Kew Gardens (Cooke).
Aug.

Occasionally larger spores were met with.
Fr. Germ. Port.

Phyllosticta berolinensis Henn. in Hedwig. 1903, p. 220. Sacc. Syll. xviii. 231. Died. 89. Mig. 29.

Spots brown, spreading over the leaf from the tip, afterwards dingy-grey, scarcely bordered. Pycnidia scattered or gregarious, erumpent and surrounded by the laciniae of the epidermis, black, 250–300μ diam., pierced by a pore; texture indistinct. Spores oblong-ellipsoid to subcylindric, obtuse at both ends, 5–7 × 2–2·5μ.

On living leaves of *Rhododendron*. Kew Gardens.   May.

A doubtful specimen. Said to be a destructive pest. See *Phoma Rhodorae* (p. 100).

Germ.

Ribes

Phyllosticta Grossulariae Sacc. Syll. iii. 17. All. vi. 82. Grove, in Journ. Bot. 1922, p. 15. Died. 91. Mig. p. 30, pl. 2, f. 1–3, pl. 4, f. 2.

Pycnidia epiphyllous, round, up to 120μ diam., on roundish or sinuous greyish brown-margined spots; texture thin, plectenchymatous, dark honey-coloured, hardly darker round the pore. Spores of two kinds, intermixed in the same pycnidium, (1) ellipsoid, biguttulate, 5–6 × 3μ, (2) oblong-linear, 3–4 × 1μ, obtuse at both ends.

On living leaves of *Ribes Grossularia*. Bute and Ayrshire (Boyd). Kent, with *Ascochyta ribesia* Sacc. & Fautr. (*q.v.*).

Aug. Sept.

Klebahn (Nebenfruchtformen der Ascomyz. p. 66) found a similar Phyllosticta in company with *Mycosphaerella Grossulariae*.

Ital. N. Amer.

Phyllosticta ribicola Sacc. Syll. iii. 17. All. vi. 82. Died. 91. Mig. 30. *Depazea ribicola* Fr. Syst. Myc. ii. 530. Curr. Simpl. Sphaer. no. 395, f. 153.

"Spots broad, milk-white. Pycnidia several on each spot, very small, black, clothed with very long deciduous hairs (?). Spores oblong, curved, rather obtuse at both ends, continuous, hyaline, 15–17μ long" (Sacc.).

On leaves of *Ribes rubrum*, and perhaps other species Penzance (Ralfs). Seamill, Ayrshire (Boyd); etc. Aug.–Oct.

Said to be common, but usually in an imperfect state.

The spots are small, roundish or irregular, ochraceous, with a narrow brown border. Pycnidia epiphyllous, few on each spot. But

I have never met with anything exactly resembling the description given by Saccardo; other mycologists have had the same experience. All the specimens I have seen were *Septoria Ribis*, *S. Grossulariae*, or *Gloeosporium Ribis*.

ROSACEAE

Cotoneaster

Phyllosticta sanguinea Sacc. Syll. iii. 6. All. vi. 72. Died. 85. *Depazea sanguinea* Desm. in Ann. Sci. Nat. 1841, xv. 142.

Spots somewhat circular, brown, margined by a narrow darker line and surrounded by a broad blood-red border. Pycnidia epiphyllous, scattered, roundish, shining-black. Spores ovoid, biguttulate, 8μ long.

On leaves of *Cotoneaster frigida*. Kew Gardens.   Aug.

The original specimens of Desmazières were on dead leaves of *Prunus Padus*.
Fr.

Crataegus

Phyllosticta monogyna All. vi. 35. Mig. 14. *Phoma crataegicola* Berl. & Bres. Microm. Trident. p. 61. Sacc. Syll. x. 141.

Pycnidia hypophyllous, scattered, covered by the epidermis, 70–100μ diam., with a small scarcely prominent ostiole; texture loose, smoky-brown. Spores numerous, oblong, often eguttulate, 4–6 × 1–1·5μ (6–8 × 2·5, Allesch.).

On living leaves of *Crataegus Oxyacantha*. Near Birmingham.

What I have found is certainly not a true *Phyllosticta*, but merely an early state of *Phleospora Oxyacanthae* (q.v.), which occurred on the same leaves. There seems no reason why *Phyllosticta crataegicola* Sacc. (Syll. iii. 6) should be anything but the earliest state of *Ph. monogyna*. Ital. Austr.

Fragaria

Phyllosticta fragariicola Desm. & Rob. Pl. Crypt. Fr. iii, no. 686, *p.p.* Sacc. Syll. iii. 40. All. vi. 122. Died. 52. Mig. 45.

Spots various, bleached when dry, with a blood-red border. Pycnidia epiphyllous, punctiform, widely scattered. Spores oblong-ovoid, straight, eguttulate, 5 × 1·5–2μ.

On living leaves of *Fragaria vesca*. Forden; Highgate; etc.

Spots small, round, pallid, surrounded by a broad purple border and resembling those produced by *Ramularia Tulasnei*, but distinguished at once by the presence of a few black dots on the upper surface. Many of the specimens under this name are merely the beginnings of the

Ramularia, but probably both are stages of the life-cycle of *Myco-sphaerella Fragariae* Lindau.

Europe, U.S.A., Australia.

Geum

Phyllosticta Gei Bres. in Hedwig. 1900, p. 325. Sacc. Syll. xvi. 831. All. vii. 766. Died. 55. Mig. 46. *Ph. fragariicola* Desm. *p.p.*

Spots fuscous-olive, irregular, epiphyllous, often extending over the whole leaf. Pycnidia subglobose or oval, pallid, 140–150μ diam.; texture thin, parenchymatous. Spores linear-ellipsoid, straight, biguttulate, hyaline, 5–7 × 1·5–2μ.

On leaves of *Geum urbanum, G. rivale*. Ayrshire (Boyd).

Oct.

Specimens somewhat doubtful.

Saxony.

Potentilla

Phyllosticta Argentinae Desm. in Ann. Sci. Nat. 1847, viii. 30. Sacc. Syll. iii. 40. All. vi. 141. Died. 82. Mig. 52.

"Spots circular, reddish-brown, with a blood-red border, becoming pale in the centre, 1–1·5 mm. across. Pycnidia only one or two in each spot, epiphyllous, very small, black, somewhat shining. Spores cylindrical, obtuse at both ends, biguttulate, 7–12 × 2–3μ" (Died.).

On living leaves of *Potentilla anserina*. Hants. (Clifford). Clyde (Trail).

Oct.

All the specimens I have seen under this name are doubtful. In many cases it has been confused with *Marssonina Potentillae* Fisch. (*Phyll. Potentillae* Desm.), *q.v.*, as in the specimens on *Potentilla reptans,* from Twycross (Bloxam) in Herb. Kew; in other cases no spores have been found in the pycnidia, as Saccardo also records in his account.

Fr. Belg. Germ. Siber.

Phyllosticta Tormentillae Sacc. Syll. iii. 40. All. vi. 152. Died. 101. Mig. 56.

Spots irregular, minute, pallid-ochraceous, with the margin nearly of the same colour. Pycnidia scattered, punctiform, lens-shaped. Spores shortly ellipsoid, hyaline (then ? somewhat brownish), 2·5–3 × 1·5–2·5μ.

On living leaves of *Potentilla Tormentilla*. Lyndhurst, Hants. (Cooke).

Aug.

The spores are only faintly tinged with colour when mature.

Germ. Ital.

Prunus

Phyllosticta circumscissa Cooke, Australian Fung. in Grevill. xi. 150 (1883). Sacc. Syll. iii. 6. *Ph. Persicae* Mich. i. 147 (1878). Sacc. Syll. iii. 8.

Spots orbicular, amphigenous, rufous-brownish, at length falling out. Pycnidia few, minute, immersed. Spores ellipsoid, hyaline, $8 \times 2\mu$, Cooke ($6-7 \times 3 \cdot 5-4$, Sacc.).

On several species of *Prunus*. Said to have been found in Britain; recorded in Australia on Plum, Peach, Apricot.

Saccardo's *Ph. Persicae* differs from *Ph. prunicola* chiefly in the total absence of the dilute olivaceous tint of the spores of the latter species, but it seems to be very similar, and perhaps identical. The spots also differ somewhat, but they both fall out and cause "shotholes".

Ital. Port. Australia.

Phyllosticta prunicola Sacc. Syll. iii. 4. All. vi. 70. Died. 84. Mig. 26. Stevens, Pl. Dis. p. 486.

Spots visible on both surfaces, subcircular, 4–9 mm. across, dingy brown or ochraceous, with a raised margin of about the same colour or darker. Pycnidia amphigenous, scattered, punctiform, slightly prominent, pierced at the summit. Spores ovoid or ellipsoid, hyaline, but at length verging upon pale olivaceous, $5 \times 3\mu$ Sacc. ($4-6 \times 2 \cdot 5-3\mu$, Allesch.; $5-8 \times 3-3 \cdot 5\mu$, McAlp.). (Fig. 2 A.)

On living leaves of *Prunus domestica, P. Cerasus*. Cheshire (Ellis.), etc. Sept. Oct.

It has been found abroad on Apricot and Peach, and other species of *Prunus*. In most cases the leaf-tissue splits round the spot, and drops clean out, thus producing a "shot-hole" effect, like *Cercospora circumscissa*, etc. Allescher gives a form on *Prunus spinosa* with more cylindrical spores, $5-8 \times 2-3\mu$. See also *Ph. Mali*.

Europe, N. Amer., Australia.

Phyllosticta prunigena Grove. *Phoma prunicola* Schwein. Syn. Amer. bor. no. 2169. Sacc. Syll. iii. 107. Grove, in Journ. Bot. 1912, p. 50. (Not *Phyllo. prunicola* Sacc.)

Pycnidia amphigenous, gregarious, seated mainly on irregular cinereous or fuscous spots which are visible on both sides of the leaf, bursting through the epidermis and surrounded by its laciniae, black, ovoid, opening by a pore

which soon becomes very wide and irregular. Spores oblong-ellipsoid, obtuse at both ends, usually faintly biguttulate, $9-10 \times 3\cdot5\mu$ $(5-10 \times 2-4\mu,$ Ellis).

On living or dry fallen leaves of *Prunus Laurocerasus*. Cheshire (Ellis). Over Whitacre, Wk.   Apr. May.

When young, the spores are smaller. Cf. *Phyll. destruens* var. *Pruni-lusitanicae* Sacc. in Mich. ii. 88; also *Macrophoma collabens, infra.*
U.S.A.

Pyrus

Phyllosticta Mali Prill. & Delacr. in Bull. Soc. Myc. Fr. 1890, vi. 181, pl. 20, f. 3. All. vi. 66. Sacc. Syll. x. 109. *Ph. prunicola* Sacc. var. *Mali.* Syll. iii. 5.

Spots numerous, small, subcircular, 2–6 mm. diam., at first brownish-ochraceous, at length dry and dingy-grey with a slightly thickened fuscous border. Pycnidia few, epiphyllous, immersed, then just piercing the epidermis, black, $130-170 \times 100-120\mu$, pierced by a pore. Spores ovoid or ellipsoid, varying much in size, biguttulate, occasionally curved, hyaline, $6-8\cdot5 \times 4-4\cdot5\mu$ $(6-8 \times 2-3\mu,$ Salmon).

On living leaves of *Pyrus Malus*. Crewkerne; Hereford; Wallasey; etc.   Aug.–Nov.

The spots are very distinct, as if stamped on the leaf. *Ph. Briardi* Sacc. Syll. x. 109 (*Ph. Mali* Briard) seems to be a young state of the same. Saccardo suggests that this is the pycnidium of his *Leptosphaeria Pomona.*
Fr. Denm.

Phyllosticta Briardi Sacc. Syll. x. 109. All. vi. 66. Grove, in Journ. Bot. 1922, p. 14. Died. 44. *Ph. Mali* Briard, Suppl. p. 79 (*non* Prill. & Delacr.).

Spots very various in form, visible alike on both sides of the leaf, brown or subochraceous, with a similar but darker (or even purplish) border, chiefly marginal or apical, up to 2 cm. across. Pycnidia epiphyllous, scattered, punctiform, immersed, black, $80-100\mu$ diam., at times aggregated. Spores cylindrical, obtuse at both ends, $4-5 \times 1\cdot5-2\mu$.

On living leaves of *Pyrus Malus*. Stevenston, Ayrshire (Boyd).   Aug.

The spots are very conspicuous, but appear as if the leaf were merely dry and dead; the pycnidia can be seen only with a lens.
Fr.

Phyllosticta pyrina Sacc. Syll. iii. 7. All. vi. 65. Died. 77. Mig. 23.

Spots roundish or sinuous, chiefly showing on the upper side, becoming by confluence as much as 6–7 mm. broad, whitish above, scarcely discoloured below. Pycnidia epiphyllous, punctiform, lens-shaped, with a projecting ostiole, 100–120μ diam., opening by a round pore. Spores oblong-ovoid, hyaline, 4–5 × 2–3μ.

On living or dead leaves of *Pyrus Malus*. Cornwall (Rilstone).

Saccardo says (Syll. i. 481) that this was accompanied at Treviso by his (*Myco*)*sphaerella Bellona*.
Fr. Germ. Ital. Port.

Rosa
Phyllosticta Rosarum Pass. Erb. Critt. Ital. no. 1092. Sacc. Syll. x. 109. All. vi. 84, with fig. Died. 92. Mig. 31.

Spots epiphyllous, scattered, grey or whitish, up to 4 mm. across, rounded, ± crowded, with a rather broad purple border. Pycnidia few, minute, black. Spores ellipsoid, hyaline, 4–5 × 2–2·5μ.

On leaves of cultivated Roses. Brighton, etc. These specimens are doubtful.

Specimens having similar spots, but containing no spores, are recorded by Cooke from King's Cliffe, Neatishead, and Scarborough; but he places them under *Ph. Rosae* Rob. & Desm., which is said to have cylindrical spores, with three or four guttules, and is probably a state of *Septoria Rosae* Desm.
Germ.

Rubus
Phyllosticta Ruborum Sacc. Syll. iii. 8. All. vi. 85. Died. 93 ? Mig. 31.

Spots minute, becoming whitish, generally aggregated along the nerves. Pycnidia few, epiphyllous, punctiform, lens-shaped, 150–180μ diam. Spores numerous, oblong-cylindrical, biguttulate, 4–5 × 1–1·5μ.

On living leaves of *Rubus fruticosus*. Lyndhurst; Forden; Helmsley, Yorks.; Ribbesford, Ws.; etc. Aug.

Spots epiphyllous, minute, angular, roundish or sinuous, at length pure shining white in the centre, with a distinct narrow purple-brown

border. Pycnidia 2–4 on each spot. Apparently merely a forerunner of *Septoria Rubi* Westd. Diedicke's species seems to be different. Fr. Germ. Ital. Australia.

Sorbus

Phyllosticta Sorbi Westd. in Bull. Acad. Roy. Belg. ser. 2, vol. ii, no. 7, p. 26 (1857). Sacc. Syll. iii. 8. All. vi. 88. T.B.M.S. iv. 292. *Ph. Aucupariae* Thüm. Beit. Pilz. Sibir. no. 611 (1878). Sacc. Syll. iii. 7. All. vi. 88. Died. 97. Mig. 33.

Spots single or crowded on each leaflet, roundish, occasionally confluent, slightly raised, 2–3 mm. diam., greyish-brown, with a dark purplish-fuscous border. Pycnidia epiphyllous, few, punctiform, black, slightly prominent, situated chiefly in the middle of each spot, perforating the epidermis with the minute ostiole. Spores ovoid or oblong, biguttulate, 6–$8 \times 2 \cdot 5 \times 4 \mu$ ($10 \times 5 \mu$, Sacc.).

On fading leaves of *Sorbus Aucuparia*. Aberdeen (Trail). Bidston Hill, Cheshire (Ellis). Sept.–Nov.

"Producing dry round spots; common in autumn" (Trail). This is quite different in appearance from "*Septoria Aucupariae* Lasch", in Rab. Fung. Eur. no. 1265, which = *S. Sorbi* Lasch, and is rather common in Britain.

Var. **torminalis** var. nov.

Pycnidia as above, seated on dry shapeless ochraceous-brown spots, which occupy nearly all the spaces between the principal nerves and have a narrow brownish border. Spores obovoid-fusoid or almond-shaped, colourless, granular within, rather acute at one or both ends, 9–10×3–4μ (up to $12 \times 4 \cdot 5 \mu$); sporophores short.

On fading leaves of *Sorbus torminalis*. Ribbesford Wood, Ws. (Rhodes). Wyre Forest. Jun.–Aug.

This is perhaps the fungus of which Cooke described and figured the spores in Seeman's Journ. Bot. 1866, iv. 97, f. 25. But to this description he prefixed, by error, the description of the pycnidia of *Phyllosticta sorbicola*, and gave to the fictitious combination the name "*Septoria Sorbi* Lasch". See Handb. 448.

Europe, Siberia, U.S.A.

Phyllosticta sorbicola All. vi. 88. Died. 97. Mig. 33. *Depazea sorbicola* Rabenh. exs. no. 548. *Phoma Sorbi* Sacc. Syll. iii. 107, *p.p.*

No spots. Pycnidia epiphyllous, minute, aggregated in little groups, semi-innate, nearly black. No spores seen.

On leaves of *Sorbus Aucuparia*. England; Scotland. Not uncommon.

The name given to the fungus at first (Depazea) indicates that it is usually found without spores; it is probably only the initial state of a Mycosphaerella or a Leptosphaeria. But some of the British specimens I have seen under the name *Phoma Sorbi* have the spores of a Septoria, for which see *Septoria Sorbi*, *infra*.

Spiraea

Phyllosticta Ulmariae Thüm. Pilzfl. Sibir. no. 806. Sacc. Syll. iii. 41. All. vi. 150. Died. 99. Mig. 233. *Ph. filipendulina* var. *Ulmariae* Sacc. *l.c.* Died. 98. Mig. 55.

Spots often minute, irregular, whitish when dry, with a very broad dingy-fuscous border. Pycnidia scattered, sometimes few or solitary, about 200μ diam., hemispherical, at length free and uncovered, black. Spores very numerous, ± cylindrical, between rounded and truncate at the ends, cloudy-granular, eguttulate, 3·5–6 × 2–2·5μ.

On living leaves of *Spiraea Ulmaria*. Lyndhurst; Dinmore; Clyde; Aberdeen. Jun.–Oct.

Saccardo's variety is merely a modified state of Thümen's species. The spots are sometimes without any sign of a fruit-body.
Fr. Germ. Ital. Siberia.

_____

Rumex

Phyllosticta Acetosae Sacc. Syll. iii. 55. All. vi. 144.

Spots mostly circular, fusco-ferruginous. Pycnidia epiphyllous, gregarious, punctiform, lens-shaped, pierced by a pore. Spores oblong or shortly cylindrical, obtuse at both ends, biguttulate, hyaline, 4–5 × 2μ.

On leaves of *Rumex Acetosa*. No certain locality known; very uncommon. Cf. *Septoria Acetosae*.

Switz. Ital.

Phyllosticta Acetosellae Sm. & Ramsb. in T.B.M.S. 1912, iv. 173.

Spots somewhat circular, about 7 mm. diam., becoming pale ochraceous and surrounded by a purple-brown border. Pycnidia epiphyllous, scattered, 130μ broad, brownish-black, pierced by a round pore. Spores ellipsoid-cylindrical, straight or slightly curved, biguttulate, 8–10 × 3–4μ.

On fading leaves of *Rumex Acetosella*. Ayrshire; Lanarkshire (Boyd). Jun.–Oct.

Sambucus

Phyllosticta Sambuci Desm. in Ann. Sci. Nat. 1847, viii. 34.
Cooke, Handb. 453. Sacc. Syll. iii. 19. All. vi. 87. Died. 94. Mig. 33.

Spots solitary or confluent, up to 10 or even 15 mm.
broad, irregular, at first brown or dark-grey, at length
whitish. Pycnidia epiphyllous, scattered, immersed, but
prominent, very minute, sometimes few in number, brownish-
black, opening by a pore; texture thin, pale-brownish. Spores
ovoid-oblong or subcylindric, biguttulate or sometimes without guttules, 5–8 × 2·5–3μ.

On living or fading leaves of *Sambucus nigra*. Shere;
Whitehall; Worcestershire; Cheshire; Ayrshire; Fife; Forth;
Inveraray; etc. Jul.–Oct.

It seems likely that *Ph. sambucina* All. vi. 245 (Mig. 33) is merely
a state of the same species, but *Phoma sambucina* Sacc. is a Phomopsis.
Fr. Belg. Holl. Germ. Austr. Ital.

Phyllosticta sambucicola Kalchbr. in Hedwig. 1864, p. 73. Sacc.
Syll. iii. 19. All. vi. 86.

Spots rather large, somewhat angular, grey, with a dark
purple-brown border. Pycnidia numerous, slightly projecting,
minute, blackish-fuscous. Spores hyaline, round or oval,
3–4μ diam. or 4–5 × 3μ.

On living leaves of *Sambucus nigra*. Whitby (Ramsbottom).
Hung.

Samolus

Phyllosticta Valerandi Brun. Flor. Myc. Saint. in Bull. Soc. Sci.
Nat. Ouest, 218. Sacc. Syll. xi. 481.

Spots white, with a brown border. Pycnidia few, black.
Spores hyaline, 4–5 × 2·5μ.

On fading stems and leaves of *Samolus Valerandi*. Cumbrae,
Buteshire (Boyd). Sept.

There are signs that this is really an immature state of an Ascochyta.
Fr.

Scrophularia

Phyllosticta Scrophulariae Sacc. Syll. iii. 46. All. vi. 146.

Spots scattered, varying in shape, 2–6 mm. diam., ochreous
with the margin almost of the same colour or brown-fuscous.
Pycnidia epiphyllous, few, scattered, punctiform, 70–90μ

diam.; texture very thin and pale. Spores ellipsoid, rounded at both ends, hyaline, "then somewhat fuscous", 5–7 × 2·5–3μ.

On living or fading leaves of *Scrophularia nodosa*, Ayrshire (Boyd). On leaves of *S. aquatica*, Dinmore (Cooke).

Aug.–Oct.

No spores of a fuscous colour have been seen in British specimens. The same spots are frequently occupied by *Ramularia Scrophulariae* Fautr. & Roum. on the lower face. Cooke's Dinmore specimens possibly belong to *Ph. scrophularinea*.
Fr. Denm. Ital.

Phyllosticta scrophularinea Sacc. Syll. iii. 46. All. vi. 146. Died. 96. Mig. 54.

Spots minute, angular, becoming pale when dry, with a broad rufous or purplish border. Pycnidia few, epiphyllous, scattered, punctiform, lens-shaped, 90–100μ diam. Spores oblong, straight or curvulous, rounded at both ends, 3–4 × 1–1·5μ.

On living leaves of *Scrophularia aquatica*, *S. nodosa*. Ockeridge Wood (Rhodes & Grove). Rugby; Ayrshire; Aberdeen; Montrose. Jul.–Oct.

The pale part of the spots is from half to a whole millimetre broad. It is probable that this is merely the younger state of the preceding species.
Germ. Ital.

Sedum
Phyllosticta Aizoi Cooke, in Grevill. xiv. 39 (as *Ph. Aizoon*). Sacc. Syll. x. 123. All. vi. 87.

Spots small, suborbicular, brown, with a darker border. Pycnidia epiphyllous, minute, immersed, membranaceous, brown. Spores ellipsoid, 3 × 1·5μ.

On leaves of *Sedum Aizoon*. Kew Gardens. *n.ex.* Aug.

Sisymbrium, see Erysimum

Solanum
Phyllosticta Dulcamarae Sacc. Syll. iii. 49. All. vi. 148. Died. 97. *Ph. perforans* Ell. & Ev. in Proc. Acad. Philad. 1893, p. 187. Sacc. Syll. xi. 480.

Spots variable in shape, often marginal, grey-brown when dry. Pycnidia epiphyllous, scattered, punctiform, lens-

shaped, 80–100μ diam., pierced by a pore. Spores globose-ellipsoid, unequal, hyaline, then with a greenish tinge, 5–6 × 3μ.

On living leaves of *Solanum Dulcamara*. Kew Gardens; Scotland.   Aug.

The Italian and French specimens are accompanied by a Septoria. It is possibly an early state of *Ascochyta solanicola* Oud.
Fr. Germ. Ital. Port. Denm. U.S.A. Canada.

Phyllosticta hortorum Speg. Nov. Add. no. 154, in Mich. ii. 277. Sacc. Syll. iii. 49. All. vi. 149.

Spots circular, fulvous, cinereous in the centre, visible on both sides, with no definite border, at length circumscissile. Pycnidia in the centre of the spot, subglobose, pierced by a pore, 80–90μ diam.; texture thin, membranaceous, fuscous-olive. Spores ellipsoid or ovoid, rounded at both ends, 4–6 × 2–2·5μ.

On fading leaves of *Solanum Dulcamara*. West Kilbride, Ayrshire (Boyd).   Sept.

Ital.

Stellaria
Phyllosticta Holosteae Allesch. in Ber. Bayer. Bot. Gesell. 1897, p. 3; Rabenh. Kr. Flor. vi. 151. Grove. in Journ. Bot. 1922, p. 16.

Spots none. Pycnidia scattered, few, chiefly epiphyllous, globose-lens-shaped, about 125μ diam., black; texture thin, pale-brown, slightly darker near the roundish pore. Spores numerous, oblong or cylindrical, rounded at both ends, hyaline, biguttulate, 5–6 × 1·5μ.

On dead bleached leaves of *Stellaria uliginosa*. Kilwinning, Ayrshire (Boyd).   July.

Allescher's specimens, on *S. Holostea*, had spores much more variable in size (3–6 × 1·5–3μ).
Germ.

Stephanotis
Phyllosticta Stephanotidis Grove, in Journ. Bot. 1886, p. 134, pl. 266, f. 3. Sacc. Syll. x. 132.

Spots rounded or irregular, whitish, bordered by a narrow dark-brown line. Pycnidia epiphyllous, numerous, scattered, black, lens-shaped, depressed, papillate, 250μ diam., the

ostiole perforating the epidermis. Spores oblong, rounded at each end, $12–16 \times 4–5\mu$.

On leaves of *Stephanotis*. Sutton Coldfield. Apr.

Differs from *Ph. Asclepiadearum* Westd. in its larger spores and pycnidia, but may be merely a variety.

Symphoricarpus, see **Lonicera**

Syringa

Phyllosticta Syringae Westd. Not. ɪɪ, in Bull. Acad. Roy. Belg. 1851, xviii. 399. Sacc. Syll. iii. 22. All. vi. 90. Died. 99. Mig. 34.

Spots broad, irregular, ochraceous when dry, usually with a fuscous border. Pycnidia epiphyllous, punctiform, lens-shaped, long covered by the epidermis, which is at length pierced by the minute ostiole; texture thin, clear-brown. Spores ovoid-oblong, hyaline, biguttulate, $5–8 \times 2–3\mu$.

On living leaves of *Syringa vulgaris*. Kew Gardens; Kent; Aberdeen; etc. Sept.

Spots rather large, occupying a great part of the leaf, more rarely small and scattered. This parasite seems to be found wherever the host-plant occurs. It has been called a form of *Ph. destructiva* Desm., but it is merely a young state of *Ascochyta Syringae* Bres., and *Depazea syringaecola* Kunze is a still younger and sporeless state. Cf. also *Ph. syringella* (Fckl.), which seems to be a form assumed by it on decaying fallen leaves.
Europe.

Teucrium

Phyllosticta Teucrii Sacc. & Speg. Syll. iii. 49. All. vi. 151. Died. 100. Mig. 56.

Spots amphigenous, variable in shape, up to 2 cm. wide, often indistinct, greyish-white when dry, with a broad brownish border. Pycnidia epiphyllous, gregarious or scattered, punctiform, covered, lens-shaped, $150–180\mu$ diam., brown, pierced by a wide pore; texture distinctly parenchymatous, olivaceous. Spores $\pm$ cylindrical, hyaline, occasionally curved, $4–5 \times 1·75\mu$.

On living leaves of *Teucrium Scorodonia*. Ayrshire (Boyd). Scotland, common (Trail). Aug.–Sept.

Germ. Ital.

Tilia
Phyllosticta Tiliae Sacc. & Speg. Syll. iii. 27. All. vi. 92. Died.
101. Mig. 35.

Spots variable, often numerous, pale-ochraceous when dry,
with a dusky margin. Pycnidia scattered, lens-shaped,
brown, 100–130μ diam., pierced at the summit; texture
loosely parenchymatous, subolivaceous. Spores ellipsoid or
oblong, obtuse at both ends, 5–7 × 3μ.

On living leaves of *Tilia europaea, T. parvifolia.* Lyndhurst; Cheshire; Forres; Aberdeen.   Autumn.

Cooke's Lyndhurst specimens have small round scattered spots,
pale in the centre, with a conspicuous blackish-brown border. Ellis's
Bebington (Cheshire) specimens have spores 10–12 × 5·5–7μ, apparently approaching Septoria.
Germ. Ital. Denm. U.S.A. Canada.

Trollius
Phyllosticta Trollii Trail, in Scot. Nat. 1889, new ser. iv. 70.
Sacc. Syll. x. 125. All. vi. 153. Mig. 56.

Spots brown, irregular, usually limited by the veins.
Pycnidia hypophyllous, crowded, depressed-globose, 120–
130μ diam., membranaceous, black. Spores very abundant,
cylindrical, truncate at both ends, 4 × 1μ.

On living leaves of *Trollius europaeus.* Hell's Glen, Loch
Lomond. *n.v.* Allescher remarks that it is often accompanied
by a Septoria.

Germ.

Ulmus
Phyllosticta bellunensis Mart. in Nuov. Giorn. Bot. Ital. 1888,
xx. 395. Sacc. Syll. x. 117. All. vi. 93. Died. 103. Mig. 233. T.B.M.S.
iii. 37.

Spots large, visible on both sides, 1–1·5 cm. across, irregular or
almost round, dark-coloured. Pycnidia chiefly hypophyllous,
punctiform, scattered over the spots, more rarely in groups,
fuscous-brown, 50–100μ diam. Spores rod-shaped, 3–5 × 1μ.

On fallen leaves of *Ulmus* spp. Isle of Wight, etc.   Oct.

Klebahn has shown (Jahr. f. wiss. Bot. 1905, xli. 498, f. 5) that this
is only an early state of *Phleospora Ulmi* Wallr. (*Septogloeum Ulmi*
Died.), which is the pycnidial phase of *Mycosphaerella Ulmi* Kleb. The
two pycnidial stages are often found in company; see Grove, in Journ.
Bot. 1919, p. 208, and cf. *Ph. Ulmi* Westd., *infra*, p. 50.
Germ. Ital.

Phyllosticta Ulmi Westd. Not. v, in Bull. Acad. Roy. Belg. ser. 2, ii. 7. Sacc. Syll. iii. 33. All. vi. 93. Died. 104. Mig. 35. *Ph. ulmicola* Sacc. Syll. iii. 33. All. vi. 92. Died. 104. Mig. 35. *Ph. lacerans* Passer. Diagn. F. Nov. III, no. 62. Sacc. Syll. x. 117. All. vi. 94. Died. 104. Mig. 35.

Spots amphigenous, roundish, 4–8 mm. diam., scattered or confluent, often greyish, without a distinct border or with a greenish border, occasionally sterile. Pycnidia few, very small, 70–80μ diam., lens-shaped, scattered, pierced at the summit. Spores oblong or ovoid, with one or two guttules or none, 6–10 × 3–5μ.

On dead or only fading leaves of species of *Ulmus*. Hereford; Renfrew; Ayrshire; Cheshire; Keswick; etc.

Jul.–Oct.

The spots when old often tear and drop out; this is *Ph. lacerans*. *Ph. ulmicola* is no doubt the same species on the living leaves, but with smaller spores, about 5 × 2μ. The spots may be brownish-ochre, with occasionally a brownish border.

Fr. Belg. Holl. Germ. Ital. U.S.A.

Urtica
Phyllosticta Urticae Sacc. Syll. iii. 53. All. vi. 153. Died. 105.

Spots visible on both sides, mostly bounded by the veins, angular, at length whitish, occasionally confluent. Pycnidia scattered, lens-shaped, 60–70μ diam.; texture thin, yellowish to brown, opening widely at the summit. Spores oblong-ovoid, obtuse at both ends, hyaline, eguttulate, 4–5 × 2–2·5μ, but occasionally much longer spores, up to 20μ long and 4μ broad, are found intermixed.

On living leaves of *Urtica dioica*. Bromsgrove, Ws. July.

On the same leaves various stages may be found between this Phyllosticta and *Septoria Urticae* (q.v.).

Germ. Ital.

Valeriana
Phyllosticta Valerianae Sm. & Ramsb. in T.B.M.S. 1915, v. 158.

Spots indeterminate, irregular, 4–5 mm. wide, with an orange border. Pycnidia epiphyllous, few, immersed, globose or lens-shaped, slightly depressed, covered by the epidermis, then erumpent by a subconical papilla, 150–200μ diam., brown; wall membranaceous. Spores straight or curvulous,

rounded at the ends, often very faintly broader above and obtuse, 8–10 × 2–3μ.

On leaves of *Valeriana officinalis*. Whiting Bay (Boyd).

Aug.

Viburnum

Phyllosticta Opuli Sacc. Syll. iii. 16. All. vi. 95. Died. 106. Mig. 36. Cf. *Ph. Lonicerae* var., *supra*.

Spots ± rounded or angular, occasionally confluent, 2–10 mm. across, pale-ochraceous, becoming dry and white in the centre, surrounded by a broad dark purple-brown border. Pycnidia few, epiphyllous, not crowded, lens-shaped, prominent, fuscous, 100–125μ diam., opening by a pore. Spores oval or oblong-ellipsoid, rounded at the ends (1-guttulate, Sacc.), 5–7·5 × 2–2·5μ.

On living leaves of *Viburnum Opulus*. Hampstead (Cooke). Cheshire (Ellis). Aberdeen (Trail). Aug. Sept.

Fr. Germ. Denm. Austr. Hung. Ital.

Phyllosticta tinea Sacc. Syll. iii. 16. All. vi. 94.

Spots somewhat circular or irregular, bleached when dry. Pycnidia epiphyllous, punctiform, flattened, about 160μ diam., pierced at the summit. Spores ovoid or oblong, 4–5 × 1μ.

On leaves of *Viburnum Tinus*. Kew Gardens; Swanscombe; Cornwall. Mar. Apr.

Spots irregular, brownish-cinereous, with a rather broad irregular border.

Fr. Holl. Austr. Ital. Port.

Vicia

Phyllosticta Viciae Cooke, in Seeman's Journ. Bot. iv. 115; Handb. 452. Sacc. Syll. iii. 43. All. vi. 154. Died. 107. *Ascochyta Viciae* Lib. *p.p. Phyllosticta Ervi* Westd.

Spots roundish, white or pallid, with a purplish margin. Pycnidia epiphyllous, minute, aggregated, black, pierced by a pore. Spores ellipsoid, biguttulate ("5–7 × 2·5–3μ", Allesch.)

On leaves of *Vicia lathyroides*. Cheshire (Ellis). Sydenham; Harborne. Apr. Oct.

This so-called species appears to be nothing else than an early state of *Ascochyta Viciae* Lib.

Fr. Belg. Germ. (on *Vicia sepium*).

Vinca

Phyllosticta Vincae-majoris All. vi. 155. Sacc. Syll. xvi. 844.
Died. 108. *Ph. Vincae* Thüm. Contr. Myc. Lusit. ii. 48, *p.p.*

Spots visible on both sides, nearly circular, ochraceous,
with a darker border. Pycnidia epiphyllous, covered by the
epidermis, then slightly projecting, globose, brown. Spores
ovoid-oblong, very obtuse at both ends, varying much in
size, 1–3 guttulate, 6–10 × 2–3μ.

On leaves of *Vinca major*. Kew Gardens; Forden.   Sept.

Germ.

Viola

Phyllosticta Violae Desm. in Ann. Sci. Nat. 1847, viii. 29. Cooke,
Handb. 454. Sacc. Syll. iii. 38. All. vi. 155. Died. 108. Mig. 58.
Duggar, 347. Maosoo, Dis. Cult. Pl. p. 412, p. 406, f. 126, 1–4.

Spots roundish, scattered or confluent, large or small,
white or whitish, without or rarely with a very narrow
brownish border. Pycnidia amphigenous, usually epiphyllous,
numerous, immersed, very small, brownish. Spores subcylindrical, straight, 8–10μ long, issuing in minute whitish
tendrils.

On living and fading leaves of *Viola odorata*. Rather common. England; Scotland.   Jun.–Aug.

Abundant on wild Violets, on which the large, often bleached and
even pure white patches are very conspicuous; more rarely on *V. hirta,*
V. tricolor. Some of the specimens seem to be young states of an
Ascochyta; and *Ramularia lactea*, which can occur on the same spots,
but on both surfaces, is probably a conidial phase of the same fungus.
Europe, U.S.A., Canada.

MONOCOTYLEDONS

Acorus

Phyllosticta acorella S. & Penz. in Mich. ii. 620. Sacc. Syll. iii.
59. All. vi. 157. Died. 18.

Spots visible on both sides, elongated, brown, later
becoming pale in the middle, up to 3 cm. long, about
5 mm. wide, scarcely bordered. Pycnidia amphigenous,
covered by the epidermis, then protruding the pore, smoky-
brown. Spores cylindric, somewhat thickened at both ends,
3·5–4 × 1–1·5μ.

On leaves of *Acorus Calamus*. Canal, Gt. Haywood, Staffs. (Grove & Rhodes). Aug.

The thickened appearance of each end of the cylindrical spore is due to the presence there of an oil-guttule.

Alisma

Phyllosticta Alismatis Sacc. & Sp. Syll. iii. 60. All. vi. 157. Died. p. 20, p. 22, f. 3. Mig. p. 58, pl. 3, f. 1–3, pl. 4, f. 3–4.

Spots broad, becoming whitish on drying, with a dusky border. Pycnidia gregarious, somewhat lens-shaped, blackish. Spores oblong-ellipsoid, rounded at both ends, biguttulate, $5–8 \times 3–3 \cdot 5\mu$.

On living leaves of *Alisma Plantago*. Cheshire (Ellis). Pembroke (Rhodes). Aug. Sept.

Spots roundish or irregular, varying in size, dusky-pallid, with a darker margin. Pycnidia epiphyllous, scattered over the spot, 130–140μ diam., punctiform, blackish; texture thin, membranaceous, translucent, pale-brown. Spores from $5 \times 2 \cdot 5\mu$ upwards. Without doubt the early stage of *Ascochyta Boydii* Grove (*q.v.*).

Germ. Ital. Port. Swed. Siberia.

Forma **santonensis** Brun. Glan. Myc. Herbor. 1892, p. 7. Sacc. Syll. xi. 482. All. vi. 158.

Spots visible on both sides of the leaf, round or oblong, abundant, up to 3 cm. broad, often concentrically zoned, pale with a brown border. Pycnidia mostly epiphyllous, immersed, just piercing the epidermis by the round pore, globose or lens-shaped, brown, darker round the pore, 150–225μ diam. Spores ovoid, $7–8 \times 3\mu$.

On living leaves of *Alisma Plantago*. Irstead (Cooke), Fung. Brit. exs. 431. Aug.

It is difficult to say what is the relation of this species to *Ph. Curreyi* Sacc. (*Sphaeria Alismatis* Curr.), found in Suffolk by Stock; *vide infra*.

Europe generally, Siberia.

Phyllosticta Curreyi Sacc. Syll. iii. 60. *Sphaeria Alismatis* Curr. Simpl. Sphaer. p. 334, f. 154. *Sphaeropsis Alismatis* Cooke, Handb. 429.

Pycnidia subglobose, chestnut-brown (at least when dry). "Spores ellipsoid, subglobose or turbinate, sometimes apiculate at the base, margined, 10–13μ long."

On leaves of *Alisma Plantago*. Epping (Cooke). Suffolk (Stock). Aug.

This does not appear to be the same as *Ph. Alismatis* S. & S., but no spores have been seen. The spots are very numerous on each leaf, small, roundish, cinereous, often scarcely bordered. Currey's so-called spores are probably subsclerotioid cells, the beginnings of a perithecium-content, as in *Phoma deusta* (*q.v.*).

Convallaria

Phyllosticta cruenta Kickx, Flor. Crypt. Flandr. i. 412. Sacc. Syll. iii. 58. All. vi. 161. Died. 79, 895. Mig. p. 60, pl. 1, f. 1–3, pl. 4, f. 1. *Sphaeria cruenta* Fr. Syst. Myc. ii. 581. *Macrophoma cruenta* Ferr. in Ann. Mycol. 1912, x. 288.

Spots numerous, 2–8 mm. diam., visible on both sides of the leaf, somewhat circular or oblong, bright blood-red when small, then becoming pallid in the centre. Pycnidia gregarious or scattered, epiphyllous, globose or lens-shaped, 100–180μ diam., at length opening by a minute pore; texture parenchymatous, rather thick, dark-brown. Spores ovoid or oblong, sometimes curvulous, up to 14–18 × 5·5–7μ, filled with thick cloudy or granular protoplasm; sporophores cylindrical, 10–12 × 4μ.

On living leaves of *Convallaria majalis*. Milton, Norths.; Earlswood, Warwicks.; etc. On *Polygonatum*, but without spores.

Frequently accompanied by *Asteroma reticulatum* (*q.v.*). A most striking species, attracting the eye by its brilliant contrast of colours. On the Continent it abounds on several species of *Polygonatum*, and is also found on *Smilacina*. The spots are much more often to be seen in this country than the pycnidia or the spores. It is not a good Phyllosticta, but to lump it into that monumental conglomeration of incongruities, entitled Macrophoma, hardly solves the difficulty of placing it, for the spores in our British specimens are ovoid and smaller, reaching at the utmost 10 × 4μ; the larger spores, described above, abound on specimens which I gathered in Germany on *Polygonatum*.

Europe, Siberia, N. Amer.

Dracaena

Phyllosticta Draconis Berk. in Plant. Port. Welw. p. 5 (*nomen nudum*). Sacc. Syll. iii. 60; xiv. 864. Grevillea, xix. 8 (*non* Karsten, in Hedwig. 1896, p. 47).

Spots irregular, pallid, with a purple margin. Pycnidia minute, pale, very thinly membranaceous, seated on the

spots, but scarcely visible to the naked eye. Spores ellipsoid, colourless, 6–7 × 3μ; on very short sporophores (in Berkeley's specimen).

On fading leaves of *Dracaena Draco*, in Portugal. This dangerous parasite is occasionally reported in our gardening papers, on leaves of *Dracaena terminalis, D. Cooperi*, etc., in conservatories.

The spots in the original specimens of Berkeley are very conspicuous, pallid, with a purple margin, and visible on both sides of the leaf. but the pycnidia in most cases contain no spores. Karsten, whose son found what he wrongly considered to be this Phyllosticta on *D. Draco* in Helsingfors, assigns to it very different spores (*l.c.*). See *Macrophoma Draconis, infra,* p. 126.

Fr. Port.

Funkia

Phyllosticta Funkiae Ferraris, in Malpigh. 1906, xx. 146. Sacc. Syll. xxii. 861.

Spots pallid, irregular, margined with brown. Pycnidia epiphyllous, gregarious, pallid with a rosy tint, pierced by a distinct pore, 115–150μ diam.; texture membranaceous. Spores obovoid or cylindrical, very numerous, rounded at the summit, hyaline, eguttulate, 9–11 × 3–3·5μ; sporophores very short.

On leaves of *Funkia ovata.* Dalry, Ayrshire (Boyd). Sept.

Ital.

Iris

Phyllosticta Pseudacori All. vi. 160. Died. 60. Mig. 230. *Phoma Pseudacori* Brun. in Bull. Soc. Bot. Fr. 1893, p. 223. Sacc. Syll. xi. 493.

Pycnidia widely scattered, minute, subglobose, erumpent, black, pallid within. "Spores subovoid, hyaline, 5 × 2·5μ" (Brun.).

On dead leaves of *Iris foetidissima.* Herm, Channel Is. (Rhodes). Bridlington. Apr. Sept.

It seems rarely to produce spores.
Fr.

Polygonatum, see **Convallaria**

Potamogeton

Phyllosticta potamia Cooke, in Grevill. 1885, xiv. 39. Sacc. Syll. x. 136. All. vi. 162. *Ph. Potamogetonis* Rostr. in Bot. Tidsskr. 1897, xxi. 48.

Spots pale-ochraceous, becoming brownish, without any distinct margin. Pycnidia numerous, hypophyllous, but

often also epiphyllous, punctiform, somewhat projecting, shining, black. Spores exactly ellipsoid, often biguttulate. up to $10–12 \times 2 \cdot 5–3 \mu$.

On leaves of *Potamogeton*. Lyndhurst; Epping Forest; Bungay (Cooke). Ayrshire (Boyd).   Aug.

Many of the spores were much smaller than the size given, even as short as 5μ, though remaining of about the same breadth. *Ph. thuringiaca* Died. (p. 82) is separated from this by Diedicke on slight grounds, but he apparently had not seen Cooke's specimens. Mr Boyd's specimens yielded spores that gave signs of becoming 1-septate, being slightly constricted in the middle.

Ruscus

Phyllosticta ruscicola Dur. & Mont. in Flor. Algér. i. 611. Cooke, Handb. 453. Sacc. Syll. iii. 58. All. vi. 162. Died. 94. *Phyllosticta Rusci* All. vi. 163 (Mig. 60) is the same, with undeveloped spores.

Spots roundish or irregular, especially situated at the tips of the cladodes, whitish or brownish, with a reddish-brown border. Pycnidia scattered over the spots, minute, globose-lenticular, at first covered by the epidermis, black. Spores oblong, biguttulate, pale yellowish-green, $7–8 \times 3 \cdot 5 \mu$.

On living and dead cladodes of *Ruscus aculeatus*. Kew Gardens; Swanscombe; Worcester; Hereford; Yorks.

Aug.–Dec.

Often associated with *Leptosphaeria Rusci* Sacc., of which it is the pycnidial stage. The pycnidia may appear on the living cladodes; the affected part then often withers and vanishes, while later the remaining part of that cladode and the other cladodes, when dead, develop the perithecia in abundance.

Fr. Belg. Austr. Ital. Port.

Sagittaria

Depazea (Phyllosticta) Sagittariae Rab. Fung. Eur. no. 553. Sacc. Syll. iii. 65.

Spots roundish, varying in size, pale-brown, surrounded by a paler zone of the leaf. Pycnidia few, epiphyllous, imperfect, containing no spores.

On leaves of *Sagittaria sagittifolia*. Bungay; Irstead, Norfolk (Cooke).   Sept.

The description is taken from Cooke's specimens.

There is a *Phyllosticta sagittifoliae* Brun. (Sacc. Syll. x. 137), with spores $8 \times 3\mu$, oblong or ovoid-oblong, straight or curvulous, without guttules, which may or may not be the same species.

Fr. Germ. Siber.

Typha
Phyllosticta typhina Sacc. & Malbr. Syll. iii. 60. All. vi. 165.
Grove, in Journ. Bot. 1922, p. 17. Died. 103. Mig. 61. *Ph. Renouana*
Sacc. & Roum. Syll. iii. 60. Mig. 61.

Spots amphigenous, at first oblong-lanceolate, 10–15 mm.
long, bright cinnamon-rust-coloured, becoming paler in the
centre, afterwards involving the whole of the leaf-tip.
Pycnidia occupying the centre of the spots, afterwards
scattered over the whole of the dead area, punctiform,
60–75μ diam., lens-shaped, black, at length opening by a
wide pore; texture thin, parenchymatous, somewhat tawny.
Spores ovoid or ellipsoid, hyaline, 4–5 × 1·75–2μ.

On the tips of the leaves of *Typha latifolia*. Kilwinning,
Ayrshire (Boyd).   July.

As shown in Journ. Bot. (*l.c.*), *Ph. Renouana* is only a stage of
growth of *Ph. typhina*, which changes remarkably in appearance as it
develops.
Fr. Germ. Bohem. U.S.A.

CRYPTOGAM

Marchantia
Phyllosticta Marchantiae Sacc. Syll. iii. 61. All. vi. 167. Died.
68. Mig. 231. Grove, in Journ. Bot. 1922, p. 16.

Spots indistinct, brownish. Pycnidia lens-shaped, punctiform, black, 70–100μ diam., pierced by a distinct pore;
texture parenchymatous, clear-brown, much darker round
the pore. Spores oblong-cylindrical, straight or faintly
curved, often biguttulate, 4–5 × 1–1·5μ.

On dead archegoniophores of *Marchantia polymorpha*,
Kilwinning, Ayrshire (Boyd). On fronds of *Conocephalus*,
Brecon.   Sept. May.

The pycnidia are chiefly situated on the upper side of the rays of
the *Marchantia*; the spores are rather those of a Phyllosticta, but the
pycnidial texture approaches that of a Phoma. The fungus on *Conocephalus* was closely similar.
Ital.

PHOMA Auct. recentior. (*nec* Fr. *nec* Desm., *neque* Sacc. *nisi p.p. minore*)

Pycnidia covered by the epidermis or the periderm, then erumpent, membranaceous or subcoriaceous, occasionally carbonaceous, globose or depressed, glabrous, without a distinct or prolonged beak, but with a small (sometimes indistinct) ostiole which may be simply impressed, but is more often papillate. Spores oblong or ovoid, more rarely fusoid or subcylindrical, seldom globose, continuous, hyaline,

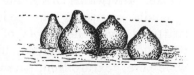

Fig. 3. A group of pycnidia of *Phoma acuta*, as seen on the wood of a dead stem of *Urtica dioica* after the outer tissues have peeled off, × 24. The dotted line shows the original position of the outer surface.

typically biguttulate; sporophores simple, sometimes very short or imperceptible. (Figs. 3 and 4.)

The species placed in this genus may occur on any part of any living or dead plant, less often on animal matter. They may be saprophytic or parasitic; but in the latter case they are usually wound-parasites. Many separations have now been made from the group as defined by the earlier authors but it remains very heterogeneous and has been used as a kind of waste heap or harbour of refuge for any Coelomycete with colourless and one-celled spores which was not fully explored or understood by its discoverer.[1] Cf. *Phyllosticta, Macrophoma, Dendrophoma, Phomopsis, Leptostroma, Plenodomus, Sclerophoma, Clinterium*, which have all been called *Phoma* in the past.

Fig. 4. Spores of: *a, Phoma complanata* on *Heracleum*; *b, P. Ilicis* on *Ilex*; *c, P. Acori* on *Acorus*; *d, P. abscondita* on *Scirpus maritimus*; all × 600.

In a typical Phoma the texture of the pycnidial wall is

---

[1] The use of the word "Phoma" has often been to the morphologist what the word "die-back" can be to the pathologist—a confession of incompetence. Nevertheless *nomen conservandum*.

more or less alike on all its sides, and may be called (pseudo)-
parenchymatous, being formed of one or a few layers of
brownish polyhedral cells, rarely darker round the ostiole.
The guttules are usually situated at the extreme ends of the
spore. It will be seen, however, that the species in the following list are very diverse. They are arranged in the same
alphabetic order (Dicotyledons first) of the host genera as
in *Phyllosticta*, except that a few species which are not confined to definite plants are placed in the forefront under the
heading Plurivorous, and that all those on CONIFERAE and
GRAMINEAE are put under the name of the family.

Plurivorous

Phoma Berkeleyi Sacc. Syll. iii. 134. All. vi. 294. Died. 149.
Mig. 237. Trail, in Scot. Nat. new ser. iii. 90, 121.

Pycnidia minute, subgregarious, immersed, then superficial, spherical, with a small papilla. Spores cylindrical,
biguttulate, very pale yellowish in mass, $8-10 \times 2\mu$.

On dead stems of *Lychnis diurna*, *Urtica dioica*, and
Sambucus nigra. Aberdeen (Trail). *n.v.* Winter.

Saccardo's species is the pycnidial stage of his *Phomatospora
Berkeleyi*, by which it is accompanied. The British record may be a
mixture of two or three species; see *P. exigua*, *P. Urticae*, but the
Phomatospora also is recorded on many hosts.
Germ. Denm. Ital.

[**Phoma chartarum** B. & C. North Amer. Fung. no. 390, in Grevill.
ii. 83 (1873). Sacc. Syll. iii. 168.

"Pycnidia scattered broadly as scarcely visible black
dots." On millboard, London, 1875 (Cooke, Fung. Brit.
no. 413).]

Examination of the original specimens, in Herb. Kew, makes it
probable that Cooke's "pycnidia" are the perithecia of *Cephalotheca
Kriegeri* Rehm (Ascom. Exs. fasc. 44, no. 1850, on white paper; cf.
Ann. Mycol. 1909, vii. 405, and Sacc. Syll. xxii. 30), with vanished
asci. See a full account in Kew Bull. 1921, p. 154.

Phoma complanata Desm. in Ann. Sci. Nat. 1851, xvi. 299. Sacc.
Syll. iii. 126. All. vi. 266. Died. p. 113, 895, p. 22, f. III, 3. Mig. 105.
Sphaeria complanata Tode, Fung. Meckl. ii. 21. *Phoma subcomplanata*

C. & M. in Grevill. xv. 107. Sacc. Syll. x. 177. *Sclerophomella com-planata* v. Höhn. in Hedwig. 1917, lix. 238.

Pycnidia varying much in size, up to 500μ diam., black, often shining, at first covered, then erumpent, at length quite superficial, soon depressed and concave, with a distinct papillate ostiole; texture of wall rather solid, parenchymatous, dark smoky-brown; contents white. Spores oblong, rounded at both ends, often slightly curved, biguttulate, 5–6 × 1·5–2·25μ. (Fig. 4a.)

On dead herbaceous stems, usually of Umbelliferae. Very common. Assigned by Fuckel to his *Sphaeria Angelicae.*

It is most abundant on *Heracleum* (*Sphondylium* and *giganteum*), but is found also on *Aegopodium, Angelica, Anthriscus, Oenanthe crocata,* etc. It is recorded also on *Rhinanthus Crista-galli,* but doubtless this is the so-called *Phoma deusta* Fckl. (*q.v.*). *P. subcomplanata* C. & M. is the same species in an earlier state; for a gradual change is observable in the appearance of this fungus according to circumstances—on dry erect stems the pycnidia are small; on those which have lain long among the damp grass they are larger and the stems are blackened around them. They are especially large on *Oenanthe*; on dry standing stems of *Heracleum* they are often under 250μ.

The pycnidia are at first covered, and have the shape of a flattened sphere, erumpent only by the papilla; they then become quite superficial as the epidermis vanishes, and at last collapse and gradually assume the form of a lunar crater with a well-marked central fumarole.

This species is given by Wehmeyer (presumably on the authority of Fuckel) as the pycnidial stage of his *Diaporthopsis Angelicae*; but this statement seems rather improbable, as there is not the remotest sign of a Phomopsis to be seen about the ordinary *Phoma complanata.*
Europe, U.S.A.

Phoma herbarum Westd. Exs. no. 965. Cooke, Handb. 896. Sacc. Syll. iii. 133. All. vi. 329. Died. 185. Mig. 109.

Pycnidia subgregarious, at first covered by the epidermis, depressed-globose, then erumpent and subumbilicate or furnished with a small papilla, blackish, opening by a round pore; texture thin, membranaceous, subtranslucent. Spores ovoid or ovoid-oblong, usually biguttulate, 5–11 × 3–4μ; sporophores very short.

On herbaceous stems—*Aristolochia, Digitalis, Malva, Menispermum,* Kew Gardens; on *Ruta,* Regent's Park; on petioles of *Catalpa,* Highgate; also on *Apium, Arctium, Angelica,*

Artemisia, Atriplex, Carduus, Campanula, Chaerophyllum, Dipsacus, Foeniculum, Galium, Humulus, Iris, Melampyrum, Phaseolus, Rumex, Sisymbrium, Stachys, Urtica, etc., in all parts of Britain. Most frequent in spring, often in company with a Pleospora.

An aggregate species, no doubt the pycnidial stage of various species of Pleospora. But, as there is probably a real multivorous *Pleospora herbarum* which can be spread to many hosts indifferently, so there is a *Phoma herbarum* corresponding to it and closely resembling it in appearance; this is distinguished from most of the other Phomas by its relatively broader and more ovoid spores, but many of the records are untrustworthy.

Distribution world-wide.

Phoma leguminum Westd. Exs. no. 1135. Sacc. Syll. iii. 147. All. vi. 187. Died. 128. Mig. 89.

Pycnidia punctiform, scattered or in groups, abundant, immersed, then erumpent, globose, black, pierced by a pore; contents whitish, then dingy. Spores ovoid or oblong-ovoid, somewhat obtuse at the ends, often biguttulate, $5-7 \times 2 \cdot 5\mu$; sporophores very short.

On pods of Leguminosae—on *Ulex, Sarothamnus, Vicia, Lathyrus,* Kew Gardens; Hampstead; Forden; etc.: on *Laburnum, Genista anglica,* Kew; Cheshire; Aberdeen: on *Colutea,* Kew Gardens.

It is very similar to and perhaps identical with *Phoma herbarum,* and is said to be the pycnidium of *Pleospora leguminum* Rab. Abroad it is recorded on pods of *Cassia, Cercis, Cytisus, Gleditschia, Robinia,* etc.

Europe, U.S.A.

Phoma longissima Westd. Not. iii, 13 (1854). Cooke, Handb. 421. Sacc. Syll. iii. 125. All. vi. 269. Died. 121. Mig. 77. *Sphaeria longissima* Pers. Syn. 31.

Pycnidia occupying long parallel cloudy black spots, which can extend even from one node to another, covered by the blackened epidermis, densely crowded, minute, lens-shaped, black, with an indistinct ostiole; texture loosely parenchymatous, brown. Spores ovoid, biguttulate, $4-6 \times 1 \cdot 5-2\mu$, often wanting.

On dead stems of various Umbellifers, e.g. *Chaerophyllum,*

Myrrhis, Heracleum. Worcs.; Yorks.; Berwick; Ireland; etc.
Locally common.   Autumn, winter.

Easily recognised by the narrow linear parallel deep-black stripes
which extend, sometimes with interruptions, for several centimetres,
even all round the stem. The colour is due to a dense weft of dark-
brown hyphae which connect the pycnidia beneath the epidermis.
Stripes from half to 2·5 mm. in breadth. The fungus is recorded
abroad on Chenopodiaceae and Rumex also.
Europe, N. America.

Phoma melaena Mont. & Dur. "Flor. Alg."(?). Sacc. Syll. iii.
135. All. vi. 268. Died. 120. Mig. 89. *Sphaeria melaena* Fr. Syst.
Myc. iii. 431, *p.p.*

Pycnidia gregarious or arranged in rows, usually crowded
on indeterminate very black patches, covered by the epidermis, subglobose, at length pierced by an indistinct pore,
100–200μ diam. Spores oblong-ellipsoid, straight, obtuse at
both ends, not or faintly guttulate, 4–7 × 2–3μ.

On dead stems and sometimes on the leaves of *Astragalus
glycyphyllos, Lychnis diurna,* and *Spiraea Aruncus.* Kew
Gardens; Warwicks.; Trench Woods, Ws.; St Cyrus, N.B.
Probably the pycnidial stage of *Sphaerella melaena* Sacc.
Syll. i. 513.   Mar.–May.

Recorded on the Continent on *Silene, Lathyrus, Vicia* and *Medicago*
also. The dense black stain often has a scorched appearance around its
margins, owing to the rich-brown hyphae, lying beneath the epidermis,
by which it is caused. *Phoma nebulosa* is less black and has larger and
less crowded pycnidia.
Europe generally.

Phoma nebulosa "Mont.", in Berk. Outl. 314. Cooke, Handb.
421. Sacc. Syll. iii. 135; x. 176. All. vi. 304. Died. 115. Mig. 83.
Sphaeria nebulosa Pers. Syn. 31. *P. Alcearum* Cooke, in Grevill. xiii.
94. Sacc. Syll. x. 172. All. vi. 304.

Pycnidia minute, gregarious, arranged more or less in lines,
forming irregular grey cloudy interrupted patches, covered,
with the ostiole sometimes subacute and prominent, at
others reduced to an impressed pore; texture at first thin,
membranaceous, of loose brown parenchymatous cells. Spores
oblong-ovoid, biguttulate, 6–9 × 3–4μ; sporophores very short.

On dead stems of various plants. A composite species,

recorded in Britain on *Althaea, Angelica, Astrantia, Conium, Daucus, Epilobium, Gentiana, Heracleum, Hyacinthus, Impatiens, Pastinaca, Rumex, Solanum, Spiraea Aruncus, Tamus, Urtica*, etc. Certainly widely distributed, but it has been often confused with other species.

It differs much on the different hosts, but is supposed always to be distinguished by its greyish-brown patches, arising from a thin subepidermal crust of brown hyphae. On examining Cooke's original specimens of *P. Alcearum* in Herb. Kew, I found that his measurement of the spores, $15 \times 5\mu$ as given in Grevillea, is incorrect; they measure about $8-9 \times 3\mu$.

Europe, U.S.A., New Zealand.

Phoma oleracea Sacc. Syll. iii. 135. All. vi. 273, with fig. Died. 124. Mig. 82. See also *P. Lingam* and *P. Urticae.*

Pycnidia scattered, lens-shaped, $250-350\mu$ diam., long covered by the epidermis, then just piercing it by the very small papilla, black; texture parenchymatous, dark-brown, often opaque. Spores oblong or subcylindrical, slightly constricted in the middle at times, obtuse at both ends, straight, uni- or bi-guttulate, $5-6 \times 1 \cdot 25-2\mu$; spore-mass often showing a faint-roseate or pinkish-pallid tinge.

On *Senecio Cineraria*, Budleigh Salterton (Rhodes). On *Tanacetum* (var. *Tanaceti* All.), Hanbury, Ws. (Rhodes). On dead stems of *Galeopsis Tetrahit*, Ayrshire (Boyd). On dead stems of *Brassica, Erysimum Alliaria*, and *Sisymbrium austriacum*; Kew Gardens; Cheshire; Ireland, etc. On dead stems of *Rumex Hydrolapathum, Scrophularia, Helianthus tuberosus, Angelica, Galium, Tamus*; Worcs.; Warwicks.; etc. Nov.–Jun.

A composite species, distinguished by its narrow spores; recorded abroad also on *Bryonia, Dipsacus, Solidago*, etc. Sometimes accompanied by *Pleospora vulgaris* Niessl, of which it is said to be the pycnidial stage; also sometimes by *Pleospora* (*Leptosphaeria*) *maculans* Tul. Carp. ii. 272, and, since these ascomycetes are plurivorous, the coelomycete is probably so also.

Europe generally.

Phoma petiolorum Desm. in Ann. Sci. Nat. 1847, viii. 16. Cooke, Handb. 421. Sacc. Syll. iii. 103.

It is, of course, absurd to think that any Coelomycete could be characterised by growing especially on petioles alone, or on legumes

alone. The form to which Desmazières' name has been chiefly applied
is *Phomopsis oncostoma* v. Höhn., on *Robinia* petioles, though the
name has also been given to fungi of the same genus on petioles of
Cytisus, Gleditschia, Sophora, etc. The name *Phoma petiolorum* Fckl.,
however, has been conferred upon petiolar fungi which do not belong
to Phomopsis, but are real Phomas; all these should likewise be attributed to other names.

Phoma porphyrogona Cooke, in Grevill. xv. 18. *P. rubella* Cooke,
in Grevill. xiv. 3 (Sept. 1885, *non* Grove, June, 1885). Sacc. Syll. x.
177. All. vi. 325.

Pycnidia collected on indeterminate red spots, semi-
immersed, somewhat depressed, black, scarcely papillate.
Spores narrowly ellipsoid, not guttulate, $7 \times 2\mu$.

On dead stems of various Umbellifers, Kew Gardens
(Cooke). On stems of *Heracleum* and *Chaerophyllum temulum*,
Cheshire (Ellis). Cf. *P. rubella* and *P. sanguinolenta*.

Phoma rubella Grove, in Journ. Bot. June, 1885, p. 162 (*non*
Cooke, in Grevill. Sept. 1885, xiv. 3). *Phoma Grovei* B. & V. in Syll.
Addit. p. 300, and x. 168. All. vi. 277.

Pycnidia gregarious, soft, lens-shaped, 250–300μ diam.,
sometimes shortly papillate, immersed, covered by the epidermis which is stained with pink or red, sparsely clothed
with pinkish hyphae, at length collapsing; ostiole pierced,
scarcely emerging; texture very thin, loosely parenchymatous,
olivaceous or pinkish-olivaceous; hyphae short, smooth,
rarely branched, about 3μ diam. Spores oblong, obtuse,
straight, biguttulate, 4–$7 \times 1{\cdot}5$–$2{\cdot}5\mu$.

On dead stems of *Cirsium arvense*; Bidston, Cheshire
(Ellis); Quinton, near Birmingham. On dead stem of *C.
lanceolatum*, Alvechurch. On *Atropa Belladonna*, Hereford.
                                                                    Apr.–Jun.

Probably the pycnidium of *Metasphaeria rubella* Sacc. which accompanied it on the *Cirsium*. Cooke's name, *rubella*, was given three
months later than mine.

It is an interesting question, how far the red colouring matter is
essential to this species and to *P. sanguinolenta* and *P. porphyrogona*.
While in many cases the colour seems to reside in and to belong to the
mycelial hyphae, there were not wanting suggestions that a form
absolutely indistinguishable might occur at times, on the same plant,
without any trace of red. See *Phoma Phaseoli, infra*, p. 96.

Phoma sanguinolenta Grove, in Journ. Bot. June, 1885, p. 162 (*non* Rostrup). Sacc. Syll. x. 168. All. vi. 278. Possibly a form of *P. rubella* Grove, unless the ascophores really differ.

Pycnidia loosely gregarious, globose or laterally subcompressed, conico-papillate, about 330μ diam., black, opaque, firm, nestling among the flexuous woody fibres of the stem which are tinged of a brilliant red or purple (as seen when the outer layers of the stem have disappeared), at length emerging, densely clothed with roughish septate branched purple hyphae which are 3μ wide; texture of crowded minute parenchymatous cells. Spores oblong, obtuse, straight, biguttulate, 6–7 × 2·5–3μ.

At the base of rotting stems of *Cirsium*, near Birmingham. On *Arctium*, Bartley Green, near Birmingham. On *Heracleum*, Cheshire (Ellis), but (?). Feb.–Apr.

Probably the pycnidium of *Leptosphaeria cruenta* Sacc., with which it was in company on *Cirsium*. The similar fungus, on a dead stem of *Heracleum*, from Cheshire, was mixed with *Phoma complanata*.

Aesculus
Phoma brunneotincta Cooke, in Grevill. xvii. 42, *p.p.*

Cooke's specimens, on the inside of dead husks of *Aesculus* (which he referred to the following species of Berkeley and Curtis by mistake) belong to a Phomopsis (probably *P. coneglanensis* Trav.). The true *Phoma brunneotincta* B. & C. is now called *Aposphaeria brunneotincta* Farlow (in Mycologia, 1922, xiv. 102), and the specimens issued in the Farlow Herbarium, no. 159, accord very well with those in Berkeley's own herbarium, to which he gave the name, except that they are slightly more superficial. Cooke's description (*l.c.*) is a confused mixture from both species.

Amorpha
Phoma Amorphae Sacc. Syll. iii. 68. All. vi. 178, 349. Died. p. 116, p. 22, f. III, 9. Mig. 89.

Pycnidia gregarious, covered by the epidermis, globose-lenticular, 100–140μ diam., pierced by a pore. Spores ovoid, rather obtuse at the ends, 6–7 × 4μ; sporophores not seen.

On twigs of *Amorpha fruticosa*. Kew Gardens (Cooke). Apr.

The specimens are somewhat doubtful. Allescher gives the size of the spores as 5–7 × 3–4μ, or in certain cases as much as 10μ long. Fr. Holl. Germ. Ital.

Apium
Phoma apiicola Kleb. in Zeitschr. f. Pflanzenkr. 1910, xx. pp. 22–33, f. 8–14, and pl. II. Sacc. Syll. xxii. 880.

Pycnidia scattered or gregarious, immersed, then erumpent, globose, blackish, 90–240μ diam., depressed above and not at all or scarcely papillate, pierced by a round pore; texture minutely but distinctly parenchymatous. Spores shortly cylindrical, rounded at both ends, hyaline, sometimes with a false partition in the middle, 3–4 × 1·2–1·8μ; sporophores merely the apiculate inmost cells of the peridium.

On stems and petioles of *Apium graveolens*, Reading; on seeds, Yorks.; on roots, Lancs.; etc.

Causing a serious disease, which can be transmitted by infected seed.
Germ.

Aralia
Phoma Araliae Cooke & Mass. in Grevill. xvi. 6. Sacc. Syll. x. 156. All. vi. 179.

Pycnidia gregarious, mostly seated on irregular blackened spots, small, subglobose, elevating and at length piercing the epidermis. Spores ovoid or ellipsoid, often biguttulate, 6–8 × 3–4μ.

On petioles of *Aralia spinosa*. Kew Gardens.

Cooke and Massee say "on stems of *Aralia spinifera*". Cf. *Macrophoma millepunctata, infra*, which occurs on the same host.

Phoma Tripolii Died. 120. Mig. 234. Aster
Pycnidia scattered or loosely gregarious, immersed, only penetrating the epidermis by the ostiole, subglobose, 75–120μ broad; texture of small brownish cells, with an indistinct pore. Spores oval-cylindrical, biguttulate, 4–6 × 1·5–2μ; "sporophores rather thick, up to 4μ broad" (Jaap).

At base of dead stems of *Aster Tripolium*. Llienawg, Beaumaris, Anglesey (Rhodes). July.

Pleospora herbarum was present on the upper part of the stems, as was also found by Diedicke in his specimens.
Germ.

Barringtonia
Phoma Barringtoniae Cooke & Mass. in Grevill. xvii. 79. Sacc. Syll. x. 143. *Dothidea Barringtoniae* B. & Br. Fung. Ceylon, no. 1172. *Phyllachora Barringtoniae* Sacc. Syll. ii. 613.

Pycnidia epiphyllous, less often hypophyllous, on large irregular glaucous spots, gregarious, subglobose, papillate, black, 250–300μ diam., covered by the thin shining epidermis which is marked over each by a pale spot and at length burst at the very apex; texture thin, parenchymatous, dark-brown. Spores elliptic-fusoid, with a guttule at each end, 10–17 × 4–5μ (13–15μ, C. & M.); sporophores subulate, at least as long as the spore or longer.

"On living leaves of *Barringtonia speciosa*. Kew."

I find the spores to be cloudy rather than guttulate, and to vary much in length. Not a good Phoma, but neither is it a Phomopsis. Excellent specimens were issued from Ceylon by Petch (Sydow, Fung. Exot. no. 278). In Berkeley's specimens of the "Dothidea", the perithecia are exactly similar to the pycnidia of the "Phoma", but the habit is different, being Asteroma-like; some of the pycnidia contained a number of imperfect asci.

Since writing the above, I see that, according to Petch, the specimens of *Phoma Barringtoniae* in Herb. Kew are not a fungus that grew at Kew on cultivated Barringtonia, but merely a part of the specimen named *Dothidea Barringtoniae* by B. & Br., collected in Oct. 1864 at Peradeniya.

Ceylon.

Bartsia, see **Rhinanthus**

Berberis

Phoma berberidicola Vestergr. in Öfv. Svensk. Vet.-Akad. Förh. 1897, no. 1, p. 18. Sacc. Syll. xiv. 866. All. vii. 789. Mig. 74. Grove, in Journ. Bot. 1930, p. 137 (*non* Brun.).

Pycnidia densely scattered, subglobose, punctiform, 100–160μ broad, covered by the epidermis, soon emerging and almost superficial, membranaceous, black; texture pale-brown, parenchymatous, darker round the slightly papillate ostiole; each surrounded by a few pale-brown branched torulose hyphae. Spores ovoid or ellipsoid, rounded at both ends, eseptate, colourless, eguttulate, 4–7 × 3μ; no pedicels seen.

Abundant on living branches of *Berberis vulgaris*, in a hedge, near Porlock, Som. On a dead hedge of the same, Fowey, Cornwall, evidently killed by the fungus. Apr.

The buds, on all the branches attacked by the Porlock fungus, were putting forth their leaves freely at the time when it was gathered.

Switz. Swed.

Phoma berberina Sacc. & Roum. Syll. iii. 72. All. vi. 180.

Pycnidia scattered or loosely gregarious, covered by the epidermis, globose-depressed, blackish-grey. Spores fusoid, biguttulate, $6-7 \times 2-2 \cdot 5\mu$.

On twigs of *Berberis vulgaris*. Kew Gardens.　　　　Mar.

This has been supposed to be the pycnidial stage of a Diaporthe. The British specimens I have seen under this name were imperfectly developed, but did not appear to belong to Phomopsis. See Kew Bulletin, 1919, pp. 179, 180, where *Phomopsis berberina* Grove is described.

Fr. U.S.A.

Beta

Phoma Betae Frank, in Zeitschr. f. Rübenzuckerind. 1892, xlii. 903, with pl.; Zeitschr. f. Pflanzenkr. 1893, iii. 90. Sacc. Syll. xi. 492. Massee, Dis. Cult. Pl. ed. 2, p. 195. Died. p. 123. *Phyllosticta Betae* Oud. in Kruidk. Arch. 1877, ii, ii. 181. Sacc. Syll. iii. 54. Died. 28. Mig. p. 40, pl. 2, f. 4–7. *Phyllosticta tabifica* Prill. in Bull. Soc. Myc. Fr. 1891, vii. 19. Prill. & Delacr. *ibid.* p. 23, pl. 3, f. 1. All. vi. 105, with fig. *Phoma tabifica* Sacc. Syll. x. 180. *Phoma sphaerosperma* Rostr. in Tidsskr. f. Landök. 1889, p. 746 (*non* Karst.).

Pycnidia densely crowded on whitish blotches of the leaves, afterwards on other parts, subglobose, black, immersed, at length often superficial, $100-180\mu$ diam., pierced by a rather wide round pore; texture of dark-brown parenchymatous thick-walled cells, darker round the slightly projecting pore. Spores ellipsoid, rounded at both ends, biguttulate, $5-7 \times 3-4\mu$, sometimes issuing in a tendril.

On the leaves, petioles, and afterwards on the "roots", etc., of *Beta* (Beets and Mangels), sometimes extending over the whole surface of a leaf. England (Kent, Surrey, Devon, Warwicks., etc.) and Ireland.　　　　Late summer.

Called "Black-leg", and often accompanied by the "Heart-rot" of Beet; it may become an epidemic and then be very destructive. *Ramularia Betae* is said to be a part of the same life-cycle. Later in the season the perithecia of *Mycosphaerella tabifica* Lindau, the ascophorous stage, can be found on the dead stalks, etc. It has been proved that the Phoma and the Phyllosticta are the same fungus (see Journ. Mycol. x. 2). It can be found on and be disseminated by the Beet "seed-balls".

Europe, Canada, U.S.A.

Betula

[**Phoma oppilata** Sacc. Syll. iii. 98. All. vi. 182. *Sphaeria oppilata* Fr. Syst. Myc. ii. 493. Cf. Sacc. Syll. iii. 449. All. vi. 968.

"Pycnidia scattered, erumpent, globose, smooth, black, with a subrimose ostiole. Spores fusoid, biguttulate, 7–10μ long."

"On twigs of *Betula alba*. Kew Gardens." The British specimens are certainly incorrectly named, but are too imperfect for further decision: not a Phoma.]

Swed.

Brassica

Phoma Brassicae Sacc. Syll. iii. 119. All. vi. 273, with fig. Died. 124. Mig. 83. (See Massee, Dis. Cult. Pl. 407.) *Aposphaeria Brassicae* Thüm. in Hedwig. 1880, p. 189. *Phoma oleracea* Sacc. Syll. iii. 135, *p.p.*

"Pycnidia superficial, rather large, densely aggregated, often confluent, hemispherical, plicate, dark-coloured, then brownish-black. Spores numerous, cylindrical, straight, rounded at both ends, eguttulate, 3–4 × 1·5–2μ."

On rotting stems and leaves of *Brassica oleracea*. The specimens on leaves of Cabbage, from Winchester, seem to me to belong to *P. oleracea* Sacc. (*q.v.*); they have oblong spores, 4–5 × 1–1·5μ, often subconstricted in the middle. I have seen no other British specimens.

Fr. Germ. Denm.

Phoma Lingam Desm. in Ann. Sci. Nat. 1849, xi. 281. Cooke, Handb. 418. Sacc. Syll. iii. 119. All. vi. 272. *Sphaeria Lingam* Tode. Fung. Meckl. ii. 51, f. 126. *Phoma Napobrassicae* Rostr. in Tidsskr. f. Landök. 1892, ii. 330; Zeitschr. f. Pflanzenkr. 1894, iv. 323. Sacc. Syll. xi. 488. Massee, Dis. Cult. Pl. 407.

Pycnidia gregarious, variable in form, convex, soon depressed and concave, rugose, dull-black, up to 1 mm. across; ostiole without definite shape, "decumbent" (Tode). Spores oblong, biguttulate, hyaline, 5–6 × 1·5–2μ; sporophores indistinct.

On fading or dead stems, fleshy roots, leaves, siliques, and seeds of *Brassica* (Cabbage, Cauliflower, Kale, Charlock, etc.) and on similar plants (Turnip, Swede, Mangel, Wallflower, Stock) in many parts of England, Scotland, Wales, and Ire-

land. It is often very destructive, especially when it occurs on seedlings.

This pest, "Dry Rot, Canker", is closely allied to *Phoma oleracea*, probably a mere form of it. Tode considered that the distinction lay in the variableness and inequality of its shape; Desmazières called it "a veritable Proteus". But I am inclined to regard that peculiarity as not essential, and as a sign that the fungus is in a subsclerotial state. See Plenodomus, *infra*. In fact the genus Plenodomus rests for its diagnosis simply upon this variability and the abnormal thickening of the cell-walls of the peridium. See T.B.M.S. 1932, xvii. 97 ff. and Sci. Proc. Roy. Dubl. Soc. 1933, new ser., vol. xx, no. 34, pp. 495–530, with two plates, for a discussion of this matter.

Var. **Napobrassicae** Rostr. in Tidsskr. f. Landök. ii. 330.

Pycnidia numerous, ovoid, black, 300–400μ diam., immersed, then superficial, appearing on the surface of wounds and cracks. Spores oblong, with rounded ends, 4–6 × 2μ, issuing as a gelatinous reddish mass or tendril.

On Turnips, etc.

Although there can be no doubt that this var. does not differ essentially from the form on Cabbage, I have included the diagnosis for completeness, since it may be biologically distinct; it is equally common all over the British Isles, except in the northern parts of Scotland. See Journ. Roy. Agric. Soc. 1903, p. 297, and Journ. Board Agric. 1900, vi. 448.

P. Siliquastrum Desm., *P. Brassicae* Sacc., and even *Phyllo. Brassicae* Curr. are forms of the same species, not to mention *Phyllo. Napi*, Sacc.

Europe, Australia, New Zealand, U.S.A.

Broussonetia
Phoma crassipes Cooke, in Grevill. xiv. 2. Sacc. Syll. x. 160; xvi. 873. Cf. *Phomopsis Broussonetiae* Died. 249; also All. vi. 182.

"Pycnidia somewhat scattered, erumpent, rather large, black, opaque, subglobose, at length with the upper half exposed. Spores oval, eguttulate, 6 × 4μ; sporophores thick, about three times as long and half as wide as the spores."

On small twigs of *Broussonetia papyrifera*. Kew Gardens.

Nothing exactly agreeing with this description can now be found on the Kew specimens, but what is considered a form of it (var. *foliicola* Tassi) has been found on the leaves of the same plant in Italy: "Pycnidia amphigenous, scattered, pitch-black, 250–500μ diam.; spores ovate-ellipsoid, 6–6·5 × 4μ" (Sacc. Syll. xvi. 873). Cooke's fungus, however, was probably the Phomopsis.

Calluna
Phoma affinis Brun. in Rev. Mycol. iv. 225. Sacc. Syll. iii. 85. All. vi. 207.

Pycnidia scattered or rarely two contiguous, black, erumpent, then almost superficial, about 100μ diam., ovoid or subhemispherical, papillate, very shining; texture thick, opaque, carbonaceous. Spores ovoid or rarely oblong, nearly always straight, rounded above, all but hyaline, often with one or two guttules, 7–8 × 2·5–3μ, slightly narrower and more acute in profile; sporophores subulate, 14–15μ long.

On dead stems of *Calluna vulgaris*. Sutton Park, Warwicks.
June.

I ascribe these specimens to Brunaud's species with little, if any, doubt.
Fr.

Phoma Callunae Karst. in Hedwig. 1884, p. 60. Sacc. Syll. iii. 85. All. vi. 207.

Pycnidia somewhat scattered, depressed-globose, always covered by the epidermis which is pierced by the minute papillate black ostiole, 200–300μ diam. Spores ellipsoid, very obtuse at both ends, eguttulate, 12–14 × 7–8μ.

On dry dead stems of *Calluna vulgaris*. Ayrshire (Boyd). Aberdeen (Trail). Kew Gardens. Winter.

Finland.

Calycanthus
Phoma aromatica Cooke, in Grevill. xiv. 4. Sacc. Syll. x. 143.

Pycnidia gregarious, covered by the slightly convex epidermis, depressed, rather minute, scarcely papillate. Spores sublanceolate, biguttulate, 8–10 × 3–3·5μ; sporophores short.

On twigs of *Calycanthus occidentalis*. Kew Gardens. Apr.

Owing to the poorness of Cooke's material, it is impossible to confirm this account altogether, but the species suggests the idea of a Phomopsis. It is not *Phoma Calycanthi* Schwein.

Castanea
Phoma eriophora B. & Br. in Ann. Nat. Hist. 1859, iii. 359. Cooke, Handb. 419. Sacc. Syll. iii. 154.

Pycnidia globose, free, at first pale, then becoming blackish, tomentose below and springing from a similar

mycelium. Spores very abundant, ellipsoid, slightly curved, biguttulate, 5–7·5 × 1·5μ.

On fruits of Spanish Chestnut (*Castanea*). Batheaston. Jan.

The specimens in Herb. Kew are in a ruined condition, but those in the British Museum are good. Saccardo, owing to a misunderstanding of the English words, says (*l.c.*) "in fructibus *Aesculi Hippocastani*".

"Pycnidia at first white, clothed more or less with white or yellowish cottony down like that of the mycelium from which they spring, at length dark, but when seen by transmitted light reddish" (B. & Br.).

Celtis

Phoma Celtidis Cooke, in Grevill. xiv. 3. Sacc. Syll. x. 162.

Pycnidia loosely gregarious, convex, prominent, covered by the epidermis and piercing it with the punctiform black ostiole. Spores oval, without guttules, 5 × 3·5μ.

On slender twigs of *Celtis occidentalis*. Kew Gardens.

Specimens very poor and doubtful. Cf. *Phoma celtidicola* Brun. (Sacc. *l.c.*). Cooke remarks that he occasionally met with another Phoma, on thicker branches, with fusiform biguttulate spores, 10 × 3μ; this latter might possibly be a Phomopsis, and the same as Brunaud's species, which *is* a Phomopsis.

Chamaerops

Phoma Chamaeropis Cooke, in Grevill. xiii. 95. Sacc. Syll. x. 182. All. vi. 334.

Pycnidia gregarious, erumpent, subglobose, black, opaque, irregular in size, pierced. Spores cylindric-ellipsoid, obtuse, often biguttulate, 4–6 × 2μ.

On petioles of *Chamaerops* and other Palms. Kew Gardens.

Not unlike *P. cocoina* Cooke (Sacc. Syll. iii. 156), but having shorter spores. It is not a good Phoma, for the spores appear to me to be in chains, and the pycnidia are very soft. Cf. Sirococcus, *infra*.

Cirsium

Phoma Cirsii Syd. in Hedwig. 1899, p. (135). Sacc. Syll. xvi. 868. Died. 130. All. vii. 794. Mig. 78.

Pycnidia gregarious on a cinereous indefinite patch which afterwards disappears, immersed, punctiform, globose, black, shining, at length protruding the vertex, up to 180μ diam. Spores oval, rounded at both ends, hyaline, eguttulate, 5–6 × 2·5–3μ.

On dead stems of *Cirsium arvense*. Sutton Coldfield. Apr.

Germ.

Clematis

Phoma vulgaris Sacc. Syll. iii. 119. All. vi. 282. *P. Clematidis-terniflorae* All. in Hedwig. xxxvi. (160). Sacc. Syll. xiv. 866. Died. 131. Mig. 97.

Pycnidia numerous, gregarious, covered by the epidermis, globose-oblong, somewhat lens-shaped, 100–150μ diam., pierced by a round pore; texture very thin, parenchymatous, clear-brown. Spores oblong-ovoid, not or indistinctly guttulate, 7–10 × 2·5–3μ.

On twigs and petioles of *Clematis Vitalba*. Cheshire (Ellis). Kew Gardens; Dartford. Apr.

Said to be the pycnidial stage of *Pleospora vulgaris* Niessl, in company with which it has been found; but see *Phoma oleracea*. It is recorded in France on *Medicago* also.
Fr. Ital.

CONIFERAE

Abies

Phoma dura Sacc. in Malpigh. 1897, xi. 306; Syll. xiv. 885. All. vii. 783.

Pycnidia scattered, amphigenous, immersed, soon erumpent, conical, hard, black. Spores cylindrical, curvulous, 5 × 1μ; sporophores fasciculate, 10–20 × 1μ.

On dead leaves of *Abies pectinata*, Italy. Reported on Douglas Fir from Surrey. *n.v.* It attacked the extreme ends of the shoots, killing the leaves and the terminal bud and forming of them a brown compact tuft. See Journ. Board Agric. 1904, xi. 501.

Araucaria

Phoma Araucariae Trav. Microm. Tremezz. in Malpigh. 1900, xiv. 469. Sacc. Syll. xvi. 876. All. vii. 787.

Pycnidia scattered, immersed, then erumpent by a minute slit, subglobose, black, 100–150μ diam. Spores ellipsoid, delicately granular, hyaline, 4–6 × 1·5–2·5μ; sporophores linear, 10–14 × 1–2μ.

On dry leaves of *Araucaria imbricata*, lying on the ground. Near Whitby; Mulgrave Woods, Yorks.; Robin Hood's Bay; Leamington; etc. Apr.–Oct.

All the spores seen appear to be incompletely developed; but there seems to be little doubt that the species is really an immature state of *Phomopsis Araucariae* (*q.v.* p. 181).

Larix
Phoma lineolata Desm. in Ann. Sci. Nat. 1851, xvi. 298. Sacc. Syll. iii. 150. All. vi. 200. Died. 149. Grove, in Journ. Bot. 1886, p. 134. Mig. 81.

Pycnidia small (250–300μ diam.), immersed, then erumpent, connate in short lines, black, pierced by a pore, at length surrounded by the longitudinally split epidermis; contents white. Spores ovoid or oblong, colourless, 5–8 × 2–2·5μ; sporophores short (?).

On outer surface of the scales of fallen cones of Larix. Hampton-in-Arden; Norwich; Herefordshire; Cheshire; N. Wales; Ayrshire. Apr.–Aug.

The pycnidia may stand singly or be connate, 2–4 together, in short lines parallel to the length of the scale, each group erumpent by splitting the epidermis. Spores ± lanceolate, on filiform sporophores about three times as long, often exuding as a tendril. (From Ellis's Cheshire specimen.)

Von Höhnel says this is a Discula; van Luyk (in Ann. Mycol. 1923, p. 137) says it is a Phomopsis, many of which are like a Discula. Probably more than one species is included under this name.

Fr. Belg. Holl. Germ. Denm. Austr. Ital.

Phoma Libertiana Speg. & Roum. in Mich. ii. 338. Sacc. Syll. iii. 73. All. vi. 193. Died. 160. Mig. 80.

Pycnidia gregarious, erumpent, globose-depressed, with a small papillate ostiole; texture parenchymatous, reddish. Spores ovoid, rather obtuse at both ends, biguttulate, colourless, 6–6·5 × 3μ.

On twigs of Larix europaea. Kew Gardens (Cooke). Said to be the pycnidial stage of Cenangium Pinastri.

It is recorded by Saccardo on Picea excelsa, and by Roumeguère on Juniperus; by Lind on Cedrus Deodara and several species of Pinus. Specimens of this name on Taxodium and Picea vulgaris Lam. had dissimilar spores. The British specimens are old and doubtful.

Fr. Belg. Germ. Denm. Spain.

Pinus
Phoma acicola Sacc. Syll. iii. 100. All. vi. 198, with fig. Died. 161, 897. Grove, in Journ. Bot. 1912, p. 50. Sphaeropsis acicola Lév. in Ann. Sci. Nat. 1848, ix. 256. Sclerophoma v. Höhn.

Pycnidia solitary or sometimes several in a row, globose, erumpent, surrounded by the split epidermis, rugulose, black, 250–300μ diam., very convex, rarely papillate, at

length pierced by an impressed pore. Spores ovoid-oblong, biguttulate, 6–9 × 3–4μ.

On leaves of *Pinus silvestris*. Cheshire (Ellis). Ripon, Yorks. (Ramsbottom). Wimbledon; Droitwich; Sutton Park; Marston Green; etc. On leaves of *P. laricio*, Hadzor Hall, Ws. Probably not uncommon. Sept.–Jun.

What has been considered to be the same species, on leaves of *Pinus Strobus*, from Glamis, has more fusoid spores, 5–7 × 2·5–3·5μ. See also *Sclerophoma pithyophila* v. Höhn. *infra*, which is a later and sub-sclerotioid state of *Phoma acicola*.
Fr. Holl. Germ. Bohem. Ital. Spain.

Phoma conicola Bayliss Elliott, in T.B.M.S. 1920, vi. 265.

Pycnidia gregarious or scattered, erumpent, spherical, 200μ diam., olive-brown or blackish, parenchymatous, covered in the lower part by minute vesicles which arise from the external layer, and fringed above by septate colourless converging hairs. Spores oblong, sometimes slightly bent, 3 × 1–1·5μ; sporophores short or longer than the spores.

On fallen cones of *Pinus silvestris*. Tanworth-in-Arden.

Accompanied by its ascomycetous stage, *Pyrenopeziza plicata* Rehm, f. *conicola*, which sometimes grew out from the pycnidium.

Phoma conigena Karst. in Rev. Mycol. 1885, p. 106. Sacc. Syll. x. 163. All. vi. 196. Mig. 82. *Phoma conophila* Sacc. Syll. x. 163. Mig. 81. See *Discella strobilina* Died. 752.

Pycnidia scattered or subgregarious, erumpent, soon superficial, varying in shape, for the most part roundish, at length dehiscing by a fissure, black, 200–300μ diam. Spores oblong-fusoid, eguttulate, 6–9μ long.

On scales of fallen cones of *Pinus*. Derbyshire; Swanscombe; Marlborough; Surrey; Worcs. Sept.

Distinguished by its soon becoming superficial. There is no doubt, however, that this is, at least in great part, merely a form of *Discella strobilina* Died. = *Sporonema strobilinum* Desm. (*q.v.*), and the same is true of its var. *abieticola* Sacc. on *Picea excelsa*.
Belg. Holl. Germ. Finland.

Phoma geniculata Sacc. Syll. iii. 102. All. vi. 200. *Sphaeropsis geniculata* B. & Br. in Ann. Nat. Hist. 1850, v. 375. Cooke, Handb. 427.

Pycnidia globose, covered, piercing the epidermis, with a prominent conical ostiole. Spores equal, cylindrical, curved, rounded at both ends, sometimes biguttulate, four or five times longer than their diameter, fixed obliquely at an obtuse angle on long slender sporophores.

On leaves of *Pinus Strobus*, sometimes with *Phoma Strobi*. Spye Park, Wilts.; Yorks.; Menmuir (Berk.). Jan. Feb.

The spores of Berkeley's specimens are exactly cylindrical, about $14-15 \times 2\mu$, rounded above, faintly pointed below, on straight sporophores about as long or shorter. But the spores were not seen in an oblique position; this point, emphasised by Berkeley, would seem to have been an accidental circumstance. The pycnidia are more or less imperfectly formed, but the material is very scanty. A specimen from Low Wood, Boynton, "on leaves of Silver Fir", but bearing the same name, is quite different. It is possible that Berkeley's species = *Fusicoccum bacillare* f. *acuum* Fautr. (*q.v.*).

Phoma pinastrella Sacc. Syll. iii. 101. All. vi. 199. Mig. 80. Grevill. xxi. 70. *Phoma Pinastri* Thüm. Beitrag. Pilz. Pin. p. 34 (*non* Lév. in Ann. Sci. Nat. 1846, v. 282, quae Diplodia junior).

Pycnidia gregarious, but never confluent, ± prominent, subglobose-conical, very black, surrounded by the burst epidermis. Spores copious, ellipsoid, straight or gently curved, tapering but rounded at both ends, usually biguttulate, the guttules being large and irregular, hyaline, $4-5 \cdot 5 \times 2-2 \cdot 5\mu$.

On dead leaves of *Pinus*. Carlisle, etc.

Fr. Germ. Denm. Austr. Siberia.

Phoma pinicola Sacc. Syll. iii. 100. All. vi. 199. Grove, in Journ. Bot. 1912, p. 50. *Pycnis pinicola* Zopf, in Hedwig. 1881, p. 146.

Pycnidia arranged in long rows, large, conspicuous, erumpent, surrounded by the laciniae of the epidermis, black, varying in shape, papillate or obtuse, thick-walled, up to 500μ diam. Spores elliptic-fusoid, rarely obovoid, with one or two guttules, always acute at both ends, not quite colourless, $8-10 \times 2 \cdot 5-4\mu$ ($8-12 \times 3-5\mu$, Sacc.); sporophores subulate, longer than the spore (up to twice as long).

On leaves of *Pinus austriaca* which were still attached to
a broken-off branch, Studley Castle, Wk. On cones of *Pinus
Strobus*, Cheshire (Ellis).   Aug. Oct.

Zopf and Winter both record it in similar circumstances, on half-
dead leaves on torn-down branches of *Pinus* (*silvestris, Pinaster*).
This is not *Sclerophoma pithyophila* v. Höhn., nor does it seem to be
quite the same as *Phoma acicola*, as von Höhnel says, yet it may be so.
Germ. Denm. Switz.

Phoma strobiligena Desm. in Ann. Sci. Nat. 1849, xi. 280. Sacc.
Syll. iii. 150. All. vi. 197. Died. 161. Mig. 81. T.B.M.S. 1913, iv. 124
(var). *Sclerophoma strobiligena* v. Höhn. in Hedwig. 1917, p. 244.

Pycnidia gregarious, erumpent and at length nearly superficial, globose, black, mouthless, somewhat rugulose, collapsing and concave, 200–250μ diam.; contents white. Spores
ovoid or ovoid-oblong, biguttulate, 6–8 × 2·5–3μ, but varying
much in size up to 10μ long, often embedded in mucus; no
sporophores seen.

On cone-scales of *Pinus excelsa, P. silvestris*. Kew Gardens;
Gamlingay; Worcs.; Cheshire; Hereford; Yorks.; Brecknock;
Glamis. Also found on *Picea* and *Abies*, and abroad on *Cedrus*
and *Thuja*.   Apr. May.

The variety *microspora* Sacc. cannot well be distinguished from the
type. There can be little doubt that this species is only the primary
or normal form of *Sclerophoma pithyophila* v. Höhn. (*q.v.*).
Europe, U.S.A.

Taxus
Phoma allostoma Died. 178 (*non* Sacc. Syll. iii. 74; All. vi. 254;
Mig. 81. *Sphaeropsis allostoma* Lév. in Ann. Sci. Nat. 1846, v. 294).
Cf. Grove in Kew Bull. 1919, p. 189.

Pycnidia scattered, chiefly hypophyllous, roundish, immersed, then erumpent, black, 100–150μ diam.; ostiole
papillate; wall of several layers of minute rather dark thick-
walled cells. Spores strictly cylindrical, straight, truncate
at both ends, furnished just within each extremity with a
round refringent guttule which makes them appear as if
thickened there, 5–8 × 1–1·3μ; sporophores densely fasciculate, persistent, linear-subulate, straight, colourless, subacute
at apex, provided with many minute guttules, 15–16 × 1–2μ,
rising direct from the inner wall of the peridium.

On dead leaves of *Taxus baccata*, Hadzor Hall, Ws.   Nov.

In plenty on both leaves and twigs at the same place
(Grove & Rhodes). Jan.

This fungus agrees well with what Diedicke found and called *Phoma
allostoma*; but it is not a true Phoma, nor is it apparently what
Léveillé called *Sphaeropsis allostoma*. The latter, as shown by a
specimen in Herb. Berk. named in Léveillé's own hand-writing, is a
Cytospora (probably *C. Taxi* Fckl.; see Grove, *l.c.*). Consequently
Sphaeropsis allostoma Lév. and the *Phoma* founded upon it by Saccardo, Allescher, and Migula (apparently without seeing the fungus)
must lapse, and the fungus must be credited to Diedicke, until it is
transferred to another genus, as will ultimately happen. The thick
pycnidial wall is quite unlike that of a typical Phoma and the same is
true of the persistent pedicels.
Germ.

Phoma hystcrella Saco. Syll. iii. 102. All. vi. 254. Died. p. 178,
p. 22, f. III, 8. Mig. 239. Grove, in Journ. Bot. 1886, p. 134.

Pycnidia amphigenous, scattered, a few here and there
aggregated in short lines, globose, papillulate, black, 200μ
diam., surrounded by the epidermis which is split open after
the fashion of a *Hysterium*. Spores obovoid, slightly pointed
below, with a large guttule or several smaller ones, 10–11 ×
5–7μ; sporophores cylindrical, half as long as the spore.

On dead leaves of *Taxus baccata*. Sussex; Surrey; Dorset;
Shrawley, Ws.; Cheshire (several places); Hampton-in-
Arden.

Saccardo considered it to be the pycnidial stage of *Physalospora
gregaria*, in company with which it was first found. Ellis's Wirral
specimens were chiefly epiphyllous, in lines parallel to the midrib,
with a longitudinal fissure over each.
Holl. Germ. Denm. Ital.

Phoma Taxi Sacc. Syll. iii. 102. *Sphaeropsis Taxi* Berk. Outl.
p. 316.

This is certainly only the immature state of *Diplodia Taxi* (*q.v.*).
Massee (Dis. Cult. Pl. 410), under the name *Macrophoma Taxi* B. & V.,
describes it as a parasite, causing living leaves to turn brown. See
M. Taxi, infra.

Thuja
Phoma thujana Thüm. Symb. Myc. Austr. iii. no. 62. Sacc. Syll.
iii. 102.

Pycnidia epiphyllous, gregarious, very minute (100–120μ
diam.), punctiform, immersed in the cortex, black, globose-

conical, emerging; texture thick, parenchymatous, dark-brown. Spores ovoid, rounded at both ends, eguttulate, 3–5 × 2–2·5μ; sporophores hyaline, short.

On leaves, especially at the leaf-bases, and twigs of *Thuja*. Lyndhurst (Cooke), in Herb. Kew.

There is, in company with it on Cooke's specimens, an early state of a pyrenomycete with young asci and long septate filiform flexuose paraphyses.

Holl. Denm. _____

Cornus

["**Phoma Corni-suecicae** (Sacc. Syll. iii. 86) on *Cornus stolonifera*", Kew Gardens (in Herb. Kew) is not that supposed species. See Sacc. Syll. xii. 524; also Allesch. vi. 350, where this species is stated to be = *Leptothyrium vulgare.*]

Crataegus

Phoma Crataegi Sacc. in Mich. i. 248; Syll. iii. 78. All. vi. 202. Died. 134. Mig. 98. T.B.M.S. vii. 224.

Pycnidia erumpent, subglobose or irregular, thin-walled, about 50μ across; texture parenchymatous, brown; contents white. Spores numerous, oblong, very minute, hyaline, 2–4 × 0·5–1·5μ; sporophores filiform, short.

On bark of branches of *Crataegus Oxyacantha*. Verdley Woods, Sussex. *n.v.* May.

Saccardo suggests that it is a pycnidial stage of *Otthia Crataegi* Fckl., to which Fuckel assigns *Diplodia Crataegi* Westd. (*q.v.*) as a pycnidial stage. The Phoma and the Diplodia were found together at Verdley Woods. Diedicke states that in one of the German specimens the pycnidia were thickly clustered over the pycnidium of a fungus resembling Fusicoccum.

Germ.

Dahlia

Phoma Dahliae Berk. in Sm. Eng. Fl. Fung. v. 284. Sacc. Syll. iii. 169. Cf. *P. fuscata* Sacc. Syll. iii. 123.

"Pycnidia (?) scattered, subhemispherical, rufescent, subpellucid, covered by the epidermis which at length bursts in the centre. Spores ellipsoid, turgid, pellucid, oozing out and forming a subglobose mass."

On decaying stems of cultivated *Dahlia*. King's Cliffe; Apethorpe, Norths. (Berk.). Kew Gardens (Cooke). Winter.

A doubtful species, as Berkeley adds "perithecium none". Cooke gives the size of the spores as "8 × 2·5μ" in the Kew specimen; but I

find them much smaller. *P. fuscata* Sacc. and *P. fusca* Preuss (Sacc. Syll. iii. 142) may be the same species, but it is impossible to decide. ? Germ. Ital. (on Dahlia).

Datura

Phoma Tatulae Kalch. & Cooke, South African Fungi, in Grevill. ix. 18. Sacc. Syll. iii. 128. All. vi. 286; vii. 799.

"Pycnidia scattered, very minute, punctiform, membranaceous, greyish-brown. Spores ellipsoid, 6·5 × 4μ."

On dead stems of *Datura Stramonium*. Kew Gardens.

Mar.

No spores could be found in these specimens. The species was originally described from South Africa on *D. Tatula*, and there is a var. *Stramonii* Pass. & Brun., with spores 5 × 3μ, on *D. Stramonium* in France (Sacc. Syll. xiv. 880).

Daucus

Phoma Rostrupii Sacc. Syll. xi. 490. All. vi. 287. Lind, Dan. Fung. p. 418, f. 31. *P. sanguinolenta* Rostr. 1888, and in Zeitschr. f. Parasitenk. 1894, p. 195, pl. 4 (*non* Grove, 1885). Massee, Dis. Cult. Pl. p. 408, f. 127.

Pycnidia hemispherical, gregarious, black. Spores ellipsoid, 4–6 × 1·5–3μ, extruded in filiform tortuous bright-red tendrils.

On roots of cultivated *Daucus Carota*. Also found on the stems. *n.v.* First observed in Denmark in 1887; a very destructive parasite, killing the attacked plants.

"Forms greyish-brown canker-like wounds that eat deeply into the root of the carrot. The mycelium persists in the root, and during the following season passes up into the flowering stem, which here and there shows depressed areas covered with the fruit of the fungus" (Mass.).

Germ. Denm.

Delphinium

[**Phoma Delphinii** Cooke, in Grevill. xx. 113.]

Cooke identified the specimens gathered by Berkeley in Northamptonshire, on *Delphinium Consolida*, with *P. Delphinii* Raben., as represented in Fiedler's exsicc. published in Klotzsch, Herb. Mycol., cent. 8; but in this he was in error. Berkeley's fungus is not a Phoma, but either an immature Leptostromatacea or, more likely, the beginnings of an ascomycete allied to Scirrhia. It forms a dense mass of dark hyphae and mycelium-cells, growing beneath the epidermis and bursting through it irregularly; the underlying cells are not spores, but part of a sclerotioid mass.

Rabenhorst's species may be described as follows: Pycnidia com-

plete, scattered, but approximate, globose-oblong, 250–300μ diam.,
immersed in the cortex, and covered by the unchanged epidermis
which is pierced by the papilla; texture thin, parenchymatous,
brownish. Spores oval, very numerous, 3–4 × 2μ; no sporophores seen.

Phoma tingens Cooke & Mass. in Grevill. xvii. 56. Sacc. Syll. x.
166. All. vi. 287. Died. 137. Mig. 97.

Pycnidia ± gregarious on large crimson spots which pene-
trate the matrix, subglobose, 330μ diam., black, papillate,
covered by the epidermis which is pierced by the ostiole,
then (when the epidermis breaks away) nearly superficial;
texture distinctly parenchymatous, thin, reddish-brown.
Spores oval or oblong, sometimes biguttulate, 3–4 × 1·5–2μ.

On stems of *Delphinium elatum*. Kew Gardens. A true
Phoma.   Jan.

It should be compared with my *Phoma sanguinolenta* which has
larger spores. The pycnidia are seated on or just within the wood, and,
when they fall away, they leave a whitish pit in the red-tinged matrix.
They are sometimes surrounded by reddish hyphae. Allescher's idea
that this species = *P. Delphinii* Raben. is only possible (although the
spores are very similar) if the red tinge is considered non-essential;
moreover in that the pycnidia are not seated on the wood.
Germ.

Diospyros
Phoma Loti Cooke, in Grevill. xiv. 2. Sacc. Syll. x. 157.

Pycnidia gregarious, globose, black, covered by the elevated
epidermis which is soon pierced by the prominent ostiole.
Spores ellipsoid, without guttules, 5 × 2μ; sporophores very
short.

On small twigs of *Diospyros Lotus*. Kew Gardens.   Apr.

The specimens are insufficient to decide with any certainty about
this species, but there appears to be only a Coniothyrium with oval
pale-olivaceous spores, measuring 3–5 × 1·5–2μ (? *C. Fuckelii*).

Elaeagnus
Phoma elaeagnella Cooke, in Grevill. xiv. 4. Sacc. Syll. x. 145.
All. vi. 206. Died. 139. Mig. 85.

Pycnidia scattered or subgregarious, minute, covered by
the convex epidermis, depressed-globose, black. Spores profuse, oval, continuous, hyaline, eguttulate, 5 × 2·5μ; sporophores indistinct.

On branches of *Elaeagnus*. Kew Gardens (Cooke).

These specimens are now somewhat battered and insufficient for determination.

Germ.

Epilobium

Phoma Onagracearum Cooke, in Grevill. xiii. 95. Sacc. Syll. x. 179. All. vi. 309.

Pycnidia scattered, seldom gregarious, lens-shaped, sometimes conspicuously papillate, covered by the epidermis which is slightly elevated and at length pierced by the papilla, black, up to 500μ diam. Spores oval or ellipsoid, sometimes biguttulate or quite hyaline ($6-8 \times 3\cdot5-4\mu$, Cooke), $8-10$ or even $12 \times 4\cdot3-5\mu$; sporophores short or imperceptible.

On dead stems of *Epilobium angustifolium* and *Oenothera biennis*, Kew Gardens (Cooke). On the former, Minworth, near Birmingham. Mar.

This might well be considered a form of *P. herbarum*. Holl.

Phoma Epilobii-parviflori Died. 139.

Pycnidia widely aggregated, immersed, then projecting, convex, $300-400\mu$ broad, opening with a wide pore. Spores cylindrical or oblong, rounded at both ends, biguttulate, $5-7 \times 2\cdot5\mu$.

On dead stems of *Epilobium parviflorum*. Hadzor Hall, Ws. Feb.

Germ.

Eupatorium

Phoma Eupatorii Died. in Ann. Mycol. x. 447; and Pilz. Brand. 896. Mig. 78.

Pycnidia loosely gregarious, occupying long grey stretches of the stems, seated on a subepidermal network of dark-brown hyphae, erumpent by the pore and at length throwing off the epidermis and becoming free, globose or elliptic, depressed, $150-250\mu$ diam.; texture rather thin, parenchymatous, dark-brown. Spores oblong-ellipsoid, rounded at both ends, biguttulate, $4-5\cdot5 \times 1\cdot5-2\mu$; sporophores inconspicuous.

On dead stems of *Eupatorium cannabinum*. Near Martley, Worcs. (Rhodes). June.

Germ.

Euphorbia

Phoma cyclospora Sacc. Syll. iii. 141. All. vi. 293.

Pycnidia subepidermal, lens-shaped, distinctly and firmly parenchymatous, pierced at the vertex by a pore. Spores subglobose or at times obtusely angular, 5·5–6·5μ diam., with 1–3 or more guttules; sporophores 5 × 1·5μ, deciduous.

On dead stems of *Euphorbia salicifolia*. Kew Gardens (Cooke).

Saccardo suggests that it may be the pycnidial stage of *Physalospora minutula* Sacc. & Speg. with which it has been found in company, but I could find no true spores (borne on sporophores) in the Kew specimens, merely loosened cells of a parenchymatous mass such as is often found in young perithecia.

Ital.

Forsythia

Phoma Forsythiae Cooke, in Grevill. xiii. 92 (1885, *non* Brun.). Sacc. Syll. x. 147. All. vi. 211.

Pycnidia very loosely gregarious, subglobose, punctiform, immersed in the bark which is slightly elevated and at length pierced by the minute ostiole. Spores cylindric-ellipsoid, with or without guttules, 4–5 × 1·5–2μ; sporophores short.

On dead twigs of *Forsythia*. Ayrshire (Boyd). Kew Gardens.   Mar.

A French form (*P. Forsythiae* Brun. in Rev. Mycol. 1886, p. 140) has spores 7–8 × 2–2·5μ, but no other difference; *P. forsythiicola* Syd. in Hedwig. 1900, p. (2), differs in its larger pycnidia (up to 650μ broad), its slightly broader spores, and its longer sporophores (12 × 1μ). The Kew specimens are poor and imperfect.

Fr. Holl.

Fraxinus

Phoma samararum Desm. Crypt. Fr. ser. 2, no. 148. Sacc. Syll. iii. 153. Cooke, Handb. 419. All. vi. 213. Died. 143. Mig. 95.

Pycnidia small, about 130μ diam., convex, black, covered by the epidermis which is at length split, pierced by a pore that sometimes becomes a fissure and is surrounded by the bleached epidermis. Spores oblong-ellipsoid, biguttulate, about 7 × 2·5μ.

On the fruit (samaras) of *Fraxinus excelsior*, chiefly on the wing. Very common.   Jan.–Apr.

It is very similar to *P. herbarum*; there is a form of it (var. *Aceris*) on the wing of Sycamore-samaras (in Cheshire). Cf. *Phomopsis pterophila*, which is quite different.

Fr. Belg. Holl. Germ. Austr. Ital. Denm.

Galax

Phoma Galactis Cooke, in Grevill. 1886, xiv. 90. Sacc. Syll. x. 178.
Phyllosticta Galactis Ell. & Ev. in Bull. Torr. Bot. Club, 1900, p. 54.
Sacc. Syll. xvi. 842. *Phoma galacticola* Henn. Not. Bot. Gart. Berlin,
xx. 382. Sacc. Syll. xvi. 870. All. vii. 803. Died. p. 143, p. 22, f. III, 7.

Spots irregular, pale-brown or cinereous, without a distinct
margin. Pycnidia amphigenous, gregarious in dense patches,
often following the course of the veins, 30–80μ diam., subglobose, punctiform, immersed in the epidermis by the base
alone, black, shining; texture loosely parenchymatous, dusky-
brown. Spores oval-cylindrical, curvulous, rounded at both
ends, with 2–4 guttules, 8–12 × 3μ (12–15 × 4μ, Cooke).

On fading and dead leaves of *Galax aphylla*. Kew Gardens.
Oct.

The pycnidia occur occasionally on distinct round spots, but they
are mainly confined to the faded or dying portions near the edges and
they also extend after death to the part which was still green and
living when the leaf fell. The fungus is probably a wound-parasite.

Cooke does not mention that the spores tend to be curved, and the
size he gives is larger than that of any of the spores I have seen. But
Phoma galacticola Henn., which grew on dead leaves, petioles, and
peduncles of the same host in the Berlin Botanic Garden and is
obviously only a more advanced state of the same species, is credited
with pycnidia up to 225μ across and ovoid or ellipsoid granular subangular "spores" measuring 8–12 × 7–9μ. This latter fungus, however,
looks like a subsclerotial state in the act of passing into the ascophorous stage.

Germ. U.S.A.

Gentiana

Phoma Gentianae Kühn, in Hedwig. 1883, p. 15. Sacc. Syll. iii.
120. All. vi. 295. Mig. 86.

Pycnidia somewhat gregarious, covered by the epidermis,
then erumpent by the minute papilla, or when the epidermis
breaks away becoming superficial, lens-shaped, blackish-
brown, at length collapsing, 125–250μ diam. Spores cylindric-
oblong, usually rounded at both ends, sometimes curved, not
guttulate, 6–7 × 1·5–2μ.

On leaves of *Gentiana acaulis*. Kew Gardens (Cooke). Aug.

Described from the British specimens. I have examined foreign
specimens, also, on stems, leaves, and calyces of *G. ciliata* and *G. lutea*,
but I could not find any trace of the bleached spots mentioned in the
original description.

Fr. Germ.

Hedera

Phoma Ralfsii Sacc. Syll. iii. 113. *Sphaeropsis Ralfsii* B. & Br. in
Ann. Nat. Hist. 1850, v. 374. Cooke, Handb. 427. ,

Pycnidia epiphyllous, scattered, covered, punctiform,
strongly collapsed, therefore resembling a Peziza. Spores
oblong or broadly oval, 7–8·5 × 4·5–5, with one or two large
guttules.

On leaves of *Hedera*. Aberystwith (Ralfs). Kew Gardens;
Kent; Sussex; Colwall; Carlisle; Menmuir; etc.   Apr.

"With *P. cylindrospora*, which was, however (in that case), confined
to the petioles. Scattered over the upper surface of the leaf, punctiform, black, strongly collapsed and presenting the appearance of
accurately defined excipula; spores oozing out on the application of
moisture from a central pore" (B. & Br.).

In my specimens (Colwall) the pycnidia were scattered widely and
singly over the dead part of the leaf, pierced by a wide pore and collapsed when old; wall very imperfect or none. I believe this is only
Gloeosporium paradoxum (*q.v.*, in Vol. ii).

Phoma leucostigma Sacc. Syll. iii. 105. *Sphaeria leucostigma*
DC. Flor. fr. vi. 144 (1815). *Macrophoma leucostigma* B. & V. *Sphaeropsis leucostigma* Lév. in Ann. Sci. Nat. 1846, v. 296. Cooke, Handb.
426, 921. *Phyllosticta leucostigma* All. vi. 47. Mig. 17.

Pycnidia scattered, immersed, convex, somewhat prominent, smooth, black, pierced by a "white" ostiole. Spores
cylindric-oblong, biguttulate, 10–12 × 2·5–4μ; sporophores
attenuated upwards, of about the same length, and narrower.

On dead leaves of *Hedera*. Kew Gardens; Lancs.; Cheshire;
Warwicks.; Cornwall; Wales; etc.

Perhaps not uncommon, but much confused; it is not the ostiole
that is white, but the fragments of the epidermis which are elevated
by it. It is said to be the pycnidium of *Metasphaeria Hederae* Sacc.
It has been recorded abroad also on *Buxus, Euonymus, Quercus* and
Rhododendron, but no doubt often incorrectly. Lind's record of it on
Hedera (spores 14–23 × 4–5μ) belongs rather to *Macrophoma cylindrospora*, and is a Ceuthospora (= *C. Hederae* Grove, *q.v.*).

It is recorded in England also on *Ilex*, but probably all these latter
specimens should be placed under *Phoma Ilicis* Desm., which resembles it in the puckered "white" ostiole.

Helleborus

Phoma effusa Desm. in Ann. Sci. Nat. 1853, xx. 220. Sacc. Syll.
iii. 144. *Phyllosticta effusa* All. vi. 125.

"Pycnidia epiphyllous, rarely hypophyllous, subgregarious,

then effused, covered by the epidermis, punctiform, 330μ diam., white within; ostiole erumpent, papillate, sometimes surrounded by a white halo. Spores oblong, rather obtuse at both ends, about 7·5 × 2·5μ."

On dry leaves of *Helleborus.* Kew Gardens (Cooke).

Mar.–Aug.

Though some of these specimens agree fairly well with those issued by Desmazières (Crypt. Fr. ser. 2, no. 357), the spores are distinctly tinged with olivaceous, and they belong undoubtedly to *Coniothyrium Hellebori* C. & M. (*q.v.*). The true *Phoma effusa* Rob. on Hellebore is said by some authors to be a Phomopsis.

Fr.

Heracleum

Phoma projecta Cooke, in Grevill. iii. 178. Sacc. Syll. iii. 126. All. vi. 325.

"Pycnidia gregarious, erumpent, globose, black, piercing the blackened epidermis with the prominent ostiole. Spores narrowly ellipsoid, with 1–3 guttules, 15μ long."

"On stems of *Heracleum.* Mickleham; Swanscombe. June."

This is probably a mistake. I can find nothing on Cooke's original specimens but *Diaporthe inquilina*, the loose younger spores of which were wrongly considered to be those of a Phoma. The fungus recorded under this name in Yorks. Fung. Flor. p. 320, "on decaying grass stems", must be something different.

Ilex

Phoma ilicicola Sacc. Syll. iii. 106. Grove, in Journ. Bot. 1886, p. 134. *Sphaeropsis ilicicola* C. & E. in Grevill. 1877, vi. 3, pl. 96, f. 28. *Phyllosticta ilicicola* Ell. & Ev., Fung. Col. no. 70.

Pycnidia amphigenous, gregarious, roundish or oblong, immersed, then erumpent, black, with a white spot over the centre of each, 200–225μ diam.; texture parenchymatous, dark-olivaceous. Spores ovoid or oblong, even somewhat pyriform, rounded at both ends, colourless, granular within, 9–12 × 5–6μ (8–14μ, Ellis); sporophores oblong, slightly tapering upwards but not always, irregular, 12–16 × 2μ.

On leaves and dead twigs of *Ilex Aquifolium.* Eastham and Bromborough, Cheshire (Ellis). Hampton-in-Arden; Edgbaston, Wk. Mar. Aug.

Named by Cooke and Ellis from the U.S.A., but the specimens which I have seen from there are ascophorous.

The spores and sporophores remind one of a young Sphaeropsis

which has not yet become coloured or (which is the same thing) of a
very young Diplodia. It is certainly not a Phoma. If it were not for
the distinct pycnidium, it would pass for a good Myxosporium. Is it
not the same as has been called *M. Nielianum* or *Gloeosporium Aquifolii*, var. *ramulorum*? See *Sphaeropsis aquifolia* Sacc. See also Died.
894. It is a much confused species. Cf. *Phyllosticta ilicicola, supra,*
p. 24.

Ital. (sp. 12–14 × 6μ, pluriguttulate), Denm. U.S.A.

Phoma Ilicis Desm. Exs. no. 1290. Sacc. Syll. iii. 106. Grove, in
Journ. Bot. 1885, p. 162. *Phyllosticta Ilicis* All. vi. 49 (*non* Oud.).
Died. 60. Mig. 17.

Pycnidia punctiform, scattered, covered by the epidermis,
globose, somewhat prominent, 200–250μ diam., black, pierced
at the summit by a pore; texture dense, formed of minute
dark-brown cells. Spores cylindrical, rounded at both ends,
often biguttulate, 12–15 × 2–3μ; sporophores 12–20 × 1–1·5μ.
(Fig. 4*b*.)

On leaves and twigs of *Ilex Aquifolium*. Lancashire;
Cheshire (Ellis). Cornwall (Hurst). Near Birmingham.

Jan.–Jul.

The pycnidia are each surrounded by a brownish stain; the epidermis is at first elevated and puckered over the centre of each to form
a little white spot, then pierced by the somewhat papillate black
ostiole.

It is similar to *Macrophoma cylindrospora* (Desm.) on leaves of
Hedera Helix, and if that belongs to *Ceuthospora Hederae* so should the
present fungus belong to *Ceuthospora phacidioides* (*q.v.*), being merely
an early state of its development. The Lancashire specimen named
Phoma Ilicis (in T.B.M.S. v. 424) has ellipsoid spores and is different.

Von Höhnel wrongly confuses Desmazières' species with the
Phomopsis crustosa which also occurs on leaves and twigs of Holly,
but the spores are totally unlike.

Var. **Euonymi-japonici** Sacc. *l.c.*

Spots whitish, irregular, ± marginal, surrounded by a
narrow brown border. Spores 11–12 × 2·5μ, biguttulate.

On leaves of *Euonymus japonicus*, Polperro (Rilstone).

June.

This should, I think, be called a Phyllosticta where I have placed
it, *supra*, p. 17, not a var. of *Phoma Ilicis.*

Fr. Belg. Germ. Ital. U.S.A.

Phoma santonensis Sacc. & Syd. Syll. xiv. 868. All. vii. 806. Grove, in Journ. Bot. 1918, p. 290.

Pycnidia somewhat crowded, and then often embedded in a thin black stroma, but often standing singly, subglobose, black, about 250μ diam., the loosened epidermis becoming whitish above the minute projecting ostiole, at length erumpent at the apex. Spores oblong, eguttulate, rounded at the ends, 6–7 × 2μ; sporophores not visible.

On dead twigs of *Ilex Aquifolium*, in company with *Camarosporium Ilicis* Oud. Quinton, Ws. Mar.

Fr.

Jasminum

Phoma domestica Sacc. Syll. iii. 81. All. vi. 210.

Pycnidia gregarious, covered by the epidermis, nearly hemispherical, pierced at the summit, about 200μ diam. Spores ovoid-oblong, hyaline, biguttulate, 3–5 × 2μ; sporophores filiform, 3–4μ long.

On thin twigs of *Jasminum officinale*. Kew Gardens. Apr.

On the same twigs was a *Coniothyrium* (? *Fuckelii*) with pale-olive ovoid spores, 4–5 × 2·5–3μ, mostly 1-guttulate; these never showed two guttules, and had not the same shape as those of the Phoma. Fr. Ital.

Lapsana

Phoma endorrhodia Sacc. in Mich. ii. 275 (1881); Syll. iii. 124. All. vi. 278. Grove, in Journ. Bot. 1922, p. 17. *Phoma Lampsanae* Dresad. in Sydow, Myc. March. no. 3193. Died. 148. Mig. 48.

Pycnidia gregarious, covered by the epidermis, blackish, globose, 200–250μ diam.; ostiole obtuse, perforating the epidermis; contents rose-pink; texture of wall thin, submembranaceous, distinctly parenchymatous, dingy ochraceous, only faintly darker round the ostiole. Spores cylindric-oblong, rounded at both ends, biguttulate, 8–9 × 1·5–2μ (or even 2·5μ).

On dead peduncles of *Lapsana communis*. Hopwood, near Birmingham; etc. Apr.

There seems to be no reason, except the presence of the rosy colouring in the spore-mass, to separate this species from *Phoma*

Lampsanae Bres. Saccardo's Italian specimens were on dead stems of *Centaurea*. Cf. *Aposphaeria Lampsanae* All. vi. 388 (Mig. 118), which is the same thing, more highly developed, on decorticated wood of the stems.

Ital.

Laurus

Phoma laurina Thüm. Contr. Fung. Lit. no. 164, pl. 1, f. 10. Sacc. Syll. iii, 82. Mig. 88.

Pycnidia gregarious, at first covered, then erumpent, round, lens-shaped, black; texture rather thick, parenchymatous, very dark brown. Spores ellipsoid, rounded at both ends, eguttulate, hyaline, $4–5 \times 1·5–2\mu$.

On dead branches of *Laurus nobilis*. Landaviddy, Polperro. Apr.

These pycnidia are smaller than those of Thümen's specimens, but have similar spores, and are probably the same species in a less advanced state of development. It is quite different from *Phomopsis laurella* (*q.v.* p. 195).

Ital.

Lavandula

Phoma Lavandulae Gabot, in N. Giorn. Bot. Ital. 1905, p. 69. Sacc. Syll. xviii. 258. Brierley, in Kew Bull. 1916, p. 113, pl. 5, 6, and f. 1–9.

Pycnidia on the stems, scattered, but sometimes very numerous and crowded, subglobose or lens-shaped, somewhat prominent, $150–200\mu$ diam., black, pierced by a round pore; texture thin, parenchymatous. Spores oval or subfusoid, uni-biguttulate, $4–5 \times 2\mu$; sporophores acicular, hyaline, up to $12–14\mu$ long.

On living and dead stems of *Lavandula*, causing the "Shab" disease. Kew Gardens; Kent; Surrey; Herts.; Yorks.; etc. A wound-parasite. Summer.

The beds at Kew were gradually destroyed. Brierley proved that the spores would not infect any genus except *Lavandula*.

Ital.

Leycesteria

Phoma Leycesteriae Henn. in Not. Bot. Gart. Berlin, 1900, p. 38. Sacc. Syll. xviii. 256. Mig. 75.

Pycnidia subglobose, black, pierced by a pore, covered by the epidermis and at length bursting it by a ragged

opening, about 150–200μ diam. Spores oblong, not quite straight, hyaline, 4–5 × 0·7μ.

On dead stems of *Leycesteria formosa*. Polperro (Rilstone). July.

Ligustrum

Phoma ligustrina Sacc. Syll. iii. 98. All. vi. 220. Died. 150. Mig. 237.

Pycnidia nestling in the bark, globose, 225μ diam. Spores sausage-shaped, 6–7 × 2·5μ; sporophores almost wanting.

On twigs of *Ligustrum*. "Kew Gardens; Regent's Park" (Cooke).

This was considered by Saccardo to be a variety of *P. endoleuca* on *Alnus*, differing in its larger pycnidia, thicker spores, and obsolete sporophores. A doubtful British species; the Regent's Park specimens are a Cytospora, with spores measuring 5–7 × 1·5–2μ.
Holl. Germ.

Lobelia

Phoma devastatrix B. & Br. in Ann. Nat. Hist. 1859, iii. 359. Cooke, Handb. 420. Sacc. Syll. iii. 132. Massee, Dis. Cult. Pl. p. 407.

Pycnidia very minute, punctiform, black, globose, pierced by a pore. Spores oblong, bi-triguttulate, 8–10 × 4–5μ.

On cultivated *Lobelia*. Shrublands, Suffolk, and elsewhere (Berk.). *n.ex.* Aug.

Massee states (*l.c.*) that in some instances the spores become 1-septate, suggesting the genus Ascochyta. Saccardo (*l.c.*) appears, by mistake, to have located "Shrublands" in North America.

"This minute species, all but invisible to the naked eye, was most destructive in the gardens of Sir W. Middleton in 1856. The pycnidia are globose and perforated with a minute round aperture" (B. & Br.).

Lonicera

Phoma minutula Sacc. Syll. iii. 70. All. vi. 221. Died. 152. Mig. 76.

Pycnidia somewhat scattered, black, globose, piercing the epidermis, about 125μ diam.; texture minutely parenchymatous, ochreo-fuliginous. Spores numerous, allantoid, 4 × 1μ: no pedicels seen.

On small living and fading stems of *Lonicera Caprifolium*, *L. Periclymenum*. Polperro; Hartlebury Common (Rhodes). Edgbaston Botanic Gardens, Birmingham. Apr.–Jul.

Other more ovoid spores, such as are mentioned by Saccardo (*l.c.*) were occasionally seen intermixed with the sausage-shaped spores. Recorded on the Continent on *L. Xylosteum*. Cf. *Phoma Xylostei, infra*. Fr. Germ. ? Argentina.

[**Phoma viventis** Cooke, in Grevill. xiv. 2. Sacc. Syll. x. 145.

"On still living twigs of *Lonicera*, Kew Gardens. Apr."] There is no *Phoma* on these specimens, but only *Coniothyrium* (? *Fuckelii*), with very pale spores, 6–7 × 2·5μ.

Phoma Xylostei Cooke & Harkn. Californ. Fung. in Grevill. ix. 82. Sacc. Syll. iii. 70.

Pycnidia scattered, punctiform, somewhat prominent, black. Spores ellipsoid, 6 × 3μ.

On twigs of *Lonicera Periclymenum*. Aberdeen (Trail). Kew Gardens (Cooke). Winter and spring.

"Pycnidia subepidermal; spores oblong or nearly ellipsoid, 5–7 × 2·5–3μ" (Trail). All the specimens I have seen, while possibly belonging to this species, were imperfectly developed. The original specimens were on *Lonicera hispidula*, from California. U.S.A.

Lycium
Phoma Barbari Cooke, in Grevill. xiv. 3. Sacc. Syll. x. 156. All. vi. 222. Died. 153. Mig. 104.

Pycnidia loosely gregarious and clustered two or three together, covered by the epidermis, globose, subpapillate, about 200–250μ diam., pierced at the summit, at length erumpent and girt by the burst epidermis; texture thin, parenchymatous, yellowish-brown, darker round the pore. Spores oval, rounded at both ends, biguttulate, 5–7 × 2·5–3μ.

On twigs of *Lycium barbarum*. Kew Gardens. Apr.

Cooke's statement "not erumpent" must be a slip of the pen; his specimens are decidedly erumpent. Germ.

Mahonia
Phoma Mahoniae Thüm. Contr. Mic. Litor. no. 161, pl. 1, f. 10. Sacc. Syll. iii. 117. *Phyllosticta Aquifolii* All. vi. 57. Mig. 21.

Spots irregular, greyish-brown, at length whitish and dry. Pycnidia epiphyllous, rarely amphigenous, densely gregarious, of moderate size, globose, black. Spores cylindric-ellipsoid, obtusely rounded at both ends, 3–4 × 1–1·5μ.

On leaves of *Mahonia Aquifolium*. Kew Gardens; Highgate; Swanscombe.   Mar.

There seems to be considerable confusion about the species on
Mahonia. There is a *Phyllosticta Mahoniae* Sacc. & Speg. (*q.v.*), which
is said to occur on fallen leaves without producing any definite spots
and to have spores 4–6 × 3–4μ.

Phoma mahoniana Sacc. in Mich. ii. 90; Syll. iii. 117. Cf. *Phyllosticta mahoniana* All. vi. 57. Died. 67.

Pycnidia on dry parts of the leaf, loosely gregarious,
globose-depressed, 150μ diam.; texture densely parenchymatous. Spores oblong, hyaline, 8–10 × 2μ (10–12 × 3–4μ, Ellis);
sporophores linear, 10–12μ long.

On dry leaves of *Mahonia Aquifolium*, accompanied by a
Phyllosticta. Lancashire; Flintshire (Ellis). Kew Gardens.
                                                         Apr.

Ellis's specimens belong rather to Saccardo's var. *sicula* (Syll. xvi.
851), with spores 8–10 × 3·5–4μ.
Saccardo remarks (*l.c.*) that this Phoma is accompanied by a
Phyllosticta. Probably *all* the five Coelomycetes of these genera here
recorded on *Mahonia* are forms of one species! See Mich. i. 153; Syll.
iii. 25, 26. The Phoma appears to come chiefly on those parts of the
leaf (mainly along the margin) which have died through want of water
and become dry and whitish. According to specimens I have seen, the
same may be said of the *Phyllosticta Mahoniae* S. & S. If there is any
real difference, it is this: the Phyllosticta grows on fully living leaves;
it may come on the margin, but often occurs on the middle part of the
leaf and makes a definite Phyllosticta-like spot—the Phoma grows on
dry dead patches, say round the edge of the leaf, which have already
become whitish or lost their colour.
Fr. Germ. Austr. U.S.A.

                                                       Malus
Phoma malorum Sacc. Syll. iii. 152. *Sphaeropsis malorum* Berk.
Outl. 316 (1860).

Pycnidia globose or subglobose, covered by the blackened
epidermis, erumpent by a rather long papilla; stroma blackish.
Spores ellipsoid, granular, greenish, about 30μ long.

Recorded on stored apples and on apples lying on the
ground. Not uncommon in England.

This is only an early state of growth of *Diplodia malorum*. *Sphaeropsis malorum* Peck in 34th Ann. Rep. N.Y. State Mus. 1881, p. 36,
pl. 4, f. 16–21 (Sacc. Syll. iii. 294) looks like a slightly later stage of the

same, but see Stevens, in Mycologia, 1933, xxv. 536, where the distinction of the two *Sphaeropses* is strongly maintained.

Phoma Bismarckii Kidd & Beaum. in T.B.M.S. 1924, x. 104.

"Pycnidia brown, subglobose, about 300μ diam., with many ostioles which are black and 30μ diam. Spores ellipsoid, hyaline, 5–8 × 2–3μ, issuing in rosy tendrils."

On Apple branch (?). "On one occasion only. The rot was dry, shallow, and brown, arising at a lenticel", T.B.M.S. *l.c.*

The many-ostioled state of the pycnidia is a frequent result of the unnatural conditions in which Petripatellists rear their unfortunate progeny. Cf. *Phoma polystoma* Tassi, in Bull Lab. Ort. Bot. Siena, 1900, p. 123, pl. 15, f. 2; Sacc. Syll. xvi. 858.

Marrubium
Phoma Labiatarum Cooke, in Grevill. xiii. 95. Sacc. Syll. x. 174.

Pycnidia scattered, punctiform, 100–200μ diam., covered by the epidermis, at length prominent, convex, black, shining, not papillate; texture thin, loosely parenchymatous, dark-brown. Spores oval, 5–6 × 2·5–3μ, but variable; sporophores short.

On dead stems of *Marrubium vulgare*. Kew Gardens (Cooke). Cleeve Hill, Cheltenham (Rhodes). Feb. Mar.

Phoma Marrubii Sacc. Syll. iii. 129 has spores 10μ long.

Mercurialis
Phoma macrocapsa Trail, in Scot. Nat. 1886, p. 327. Sacc. Syll. x. 180. All. vi. 307. Died. 155. Mig. 237.

Pycnidia subepidermal, at length nearly superficial, depressed-globose, 600–700μ diam., reaching to a height of 250μ (exclusive of the ostiole which is about 100–150μ in length), dark-brown; texture very thick, of small dense parenchymatous cells. Spores oblong, subacute at both ends, 4–5 × 1–1·5μ.

On dead stems of *Mercurialis perennis*. Near Old Aberdeen. *n.v.* "Remarkable for its large pycnidia." May.

Sydow (Mycoth. germ. no. 1050) issued the same fungus, in company with *Leptothyrium Mercurialis* Kab. & Bub.
Germ.

Morus
Phoma Mororum Sacc. Syll. iii. 95. All. vi. 225.

Pycnidia gregarious, covered by the epidermis, scarcely erumpent, globose, ± depressed, about 200μ diam., obtuse, pierced at the summit; texture thin, brownish-yellow, parenchymatous. Spores oblong or ovoid, obtuse, without guttules, 6–8 × 2·5–3μ; sporophores none or indistinct.

On twigs of *Morus alba*. Kew Gardens. Apr.

Saccardo states that, in the spring of 1884, it appeared in northern Italy in great abundance on unhealthy (but still living) twigs of *Morus alba*, to which it did great harm. There could scarcely be found a more perfect example of the difference between Phoma and Phomopsis than in the two fungi on the Mulberry, this and *Phomopsis moricola*; the mycelium described (*l.c.*) by Saccardo was not to be seen in the British specimens.
Holl. Ital.

Mühlenbeckia
Phoma Mühlenbeckiae Cooke & Mass. in Grevill. xvi. 6. Sacc. Syll. x. 157. All. vi. 226.

Pycnidia exceedingly minute, densely gregarious, covered by the epidermis, subglobose, membranaceous, papillate. Spores ellipsoid, 3 × 2μ; sporophores short.

On dead stems of *Mühlenbeckia*. Kew Gardens. *n.ex.* May.

Nelumbium
Phoma Nelumbii Cooke & Mass. in Grevill. xvi. 78. Sacc. Syll. x. 172. All. vi. 307.

Pycnidia scattered, erumpent, soon becoming naked and prominent, almost superficial, subglobose, black, opaque, 160μ diam.; texture very thin, parenchymatous, umber-brown. Spores oval, cloudy-granular, rounded at both ends, with a distinct central guttule, 8–10 × 5–6μ.

On fading stems of *Nelumbium speciosum*. Kew Gardens.
Feb.

The wall of the spore is not thick, as stated in Grevillea.

Nepenthes
Phoma Nepenthis Cooke & Mass. in Grevill. xviii. 73. Sacc. Syll. x. 179. All. vi. 308.

Pycnidia scattered, immersed, black, membranaceous, pierced. Spores ellipsoid, biguttulate, 7 × 3–3·5μ; sporophores short.

On dead pitchers of *Nepenthes*. Redlands, Glasgow (Boyd).
n.ex.   Jan.

Ononis

Phoma Zopfiana All. in Hedwig. xxxiii. 123 (as *P. Zopfii*); Krypt.
Flor. vi. 309. Sacc. Syll. xi. 489. Died. 156. Mig. 92.

Pycnidia scattered or gregarious, subepidermal, then
erumpent, depressed but papillate; texture parenchymatous.
Spores numerous, oval-oblong, obtuse at both ends, eguttulate, hyaline, $5-8 \times 2-3\mu$; sporophores not seen.

On *Ononis repens*. Sea shore, Llandanwg, Mer. (Rhodes).
                                                        Aug.

P. Ononidis All., found on the stems of *O. spinosa* in Germany by
Zopf, is said to differ in having larger spores and filiform sporophores
(? identical).
Germ.

Paulownia

Phoma Paulowniae Thüm. Contr. Fung. Lit. no. 171, pl. 1, f. 33.
Sacc. Syll. iii. 92. All. vi. 229.

Pycnidia thinly scattered, globose, black, at first covered
by the epidermis, then perforating it sometimes in long
fissures. Spores minute, cylindrical or cylindric-ovoid, between rounded and acute at the ends, without guttules,
$3\cdot5-5 \times 1\cdot5\mu$.

On dry twigs of *Paulownia imperialis*. Kew Gardens
(Cooke).

Among the fungi on these specimens is one which may be identical
with Thümen's species, but it is very doubtful. In French specimens
the spores are cylindrical, tapering at the ends, $5-6 \times 2\mu$; nothing
exactly resembling this could be found in Cooke's specimens, although
there is an immature *Coniothyrium* (? *Fuckelii*) and possibly a
Phomopsis.
Fr. Holl. Austr.

Phaseolus

Phoma Phaseoli Desm. Descr. Esp. nouv. crypt. 1836, p. 13.
Sacc. Syll. iii. 120. All. vi. 312. Died. 158. Mig. 92.

Pycnidia orbicular, convex, with a round pore. Spores
oblong, colourless, biguttulate, $10-12\mu$ long.

On stems of *Phaseolus multiflorus*. Edgbaston, Birmingham; etc.

A form with shorter spores, at Edgbaston in Dec. 1908, on purplish or red spots, I call *rubriseda*. Cf. *Phoma rubella, supra*, p. 64.
Fr. Belg. Germ.

Philadelphus

Phoma Philadelphi Cooke, in Grevill. xiii. 93. Sacc. Syll. x. 148. All. vi. 230.

"Pycnidia generally gregarious in lines, rather small, covered by the epidermis which is scarcely elevated, immersed in the bark, depressed, black, pierced. Spores cylindrical, obtuse at the ends, eguttulate, hyaline, 12 × 2·5μ."

On branches of *Philadelphus*. Kew Gardens. Apr.

It is stated by Cooke to differ in habit and in spores from *Phomopsis Landeghemiae*, which occurred on the smaller branchlets of the same host. There is a Phoma on the branches of Cooke's specimen, but no spores could be found in it.
Fr.

Phlomis

Phoma Phlomidis Cooke, in Grevill. xiii. 44. Sacc. Syll. x. 173. (Not *Dothidea Phlomidis* Lév. Voy. Demid. ii. 108, pl. 5, f. 2; nor *Phoma Phlomidis* Thüm. Sacc. Syll. iii. 129.)

Pycnidia scattered or gregarious, erumpent and at length superficial, globose or subconical, black, shining, about 1 mm. diam. "Spores cylindrical, simple, pellucid, obtuse, 20 × 4μ" (Cooke, *l.c.*).

On stems of *Phlomis fruticosa*. Kew Gardens. May.

I could find no spores in this specimen, which is therefore doubtful; but it is not *Phomopsis Desmazieri* var. *Phlomidis* Grove, in Journ. Bot. 1930, p. 272, on the same host. Léveillé's specimens were on the leaves, as were those of Karsten and Hariot (Journ. de Bot. 1890, iv. 358) who named theirs also *Phoma Phlomidis*; both have cylindrical spores 4–6 × 1μ; Thümen's spores measured 10–12 × 2–2·5μ.

Plantago

Phoma polygramma Sacc. Syll. iii. 130. All. vi. 270. Died. 122. Mig. 88. *Sphaeria polygramma* Fr. Syst. Myc. ii. 432. *Sphaeropsis polygramma* Fr. Sum. Veg. Scand. 419.

Pycnidia covered by the epidermis, then piercing it and often becoming nearly superficial, arranged in rows of some-

times considerable length, occasionally confluent, connected with one another by subepidermal hyphae, at first clear-, then dark-brown, 70–100μ diam. Spores oblong-ovoid, obtuse at both ends, with or without guttules, 5–7 × 2·5–3μ.

On dead peduncles of *Plantago lanceolata*. Not common. Recorded abroad on *Ballota nigra* and *Galeopsis* also.

Akin to *Phoma nebulosa*, but the pycnidia are in lines, and do not form such grey cloudy patches, and are also smaller than in that species. Probably the pycnidium of *Mycosphaerella polygramma* Joh. & Magn. Quite unlike *Phomopsis subordinaria*.
Germ. Swed.

Platanus

Phoma dispersa Cooke, in Grevill. xiii. 93. Sacc. Syll. x. 161.

Pycnidia hypophyllous, thinly scattered, subglobose or lens-shaped, erumpent, then ± superficial, at length collapsed, opaque, black, about 300μ diam.; texture very soft and thin, parenchymatous, brownish. Spores numerous, ellipsoid or ovoid-oblong, rounded at both ends, hyaline, eguttulate, 8–11 × 4–5μ; sporophores very short.

On dead fallen leaves of *Platanus*. Kew Gardens (Cooke).

May not this be merely a state of *Gloeosporium nervisequum* (*q.v.*)? The spore-measurements (15 × 6μ) given by Cooke (*l.c.*) seem to be erroneous.

Phoma hapalocystis Sacc. Syll. iii. 94. All. vi. 232. Died. 163. Mig. 96.

"Pycnidia in clusters underneath the bark which is at length fissured, globose, papillate, black. Spores cylindrical, curved, 3 × 1μ."

On dead branches of *Platanus*. Kew Gardens. *n.v.*

This is said to be the pycnidial stage of *Pseudovalsa hapalocystis* Sacc., but the same is said of *Fusicoccum hapalocystis* Sacc.; so that the Pseudovalsa is credited with two imperfect stages. There are no specimens at Kew.
Germ.

Polemonium

Phoma Polemonii Cooke, in Grevill. xiii. 94. Sacc. Syll. x. 174. All. vi. 314. Died. 164. Mig. 97.

Pycnidia gregarious, globose-depressed, black, shining, soon becoming naked by the falling away of the thin epi-

dermis; ostiole distinct, acute. Spores narrowly ellipsoid, rounded at both ends, often biguttulate, $5-7 \times 2 \cdot 5\mu$.

On stems of *Polemonium coeruleum*. Kew Gardens (Cooke). Shrewsbury. Jan.–Mar.

The size of the spores given (*l.c.*) by Cooke ($10 \times 3\mu$) is not in accordance with his original specimens.
Germ.

Polygonum

Phoma anceps Sacc. Syll. iii. 120. All. vi. 305 (on *Medicago*). Var. **Polygoni** Grove, in Journ. Bot. 1918, lvi. 289.

Pycnidia gregarious or densely effused on the lower part of the stem, about 100μ diam., lens-shaped, orbicular, black, nestling beneath the epidermis, then $\pm$ erumpent; texture soft, parenchymatous, smoky-brown, irregular. Spores rod-shaped or narrow-oblong, rounded at both ends but somewhat narrower below, 2–4-guttulate, $11-15 \times 2-2 \cdot 5\mu$, but sometimes as much as 20μ long; sporophores similar, but shorter and slightly narrower.

On dead stems of *Polygonum cuspidatum*. Botanic Gardens, Edgbaston, Birmingham. Mar.

Intermediate between *P. anceps* and *P. bacillaris* Sacc. Probably it is a Macrophoma.
Fr. Austr.

Phoma Polygonorum Cooke, in Grevill. xiv. 3. Sacc. Syll. x. 179. All. vi. 315.

"Pycnidia loosely gregarious, minute, punctiform, covered by the epidermis which is soon pierced by the minute ostiole. Spores narrowly ellipsoid, hyaline, eguttulate, $12 \times 3\mu$."

On stems of *Polygonum cuspidatum*. Kew. See p. 208.

Prunus

[**Phoma prunicola** Schwein. Syn. Amer. bor. no. 2169. Sacc. Syll. iii. 107.

Spots effused, broad, cinereous, irregular, at length dry. Pycnidia ovoid, roundish, or squarish, erumpent, fuscous-black, pierced by a round pore, at length opening widely.]

The British records of this species all refer to Phyllosticta.

Phoma gallarum Briard, Suppl. 89. Sacc. Syll. x. 161. All. vi. 236.

Pycnidia numerous, scattered, spherical, often depressed, black, rugulose, immersed at the base only, 200–250μ diam. Spores somewhat irregular, ovoid-oblong or ellipsoid, obtuse or slightly acute at the ends, often biguttulate, 8–9 × 3–4·5μ.

On Oak galls (*Quercus*). Hastings (Connold). Ockeridge Wood, Ws. (Rhodes).

Not a good Phoma. In these specimens I find the spores are often fusoid, very numerous, rarely guttulate, 8–10 × 3–3·5μ (rarely 4μ), on pedicels about as long as the spore. The pycnidia are globose with a short papillate ostiole, immersed (not by the base only), and grouped together closely in erumpent pustules. Perhaps not Briard's species, but *Phomopsis glandicola* Grove, f. *major* (*q.v.*).

Phoma Quercus Sacc. Syll. iii. 108. *Sphaeropsis Quercus* Lambotte, Myc. Belg. iii. 60. *Phyllosticta Lambottei* All. vi. 75.

"Pycnidia epiphyllous, aggregated here and there, immersed, greyish-black, pierced at the summit by a distinct round pore. Spores ovoid, hyaline, without guttules."

On dry leaves of *Quercus*, Oxford. *n.v.* On "marble-galls" of *Quercus Cerris*, Cheshire (Ellis). A doubtful species.

Ellis's specimen is not a Phoma, but a Leptothyrium (*L. quercinum*, f. *minus*) having spores 4–5 × 1μ.
Belg.

Phoma deusta Fckl. Symb. Myc. 377. Sacc. Syll. iii. 155. All. vi. 316. Grove, in Journ. Bot. 1912, p. 51. See Died. 168. *Zythia Rhinanthi* Fr. Summ. Veg. Sc. 408 (the young state). Sacc. Syll. iii. 615. All. vii. 302. Died. 692. *Sphaeronaema Rhinanthi* Lib. exs. no. 263. Cf. *Doassansia Rhinanthi* Lagerh. in Sydow, Ustilag. no. 95.

Pycnidia scattered, black, round, depressed, 250–600μ diam., each surrounded by a zone of brown hyphae which imparts a scorched appearance; peridium one cell thick, parenchymatous, dark-brown; contents very hard. "Spores" oblong, straight, 6–10 × 1·5–2μ.

On dry bracts, capsules, peduncles, and stems of *Rhinanthus Crista-galli* and *Bartsia Odontites*. Frequent, England and Scotland.   Sept.–May.

The "spores" are merely sclerotial cells, forming at first a thick, compact mass, but afterwards loose. An immature pyrenomycete.
Fr. Belg. Germ. Ital. Finland.

Rhododendron

Phoma Rhodorae Cooke, in Grevill. xiv. 3. Sacc. Syll. x. 148.

Spots large, irregular, occupying the margins or the tip of
the leaf, rusty-brown with a darker border. Pycnidia epiphyllous, minute, gregarious, punctiform, black, immersed,
but rather prominent. Spores subellipsoid, lanceolate, or even
slightly clavate, acute at both ends, biguttulate, $6-8 \times 2\mu$
($4-5 \times 2\mu$, Cooke); sporophores short, but perceptible.

On living leaves of *Rhododendron*. Kew Gardens (Cooke).
Renfrewshire (Boyd). Marlborough (Cotton). Bidston,
Cheshire (Ellis); etc.   May–Oct.

Cooke suggests that it is the pycnidial stage of his *Sphaerella
Rhodorae* (in Grevill. xiii. 99), i.e. *Laestadia Rhodorae* B. & V. (Sacc.
Syll. Addit. 62), which was found by him in company with it. Some-
times the pycnidia occupy nearly the whole of the apical half of a leaf.
Is not this *Phyllosticta berolinensis* Henn. and perhaps also *Ph.
Rhododendri* West.?
Denm.

Phoma Rhododendri Cooke, in Grevill. xiii. 93. Sacc. Syll. x.
148.

Pycnidia subgregarious, on small dead twigs which are
bleached, subglobose, black, rather less than 250μ diam.,
covered by the epidermis which is elevated, but scarcely discoloured. Spores oval, without guttules, $4-5 \times 2\mu$.

On twigs of *Rhododendron*. Kew Gardens.

These specimens have a true Phoma pycnidium, but I could find no
spores. It appears to be a form (*ramulicola*) of *P. Rhodorae*.
Holl.

Rhus

Phoma rhoina Cooke, in Grevill. xiv. 27.

The specimens on *Rhus* (Whitehall; Swanscombe), published under
this name by Cooke (*l.c.*) belong undoubtedly to *Phomopsis Rhois*
Trav. (*q.v.*), which is *Phoma Rhois* Sacc. Syll. iii. 85. The change of
name to *rhoina* was merely a slip of the pen. They are quite distinct
from *Macrophoma rhoina* Sacc. Syll. xi. 495.

Ribes

Phoma Grossulariae Sch. & Sacc. Micr. Slav. no. 43. Sacc. Syll.
iii. 88. All. vi. 239. Grove, in Journ. Bot. 1912, p. 50.

Pycnidia gregarious, globose-depressed, at first covered by
the epidermis, then emerging by the short obtuse ostiole,.

black, shining, somewhat collapsed, 200–300µ diam.; texture
parenchymatous, olive-brown. Spores oblong-oval, 6–9 × 4µ.

On twigs of *Ribes Grossularia*. Studley Castle, Wk.;
Badsey, Ws.; Ireland; etc.

No sporophores could be seen. On the same bush, at Studley, there
was *Phomopsis pungens*, and some pycnidia with cylindrical spores,
5 × 1µ, on very conspicuous and branched sporophores; the latter is
probably *Dendrophoma pleurospora* Sacc. (*q.v.*).
Holl. Austr. Slav.

[**Phoma suspecta** Mass. Dis. Cult. Pl. ed. 2, 1915, p. 406, f. 126.
Sacc. Syll. xxii. 873.

On twigs of Gooseberry.]

This supposed *Phoma* is nothing but the young state of the common
Coniothyrium of Gooseberry, in which Massee did not recognise the
tint of olive-colour always to be seen if looked for.

Robinia

Phoma capsularum Cooke & Harkn. Californian Fungi, in Grevill. 1881, ix. 82. Sacc. Syll. iii. 147.

Pycnidia crowded and collected in roundish spots, erumpent, shining, black. Spores ellipsoid, 5–6·5 × 2·5–2·8µ.

On pods of *Robinia*, etc. Highgate (Cooke).

The British specimens, from which the description given above is
taken, differ from *P. leguminum* Westd. (*q.v.*) merely in having the
pycnidia clustered and a little larger. They have a true Phoma-like
pycnidium. But those of Cooke and Harkness (N. Amer. Fung. no.
1448) from California do not seem to be the same, being mostly
ascigerous.
U.S.A.

Rosa

Phoma rhodophila Sacc. Syll. iii. 98 (as var. of *P. endoleuca*).
Phoma Rosarum Sacc. in Mich. ii. 91 (*non* Mont.). All. vi. 243.

Pycnidia covered, then erumpent, whitish within. Spores
cylindrical, rather obtuse at both ends, hyaline, 2–3-guttu-
late, 6 × 2µ; sporophores 6–10µ long.

On twigs (and on a woody gall) of *Rosa canina*. Blockley,
Oxon.   Apr.

Saccardo places this, in the Sylloge, as a variety of his *Phoma
endoleuca* on *Alnus glutinosa*; there seems to be little to recommend
this ascription, except the size of the spores.
Fr.

Phoma aculeorum Sacc. Syll. iii. 76. All. vi. 243. Died. 169.
Grove, in Journ. Bot. 1930, p. 137.

Pycnidia scattered or subgregarious, subepidermal, punctiform, black, 100–150μ diam., bursting the epidermis by a
minute papilla, the epidermis above the pycnidium appearing
faintly blackened. Spores cylindric-oblong, curvulous, often
biguttulate, hyaline, 2–4 × 1·5μ; no pedicels seen.

On dead prickles of *Rosa canina*, Goosehill Woods, near
Droitwich, Oct.; Traeth Mawr, Brecknock, May; Surrey.
Also on dead stems of *Rosa canina*, Ockeridge Wood, Worcs.
(Rhodes).

The pycnidial stage of *Physalospora rosicola* Sacc. (see Journ. Bot.
ibid. p. 68).
Fr. Germ.

Phoma pusilla Sch. & Sacc. Micr. Slav. no. 48. Sacc. Syll. iii. 77.
All. vi. 242.

"Pycnidia immersed in the bark, scattered, globose, depressed, 100–200μ diam., pallid within; ostiole obtuse, indistinct. Spores oblong, straight, 4–5μ long; sporophores
filiform, fasciculate, three times as long."

On branches of *Rosa canina*. Kew Gardens (Cooke).

Apr.

A very doubtful Phoma, much more probably the young state of a
Phomopsis; it is very black, covering the whole stem, like a Diaporthe.
No Phoma spores could be found, only those of a Diplodia.
Holl. Austr.

Phoma rubiginosa Brun. in Act. Soc. Linn. Bord. 1898, p. 10
(extr.). Sacc. Syll. xiv. 873. All. vii. 824. Died. 170, 897. Mig. 100.
Var. **circumstipata** Grove, in Journ. Bot. 1916, liv. 186.

Pycnidia of two kinds, 1–3 larger ones (160–200μ diam.)
surrounded by groups of smaller ones, black, erumpent by a
short neck through a longitudinal fissure. Spores oblong-
ovoid, usually without guttules, 6–10 × 2–3μ.

On prickles of *Rosa canina*. Lapworth, Wk.   May.

The pycnidia form conspicuous greyish patches. This variety is
connected with the type (which has spores 5 × 2μ and has not yet been
found in Britain) by the variety *major* Syd. (Sacc. Syll. xvi. 860). The

latter has scattered or gregarious pycnidia, erumpent by a fissure, and oblong eguttulate spores, 6–10 × 3μ; on dry fruits of *Rosa*, and (?) on stems, Herm (Rhodes).

Fr. Germ. Austr. Denm.

Salix

Phoma salicifolia Cooke, in Grevill. xvi. 48. Sacc. Syll. x. 158. *Phyllosticta salicifolia* All. vi. 86.

Pycnidia epiphyllous, scattered or more commonly gregarious in small orbicular patches, very minute, punctiform. Spores subglobose or oval, 6 × 4μ.

On dead leaves of *Salix*. Kew Gardens.

Very doubtful specimens; I cannot confirm the description.

Phoma salicina Westd. in Bull. Acad. Roy. Belg. ser. 2, vol. ii, no. 7. Sacc. & Roum. Rel. Lib. v, no. 63; Syll. iii. 97. All. vi. 245.

Pycnidia gregarious, subcutaneous, globose-depressed. Spores oblong, hyaline, 6–7 × 2–2·5μ; sporophores fasciculate, as long as the spore.

On bark of branches of *Salix alba, Caprea, viminalis*, etc. Cheshire (Ellis).

These are probably all the same as *Phomopsis salicina* Died., or at any rate those on *viminalis* are so.

Fr. Germ.

Phoma saligna Fr. Syst. Myc. ii. 546. Berk. in Sm. Engl. Flor. v. 283. Trail, in Scot. Nat. 1887, p. 90. Sacc. Syll. ii. 354.

"On fallen sallow leaves. Winter and spring. Sowerby, Greville, Johnston." "On decayed leaves of *Salix cinerea*. Aberdeen (Trail). Feb."

This is merely one of those sterile subsclerotioid stages of an ascomycete which have been so often mistaken for a Phoma. The so-called "spores" are the loosened cells of the pseudoparenchymatous mass which fills the perithecium (more or less) instead of and before the asci. This "Phoma" is such a stage of *Linospora Capreae* Fckl., of which the mature ascophorous stage accompanies it. See Berk. in Ann. Nat. Hist. 1841, vi. 364.

Belg. Fr. Germ. Ital. Swed. Finl. Siber.

Phoma glyptica Cooke & Massee, in Grevill. xv. 107. Sacc. Syll. x. 158. All. vi. 245.

"Pycnidia subepidermal, circinate, subglobose; ostiole

punctiform, piercing the epidermis. Spores oval, $4-5 \times 3\mu$, on long sporophores" (C. & M.).

On branches of *Salix*. Frant; Tunbridge Wells.   Apr.

"The circular groups of pycnidia are surrounded by a more or less distinct line, and externally are not distinguishable from *Valsa glyptica* B. & C." (C. & M.). In fact, it is the *Valsa* not fully developed; all the specimens seen have no true spores, on sporophores.

Sambucus

Phoma exigua Desm. Exs. no. 1869. Cooke, Handb. 420. Sacc. Syll. iii. 134. All. vi. 302. Died. 172.

Pycnidia numerous, approximate or more rarely scattered, about 250μ diam., globose, long covered by the epidermis, opening by a pore, brownish when moist, "when dry blackish and rather shining"; texture thin, parenchymatous, brown; contents white. Spores numerous, ellipsoid, rounded at both ends, faintly biguttulate (at the very extremities), $5-7 \times 2-3\mu$.

On dead shoots of *Sambucus nigra*. Batheaston; Mickleham; Leicester; Heythrop Park, Oxon.; Warwickshire; Yorks.; Lancs.; Cheshire; Ayrshire; etc. Probably common.

Feb. Mar.

The pycnidia occur in troops, just below the slightly elevated epidermis and partly immersed in the thin layer of cork which lies beneath it. When this layer scales off the dead young shoots, the pycnidia come with it and can be seen clinging to its under surface like a number of little brown dots.

Fr. Holl. Germ. Austr. Ital.

Phoma mutica Sacc. Syll. iii. 98. All. vi. 177. Died. 115. Mig. 74. *Sphaeropsis mutica* B. & Br. in Ann. Nat. Hist. 1850, v. 376. Cooke, Handb. 428.

Pycnidia $\pm$ caespitose, erumpent, globose, obtuse, black, shining. Spores very minute, ellipsoid or obovoid.

On small branches of Elder, *Sambucus nigra*. Penzance; Batheaston. *n.ex.*   Mar.

"It has exactly the habit of a Diplodia" (B. & Br.). Saccardo makes a mistake by taking "Elder" to mean Alder, and assigns the species to *Alnus*; this mistake is copied by Allescher, Diedicke, and Migula. The foreign records of *P. mutica* are all therefore incorrect.

Phoma sambuciphila Oud. Cat. Rais. Champ. Pays-Bas, p. 415.
Phoma vicina Sacc. in Mich. i. 525; Syll. iii. 71. All. vi. 246. (*Non*
Desm.)

Pycnidia punctiform, black, globose-elliptic, 100–150 × 50–
60μ, with a minute ostiole, the base of the pycnidium sunken
in the wood. Spores oblong, somewhat curved, eguttulate,
hyaline, 5 × 2μ; sporophores not visible.

On decorticated branches of *Sambucus nigra*. Whitehall;
Ascot (Cooke)! in Herb. Kew (named *Phoma vicina* Desm.).

Holl.   Sept.

Saxifraga

Phoma Saxifragarum Westd. Not. vi, p. 23. Sacc. Syll. iii. 145.
Phyllosticta Saxifragarum All. vi. 145.

Pycnidia gregarious, immersed, then erumpent, punctiform, globose, pierced by a pore. Spores oblong, obtuse at
both ends, sometimes subconstricted in the middle, biguttulate, 6–7 × 2·5μ.

On fading leaves of *Saxifraga* (*Megasea*) *crassifolia*. Shrewsbury (Leighton).   Jan.

Specimens very doubtful.
Fr. Belg. Germ.

Scabiosa

Phoma superflua Sacc. in Mich. i. 522; Syll. iii. 139. All. vi. 320.

Pycnidia gregarious, punctiform, 80–90μ diam., covered by
the epidermis, opening by a minute pore, dusky-olive or
dark-brown. Spores nearly cylindrical with rounded ends,
straight or slightly curved, with 1–3 guttules or very faintly
1–3-septate, 10–15 × 3–4μ.

On dead stems of *Scabiosa succisa*. Aberdeen (Trail). May.
n.v.

Saccardo says that it resembles in habit *Mycosphaerella superflua*.
Fr.

Solanum

Phoma alternariacea Brooks & Searle, in T.B.M.S. 1921, vii. 193.

"Pycnidia aggregated, glabrous, subglobose, brown or
black, papillulate, pierced with one or two pores, 100–250μ
diam. Spores ovate, subacute at both ends, hyaline, con-

tinuous, sometimes faintly biguttulate, $3-7\cdot5 \times 2-3\cdot5\mu$ (average $6 \times 3\mu$), issuing in a rosy tendril; sporophores simple."

On both green and mature fruits of *Solanum Lycopersicum*, causing them to rot. *n.v.*

The authors state (*l.c.*) that on the aerial mycelium surrounding the pycnidia, in their cultures, dark-brown multiseptate spores of the Alternaria type, $40-80 \times 12-18\mu$, appeared in chains; they considered that these were genetically connected with the "Phoma", which, however, I should deem to be merely an early state of *Ascochyta Lycopersici*.

Phoma dulcamarina Sacc. Syll. iii. 127. Cooke, in Grevill. xvi. 6. All. vi. 322. *Phoma Dulcamarae* Thüm. Contr. Myc. Lus. no. 569 (*non* Nits. Sacc. which is a Phomopsis).

Pycnidia scattered, rather small, sometimes confluent, punctiform, generally emergent, black. Spores ellipsoid, somewhat rounded at both ends, often 1-guttulate, $5 \times 2\cdot5\mu$ ($3 \times 2\mu$ Sacc.).

On dead stems of *Solanum* sp. Kew Gardens (Cooke).

The identification is very doubtful. Cooke's specimens are more likely to be a Coniothyrium; the spores do not measure "$3 \times 2\mu$", as Saccardo's did.

Holl. Port.

Phoma solanicola Pr. & Delacr. in Bull. Soc. Myc. Fr. 1890, p. 179, pl. 20, f. 2. Sacc. Syll. x. 175. All. vi. 323.

"Spots large, white or somewhat yellowish. Pycnidia gregarious, immersed, roundish, somewhat prominent, papillate, $135-145 \times 110-115\mu$. Spores ovoid, biguttulate, $7\cdot5 \times 3\mu$."

On living stems of *Solanum tuberosum*, which it causes to dry up; Ireland (Census Catalogue of Irish Fungi, in Proc. Roy. Irish Acad. 1910, p. 148). On stems of the same, Botley, Hants (Cotton). On dead potato haulm, lying in the fields, Wishaw, etc. Wk., in great plenty.

In the Wishaw specimens the spores were abundant, ovoid to ellipsoid, colourless, biguttulate, mostly $5-8 \times 2-3\cdot5\mu$, without any sign of a septum. The pycnidia were those of a typical Phoma, $100-120\mu$ diam., subglobose, black, immersed, then erumpent by the vertex, and forming large dusky patches on the stems. The haulm would undoubtedly infect the next year's crop, if the same field were used again for Potatos.

Fr. Germ.

Phoma tuberosa Melh. Ros. & Sch. in Journ. Agric. Research, 1916, vii. 251, with plates. *P. solanicola* Pr. & Delacr. is perhaps the same species.

Pycnidia black, generally scattered over the entire surface of the affected spot, immersed, irregular, subglobose to spherical, 80–160 × 90–160μ, with a pierced ostiole. Spores oblong-ovoid, 4–6 × 2–3·5μ.

On wounded parts of tubers of *Solanum tuberosum*. Kew Gardens (Cotton). Yorkshire; Carnarvonshire; etc., but reputed uncommon.

The lesions are brownish to dark-grey or black, 6–25 mm. diam., sunken, membranous, with an irregular and sharply defined margin. The authors describe the spores as "subglobose", but do not figure them so. They proved that the Phoma appeared on wounds caused by *Spongospora subterranea*; A. D. Cotton found it on tubers already attacked by *Phytophthora* and *Fusarium Solani*. An unsatisfactory description.
U.S.A.

Solidago

Phoma Solidaginis Cooke, in Grevill. xiii. 95. Sacc. Syll. x. 169. All. vi. 323.

Pycnidia numerous, gregarious, at first covered by the epidermis, then convex, black, shining, pierced by a minute pore; texture thin, parenchymatous, pale-brown. Spores narrowly ellipsoid, rounded at both ends, biguttulate, 9–10 × 2μ; sporophores very short.

On stems of *Solidago canadensis*. Kew Gardens; Whitehall.

Dec.–Mar.

A true Phoma.

Sorbus, see *Phyllosticta sorbicola*

Spiraea

Phoma Spiraeae Cooke, in Herb. (*non* Desm. Obs. Crypt. 1830, p. 13, *quae* Phomopsis; Sacc. Syll. iii. 132). See All. vi. 324; Died. 175; Mig. 100; which also include Phomopsis. Also Sacc. Syll. xiv. 874.

Pycnidia numerous, minute, slightly raising the epidermis and just piercing it with the ostiole, about 100μ diam., roundish, black; texture thin, parenchymatous. Spores oval, faintly guttulate, 5–6 × 2·5μ; no sporophores visible.

On dead stems of *Spiraea Ulmaria*. Hartlebury Common,

Ws., accompanied by *Pleospora* (? *herbarum*). Apr. Also Kew Gardens, Irstead, and Tottenham (Cooke).

Of these latter specimens collected by Cooke, those from Kew are certainly a Phoma, not a Phomopsis; the other two do not seem to have been preserved.

The Hartlebury specimens were accompanied, upon the same stems, by *Leptostroma spiraeinum* Vestergr., which it has been suggested is a pycnidial stage of *Diaporthe Lirella* Nits.; the normal pycnidial stage of the Diaporthe, however, is probably *Phomopsis Spiraeae* (Desm.) Gr. The Hartlebury and the Kew specimens of the Phoma both had, in the same pycnidia with the oval ($5-6 \times 2 \cdot 5\mu$) spores, others Cytospora-like such as I have mentioned previously, which were curved, allantoid, and measured about $5 \times 1\mu$.

Statice

Phoma Statices Tassi, in Bull. Labor. Ort. Bot. Siena, 1898, p. 167, pl. 12, f. 3. Sacc. Syll. xvi. 868. All. vii. 828. Died. 176. Mig. 239.

Pycnidia scattered, raising the epidermis a little, depressed-globose, $200-500\mu$ diam., with a small torn pore; texture of small brownish cells, rather indistinct. Spores linear-ellipsoid, obtuse at both ends, faintly biguttulate, hyaline, $3 \cdot 5-4 \times 1 \cdot 5-2\mu$; sporophores not seen.

On dry dead stems of *Statice Limonium*. Salt-flats, Three-mile Bridge, Holy Island, Anglesey (Rhodes).   Aug.

Germ. Ital.

Suaeda

Phoma Suaedae Jaap, in Schr. nat. Ver. Schles.-Holst. 1907, xiv. 27. Sacc. Syll. xxii. 890. Died. 177. Mig. 77. Grove, in Journ. Bot. 1930, p. 138.

Pycnidia gregarious, soon erumpent and becoming superficial, punctiform, black, $150-200\mu$ wide, with a short conical ostiole; peridium parenchymatous, pale yellowish-brown, darker round the ostiole. Spores ellipsoid, ovoid, or sub-cylindrical, rarely subclavate, rounded at both ends, straight or curvulous, colourless, often biguttulate or with three or four smaller guttules, $5-8(-10) \times 2 \cdot 5-4\mu$, at length faintly yellowish.

On dry branches of *Suaeda maritima*, Llandysilio, near Menai Bridge, Anglesey (Rhodes).   Aug.

Differs from the type only in a few details.
Germ.

Syringa

Phoma enteroleuca Sacc. Syll. iii. 75. All. vi. 231. Died. 162. Mig. 96.

"Pycnidia in little groups here and there, covered by the epidermis, then erumpent, globose, 250μ diam., scarcely papillate, for a long time filled with white contents. Spores ovoid-oblong, eguttulate, $4 \times 1 \cdot 5\mu$; sporophores not seen." "On capsules of *Syringa vulgaris*. Kew Gardens."

I find that these specimens are merely *Coniothyrium Fuckelii*.

This species is recorded, on the Continent, on twigs of *Fraxinus*, *Pyrus*, as well as *Syringa*, but I think most of the records are founded upon error and refer to states of other species, possibly of imperfectly developed Pyrenomycetes.

Fr. Belg. Germ.

Tamarix

Phoma tamaricina Thüm. in Oesterr. Bot. Zeit. 1877, p. 12. Sacc. Syll. iii. 93. All. vi. 253. Died. 177. Mig. 104. *P. tamaricella* Sacc. Syll. iii. 93.

Pycnidia gregarious, semi-immersed, erumpent, subglobose, black, up to 250μ diam. Spores cylindrical, nearly straight, obtuse at both ends, hyaline, $5-6 \times 1-1 \cdot 5\mu$; sporophores very short.

On dead twigs of *Tamarix*. Kew Gardens; Walmer; Budleigh Salterton; Barmouth. Mar. Apr. Aug.

Some of the spores of the Phoma measured as little as 3–4μ long. Frequently mixed with it was a Coniothyrium which has broader spores, 2·5–3μ wide and tinged with olivaceous. *Phoma tamaricella* is only a less developed form of *P. tamaricina*, with spores measuring $4 \times 0 \cdot 75\mu$.

Fr. Germ. Austr.

Phoma Tamarisci Sacc. Syll. iii. 94. All. vi. 253. Died. 178. Mig. 104. *Clisosporium Tamarisci* Mont. Cent. vii, no. 11, in Ann. Sci. Nat. 1856, v. 341. (Not *Sclerothyrium Tamarisci* v. Höhn. in Hedwig. 1918, lx. 181.)

"Pycnidia scattered or gregarious, 100–300μ diam., covered, then naked, globose when moist, black, opaque, depressed and umbilicate on drying, then apparently ostiolate, but at length dehiscing irregularly; texture membranaceous, very thin. Spores very numerous, globose-oblong, about 6·5μ diam.

"On twigs of *Tamarix gallica*. Kew Gardens" (Cooke).

These British specimens, however, have distinctly coloured spores, and are probably *Coniothyrium Tamaricis* Oud. (*q.v.*); the spores have a large single guttule and do not resemble those of Phoma. The thin, soft, parenchymatous peridium is also characteristic of Coniothyrium. Montagne does not mention the colour of his spores.
Fr. Holl. Germ.

Tecoma

Phoma radicantis Cooke, in Grevill. xiii. 92. Sacc. Syll. x. 155. All. vi. 255. Died. 179.

Pycnidia gregarious, on bleached spots, covered by the thin epidermis, minute, 100μ diam., punctiform, flattened. Spores numerous, ovoid or oval, $3\text{–}4 \times 1\cdot5\text{–}2\mu$; sporophores not distinct.

On living branches of *Tecoma radicans*. Kew Gardens (Cooke).

It is very likely that Cooke's specimen is merely the young state of *Coniothyrium Fuckelii*, var. *Tecomae*.
Germ.

Thalictrum

Phoma Jacquiniana Cooke & Mass. in Grevill. xvii. 56 (1889). Sacc. Syll. x. 166. All. vi. 287.

Pycnidia densely scattered, about 200μ diam., globose, papillate, black, covered by and adhering to the epidermis. Spores ellipsoid, rarely biguttulate, rounded at both ends, $9\text{–}10 \times 4\text{–}5\mu$; sporophores not perceptible.

On stems of *Thalictrum Jacquinianum* (= *minus*). Kew Gardens. Jan. In company with *Didymella Heribaudii* Har. & Br. (in Rev. Mycol. 1890, p. 131).

The name "Delphinium" used for the host by Cooke (*l.c.*) is a mere *lapsus calami*. The length of the spores there given, 15μ, is incorrect; I found the spores did not exceed 10μ, even when swelled up again by potassic hydrate solution.

Tussilago

Phoma Tussilaginis Cooke & Mass. in Grevill. xv. 108. Sacc. Syll. x. 169.

Pycnidia epiphyllous, gregarious on large brown spots which become pale in the centre, at first covered, then hemispherical, minute, punctiform, black, pierced at the apex; texture thin, parenchymatous. Spores oval or ovoid, $8\text{–}10 \times 5\text{–}6\mu$ or $6\text{–}7 \times 4\text{–}5\mu$.

On fading leaves of *Tussilago Farfara*. The Old Canal bank, Hereford (Cooke)! Dinmore (Vize). Ayrshire (Boyd). Earlswood and Wishaw, Wk.   Aug. Sept.

"A most distinct and interesting species, not at all like the ordinary forms of *Phoma*, but approaching *Asteromella*" (Cooke). I found the fungus in the exact locality indicated by Cooke, but the "spores" seem to be more of the nature of sclerotial cells than true spores. The Ayrshire specimens had a large number of curved fusoid guttulate spores, mixed with those of the "Phoma". Cf. *Asteroma impressum*.

My explanation of the appearances is that they are all stages in the development of *Stagonospora Tussilaginis* (*q.v.*). The "Phoma" spores show by their *unfinished* look that they are only those loose subsclerotial cells which are often found in young perithecia or pycnidia. Then the true spores are produced, passing through a gradual series of transformations, from the fusoid spores, $10 \times 2\mu$, through oblongfusoid granular spores $16 \times 2 \cdot 5\mu$, etc. up to the perfect form shown in *S. Tussilaginis*. Any other explanation would fail to account for the long series of graduated intermediate forms which can be found in the pycnidia upon the same "spot".

                                                            Ulex
Phoma Ulicis Syd. in Ann. Mycol. iii. 420. Died. 181. Mig. 93.

Pycnidia scattered, covered, at length erumpent, globose, black, up to 300μ diam., opening by a wide pore; texture thin, indistinct, brownish. Spores ovoid or obovoid, biguttulate, colourless, $5-6 \times 2-2 \cdot 5\mu$, issuing in tendrils: sporophores filiform, "$10-13 \times 1-1 \cdot 5\mu$" (Died.).

On dead spines of *Ulex europaeus*. Rather common; Bromsgrove, Ws.; Cornwall; etc.; but often not fully developed.

                                                          Summer.
Germ.

                                                            Urtica
Phoma acuta Fckl. Symb. Myc. 125. Sacc. Syll. iii. 133. All. vi. 326. Died. p. 182, p. 22, f. iii, 2. Mig. 88. *Aposphaeria acuta* Berk. Outl. 315. Cooke, Handb. 901.

Pycnidia rather large, up to 500μ diam., between conical and globose, papillate, black, smooth, shining, seated on the wood, at first concealed by the epidermis which is pierced by the often rather wide pore of the conical ostiole, at length naked when the epidermis breaks off; texture thick and dark. Spores oblong, biguttulate, quite colourless in mass, $4-5 \times 1 \cdot 5-2\mu$ (Fig. 3, p. 58).

On dead stems of *Urtica dioica*, chiefly at the base. Rather
common.   Mar.–May.

The pycnidial stage of *Leptosphaeria acuta*, with which it is frequently associated and which it much resembles in shape. I have
found very similar pycnidia, once on *Cirsium arvense*, and once on
Ballota nigra.

Phoma Urticae, which is also common on the Nettle, is easily distinguished by its smaller size, its different shape, the much thinner
peridium, the slenderer spores, and the presence of a pallid roseate
tinge in the mass of spores.

A form of *Phoma acuta* (*P. amplior* Sacc. & Roum.), with longer
spores ($7 \times 2\mu$) and pycnidia perhaps a little larger, is found in France
and Germany on dead stems of *Foeniculum*.

Europe, N. Amer.

Phoma Urticae Sch. & Sacc. Syll. iii. 140. All. vi. 326. Died. 182.
Mig. 107.

Pycnidia scattered, but often rather densely, subglobose,
much depressed, 160–300μ diam., black, closely covered by
the adherent epidermis and showing through it as a blackish
spot, then piercing it by a minute pore, at length superficial as
the epidermis vanishes; texture loosely parenchymatous,
brown, thin; contents pallid or subroseate. Spores cylindric-
oblong, often biguttulate, rounded at both ends, $4–6 \times 1–2\mu$.
The upper half of the pycnidium often falls away, leaving an
excipuliform black base.

On dead stems of *Urtica dioica*. Common in England;
Wales; Ireland (Antrim).   Sept.–May.

This species seems to be much like *P. oleracea*, except in the absence of a distinct papilla from the much depressed pycnidium.
P. acuta, which may occur on the lower part of the same stem, is very
different.

Holl. Germ. Denm. Austr. Ital. Spain, Siber.

Verbascum

Phoma verbascicola Cooke, in Rav. Amer. Fung. no. 141 (1878).
Sacc. Syll. iii. 129. All. vi. 327, with fig. on p. 170. Died. 183. Mig.
103. *Sphaeria verbascicola* Schwein. Syn. Fung. Am. bor. no. 1726
(1834). *Phoma errabunda* Desm. in Ann. Sci. Nat. 1849, xi. 282. Sacc.
Syll. iii. 128. *Sclerophomella verbascicola* v. Höhn.

Pycnidia gregarious, numerous, depressed-globose, black,
somewhat shining, about 200μ diam., not prominent, covered
by the epidermis which is at length pierced by the minute

papilla; texture rather thin, distinctly parenchymatous, smoky-brown. Spores ovate or ellipsoid, 3–4·5 × 1–2μ; sporophores very short; tendrils whitish.

On dead stems of *Verbascum*. Darenth (Cooke). Mickleham, on *V. nigrum*.

Von Höhnel mistakenly has stated that this is the same as *P. complanata* Desm. Cooke's specimens, Fung. Brit. no. 619, include several other species, besides that described above.

Fr. Belg. Holl. Germ. Austr. Spain, U.S.A.

Viola

[**Phoma Violae** Westd. Exs. no. 525. Sacc. Syll. iii. 145.]

The only British specimens of this which I have seen, on stems of cultivated Violas, Kew Gardens, attacked by *Puccinia aegra* Grove, were undoubtedly, like those of Westendorp, the ordinary *Darluca Filum* Cast. But several real species of Phoma on *Viola* have been found in other countries.

Viscum

Phoma Visci Sacc. Syll. iii. 113. *Phyllosticta Visci* All. vi. 96.

Pycnidia aggregated on spots of the leaves which become yello.vish on drying, covered by the epidermis, then erumpent, subglobose, black, 200–250μ diam., with a small papilla; texture rather solid. Spores oblong-ovoid, straight, biguttulate, 5 × 2·5μ.

On leaves of *Viscum album*.

The spots recall a Phyllosticta, but the pycnidia are of a more solid character. I have seen no authentic British specimens, but it has occurred on imported Mistletoe.

Fr. Germ. Austr.

Vitis

Phoma viticola Sacc. in Mich. ii. 94; Syll. iii. 79 (neque *P. viticola* Sacc. Syll. iii. 110, quae *Macrophoma*; nec *P. viticola* Sacc. in Mich. ii. 92, quae *Phomopsis*. See Grove, in Kew Bull. 1917, p. 67).

Pycnidia scattered, covered by the epidermis, globose, papillate, 150μ diam., black; texture soft, indistinct, rather thick, fuliginous-olive. Spores ellipsoid to ovoid, subinequilateral, eguttulate, perfectly hyaline, 6–7 × 3–4μ; no pedicels visible.

On thin shoots of *Vitis vinifera* (an old plant) growing on a wall at St Ambrose's Presbytery, Kidderminster, Mar. 3, 1930.

Fr.

Phoma Cookei Pirotta, Fung. Vit. p. 55, pl. 12, f. 21. Thüm. Pilz. Weinst. p. 151, pl. 2, f. 12. Sacc. Syll. iii. 80. All. vi. 259. *Phoma Vitis* Cooke, Exs. i, no. 618 (*non* Bonord.), but not his Exs. ii, no. 14, with fig., or Grevill. iii. 177. *Cylindrophoma Cookei* v. Höhn. in Sydow, Mycoth. Germ. no. 1657. *Ceuthospora Cookei* Thüm. Cf. *Leptothyrium perpusillum* Pass. & Thüm.

Pycnidia minute, scattered, punctiform, black, globose or subglobose, at first covered by the epidermis, then erumpent, 100–125μ diam. Spores linear, curved, very obtuse at both ends, continuous, hyaline, 13 × 4·5μ; sporophores crowded, filiform, flexuous, hyaline.

On rods of *Vitis vinifera*, near the nodes. King's Lynn (Plowright).

Cooke's two exsiccata seem to be different, and nothing approaching his figure could be discerned, although other fungi are present such as a Cytospora and a Hendersonia.
Denm.

Phoma Vitis Bon. Abhandl. Myc. 141. Sacc. Syll. iii. 79. All. vi. 259. Died. 184. Mig. 108. Pirotta, Fungh. Vit. p. 54, pl. 12, f. 18–20.

Pycnidia scattered, punctiform, very minute, black, globose-depressed, perforating the epidermis by the minute ostiole. Spores varying from ellipsoid to ovoid, with a refringent guttule at each extremity, 3–4 × 1·5–2μ; sporophores rather short (fusoid or ampulliform, 8–12 × 1–2·5μ, Died.).

On dead rods of *Vitis vinifera*. Kew Gardens; Shere; King's Lynn, etc.

Often wrongly recorded. This species has a complete parenchymatous peridium; it is said to be the pycnidial stage of *Gibbera Vitis* Sch. Not to be confused with *Phomopsis viticola* Sacc. or *Phoma Cookei* Pir.
Fr. Germ. Holl. Ital. Austr. U.S.A.

Weigelia

Phoma Weigeliae Speg. in Mich. i. 481. Sacc. Syll. iii. 70. All. vi. 260.

"Pycnidia nestling beneath the epidermis, lens-shaped, 110–120μ diam.; ostiole cone-shaped, papillate, rather acute; texture carbonaceous. Spores ellipsoid or ovoid, obtuse at the ends, eguttulate, hyaline, then pale yellowish-green, 3–5 × 1–2μ."

On dead twigs of *Diervilla* (*Weigelia*) *rosea*. Kew Gardens.
                                                       Mar.–Jun.

A very doubtful British species; the imperfect Kew specimens are
not apparently a Phoma at all, and also do not resemble in the slightest
degree *P. Weigeliae* (Roum. Fung. Gall. no. 3355), which indeed appears to be a Phomopsis.
Fr. Holl. Denm. Ital.

MONOCOTYLEDONS
Acorus
Phoma Acori Cooke, in Grevill. xiii. 95. Sacc. Syll. x. 183. Grove,
in Journ. Bot. 1930, p. 137.

Pycnidia scattered, depressed-globose, black, 100–200μ
diam., opening by a distinct pore; texture very thin, dusky-
translucent, much darker round the pore. Spores numerous,
roundish, oval, or ellipsoid, 5–10 × 4–5μ, not biguttulate but
oily-granular within, quite colourless; no pedicels seen
(Fig. 4*c*).

On dead submerged leaves of *Acorus Calamus*, in the canal,
near Gt. Haywood, Staffs.   Aug.

Cooke's record (*l.c.*) is for Kew and Totteridge; Vize afterwards
issued the Totteridge form (in Myc. Fung. Brit. no. 526) as *Phyllosticta
Acori*, a title given to a fungus found in Holland (Oud. Aan. Myc.
Nederl. 1876, p. 6), but the fungus of that name is quite unlike Cooke's
specimens. Cooke's description is as follows:
"Pycnidia very numerous, gregarious, subepidermal, minute,
punctiform, scarcely visible when dry, membranaceous, brown.
Spores oval or ellipsoid, obtuse, 6–8 × 3μ. On dead leaves of *Acorus
Calamus*. Totteridge; Kew; March. In conjunction with *Leptosphaeria
acorella*."

Asparagus
Phoma Asparagi Sacc. Syll. iii. 162. All. vi. 333. Died. 120.
Mig. 94.

Pycnidia gregarious, 170–200μ long, black, covered by the
epidermis, but scarcely elevating it, and at length piercing it
by the minute ostiole; texture thin, parenchymatous, dusky-
brown. Spores oblong, scarcely at all fusoid, rather obtuse at
both ends, sometimes biguttulate, 7–8 × 2·5–3μ; sporophores
not seen.

On dead stems of *Asparagus officinalis*. Forden; Hampstead.

I have seen no good British specimens; the European ones generally
(except Saccardo's) seem to be a Phoma, while most of the Italian and

American ones, which are much larger and surrounded by a dark halo,
are a true Phomopsis with a thick pycnidial wall and long sporophores.

Fr. Denm. Germ. Ital. Siberia, U.S.A.

GRAMINEAE

Ammophila

Phoma Ammophilae Dur. & Mont. in Flor. Alg. p. 564. Sacc.
Syll. iii. 166. Died. 116. Mig. 234. Jaap, in Schrift. nat. Ver. Schles.-
Holst. xiv. 27.

Pycnidia thickly scattered, subglobose, immersed, black,
about 200μ diam.; texture loose, irregular, parenchymatous,
brown. Spores oval or ellipsoid, acute or obtuse at the ends,
faintly biguttulate, hyaline, 4–6 × 2–3μ (about 5 × 3μ, Jaap;
4–5 × 1·5–2μ, Sacc. in Syll. Addit. p. 305); sporophores 25–
30 × 3μ, or even longer.

On dead leaves of *Ammophila arundinacea*. Tal-y-bont,
Mer. Not a true Phoma.   Apr.

Germ. Alger.

Gynerium

Phoma gyneriicola Cooke & Mass. in Grevill. xvi. 7. Sacc. Syll.
x. 186.

Pycnidia minute, scattered or gregarious, soon becoming
superficial, membranaceous, subglobose, dark-brown, not
more than 30μ diam. Spores ellipsoid, 3 × 1μ.

On leaves of *Gynerium argenteum*. Kew Gardens. *n.ex.*

Phragmites

Phoma stagonosporoides Trail, in Scot. Nat. 1889, iv. 71. Sacc.
Syll. x. 186.

Pycnidia scattered, immersed, depressed-globose, papillate,
120–150μ diam. Spores ellipsoid, faintly 4-guttulate, 10–12 ×
3–4μ.

On dead leaves of *Phragmites communis*. Loch Achray
(Trail). *n.v.* Approaching Stagonospora.

Phoma rimosa Westd. Not. iii, p. 13. Sacc. Syll. iii. 165. All. vi
337. *Phyllosticta rimosa* Oud. N.K.A. ser. 2. vi. 598.

Pycnidia ovoid, ± compressed, arranged in rows which are
closely connected laterally in a stroma so as to form little

black convex elliptic-lanceolate pustules about 1 mm. long,
which are covered by the blackened epidermis. Spores narrow, subcylindric, curvulous, acute at both ends, indistinctly
biguttulate, $3 \times 0.5\mu$.

On both surfaces of leaves of *Phragmites communis*. Lyndhurst (A. L. Smith). *n.ex.*   Oct.

Probably the pycnidial stage of *Scirrhia rimosa* Fckl., which it much
resembles.

Belg. Holl.

Phoma arundinacea Sacc. Syll. iii. 164. All. vi. 337. Died. 160.
Mig. 86. *Sphaeria arundinacea* Sow. Engl. Fung. vol. iii, pl. 336.
Sphaeropsis arundinacea Lév. in Ann. Sci. Nat. 1846, v. 294. Berk.
Outl. 316.

Pycnidia arranged in short rows of two, three, or more,
somewhat connate, bursting the epidermis in longitudinal
fissures, but hardly emerging, black, white within, about 200μ
broad; ostiole short, indistinct. Spores oval-oblong, biguttulate, $8-9 \times 2.5-3\mu$.

On culms of *Phragmites communis*. Cheshire (Ellis). On
culms of *Calamagrostis Epigejos*, Goosehill Woods, Worcs.,
but with more acute spores; with it was a pyrenomycete,
probably a Mycosphaerella, but undeveloped.   Apr. Oct.

Fr. Germ. Ital.

_____

                                                    Iris
Phoma iridina Maire & Sacc. Syll. xvi. 1154. Grove, in Journ.
Bot. 1916, p. 188.

Pycnidia scattered, oblong or lanceolate, immersed, at
length erumpent, convex, black, up to 250μ long, surrounded
at the base by a few brown hyphae; texture parenchymatous,
dark-brown. Spores oblong-fusoid, subacute at both ends,
especially below, $7-9 \times 2-2.5\mu$.

On dead bleached peduncles of *Iris Pseudacorus*. Quarry
pool, Hamstead, St.   Apr.

The Corsican specimens to which the name was originally applied
had larger pycnidia ($500-750\mu$ diam.) but had similar spores; they
were on *I. foetidissima*.

Phoma Iridis Cooke, in Grevill. xv. 108. Sacc. Syll. x. 182.

Pycnidia scattered, punctiform, covered by the epidermis, convex, black. Spores narrowly ellipsoid, with or without guttules, obtuse at both ends, $7 \times 2\mu$; sporophores short. On leaves of *Iris foetidissima*. Kew Gardens; Somerton; Breinton.

A doubtful species, the specimens of Cooke which I have seen being partly or wholly Coniothyrium.

Juncus

Phoma neglecta Desm. in Ann. Sci. Nat. 1853, xx. 220. Sacc. Syll. iii. 164. All. vi. 336. Trail, in Scot. Nat. 1887, p. 124.

Pycnidia rather scattered, subepidermal, ovate, 160–200μ diam., shortly papillate, prominent, black, shining, white within, pierced by a pore; texture rather solid. Spores oblong, 4–$5 \times 1 \cdot 5$–2μ.

On dead stems of *Juncus effusus*, Aberdeen (Trail). Of *Juncus maritimus*, Borth (Bayliss Elliott). May.

Phoma juncicola Brun. Champ. Saint. 1889, p. 338 (Sacc. Syll. x. 184. All. vi. 336. Died. 147. Mig. 87), on *Juncus acutus*, seems to differ in no respect, except in being densely crowded. The pycnidia of Desmazières' *P. neglecta* were on the perianth and pedicels, and were described by him as being "few".

Fr.

Potamogeton

Phoma microscopica B. & Br. in Ann. Nat. Hist. 1850, v. 370. Cooke, Handb. 420. Sacc. Syll. iii. 159.

Pycnidia scattered over discoloured spots, subglobose, minutely papillate, about 150μ diam., smooth, covered by the epidermis which is darkened around the ostiole, pierced by a pore; texture parenchymatous, thin, pale-brown. Spores oblong-ellipsoid, occasionally curved, often biguttulate, 7–$8 \times 2 \cdot 5$–3μ.

On dying stems of *Potamogeton*. Berkeley's exsiccatum, no. 44, examined.

These specimens should rather be referred to Phyllosticta.

Richardia

Phoma Richardiae Mercer, in Mycol. Centralbl. 1913, ii. 244 ff., with figs. Sacc. Syll. xxv. 113. *Phyllosticta Richardiae* Halsted, in New Jers. Agric. Exp. Sta. 1893, p. 400, without diagnosis.

Pycnidia globose-ovoid, 120–150μ diam., at first yellow,

then dark-brown; ostiole conical, rather short, pore about 20–30μ wide. Spores ovoid, hyaline, with one, two, or three small guttules at each end, 6–7 × 4μ, seated directly on the proliferous stratum.

Recorded on leaves and "flowers" (i.e. spathes) of *Richardia africana* (cult.), in many parts of England from the Scilly Isles to Cumberland and Northumberland. *n.v.*

This appears to be the same fungus as *Phyllosticta Richardiae*, which has been recorded for the same areas in this country. But Halsted gives no proper description, mentioning merely dark-coloured pycnidia seated on large grey spots. Mercer mentions no definite spots. He maintains that his Phoma produces a species of Alternaria as a conidial stage; cf. *P. alternariacea*, p. 105.
Germ. U.S.A.

Ruscus
Phoma Rusci Westd. in Bull. Acad. Belg. ser. 2, pl. 7, no. 5. Sacc. Syll. iii. 162. *Phyllosticta Rusci* All. vi. 163. See also p. 222.

Pycnidia amphigenous, scattered, immersed, black, minute; ostiole papillate, elevating and perforating the epidermis. Spores elongate-ovoid, eguttulate, "7 × 2μ".

On stems and cladodes of *Ruscus aculeatus*. Kew Gardens; Yorkshire, etc.   Apr. May.

I have seen only very imperfect specimens. One from Sussex (J. W. Ellis) had very variable "spores", mostly 8–15 × 3–4μ. These appeared to be sclerotial cells, and the fungus was probably a preliminary sclerotioid state of *Leptosphaeria Rusci* Sacc., whose pycnidial stage is *Phyllosticta ruscicola* (*q.v.*).
Belg. Germ. Austr. Port.

Phoma cladodii C. & M. in Grevill. xvi. 6. Sacc. Syll. x. 184.

Pycnidia amphigenous, very numerous, minute (200μ diam.), punctiform, densely gregarious, sometimes occupying the whole surface, subepidermal, black; spores "almond-shaped, 10 × 5μ, on short sporophores".

On cladodes of *Ruscus Hypoglossum*. Kew Gardens, May, 1887.

No spores such as described can now be found in these specimens; all the pycnidia examined were empty! No doubt it = *P. Rusci*.

Scirpus

Phoma abscondita Passer. Diagn. Fung. Nuov. IV. no. 90. Sacc.
Syll. x. 185. All. vi. 339.

Pycnidia entirely immersed in the unchanged substance of
the matrix, subglobose, black, with a minute papilla. Spores
oblong, rounded at both ends, very faintly greenish-yellow-
hyaline, $12 \cdot 5$–$15 \times 3 \cdot 5$–4μ (Fig. 4d).

On withered tips of barren stems of *Scirpus*. Brackish inlet,
Newgale, Pembr. (Rhodes).   July.

Ital.

Typha

Phoma Typharum Sacc. Syll. iii. 163. Scot. Nat. 1887, p. 124.
Phyllosticta Typharum All. vi. 166. Died. 102. Mig. 61.

Pycnidia minute, black, nearly free, globose-conical;
ostiole about as long as the pycnidium. Spores cylindrical,
tending towards ellipsoid or ovoid, obtuse at both ends, often
slightly curved, 4–$6 \times 1 \cdot 5$–$2 \cdot 5\mu$ (3–$4 \times 0 \cdot 5$–1μ, Trail).

On rotting leaves of *Typha angustifolia*. Kew Gardens
(Cooke). Sutton Coldfield. On dead leaves of *T. latifolia*,
Aberdeen, in company with *Leptosphaeria Typharum* Karst.
of which it is the spermogonial stage (Trail).   Apr.

The Sutton specimens were on dead leaves lying in the water; the
pycnidia were solitary, minute, punctiform, placed singly in the
grooves of the leaf, at first projecting by the short ostiole, then half-
free; spores 4–$6 \times 1 \cdot 5$–$2 \cdot 5\mu$. *Phoma Typhae* Pass. and *Phoma typhicola*
Oud. seem to be the same species, just as *Leptosphaeria Typharum*
Karst. is merely the older state of *L. Typhae* Karst. So the specimens
may belong to *Phoma Typhae* Pass. in Brun. List. Sphaerops. p. 20
(Sacc. Syll. x. 134) = *Phyllosticta Typhae* All. vi. 166 (Died. 102), which
is described as follows:
"Pycnidia scattered, punctiform, depressed, black, at first covered
by the epidermis, then free. Spores cylindric, straight, hyaline.
On leaves of *T. latifolia*, with *Leptosphaeria Typhae*. France."
Europe, U.S.A.

Selaginella

Phoma Selaginellae Cooke & Mass. in Grevill. xvi. 102. Sacc.
Syll. x. 187.

Pycnidia scattered, immersed, small, punctiform, black.
Spores ellipsoid, $5 \times 3\mu$.

On dead stems of *Selaginella Willdenovii*. Kew Gardens.
n.ex.

Equisetum

Phoma epitricha Sacc. Syll. iii. 168. All. vi. 341. *Sphaeropsis epitricha* B. & Br. in Ann. Nat. Hist. 1850, v. 375. Cooke, Handb. 427.

Pycnidia globose, completely covered by the epidermis, seated on a sparse brown floccose branched subiculum, at length piercing the epidermis with a rather broad opening. Spores oblong, but somewhat pointed at one or both ends, 6–7 × 2μ.

On dead stems of *Equisetum* (*palustre* and others). Wiltshire; Yorkshire; Aberdeenshire.   Jan. Feb.

"Pycnidia globose, seated beneath a discoloured cinereous spot, springing from forked septate threads which have obtuse apices and are very remarkable." (B. & Br.) But see p. 326.
Holl.

Musci

Phoma muscicola A. L. Smith, in T.B.M.S. 1910, iii. 221. Sacc. Syll. xxii. 896. *P. Orthotrichi* Sm. & Ramsb. in T.B.M.S. 1914, iv. 326.

Pycnidia minute (120–150μ diam.), opening by a small pore. Spores oblong-ellipsoid, about 5 × 2μ.

On capsules of Mosses (*Bryum calophyllum, B. Warneum, Hypnum* sp.). Sand-dunes, Freshfield, Lancs. (Wheldon).

Jan.

P. Orthotrichi is said to be distinguished by its smaller spores (3 × 1μ), on capsules of *Orthotrichum*, Ayrshire (Boyd); but the pycnidia are also smaller and therefore perhaps younger. It is not uncommon to find the very young state of a Phoma with smaller spores than the mature state.

———————

There are a number of "Phomas", so described as observed mycorhizally on roots, such as *P. radicis-Andromedae, P. radicis-Ericae, P. radicis-Tetralicis, P. radicis-Oxycocci, P. radicis-Vaccinii* (all named by Ternetz). But there is no reason to believe that they are really members of this genus, or that they are all specifically distinct; some of them showed the usual monstrosities of laboratory-growth.

MACROPHOMA Berl. & Vogl. in Sacc. Syll. Addit. 306.

Pycnidia resembling those of Phoma, but differing in having longer spores, which may be over 15μ long, and are seldom biguttulate; the spores may be cylindrical or ellipsoidal. (Fig. 5.)

The species of this genus can occur on leaves as often as on stems, and the texture of the peridium can vary from being many-layered (almost sclerotial) to thin-walled (like a typical Phoma). But it is at present a purely artificial genus; only the section Cylindrophoma is justified, most of the others being merely young states of a Sphaeropsis or a Diplodia. See Kew Bulletin, 1919, p. 178.

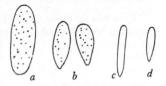

Fig. 5. Spores of: *a*, *Macrophoma Candollei*; *b*, *M. Mirbelii*; *c*, *M. cylindrospora*; *d*, *M. nitens*; all × 600.

Plurivorous

Macrophoma collabens Berl. & Vogl. in Sacc. Syll. Addit. 309; Syll. x. 195. All. vi. 371. *Phoma collabens* Cooke, in Grevill. 1885, xiii. 94 (*non* D. & M. in Sacc. Syll. iii. 131).

Pycnidia epiphyllous on fallen leaves or scattered over brown spots of dead tissue on living leaves, orbicular, shining, rugose, soon depressed and even concave, subsuperficial, 200–250μ diam. Spores oblong-ellipsoid, eguttulate or filled with many minute guttules, 15–25 × 3·5–5μ; sporophores oblong-linear, 15–16 × 2μ.

On living or fading leaves of *Prunus lusitanica*, Kew Gardens; Wimbledon; Derbyshire; Tibberton and Hadzor, Worcs.; etc. On tip of living leaves of *P. Laurocerasus*, Ayrshire (Boyd). Arthog; Yorkshire.

The spots in the Welsh (Arthog) specimens are large, fuscous, and surrounded by a broad reddish-brown border. The Ayrshire specimens were accompanied on the same plants, but not on the same leaves, by *M. cylindrospora*, so that these two species of Macrophoma may be identical, for *M. cylindrospora* differs very slightly except that the spores are narrower than those of *M. collabens*.

Var. **aucubina**, v.nov.

Pycnidia somewhat larger. Spores smaller, 10–15 × 4μ, more oblong, slightly irregular and containing a few minute guttules.

On tip of fallen leaves of *Aucuba japonica*. Ayrshire (Boyd).

Germ.

Macrophoma cylindrospora Berl. & Vogl. in Sacc. Syll. Addit. 313; Syll. x. 203. All. vi. 365, with fig. Died. 190. Mig. p. 110, pl. 7, f. 7, 8. *Sphaeropsis cylindrospora* Desm. in Ann. Sci. Nat. 1849, xi. 277. B. & Br. in Ann. Nat. Hist. 1850, v. 374. Cooke, Handb. 426. *Phoma cylindrospora* Sacc. Syll. iii. 113.

Pycnidia gregarious, very numerous, punctiform, covered by the epidermis, globose, black, somewhat shining, at length collapsing, pierced at the vertex by a pore, up to 350μ diam.; texture thick, of small dark cells. Spores cylindrical, obtuse at both ends, straight or rarely curved, faintly granular, 20–25 × 2–3·5μ; sporophores filiform, simple or branched, hyaline, 15–16 × 1·5–2μ, often very similar to the spores. (Fig. 5c.)

On dead leaves of *Aucuba japonica* and *Escallonia macrantha*, Ayrshire (Boyd). On leaves of Rhododendron and Pear, Scotland (Trail)? On leaves of *Prunus lusitanica* and *P. Laurocerasus*, Highgate (Cooke). Heythrop Park, Oxon; Harborne Hall, etc., Birmingham. On *Ilex Aquifolium*, Liverpool (Travis). Commonly recorded also on *Hedera*, but see below.

The cylindrical spores vary from 15μ or even less to over 20μ in length; the pycnidia are much smaller and more crowded than in the similar-looking *Phoma leucostigma*.

This much confused species is recorded on the Continent also on *Vinca*, *Euonymus japonicus* and *Quercus Ilex*. See *M. collabens*, *Ceuthospora Hederae*, *C. Feurichii*, and *C. Euonymi*; *Hedera* especially doubtful.

Var. **Arbuti**, v.nov.

I have found, on fallen leaves of *Arbutus Unedo* at Kemerton, Glos., a fungus which presents the appearance sometimes of *Ceuthospora*, sometimes of *Macrophoma*; it has cylindrical spores, 16–25 × 3–4μ, when in the best condition, but usually the spores are imperfectly developed and assume irregular shapes. This is probably the fungus which was called *Cheilaria Arbuti* by Desmazières, and is referred to

by Saccardo in Syll. iii. 23 (under *Phyllosticta Arbuti*, a mistake which he afterwards corrected on p. 648). It occurs nearly always in the Depazea condition, and looks often as if it were in an immature pyrenomycetous stage. It might well be a Ceuthospora. Trail's records also (*supra*) on Pear and Rhododendron are very doubtful, and the latter might be a Ceuthospora. Cf. also *Phyllosticta Arbuti, supra.*
Europe.

Macrophoma leucostigma B. & V.,
see **Phoma leucostigma**

Acer

Macrophoma samaricola Berl. & Vogl. in Sacc. Syll. Addit. 310; Syll. x. 197. All. vi. 355. *Phoma samaricola* Sacc. Syll. iii. 153.

"Pycnidia immersed, covered by the epidermis, depressed-globose, black; contents white. Spores oblong, granular within, 20–30 × 7–8μ; sporophores rather long."

"On samaras of *Acer*, but apparently on the fruit only, not on the wing." Swansea (Ellis). *n.v.*   Sept.

This so-called Macrophoma seems to present all the characters of an immature Diplodia, probably *D. subtecta.* But cf. *M. Negundinis* Ell. & Ev., on branches of *Acer Negundo*, which is very similar.
Fr. Port.

Aralia

Macrophoma millepunctata Berl. & Vogl. in Sacc. Syll. Addit. 309; Syll. x. 195. All. vi. 356. *Phoma millepunctata* Penz. & Sacc. Fung. Mortol. p. 10, pl. 4, f. 8. Sacc. Syll. iii. 105 (*non* Lév.). *Macrophoma Araliae* Sacc. & Berl. in Syll. x. 195. Berl. & Vogl. in Atti Soc. Ven.-Tr. 1886, p. 180, pl. 5, f. 2.
Var. **spinosae**, v.nov.

Pycnidia densely gregarious, mostly on blackened spots, oval or circular, depressed, up to 200μ long, black, covered by the epidermis, then emerging by a rather wide pore; peridium thick, subcarbonaceous, very dark brown. Spores cylindrical, rounded at both ends, straight, with 1–4 guttules, 13–20 × 3–4μ; sporophores short, straight, 6–8 × 2–3μ.

On petioles of *Aralia spinosa.* Kew Gardens, in company with *Phoma Araliae* C. & M. (*q.v.*), which is (?) part of the same life-cycle.

This variety differs from the type (which was on *A. pulchra*) by its much narrower and truly cylindrical spores, and by its thicker-walled peridium.
Ital. Alger.

Buxus

Macrophoma Mirbelii B. & V. in Sacc. Syll. Addit. 308; Syll. x.
194. All. vi. 358, with fig. Died. p. 187, p. 22, f. iv, 5. Mig. 240.
Sphaeria Mirbelii Fr. in Linnaea, 1830, v. 548. *Phoma Mirbelii* Sacc.
Syll. iii. 105. *P. delitescens* Sacc. iii. 105. *Macrophoma Candollei* B. &
V., *l.c.* Died. p. 187, p. 22, f. iv, 4. Mig. 240. *Sphaeropsis Candollei*
B. & Br. in Ann. Nat. Hist. 1850, v. 376. Cooke, Handb. 426, 922.
Phoma Candollei Sacc. Syll. iii. 105. See also Syll. ii. 455; xviii.
272.

Pycnidia gregarious, amphigenous, but mostly hypophyllous, also on the twigs, subglobose, immersed, then elevating the epidermis and piercing it by the ostiole, somewhat
prominent, black, 300–400μ diam.; peridium minutely parenchymatous, fulvous or fuscous, afterwards becoming darker.
Spores ovoid, apiculate below, 13–18 × 8–9μ, then oblong or
broadly cylindrical, obtuse at the base, cloudy-granular,
sometimes with one or two guttules, 28–40 × 10–12μ; sporophores at first short, hyaline, then 5–8 × 1–2μ. (Fig. 5a, b.)

On fading or dead leaves and terminal twigs of *Buxus sem-
pervirens*. Swanscombe; Hampton-in-Arden; Snitterfield
Bushes; Kent; Sussex; Surrey; Wenlock Edge; Liverpool;
Heyshott; Spye Park, Wilts.; Shropshire; Durham.

This occurs alike on leaves and twigs, the more advanced state,
M. Candollei, on the latter; *M. Mirbelii*, which is called *Sarcophoma
Mirbelii* by von Höhnel in Hedwig. 1918, lx. 133, is less well-developed;
and presumably *Phoma phacidioides* and *P. delitescens* are very young
states. Both Cooke and Saccardo suggest that *Hyponectria Buxi* Sacc.
(*Sphaerella Buxi* Cooke) is its ascophorous stage, but this is doubtful.
S. and W. Europe, U.S.A.

Calamagrostis

Macrophoma graminella B. & V. in Sacc. Syll. Addit. 314; Syll.
x. 205. Mig. 110. *Phoma graminella* Sacc. Syll. iii. 166.

Pycnidia gregarious, immersed, globose-depressed, 160–
200μ diam., black, emerging by the short obtuse papilla;
texture of wall parenchymatous, wide-celled, fuliginous.
Spores ovate-fusoid, straight, acute at both ends, hyaline,
15–18 × 4μ.

On leaves of *Calamagrostis Epigejos*. Goosehill Woods, Ws.
(Rhodes).

Germ.

Delphinium

Macrophoma xanthina Berl. & Vogl. *l.c.* 307. Sacc. Syll. x. 192.
Phoma xanthina Sacc. Syll. iii. 118. *Sphaeropsis Delphinii* Cooke &
Mass. in Herb. Kew.

Pycnidia gregarious, covered by the slightly swollen epidermis, globose-depressed, 200–330μ diam., with a small
erumpent ostiole; texture parenchymatous, smoky-brown.
Spores cylindrical or cylindric-oblong, obtuse at the ends, at
times curvulous, 2–3-guttulate, singly nearly hyaline, but
yellowish in mass, 14–15 × 4–6μ; sporophores very short.

On stems of *Delphinium*. Kew Gardens. Nov. 1887.

Cooke and Massee give the size of the spores as 17–20 × 6–8μ. The
wall of the spore is colourless, but the protoplasm is distinctly yellowish, which shows plainly when the spores are in a mass; they are often
irregular and not always guttulate. It is an immature Diplodia.
Fr.

Dracaena

Macrophoma Draconis All. in Rab. Krypt. Flor. vii. 836.
Phyllosticta Draconis Karsten, in Hedwig. 1896, p. 47 (*non* Berk.).

"Pycnidia immersed, then projecting, subglobose, black,
pierced, punctiform, seated on a pallid spot. Spores cylindrical, obtuse at both ends, slightly constricted in the middle,
guttulate, hyaline, up to 20 × 3μ; sporophores filiform, up to
25 × 1·5μ." (Karsten.)

On leaves of cultivated Dracaenas in conservatories.

Probably this is not the fungus reported in our gardening papers as
Phyllosticta Draconis (*q.v.*), for Allescher, who named it *Macrophoma
Draconis* (Berk.), was not aware of the size of the spores of Berkeley's
plant, which is 6–7 × 3μ! Evidently Karsten's fungus is not the same
as Berkeley's.
Finland.

Fraxinus

Macrophoma Fraxini Delacr. in Bull. Soc. Myc. Fr. 1890, p. 140.
Sacc. Syll. x. 191. All. vi. 365, with fig. Died. 189. Mig. 240. Ellis, in
T.B.M.S. iv. 124. *Phoma hyalina* Sacc. *p.p.*

Pycnidia gregarious, subcutaneous, convex, covered, then
elevating the epidermis and causing the surface of the twig to
appear like a rasp, at length projecting through a torn opening, black, about 300μ diam.; peridium many-layered, firm,
parenchymatous, blackish-brown without, with a few brown
hyphae; contents white. Spores oblong-ellipsoid, obtuse at

both ends, thick-walled, filled with granular and guttulate protoplasm, colourless, 20–30 × 7–10μ or even broader; sporophores crowded, nearly straight, hyaline, acute, 10–20 × 2–4μ.

On fallen twigs of *Fraxinus excelsior*. Kew Gardens; Derbyshire; Oxfordshire; Herefordshire; Cheshire; Flintshire; etc.   Feb.–May.

The spores often have the protoplasm divided in the middle, and sometimes show a faint constriction. The pycnidia usually stand singly, but occasionally 2–5 may be found in a botryose cluster. There cannot be the slightest doubt that this is merely a young state of *Diplodia inquinans* (*q.v.*).

Fr. Germ. Denm. U.S.A.

Passiflora

Macrophoma passifloricola Grove. *Diplodia passifloricola* Henn. in Verh. Bot. Ver. Prov. Brand. xl. 167. Sacc. Syll. xvi. 917. Died. 622. Mig. 330.

Pycnidia gregarious, subglobose, shining, black, roundish or oblong, about 100μ diam., immersed, then erumpent by the vertex. Spores oblong-cylindrical or subclavate, straight, rounded at both ends, nearly or quite colourless, but cloudy or granular within, faintly guttulate, 18–24 × 5–6μ; no sporophores seen.

On dead stems of *Passiflora*. School House, Polperro (Rilstone).   May.

The spores sometimes looked as if they might become 1-septate in the middle, but they never formed a distinct septum. This seems to be the fungus originally described by Hennings as a Diplodia, but afterwards recognised by Diedicke (*l.c.*) from the same specimens as probably a Macrophoma. It is certainly no Diplodia; ?Diplodina.

Germ.

Picea

Macrophoma parca Berl. & Vogl. in Sacc. Syll. Addit. 313. All. vi. 354. *Sphaeropsis parca* B. & Br. in Ann. Nat. Hist. 1850, v. 375. Cooke, Handb. 427. *Phoma parca* Sacc. Syll. iii. 100.

Pycnidia immersed, minute, collapsing when dry, ostiole erumpent by a minute fissure; peridium soft, parenchymatous, brown, ostiole darker. Spores oblong, somewhat cylindrical, obtuse, but attenuated at the lower end, very granular and semi-opaque, with 2–6 large guttules.

On leaves of *Picea excelsa*. Batheaston (B. & Br.).   Jan.

"Scattered sparingly on the leaves. Pycnidia collapsed when dry, so as not to rise at all above the surface, black. Spores obtuse at both ends, but often suddenly attenuated at one extremity. Resembling very much *Sphaeria Buxi* DC. [i.e. *Macrophoma Candollei* B. & V.], which belongs to the same genus, but differing in its collapsed pycnidia and narrower spores." (B. & Br.)

Fr. Belg. Germ. Ital. U.S.A.

Pinus

Macrophoma Strobi Berl. & Vogl. in Sacc. Syll. Addit. 313; Syll. x. 202. *Sphaeropsis Strobi* B. & Br. in Ann. Nat. Hist. 1850, v. 375. Cooke, Handb. 427. *Phoma Strobi* Sacc. Syll. iii. 101.

Pycnidia scattered or subgregarious, immersed, punctiform, black, about 200μ across, at length piercing the epidermis by the shining papilla. Spores cylindrical, straight, rounded at the apex, subacute at base, $12–20 \times 2–2\cdot5\mu$.

On leaves of *Pinus silvestris*, Mickleham Down (Bloom). Of *P. austriaca*, Brace's Leigh Wood and Hartlebury Common (Rhodes). Of *Cryptomeria*, Hadzor Hall, Droitwich.

Jan.–Jun.

There is every reason to believe that this is merely an early state of *Diplodina Strobi* Grove (*q.v.*), before the septum is developed.

Quercus

Macrophoma dryina Berl. & Vogl. in Sacc. Syll. Addit. 307. *Sphaeropsis dryina* B. & C. N. Amer. Fung. no. 411, in Grevill. 1874, ii. 180. *Phoma dryina* Sacc. Syll. iii. 96.

"Pycnidia papilliform, black, surrounded by the epidermis, which gives them a pale appearance. Spores obovoid, hyaline, $15 \times 6–7\mu$."

On slender twigs of *Quercus coccinea*. Kew Gardens (Cooke).

Apparently identical with the American form, but probably introduced with the host. The spores are oval-oblong or somewhat obovoid, thick-walled, filled with dense protoplasm or very granular, not guttulate, $18–20 \times 7–8\mu$; sporophores short, thick, about as long as the spore and $5–6\mu$ wide. No doubt it is an immature Diplodia.

N. Amer. (on *Quercus*).

Macrophoma nitens Berl. & Vogl. in Sacc. Syll. Addit. 314; Syll. x. 204. All. vi. 373. Died. p. 191, p. 22, f. IV, 1. Mig. 241. *Phoma nitens* Sacc. Syll. iii. 151.

Pycnidia gregarious, crowded in a crust-like layer, nearly superficial, black, shining, hemispherical, then collapsing,

but still protruding the vertex, 180–250μ diam.; peridium dense, many-layered, indistinctly fibrous, dark-brown without, paler within. Spores cylindrical, straight, obtuse at both ends, 13–18 × 2–3μ; sporophores short, 5 × 1–1·5μ. (Fig. 5d.)

On leaves of *Quercus palustris*, Hadzor Hall (Rhodes). On twigs of *Quercus Ilex*, Hadzor Hall, Ws.

The German and Belgian specimens were on fallen acorns. The spores resemble those of *M. cylindrospora*, but the pycnidia are different. Belg. Germ.

Rhododendron
Macrophoma Falconeri Henn. in Zeitschr. f. Pflanzenkr. 1904, p. 143. Sacc. Syll. xviii. 271. Died. 191. Mig. 241. T.B.M.S. v. 244. *Phoma Falconeri* Henn. in Hedwig. 1903, p. 219.

"Spots large, marginal, reddish-brown, becoming bleached. Pycnidia gregarious or scattered, bursting the epidermis and becoming somewhat prominent, girt by the torn laciniae, depressed-globose, thick-walled, black, shining, 250–300μ diam.; texture indistinct, subsclerotial. Spores oblong, obtuse at both ends, rather thick-walled, guttulate or somewhat granular-cloudy, 15–30 × 10–14μ; sporophores oblong or subclavate, 10–25 × 3–4·5μ."

On fading leaves of *Rhododendron Falconeri*. Gower, Swansea (Rees). Oct.

These specimens differ from those found at Berlin, on the same host, in that the spots were not always marginal, the pycnidia were not quite so large, and the spores seldom measured more than 18 × 7μ. It is an immature Diplodia. Germ.

Taxus
Macrophoma Taxi Berl. & Vogl. in Sacc. Syll. Addit. 308; Syll. x. 194. All. vi. 375. Died. 193. Mig. 112. *Sphaeropsis Taxi* Berk. Outl. 316. Cooke, Handb. 428. *Phoma Taxi* Sacc. Syll. iii. 102.

Pycnidia epiphyllous, gregarious or in rows, covered by the epidermis which is at length pierced by the raised but hardly projecting ostiole, about 300μ diam.; peridium many-layered, of indistinct cells, fuscous outside. Spores ovoid-elongate, with somewhat attenuated but obtuse ends, 16–20 × 5–7μ (Allesch. 20–22 × 8–9μ); sporophores filiform, subacute, 10 × 2μ.

On dead leaves of *Taxus baccata*.

This is nothing but a young state of *Diplodia Taxi* de Not. (*q.v.*).

Thuja
Macrophoma thujana Cooke & Mass. in Grevill. xvi. 7. Sacc.
Syll. x. 192. All. vi. 376.

Pycnidia somewhat scattered, subepidermal, globose, elevating and at length piercing the epidermis. Spores ellipsoid,
$25 \times 10\mu$.
On twigs of *Thuja*. Kew Gardens.

I could find no spores in any of the specimens. There is no reason to
suppose this to be anything but a young state of *Diplodia thujana*
Peck & C. or *Diplodia Thujae* Westd.

Vinca
Macrophoma Vincae Berl. & Vogl. in Sacc. Syll. Addit. 309. All.
vi. 377. *Sphaeropsis Vincae* Curr. Simpl. Sphaer. 333. *Phoma Vincae*
Sacc. Syll. iii. 145. *Macrophoma cylindrospora* Died. 190, *p.p.* Mig.
110, *p.p.*

No spots. Pycnidia scattered all over the leaf, amphigenous, abundant, globose, 200–250μ diam., erumpent, rather
prominent, smooth, black, pierced by a pore; contents whitish.
Spores oblong-ellipsoid or subcylindrical, $12 \times 2\mu$ (15–18μ
long, Sacc.).
On dead leaves of *Vinca minor* (not *major*). Bungay;
Ditchingham; Forden.

The pycnidia chiefly followed the course of the venules. Is not this
the simple state of *Ceuthospora Feurichii* Bub. ?; *vide infra.*
Belg.
See *Macrophoma Ulmi* in Sacc. Syll. iii. 99.

HAPALOSPHAERIA Sydow, in Ann. Mycol. 1908, vi. 305.

Pycnidia clear-brown, rather soft, with a relatively thick
wall which, however, easily breaks up, pierced at the apex
by a pore. Spores globose, continuous, hyaline; sporophores
conical.
   Parasitic in flowers and fruiting in the anthers; after the
collapse of the pycnidia, the flowers are filled with the dust-
like spores.—This genus is out of place in its present position.

Rubus
Hapalosphaeria deformans Syd. in Ann. Mycol. 1908, vi, 305.
T.B.M.S. 1921, vii. 84. Died. p. 12, p. 22, f. 1. Mig. p. 226, pl. 31,

f. 6–8. *Paepalopsis deformans* Syd. in Ann. Mycol. 1907, v. 398.
T.B.M.S. vii. 84.

Pycnidia solitary or clustered, formed in the outer wall of
an anther, at length subsuperficial, subglobose or conical; texture parenchymatous, clear-brown; wall rather thick, of
several layers of minute cells. Spores numerous, globose,
3–5μ diam.

On anthers of *Rubus fruticosus*. Aberlady, Haddington-
shire, 1904 (Dr Borthwick). *n.v.*

The mycelium apparently arises first in the epidermis of the young
flower-bud, later penetrating into the anthers or creeping over their
surface. It is said to cause sometimes the formation of a kind of
"witches' broom" in the inflorescence.
Germ. Spain.

CLINTERIUM Fr. Sum. Veg. Sc. 418.

Pycnidia erumpent, then free, $\pm$ globose, carbonaceous,
composed below of (pseudo)parenchymatous hyphae which
in the upper part become prosenchymatous and converge towards the summit, and, in consequence, dehiscing by cracks
or fissures. Spores somewhat elongated, hyaline, continuous
or pseudoseptate.

Distinguished from Phoma by its texture and mode of de-
hiscence. Supposed by Fries to be an imperfect stage of Gibbera, which it somewhat resembles in texture.

Ericaceae

Clinterium obturatum Fr. Summ. Veg. Scan. 418. Cooke,
Handb. 429. *Sphaeria obturata* Fr. Syst. Myc. ii. 495 (see also *Gibbera
obturata* Fr. S.V.S. 402). Currey, Simpl. Sphaer. 329. *Phoma obturata*
Sacc. Syll. iii. 85. All. vi. 207. *Sporonema obturatum* Sacc. Syll. iii.
678, *p.p.* All. vii. 412. See Starbäck, I, 1894, p. 57, pl. 2, f. 36a, b.

Pycnidia scattered, subglobose, at first mouthless, smooth,
then rugose and collapsing, erumpent and nearly free, black,
horny, 500–700μ diam., at length dehiscing by several minute
fissures as the apical converging filaments of the peridium
separate. Spores abundant, cymbiform-fusoid, often somewhat curved or arcuate, subobtuse at both ends, 10–12 ×
2–2·5μ, variously guttulate, at last pseudo-uniseptate in the
middle; sporophores varying in length.

On leaves of *Calluna*, Appin. On branches of *Erica*, Lynd-hurst; Clare Island, Ireland.

It has also been found in Sweden on branches of *Arbutus* and on leaves of *Vaccinium Oxycoccus*, and elsewhere on leaves and branches of other Ericaceae. It is no doubt allied to the Phacidiaceae. Cf. *Phoma cymbispora* (B. & C.) Sacc. Syll. iii. 85, which seems to be the same or a closely allied species, having a similarly formed pycnidium and similar spores.

DENDROPHOMA Sacc. in Mich. ii. 4.

Pycnidia immersed or superficial, of prosenchymatous or even subsclerotial thick brown almost carbonaceous texture, always unilocular and usually furnished with a pore. Spores very small, sub-cylindrical or ovoid; sporophores with whorled or irregular branches which are sometimes reduced to mere teeth.

The characters of the genus reside in the 1-locular pycnidia with thick brown walls, the branched sporo-phores, and the small more or less oblong or ovoid spores. (Fig. 6.)

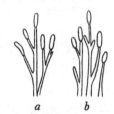

Fig. 6. Spores and sporo-phores of: *a*, *Dendrophoma Convallariae*, var. *Cliviae*; *b*, *D. pleurospora*; both × 600.

Plurivorous

Dendrophoma pleurospora Sacc. Syll. iii. 178. All. vi. 405. Died. p. 196, p. 202, f. III, 2. Grove, in Journ. Bot. 1912, p. 50; 1922, p. 17.

Pycnidia scattered, globose-conical, pierced, 140–200μ diam.; contents pallid; texture parenchymatous, smoky-brown. Spores shortly cylindrical, 4–4·5 × 1–1·5μ, obliquely sessile at the apex and sides of the sporophores, which are thick, slightly tapering upwards, ± straight, 30–50 × 2–3·5μ. (Fig. 6*b*.)

On wood of *Populus*, Cheshire (Ellis). On twigs of *Salix fragilis*, Quinton. On twigs of *Ribes Grossularia*, Studley Castle. Mar. Nov.

Forms of this Dendrophoma are recorded on *Ribes rubrum*, as well as on *Laurus nobilis*, *Prunus*, *Quercus*, *Rosa*, and *Vitis*. When old, the sporophores seem to vanish.

Fr. Germ. Ital.

Cladonia

Dendrophoma podetiicola Keissl. in Oesterr. Bot. Zeitschr. 1910, lx. 57. T.B.M.S. iii. 282. *Lichenosticta podetiicola* Zopf, in Nov. Act. Leop.-Carol. 1898, lxx. 263, f. 22–5. Sacc. Syll. xvi. 851. ? *Aposphaeria Cladoniae* All. & Schnab. in Ber. Bayer. Bot. Ges. 1895, p. 32. See All. Krypt. Flor. vi. 385. Sacc. Syll. xiv. 895.

Pycnidia semi-immersed, black or brownish-black, about 150μ diam. Spores kidney-shaped, with usually two small guttules, about 6–8 × 3μ; sporophores branched.

Parasitic on the podetia and squamules of *Cladonia*. Has been considered as belonging to a Lichen, Lindsay in Trans. Roy. Soc. Edin. xxii. 161, pl. 8, f. 3. *n.v.*

Germ. Switz. Austr. N. Amer.

Clivia

Dendrophoma Convallariae Cav. Mat. Lomb. 18. Sacc. Syll. x. 211. All. vi. 401, with fig. Died. 194. Mig. p. 121, pl. 8, f. 5–9.
Var. **Cliviae** Grove, in Journ. Bot. 1930, p. 138.

Spots large, indefinite, grey, with a narrow fuscous border. Pycnidia innate, scattered, about 500μ diam., flatly lens-shaped, black, unilocular, remaining immersed, but pierced by an indistinct pore; wall of several layers thick (somewhat like a Ceuthospora), composed of numerous minute indistinct dark olivaceous cells which get gradually paler inwards and bear on the inner surface crowds of filiform and alternately-branched pedicels as long as 30μ or more. Spores Cytospora-like, about 5 × 1μ, slightly curved, not thickened at the ends, hyaline. (Fig. 6a.)

On base of leaves of *Clivia*, in greenhouse, Erdington, Warw. (Rhodes).

Crataegus

Dendrophoma pulvis-pyrius Sacc. Fung. Ven. Nov. ser. 3, no. 18; Syll. iii. 181. All. vi. 400. Died. 194. Mig. 121.

Pycnidia globose, somewhat depressed, irregular, hardly papillate, about 300μ diam. Spores cylindrical, hyaline, 3–4 × 0·7μ; sporophores once or twice verticillately branched, 18–25 × 1μ.

On a dead twig of *Crataegus Oxyacantha*, Holyhead, Anglesey. On dead wood, Sutton Coldfield, etc. Apr. May.

Recorded abroad on *Alnus, Carpinus, Pyrus, Quercus, Robinia*, etc. Fr. Germ. Ital. etc.

Ilex

Dendrophoma phyllogena Trail, in Scot. Nat. 1887, p. 87. Grevill. xv. 108. Sacc. Syll. x. 210. All. vi. 404.

Pycnidia numerous, on pale spots, subepidermal, ellipsoid, slightly papillate, black. Spores cylindrical, $8-12 \times 1 \cdot 5-2\mu$; sporophores hyaline, branched, fasciculate, $30-35\mu$ long, 2μ thick at the base; branches short, alternate, each tipped by a spore.

On leaves of *Ilex Aquifolium*, on dead spots near the tip. Aberdeen. *n.v.* (On the same, in Spain also.) May.

NEOTTIOSPORA Desm. in Ann. Sci. Nat. 1843, xix. 346.

Pycnidia completely immersed and remaining so, globose, membranaceous, opening by a round or irregular aperture. Spores oblong-fusoid, continuous, hyaline, provided at the apex with a tuft of little mucoid setae which readily disappear. (Fig. 7.)

Carex

Neottiospora Caricum Desm. in Ann. Sci. Nat. 1843, xix. 346. Cooke, Handb. p. 457, f. 169. Sacc. Syll. iii. 216. All. vi. 444. B. & Br. in Ann. Nat. Hist. 1850, v. 379. *Zythia maxima* Fautr.

Pycnidia amphigenous, scattered, very minute, rusty-brown, at length umber, immersed, globose, covered by the discoloured epidermis; texture parenchymatous, greenish-olive; contents rosy, sub gelatinous, mixed when young with globules of rose-coloured oil; ostiole round, broad, becoming black. Spores fusoid or oblanceolate, nearly hyaline, $12-14 \times 3\mu$, with three or four guttules, bearing at the apex a little brush of three or four short, sometimes forked, bristles, which soon disappear and are scarcely to be recognised in dried specimens.

Fig. 7. Spores of *Neottiospora Caricum*, × 600.

On dead leaves of *Carices* (e.g. *C. paludosa*, *C. paniculata*, *C. pendula*). Spye Park, Rudloe, Wilts.; Batheaston, Somerset (Broome). Scarborough; Linley, Salop (Ellis). Moray

(Trail). Pembrokeshire (Rhodes). Devon; Goosehill Woods, Ws. Rare, but not uncommon in Worcestershire, though not easy to detect.   Spring.

"Remarkable for the appendage of short hyaline threads, with which the spores are furnished at one extremity" (B. & Br.). Berkeley records a variety with larger and olive-coloured spores. I have seen the spores also with a distinct bluish tinge. Diedicke records three species of Neottiospora in his Flora, one on dung, another on *Eriophorum*, and a third (*N. arenaria*) on *Carex arenaria* (spores 22–35 × 5·5–8μ).

Fr. Germ. Denm. Ital. etc.

SIROCOCCUS Preuss, Fung. Hoyersw. no. 306 (in Linnaea, 1854, xxvi. 716).

Pycnidia complete, subcarbonaceous, erumpent or superficial, often mouthless. Spores subglobose to cylindrical, concatenate, arising from filiform sporophores.

The pycnidia resemble those of a typical Phoma, but the numerous spores are arranged distinctly in chains, by which two characteristics this genus is distinguished from all others.

Delphinium
Sirococcus gibberoideus Grove. *Phoma gibberoidea* Cooke & Mass. in Grevill. xvii. 56. Sacc. Syll. x. 166. All. vi. 287.

Pycnidia scattered or arranged more or less in rows, covered, oblong, black, up to 500μ long, papillate, the papilla piercing the epidermis; peridium rather thick when old, parenchymatous or subcarbonaceous, but soft, dark-brown. Spores profuse, concatenate, cylindrical, subtruncate at the ends, straight, 2–5-guttulate, 9–14 × 1–2μ; chains long, parallel, crowded, adherent, arising from fasciculate sparingly branched sporophores which resemble the spores.

On dead stems of *Delphinium elatum*. Kew Gardens. Jan. In company with *Leptosphaeria vagabunda* Sacc.

This is the first species of the genus which has been recognised in this country; it is allied to *S. pulcher* Sacc. (Syll. xvi. 905) on *Erica carnea* and *S. cylindroides* Sacc. (Syll. iii. 217) on *Adenostyles*. There are also one or two species on cones, which should be found here.

APOSPHAERIA Berk. Outl. 315.

Pycnidia occurring on bark or wood, superficial or immersed by the base alone, globose or ovoid, sometimes variable in shape, papillate; texture usually ± prosenchymatous, at length somewhat carbonaceous. Spores oblong, ovoid, subglobose, or subfusoid, continuous, hyaline; sporophores short (up to 10μ), simple, sometimes inconspicuous.

Similar to Phoma, but always superficial or nearly so, never erumpent. The pycnidia are generally hard and brittle, and are commonest upon hard wood.

Plurivorous

Aposphaeria agminalis Sacc. Syll. iii. 171. All. vi. 382. *Phoma myriocarpa* Cooke, in Herb. Kew (*non* Dur. & Mont.).

Pycnidia scattered or here and there clustered in groups, nearly superficial, punctiform, globose-conical, shining-black, $90–100\mu$ diam.; wall thick, carbonaceous. Spores abundant, ellipsoid or oblong, obtuse at both ends, biguttulate, $3 \times 2\mu$.

On bare wood of *Juglans regia*, Kew Gardens (Cooke). On a decorticated trunk of *Betula*, Ayrshire (Boyd). On wood of *Pinus*, Sydenham (Cooke)! Forhill, Ws. (Chesters).

Probably the pycnidial stage of some Zignoëlla. I find many of the spores to measure $3–3·5 \times 1·5\mu$, though the $3 \times 2\mu$ occur mixed with them. The two guttules are very distinct in nearly every spore. Ital.

Aposphaeria fibricola Sacc. Syll. iii. 176. All. vi. 386. *Phoma fibricola* Berk. in Hook. Journ. Bot. Kew, 1853, v. 41, pl. 3, f. 1. Cooke, Handb. 422.

"Spots indeterminate. Pycnidia elongated, scattered or here and there aggregated, following the course of the fibres. Spores ovoid or subellipsoid, without guttules, 6μ long, of a delicate olive-green colour" (Berk.).

On decorticated wood of *Tilia*, Ayrshire (Boyd). On chips of wood of *Fraxinus*, *Populus*, *Quercus*, and *Ulmus*; King's Cliffe; Forden; Lyndhurst; Scarborough; etc.   Aug.–Nov.

The citation by Berkeley of *Pinus* as a host, in the "Outlines", is probably a slip of the pen. So far as British specimens go, this species is merely the immature state of *Diplodiella fibricola* Sacc. (*q.v.*).

Berkeley's original specimens (King's Cliffe) have brownish 1-septate spores, 7–8 × 2–2·5μ. Others may be different.

Aposphaeria glomerata Sacc. Syll. iii. 175. All. vi. 396, with fig. Mig. 117. *Coniothyrium glomeratum* Corda, Icon. iv. 39, f. 108. Cooke, Handb. p. 416, f. 148.

Pycnidia collected into minute black tufts, superficial, convex, rugulose, brown. Spores oblong, rounded at the ends, colourless, 5–6μ long.

"In the cracks of planks of *Ulmus*, especially on the medullary rays, King's Cliffe, Nov." (Berk.). Boynton, Yorks. On bare weathered planks,. Warwickshire. On a dead ash-stick, Hartlebury Common, Ws.   Apr. May.

Berkeley's specimen is mixed with *Dinemasporium hispidulum*. Bohemia.

Aposphaeria Pulviscula Sacc. Syll. iii. 175. All. vi. 394. Died. 207. Mig. 116. *Phoma Pulviscula* Sacc. in Mich. i. 258.

Pycnidia on wood, gregarious, nearly superficial, subglobose, about 100μ diam., with a minute papilla; peridium thin, minutely parenchymatous, smoky-brown. Spores oblong-ovoid, 4–5 × 1·5–2μ (or even as much as 3μ broad); sporophores oblong or attenuated upwards, 5–8 × 2μ.

On a rotten stump of *Salix*, Oxford. On very old bark, Piper's Hill Common, Ws.   Feb. Mar.

Probably the pycnidium of *Zignoëlla Pulviscula* Sacc. Fr. Germ. Denm. Ital.

Acer
Aposphaeria inophila Sacc. Syll. iii. 175. All. vi. 380. Mig. 114. *Phoma inophila* Berk. in Hook. Journ. Bot. 1853, v. 40, pl. 3, f. 4. Cooke, Handb. 421.

Spots indeterminate, silky-shining. Pycnidia gregarious, oblong, black, immersed among the fibres, compressed, at length superficial, about 200μ diam.; texture of wall rather parenchymatous, dark fuscous-brown. Spores oblong, biguttulate, 1·5–2μ long.

On planks of *Acer campestre* and ? *Ulmus*. King's Cliffe (Berk.).   Nov.

Resembling *A. epileuca*; growing on shining patches, which contrast strongly with the rest of the surface. As will be seen from what

follows, these specimens of Berkeley here described have probably immature spores.

Var. **Pseudoplatani** Grove, in Journ. Bot. 1886, p. 135. Allescher, in Hedwig. 1895, xxxiv. 206; Krypt. Flor. vi. 382. Mig. 114.

Pycnidia effused, gregarious or a few at times connate, very varied but chiefly globose, scarcely or distinctly papillate, black, rugose, 80–160μ diam., nestling among the whitish-cinereous silky shining wood-fibres, at length superficial, collapsing, pierced by a pore. Spores oblong or ovoid, with two guttules or none, singly hyaline, in mass faintly yellowish, 4–5μ long.

On wood of decorticated trunks of _Acer Pseudoplatanus_. Sutton Coldfield. Jan.–Mar.

Spores more than twice as long as in the type. Karsten's var. _opaca_ (Sacc. Syll. x. 208), on _Acer platanoides_, has exactly inter-mediate spores.

Germ. Finland.

Pinus

Aposphaeria bicuspidata Sacc. Syll. iii. 71. All. vi. 390. Mig. 114. _Phoma bicuspidata_ Berk. in Hook. Journ. Bot. 1853, v. 41, pl. 3, f. 6. Cooke, Handb. 422. _A. Broomeiana_ Cooke, in Grevill. xvi. 7. Sacc. Syll. x. 208. All. vi. 399. _Phoma Broomeiana_ Berk. in Herb. no 6490.

Pycnidia elongated, minute, immersed, arranged in the line of the fibres, at first scattered, occasionally confluent, black. Spores shortly fusoid, biguttulate, sometimes with a small papilla at each end, 7–8 × 2μ; sporophores short and slender.

On planks of _Pinus_. Woodnewton (Berk.). Dec. Jan.

Externally very similar to _A. ulmicola_. The spores vary in size and in degree of acumination. _A. Broomeiana_, on wood of _Ulmus_, King's Cliffe (Berk.) and on charcoal, Mortlake (Cooke), is partly at least the same species. The King's Cliffe specimen, under that name, has vari-able spores, some as bicuspidate as in Berkeley's figure (_l.c._), others oblong, 2–3μ long and with sporophores like those of _A. mucifera_, while some of the pycnidia were filled with a mass of sclerotioid cells, probably the beginning of the ascophorous state.

Germ.

Aposphaeria epileuca Sacc. Syll. iii. 169. All. vi. 390. _Phoma epileuca_ Berk. in Hook. Journ. Bot. 1853, v. 41, pl. 3, f. 2. Cooke, Handb. 422.

Spots indeterminate, white. Pycnidia scattered, erumpent, superficial, ± elongated, black, about 200μ wide, opening by

a minute pore; texture parenchymatous, dark-fuscous. Spores oblong or subclavate, sometimes slightly curved, occasionally with one or two guttules, colourless, $2 \cdot 8$–$3 \cdot 8 \times 1$–$1 \cdot 25 \mu$.

On bleached planks of *Pinus*. Woodnewton.   Dec.

Pycnidia following the direction of the fibres.
Ital. Siberia, U.S.A.

Aposphaeria mediella Karst. in Hedwig. 1884, p. 59. Sacc. Syll. iii. 170. All. vi. 390. Died. 205.

Pycnidia erumpent, becoming superficial, solitary or caespitose, varying in shape, roundish or angular or somewhat depressed, scarcely papillate, at length opening by a wide pore, black, 200–300μ diam.; wall carbonaceous. Spores oval, 4–7×2–3μ.

On dead bark of *Pinus silvestris*. Bidston and Bromborough, Cheshire (Ellis).   May.

Germ. Finland.

[**Aposphaeria nitens** Cooke & Mass. in Grevill. xvi. 7. Sacc. Syll. x. 208. All. vi. 391.

"Pycnidia rather small, gregarious, erumpent, at length nearly superficial, globose, papillate, black, shining. Spores cylindrical, obtuse at both ends, 10×2–3μ."]

On decayed wood of *Pinus*. Kew Gardens (Cooke).

On examination, this specimen is seen to be a pyrenomycete, with asci. It may be *Wallrothiella minima*, but its condition is so poor that it is impossible to decide the question.

                                                        Populus
Aposphaeria populea Sm. & Ramsb. in T.B.M.S. 1914, iv. 325.

Pycnidia superficial, sparsely gregarious, when young globose, at length depressed, glabrous, smooth, blackish-brown, 200–300μ diam., pierced by a round pore. Spores rounded at both ends, 7–8×2–3μ.

On decorticated wood of *Populus*. Stevenston, Ayrshire (Boyd). *n.v.*   Feb.

A. populina Died. appears to differ only in its smaller and probably younger spores (4–$5 \times 1 \cdot 5 \mu$).

Ulmus

Aposphaeria ulmicola Sacc. Syll. iii. 175. All. vi. 396. *Phoma ulmicola* Berk. in Hook. Journ. Bot. Kew, 1853, v. 40, pl. 3, f. 3. Cooke, Handb. 422.

Pycnidia nestling between the fibres, at length superficial, here and there densely gregarious and forming little oblong dark-brown patches, black. Spores ellipsoid, scarcely guttulate, 2μ long.

On planks of *Ulmus*, exposed to the weather. King's Cliffe. Nov.

Closely resembling *A. agminalis*, of which it may be the immature state, but smaller. All these Aposphaerias published by Berkeley in Hooker's Journ. Bot. Kew, are very similar, and several of them may be forms of one species.

Aposphaeria mucifera Sacc. Syll. iii. 175. All. vi. 396. *Phoma mucifera* Berk. in Hook. Journ. Bot. Kew, 1853, v. 40, pl. 3, f. 5. Cooke, Handb. 422.

Pycnidia scattered, immersed among the fibres, then superficial, oblong, about 150μ diam., black, shining, sometimes papillate. Spores oblong-ellipsoid, involved in mucus, nearly all biguttulate, $2 \cdot 5 – 4 \times 0 \cdot 75 – 1\mu$, at length expelled in a tendril; sporophores crowded, filiform, $10–12\mu$ long, rising from a dark basal stratum.

On planks of *Ulmus*. King's Cliffe. Nov.

Among pycnidia, such as are described above, were found some which had 1-celled dark-olive spores, $5–7 \times 2–3\mu$, immersed in a very persistent mucus. These are perhaps the fully mature pycnidia, and show that the species should be called *Coniothyrium muciferum* (*q.v.*). Berkeley himself noted these, but wrongly assigned them (*l.c.* p. 41) to *C. glomeratum*.

Paint

Aposphaeria violacea Bertel, in Oesterr. Bot. Zeitschr. 1904, p. 205. Sacc. Syll. xviii. 277. Mig. 118. *Phoma pigmentivora* Massee, in Kew Bull. 1911, p. 325, with coloured figs., and Dis. Cult. Pl., ed. 2, Suppl. p. *15. Grove, in Journ. Bot. 1913, p. 43.

Spots caused by the mycelium (on paint) roundish, indeterminate, bright-rosy or rosy-purple, up to 8 cm. or more long. Pycnidia loosely gregarious on the spots or occasionally crowded, slightly prominent, purplish-black, subglobose, hardly papillate, $125–150\mu$ diam.; texture loosely parenchy-

matous. Spores ellipsoid, hyaline, $4-6 \times 2-2 \cdot 5\mu$ $(6 \cdot 8 \times 3 \cdot 2\mu$, Bertel).

On new white paint, especially in hothouses at Botanic Gardens, etc. Kew; Birmingham; Durham; Studley Castle, Wk.; Essex; etc.

The pink colour is contained in the mycelium; when the spores germinate in pure linseed-oil, the mycelium was said to be colourless, but on the carbonate of lead paint to become coloured. When it grew upon the fresh oil-paint in a warm house, its metabolism was thought to decompose the linseed-oil-lead-carbonate complex with disengagement of water and carbon dioxide, thus producing various oxides of lead. But Mr J. Ramsbottom has grown it in cultures for many years on various media (such as Sabouraud's) in which presumably no metal was contained, and the pink or violet colour was still produced.

In the specimens which occurred, on paint at the Prague University, the pycnidia are described as having two or three ostioles on each.

It would seem likely that this interesting species is a sport from some Phoma which had been introduced into the hothouses, say on an oil-palm, from the Tropics. It cannot have been evolved on oil-paint, which is a comparatively modern invention.

RHIZOSPHAERA Mang. & Har. in Bull. Soc. Myc. Fr. 1907, xxiii. 56.

Pycnidia superficial, subglobose, black, parenchymatous, subcoriaceous, pierced at the apex, attenuated downwards into a narrow stipe, which is immersed in the parenchyma of the leaf and ends in a branched mycelial filament. Spores hyaline, continuous, ovoid, smooth; sporophores short, simple, monosporous.

Coniferae

Rhizosphaera Kalkhoffii Bubák, in Ber. Deutsch. Bot. Ges. 1914, xxxii, 190. Wilson, in Trans. Roy. Scot. Arbor. Soc. xl. 34–6, f. 1–4. T.B.M.S. xiii. 152, pl. 8, f. 1. *Sphaeronema*[1] *Pini* Desm. in Ann. Sci. Nat. 1848, x. 347. *Phoma Pini* Sacc. Syll. iii. 101. *Sclerophoma Pini* v. Höhn. in Sitz.-ber. Akad. Wiss. Wien, 1909, cxviii. 1234.

Pycnidia resembling those of *Rh. Pini* in form, structure and mode of origin, ovoid, narrowed below, rough, dull-black, $80-150\mu$ diam., dehiscing without a definite pore at the vertex. Spores ovoid, continuous, hyaline, conglutinate, eguttu-

---

[1] Misquoted "Sphaeropsis" by Saccardo, *l.c.*

late, 7·10 × 3–4μ, springing direct from the cells of the peridium.

On living leaves of *Picea pungens*, var. *argentea* and *glauca* (chiefly), *P. sitkensis* and other species of *Picea, Abies nobilis, A. pectinata, Pseudotsuga Douglasii, Pinus austriaca* and *P. montana.* England; Scotland; Ireland. Aug.–Apr.

A deadly parasite. Each pycnidium, as it pushes up through the stoma, may carry with it a minute whitish waxy lump (Saccardo's "*globulus minutus albus*") which had lain in the pore, and this may remain as a white spot on its apex. The same is true of the other Rhizosphaera.

Fr. Germ. Bohem. Tyrol.

Rhizosphaera Pini Maubl. in Bull. Soc. Myc. Fr. 1907, xxiii. 171, f. 6. T.B.M.ß. xiii. 151. Died. 899. *Coniothyrium Pini* Corda, Icon. Fung. iv. 38, f. 105 (*non* Oud.). *Sacidium Pini* Fr. Summ. Veg. Scand. 420. *Leptothyrium Pini* Sacc. Syll. iii. 627. *Rhizosphaera Abietis* Mang. & Har. in Bull. Soc. Myc. Fr. 1907, xxiii. 56, f. 1–6.

Pycnidia densely congregated ± in rows, hypophyllous, globose, superficial, black, 90–120μ diam.; texture distinctly parenchymatous, of dark, thick-walled, angular cells. Spores numerous, oval-oblong, 16–20 × 8μ; sporophores acuminate, short, i.e. the inner cells of the peridium.

On leaves of *Abies grandis*. Bagley Wood, Oxon (Wilson), Feb. 1927.

The occurrence of the pycnidia in rows arises from the serial arrangement of the leaf-stomata.

Fr. Germ. Austr. Ital. N. Amer.

ASTEROMA DC. in Mém. Mus. iii, pp. 329, 336.

This genus is represented, for the most part, only by the mycelial beginnings of parasitic fungi on leaves or herbaceous stems; either no fruit-body at all is produced or, if there is the semblance of one, it usually contains no spores. The marks on leaves to which these names are given are generally caused by radiating fibrils of brown hyphae growing in the host-tissue, but sometimes nothing can be seen but discoloured mesophyll or epidermal cells. Unless spores are present, such productions are not worthy of a name, since the fibrils may belong

either to a perfect fungus or to one of the Fungi Imperfecti,
i.e. a Coelomycete or a Hyphomycete. For instance, *Asteroma
Prunellae* Purt. is the early state of *Excipula Prunellae*, and
Asteroma Mali Desm. is the early state of *Fusicladium dendriticum*. Asteroma is included here only because it has been the
custom to reckon it among the Coelomycetes.

Plurivorous

Asteroma vagans Desm. in Ann. Sci. Nat. 1847, viii. 37. Sacc.
Syll. iii. 204. All. vi. 472. Died. 225. Mig. 141.

"Spots amphigenous, round, brown, greyish, when dry;
fibrils very slender, jointed, branched, divaricate, radiating
irregularly in all directions, covered by the epidermis; joints
half as long again as their diameter, constricted at the septa.
Pycnidia scattered, globose, semi-emergent, about 50μ diam.,
black."

On fading leaves of various trees.

A useless collective name; there are mentioned as hosts *Acer, Carpinus, Populus, Rhamnus, Syringa, Tilia, Viburnum*. On *Tilia* there
are two forms; the second, *A. Tiliae* Rud., differs in its dendroid, not
round, spots and its fibrils covered with greyish arachnoid threads.
Fr. Germ. Ital.

Acer

Asteroma Aceris Rob. & Desm. in Ann. Sci. Nat. 1843, xix. 348.
Sacc. Syll. iii. 207.

Amphigenous, spot-like; fibrils very slender, branched,
flexuous, reddish-brown, irregularly radiating in all directions.
Pycnidia scattered, globose, semi-emergent, black.

On dry leaves of *Acer campestre*. Darenth (Cooke). Spring.
Fr.

Betula

Asteroma Betulae Rob. & Desm. in Ann. Sci. Nat. 1843, xix. 349.
Sacc. Syll. iii. 208. All. vi. 454. Died. 217.

Amphigenous, spot-like; fibrils immersed in the leaf,
brown, branched and radiating from the centre; branches
numerous, diverging at the apex. Pycnidia filled with sclerotial cells, mostly hypophyllous, numerous, scattered, erumpent, black, about 80μ broad.

On fallen leaves of *Betula*. Wimbledon, etc.

No specimens of this, wherever gathered, seem ever to have yielded
spores on sporophores. It is therefore probably an immature pyren-

omycete, and Diedicke (Ann. Mycol. ix. 539), finding at times two or
three upright bristles upon the conceptacles, considers it to be an early
state of *Venturia ditricha* Karst., i.e. not a spermogonial stage of that
species, as Fuckel surmised, but merely the not fully developed perithecial stage.

Fr. Belg. Holl. Germ.

Colutea

Asteroma delicatulum Desm. in Ann. Sci. Nat. 1851, xvi. 303.
Sacc. Syll. iii. 213. All. vi. 458. Died. 223. Mig. 138.

Spots minute, round, occasionally confluent, when moist
tending towards olive colour, when dry greyish-black; fibrils
immersed in the leaf, very delicate, flexuous, radiating from
the centre; branches few, elongated, subdichotomous, jointed,
each joint as long as it is broad. Pycnidia very minute, scattered, globose.

On pods of *Colutea arborescens*. Kew Gardens. Recorded
abroad also on pods of *Lunaria*. Probably merely the beginnings of mycelial growth.

Fr. Belg. Holl. Germ. Switz. Port.

Cornus

Asteroma Corni Desm. in Ann. Sci. Nat. 1843, xix. 348. Sacc.
Syll. iii. 207. All. vi. 459. Died. p. 219, p. 202, f. vii, 4. Mig. 136.
A. obscurum Desm. in Ann. Sci. Nat. 1851, xvi. 303. Sacc. Syll. iii.
207. All. vi. 159. Mig. 136.

Spots epiphyllous, rarely hypophyllous, variable in size,
suborbicular, crowded, at times confluent, blackish; "fibrils
immersed, numerous, branched, anastomosing, fuscous-black;
branches radiating at the margin. Pycnidia very minute,
hardly perceptible".

On half-decayed leaves of *Cornus sanguinea*, Dartford. On
fading and reddening leaves of *Cornus alba*, Hadzor Hall,
Worcs.   Sept. Oct.

The "fibrils" are apparently composed of nothing but the discoloured cells of the mesophyll, which are closely embraced by the
mycelium.

Fr. Germ. Switz. Ital.

Crataegus

"**Asteroma Crataegi**", on leaves of *Pyrus communis*; Tonbridge;
King's Cliffe. So far as British specimens are concerned, this is merely
Fusicladium pyrinum; and the same may be said of "*Asteroma*(?)

Pyri", on leaves of the same host, King's Cliffe, and Terrington, Yorks. They are the leaf-forms of *Fusicladium*.

In Brit. Mus. there are specimens, from Berkeley's herbarium, of what might be *Actinonema Crataegi* Pers., on *Sorbus torminalis*, but without locality; Diedicke says that *Act. Crataegi* Pers. is *Fusicladium orbiculatum* (Detm.) Thüm.

Euphorbia

Asteroma euphorbiaceum Grove.

Spots roundish, small, 2–3 mm. diam., dark-brown, a little paler in the centre, several on each leaf, most visible on the upper side. Fibrils obscure, blackish-brown, branched, radiating just beneath the epidermis. Pycnidia exceedingly minute.

On leaves of *Euphorbia amygdaloides*. Wyre Forest. Oct.

Hedera

Asteroma Hederae Quest. *in litt. apud* Desm. Pl. Crypt. exs., ser. II, no. 774. Sacc. Syll. xi. 502. *Asterina Hederae* Desm. *ibid.*

Cooke's Norfolk specimens on Ivy leaves (Grevill. xiv. 75) are exactly like those of Desmazières. In them there are only faint reddish radiating markings on the upper surface of the leaf; no signs of pycnidia. Mr Boyd sent me some specimens from Ayrshire in which the fibrils are much more strongly developed. It is an imperfect Asterina. But sometimes faint cloudy markings are found on Ivy and named Asteroma, which are only the beginnings of *Ceuthospora Hederae*.

Fr. Holl.

Ilex

Asteroma Ilicis Grove.

Spots many on each leaf, indeterminate, irregular, confluent, olivaceous-brown; no fibrils visible.

On leaves of *Ilex Aquifolium*. Rissbury Camp, Hereford.

June.

Polygonatum

Asteroma reticulatum Chev. Fl. par. i. 447. Cooke, Handb. 460. Sacc. Syll. iii. 214. All. vi. 458. Died. 218. Mig. 139. *Sphaeria reticulata* DC. Flor. fr. vi. 138. *Dothidea reticulata* Fr. Syst. Myc. ii. 560.

Epiphyllous, black, spread over the leaf, not seated on distinct spots; fibrils free, creeping longitudinally, occasionally branched, connecting the pycnidia which are arranged somewhat in rows. No spores ever seen.

On the stems and still green leaves of *Polygonatum*. Ireland.
Also recorded on *Convallaria*.

A German specimen, which I gathered on the Drachenfels, on *P.
officinale*, shows numerous thick black pycnidia, arranged in reticulated rows and connected by short lengths of creeping branched
hyphae. They were found to be always empty.

It is suggested that the fungus on *Convallaria* may be the early state
of *Mycosphaerella Asteroma* Karst., and that the so-called variety on
Eryngium belongs similarly to *Mycosphaerella Eryngii* (Cooke). Another fungus of the kind, common in Denmark and parasitic on *Convallaria*, is *Asteroma subradians* Fr. (S. Veg. Scand. 425) which is
merely a state of *Septoria brunneola* Niessl; see Sacc. Syll. iii. 573, and
Lind's Danish Fungi, p. 451.

Fr. Holl. Germ. Port. Ital. Siberia.

Salix

Asteroma Salicis Rob. & Desm. in Ann. Sci. Nat. 1843, xix. 350.
Sacc. Syll. iii. 208. All. vi. 474. Died. 226. Mig. 140.

Spots epiphyllous, cinereous or lead-coloured; fibrils immersed, black, branched, radiating from the centre; branches
rather short, divaricate, somewhat fastigiate, compressed and
dilated at the apex. Pycnidia unknown.

On fallen leaves of *Salix*, Audley End (Cooke). Of *Salix
fragilis*, West Kilbride, Ayrshire (Boyd). Winter.

Fr. Belg. Denm. Germ. Austr. Ital.

Scrophularia

Asteroma Scrophulariae Brun. Misc. Myc. i., in Act. Soc. Linn.
Bord. 1888, xlii. 98.

Spots small, numerous, elongated in the direction of the
stem, 3–10 mm. long, rich umber-brown. Fibrils creeping just
beneath the epidermis, branched, tree-like, dark-brown.
Pycnidia not seen.

On dead stems of *Scrophularia nodosa*. West Kilbride, Ayrshire (Boyd). Jan.

Brunaud found numerous pycnidia on the fibrils.

Fr.

Solidago

Asteroma Solidaginis Cooke, in Grevill. xiv. 40 (1885). Sacc.
Syll. x. 219. All. vi. 475.

Pycnidia minute, collected in dark suborbicular patches,
seated on a delicate brown, reticulated, "cuticular" mycelium,

which is more or less radiating. Spores minute, ellipsoid, hyaline, continuous.

On fading leaves of *Solidago elliptica*. Kew Gardens.

It is quite possible that this is the same as *Asteroma atratum* Chev. Flor. par. 449 (1826); Sacc. Syll. iii. 212. For that species is recorded on *Cacalia*, *Centaurea montana*, and *Solidago Virgaurea*.

Fr. Germ.

Spiraea

Asteroma vernicosum Fckl. Symb. Myc. 385. Sacc. Syll. iii. 211. All. vi. 457. Died. 218. Mig. 141. Grove, in Journ. Bot. 1922, p. 46. *Sphaeria vernicosa* DC. Flor. fr. vi. 138.

Spots oval, 5–8 mm. long, smooth, shining, inky-black, with a paler radiating margin. Pycnidia mostly in the centre of the spot, convex or subconical, rather prominent, mouth-less, very black. Spores very few, oval, continuous, 7–8 × 2·5–3μ.

On dead stems of *Spiraea Aruncus*. Edgbaston Botanic Gardens, in company with an immature pyrenomycete.

Apr. May.

Exactly like Rabenh. Fung. Eur. no. 1274. Recorded abroad also on *S. Ulmaria*, *Anthriscus*, *Chaerophyllum*, and *Heracleum*.

Fr. Holl. Germ. Austr. Switz. Hung.

Stellaria

Asteroma graphoides Rob. & Desm. in Bull. Soc. Bot. Fr. 1857, iv. 995. Sacc. Syll. iii. 209. All. vi. 476. Died. 227. Mig. 141.

Spots epiphyllous, more rarely hypophyllous or on the stems, small, brown, occasionally wanting; fibrils rather prominent, deep reddish-brown, branched, radiating from the centre; branches divaricate, rather short. Pycnidia unknown.

On leaves of *Stellaria Holostea*. Very uncommon; no certain locality known.

Fr. Germ.

Triglochin

Asteroma Juncaginacearum Rabh. Deutsch. Kr. Flor. no. 1269. Sacc. Syll. iii. 214. All. vi. 477. Died. p. 227, p. 202, f. vii, 2. Mig. p. 142, pl. 12, f. 4. *A. Calvadosii* Desm. in Ann. Sci. Nat. 1851, xvi. 302.

Spots epiphyllous and on the stems, at first olivaceous, then black, smooth, somewhat shining, ovate or elongated; fibrils

pitchy-black, closely adherent, compressed, branched, radiating from the centre; branches straight, fasciculate; branchlets somewhat palmate, at times fastigiate. Pycnidia scattered, minute. No spores known.

On *Triglochin palustre*, forming black spots on the fading stems and leaves, etc. Peat-mosses near Aberdeen (Trail). Ayrshire (Boyd). On *T. maritimum*, Merioneth (Rhodes). Whitstable. Aug.

Spots often 12 mm. or more long, with dark branched fibrils radiating outwards in bundles, on which are seated the dark pycnidia. Fr. Belg. Germ.

Tropaeolum
Asteroma tenerrimum Grogn. Crypt. Saône, 125. Sacc. Syll. iii. 212.

Spots reddish-brown, then greyish-olive; fibrils very delicate, short, tortuous, scarcely anastomosing and very slightly radiating. Pycnidia rounded, a little prominent, rather large, opaque.

On dead petioles of *Tropaeolum majus*. West Kilbride, Ayrshire (Boyd); a doubtful specimen. Oct.

Varieties of *tenerrimum* are recorded by Grognot (*l.c.*) also on *Lilium, Iris, Aconitum, Petroselinum, Phlox, Geum, Sambucus*, and *Centranthus*. He says that on *Tropaeolum* the fibrils are elongated, distinct, brown, and the pycnidia are depressed. Fr.

Tussilago
Asteroma impressum. Fckl. Symb. Myc. Nachtr. II. 82. Sacc. Syll. iii. 211. All. vi. 477. Died. 900. Mig. 465. (Not *Excipula impressa* Died. in Ann. Mycol. ix. 535.)

Spots brown or reddish, indistinctly bordered. Fibrils blackish-brown, running below the cuticle, dichotomous or irregularly branched, knotted. Pycnidia thin-walled, closed, then open, black, up to 200μ diam. Spores rare, fusoid, more or less falcate, eguttulate, 8–$10 \times 1 \cdot 5$–2μ, on short sporophores.

On living and fading leaves of *Tussilago Farfara*.

Rather common, but mostly without spores. I think this is nothing but the beginnings of *Stagonospora Tussilaginis* (*q.v.*). Cf. *Phoma Tussilaginis*. Germ.

Ulmus

Asteroma Ulmi "Klotzsch", in Cooke, Handb. 460. Greville, Flor. Edin. 368. Sacc. Syll. iii. 209. All. vi. 478. Died. 228.

"Fibrils very delicate, much branched, radiating, subdichotomous, flexuous, seated on a brownish spot."

On living leaves of *Ulmus campestris, U. montana.* Darenth; Highgate; Bungay; Sanquhar; Inveraray; Aberdeen; North Highlands; Heythrop Park, Oxon.; Hanbury, Pershore, and Hadzor Hall, Worcs. Sept.–Nov.

The specimens placed under this name are a mixture of two distinct kinds. When they show merely a dark roundish patch on the green leaf, with no visible external structure, it is probably the beginning of *Gloeosporium inconspicuum* Cav. (*q.v.*), but Greville's and others are the beginnings of *Piggotia astroidea* B. & Br. (*q.v.*).

Fr. Holl. Germ. Denm. Port.

Umbelliferae

Asteroma Robergei Sacc. Syll. iii. 210. All. vi. 465. Died. 221. Mig. 137. *Actinonema Robergei* Desm. in Ann. Sci. Nat. 1840, xiii. 181.

Fibrils branched; branches few, fuscous-black (under the microscope, olivaceous), jointed, nodular, the joints as long as broad or three to four times as long, 20–40μ thick at the base. Pycnidia unknown.

On stems of *Conium*, King's Cliffe (Berk.); of *Ligusticum*, Ayrshire (Boyd); of *Heracleum*, Goosehill Woods, Ws. and Mickleham, etc.

It is quite common to find long barren creeping brown hyphae on or under the epidermis of *Chaerophyllum* (on which *A. Robergei* has been recorded) and other Umbellifers. Berkeley's specimens (in Herb. Kew) consist of roundish brown blotches on the leaves (2–3 mm. diam.) composed of delicate radiating fibres, on which are a few subglobose bodies containing irregular oval cells (not spores). They resemble continental specimens named *Ast. Robergei*, but not the original ones of Desmazières (which were inside *Heracleum* stems).

Veronica

Asteroma Veronicae Desm. Pl. Cr. Fr. ser. i, 1836, no. 778, with fig. Berk. Outl. 322. Cooke, Handb. 934. See Stevenson, Mycol. Scot. 356.

"Pycnidia seated on a mycelium of radiating branched black threads, hemispherical, minute, rupturing irregularly in laciniae. Spores oblong, uniseptate, hyaline."

On leaves of *Veronica officinalis*. Shere (Capron). Scotland, up to 1000 ft.

This is merely the ascomycete *Dimerosporium abjectum* Fckl., misunderstood. See Grevill. v. 122.

Viburnum

Asteroma dendriticum Desm. in Ann. Sci. Nat. 1848, x. 349. Sacc. Syll. iii. 205. All. vi. 479. Died. 229. Mig. 142.

Spots epiphyllous, roundish, occupying the greater part or even the whole of a leaf, blackish-brown, formed by radiating irregular much-branched fibrillae. These fibrils are composed of hyphae which run just beneath the cuticle. Pycnidia in rows, inconspicuous.

On fading or dead leaves of *Viburnum Opulus*. Trench Woods, Droitwich; Heythrop Park, Oxon.; etc. Oct. Nov.

Germ.

CICINNOBOLUS Ehrenb. in Bot. Zeit. 1853, p. 16.

See Zeitschr. f. Pflanzenkr. 1910, xx. 449.

Pycnidia small, globose, oblong, or somewhat pyriform, often pedicellate, membranaceous, dark-ochreous, pierced at the vertex. Spores ovoid, continuous, hyaline, emerging in tendrils. (Fig. 8.) Parasitic in or on the hyphae of species of Erysipheae. It was formerly considered, as by Tulasne (Carp. i. 192, pl. 3–5), that they were part of the life-cycle of those fungi on which they are parasitic.

Fig. 8. *Cicinnobolus Cesatii*: *a*, three pycnidia on erect hyphae of *Oidium*, ×180 (after Tulasne); *b*, spores of the same, ×600.

Cicinnobolus Cesatii de Bary, Beitr. z. Morph. u. Phys. Pilz. ser. 3, p. 71, pl. 12, f. 5–13; Vergl. Morph. u. Biol. Pilz. p. 268, f. 119. Sacc. Syll. iii. 216. All. vi. 481, with fig. Died. p. 230, p. 202, f. VIII. Mig. p. 130, pl. 9, f. 11.

Pycnidia growing in the hyphae of various species of *Oidium*, clavate, pyriform, or lemon-shaped, very minute, 25–35 × 9–15µ (25–60 × 10–25µ, Died.), pierced at the vertex; texture

thin, minutely parenchymatous, dusky-ochraceous. Spores oblong-cylindrical or narrow-ovoid, straight or somewhat curved, rounded at both ends, colourless, often containing one or more guttules, $2 \cdot 5 - 3 \times 1 - 1 \cdot 5\mu$, Sacc. ($5-10 \times 2-4\mu$, Died.), issuing in long tendrils.

In the cells of the erect hyphae of the *Oidium*-stage of Erysipheae on various hosts, e.g. *Pisum, Rosa, Crataegus*, etc. Wyre Forest; Malvern; etc., but not common.

Besides that described above there are several other forms which may be varieties or distinct species, differing in the shape and size or occasionally in the colour of the pycnidium, and in the size of the spores. The pycnidium may reach 75μ in length or 50μ in breadth. De Bary's original figures give spores of very different sizes. *Bysso-cystis textilis* Riess (in Hedwig. i. 23) is a species that has blackish pycnidia and larger spores ($9-10\mu$). It is said to grow on *Erysiphe lamprocarpa*, on *Plantago major*.

Europe, Egypt, N. America.

Cicinnobolus Ulicis Adams, in Irish Nat. 1907, xvi. 168, with figs. Smith & Rea, in T.B.M.S. 1908, iii. 38.

Pycnidia pedicellate, brownish-black, about $34-62 \times 27-42\mu$. Spores ovoid to oblong, $4-8 \times 2-3\mu$.

Parasitic on a species of Erysipheae, on stems and leaves of *Ulex europaeus*. Gt. Sugar Loaf, Co. Wicklow (J. Adams). *n.v.*

Bubák describes also, under the name *C. Hieracii*, a species on leaves of *Hieracium* (probably parasitic on *Sphaerotheca Humuli*) to which he assigns yellowish-brown pycnidia $49-62 \times 28-35\mu$, with ovoid-oblong spores $6-11 \times 3 \cdot 5 - 4 \cdot 5\mu$.

PYRENOCHAETA de Not. Microm. Ital. v. 15.

Pycnidia globose or conical, immersed, then erumpent, membranaceous or subcarbonaceous, pierced at the apex, beset with stiff bristles, especially towards the top; texture parenchymatous or prosenchymatous. Spores 1-celled, of various shapes, hyaline or faintly coloured; sporophores slender. (Fig. 9.)

The characteristic of this genus lies in the possession of

bristles clothing the external surface of the pycnidium; these are not so thick and stiff as those of Vermicularia.

Ilex

Pyrenochaeta Ilicis Wilson, in Scot. Bot. Rev. 1912, i. 161. T.B.M.S. 1913, iv. 175. Sacc. Syll. xxv. 188.

Pycnidia amphigenous, scattered, ovoid or subglobose, immersed, then erumpent, 250–500μ diam., subcarbonaceous, black, clothed with many rigid black bristles 200–400μ long; ostiole round, somewhat prominent. Spores cylindrical, obtuse at both ends, 6–7 × 1–2μ; sporophores filiform, persistent, branched; branches alternate, short. (Fig. 9.)

On dead leaves of *Ilex Aquifolium*.

Fig. 9. Pycnidium of *Pyrenochaeta Ilicis*, emerging through the epidermis of a dead Holly leaf, × 30; spores and sporophores of the same, × 600.

Wimbledon Common (W. Nowell). Tanworth-in-Arden (Bayliss-Elliott). May–Jul.

The sporophores are described from the Tanworth specimens; the spores often became separate with the pedicel still attached; the bristles were often closely septate, not continuous, and arose from every visible part of the pycnidium. On the same leaves were *Microthyrium microscopicum*, *Aulographum vagum*, and *Stegia Ilicis*.

Phlox

Pyrenochaeta Phlogis Massee, in Kew Bull. 1907, p. 241, f. 1, 2 (as *Phloxidis*); Dis. Cult. Pl. p. 420, f. 131. Sacc. Syll. xxii. 932.

Spots elongated. Pycnidia gregarious, globose, partly buried in the substance of the stem, erumpent, black, 130–180μ diam., ornamented with long brown rigid spines, 70–120 × 6–7μ, especially around the distinct pore-like opening; peridium thin, parenchymatous, smoky-brown under the microscope. Spores oblong-ellipsoid, 4–5 × 2–3μ; sporophores linear, hyaline, very slender, about twice as long as the spore.

On stems of cultivated species of *Phlox*. Kew Gardens. June.

The stem is attacked just above the ground-line; the leaves turn yellow and drop off, the stem breaks easily near the base.

Allied to *P. ferox* Sacc., which infests Potato stems, but that has pellucid spines and much longer spores.

Solanum
Pyrenochaeta ferox Sacc. Syll. iii. 220. All. vi. 490. *Sphaeronema ferox* de Not. Microm. Ital. iii. 12, pl. 9.

Spots on the stems brownish. Pycnidia densely gregarious, covered by the epidermis, depressed-globose or bluntly conical, fuscous, thin; ostiole rather broad and beset round about with somewhat rigid more or less abundant spreading pellucid setae. Spores cylindrical, obtuse at both ends, opalescent, 8–9 × 1–1·5μ, at length issuing as a powdery mass.

On living stems of *Solanum tuberosum*. Bridgwater. July.

It attacked the lower part of the stems and extended for some distance upwards.
Ital.

PLENODOMUS Preuss, Fung. Hoyersw. no. 150 (1851).

Pycnidia almost or quite superficial, irregular in shape and size, black; peridium consisting of many layers, formed of hard thick-walled sclerenchymatous cells. Spores continuous, oblong or ovoid, hyaline; sporophores very short or imperceptible.

Distinguished from Aposphaeria by its sclerotial wall, which is tough and not fragile as in Aposphaeria; from Phomopsis it is distinguished by its complete pycnidium which surrounds the spore-mass on all sides, below as well as above, and by not having long persistent sporophores.

But the veritably protean forms placed by authors in this genus seem to me to be merely subsclerotioid states of species of Phoma (they are mentioned separately here because they are frequently treated so). For instance, *Plenodomus Lingam* is merely a sclerotioid state of *Phoma oleracea* Sacc., and occurs on the same hosts, though there is a tendency to consider it as confined to *Brassica* and then to call it *Phoma Lingam*. At Spernal and Studley Castle in Warwickshire, and at Smethwick in Staffordshire, I have found an exactly similar fungus on old dead stems of *Urtica dioica*; this I have no doubt is *Plenodomus acutus* Bubák, and stands in the same relation to *Phoma acuta* as *Pl. Lingam* does to *Phoma oleracea*.

It may be justifiably maintained that these abnormal and frequently distorted states are induced in a typical Phoma by unknown conditions of the environment and are not distinct species. Other so-called species of Plenodomus will meet with the same fate in the future. As Migula has figured four of them, I will enumerate them here, with the addition of the plate on which they are figured:

Pl. Chondrillae Diet. on *Chondrilla juncea* (Mig. pl. 18, f. 12–14).

Pl. herbarum All. on *Convallaria majalis* (pl. 20, f. 7–9), All. vi. 417, fig.

Pl. microsporus Berl. on *Sedum maximum* (pl. 20, f. 1–3).

Pl. Salicum Died. on *Salix viminalis* (pl. 20, f. 4–6).

That a change of environment can produce unexpected distortions is shown by that curious and, I fear, misbegotten genus Polyopeus (*q.v.* p. 162).

Plenodomus Lingam v. Höhn. in Sitz.-ber. k. Akad. Wien, cxx. i, p. 82 (1911). Died. p. 235, p. 240, f. 1. *Sphaeria Lingam* Tode, Fung. Meck. sel. ii. 51, p. 126 (1791). *Plenodomus Rabenhorstii* Preuss, Fung. Hoyersw. no. 150, in Linnaea, xxiv. 145 (1851). Sacc. Syll. iii. 185. All. vi. 417. Mig. p. 175, pl. 19, f. 5–10. *Sclerophoma* v. Höhn. in Hedwig. 1917, p. 244.

Pycnidia gregarious, often confluent, nearly superficial, dull-black, irregularly wart-shaped or pulvinate, somewhat depressed and rugose or at length papillate, up to 1 mm. wide; peridium sclerotioid, dark outside, paler within; the base of the cavity often raised up within in the form of a convex cushion; ostiole very variable, often oblique or decumbent. Spores numerous, subcylindric-oblong to ovoid, sometimes curved, biguttulate, 4–6 × 1·5–2 or 3μ; sporophores unseen.

On rotting stems of *Brassica*, not uncommon. On *Conium*, Ham Bridge, Ws. (Rhodes). On *Arctium*, Hams Hall, Wk. Recorded abroad also on *Foeniculum*, *Hesperis*, *Alliaria*, etc., and on wood. See *Phoma Lingam*, *supra*, p. 69.

Europe, U.S.A., Canada.

Plenodomus acutus Bubák, in Ann. Mycol. 1915, xiii. 29.
Leptophoma acuta v. Höhn. in Hedwig. 1918, lix. 262. *Phoma acuta*
Fckl. *p.p.*

This fungus, on *Urtica*, has been given many names and listed in
half-a-dozen genera, and little reliance can be placed upon any of the
statements made about it and its allies by recent authorities. It and
the similar forms on *Leonurus, Melilotus, Senecio*, etc., which have
been classed under Plenodomus, need to be worked out afresh funda-
mentally. They are not normal forms in any case, and are not neces-
sarily congeneric.

SCLEROPHOMA von Höhnel, in Sitz.-ber. k. Akad.
Wiss. Wien, 1909, cxviii. 1232.

This genus resembles Phoma in many respects, but there is
no distinct ostiole, and the pycnidia are very thick-walled, the
parenchymatous outer layer being dark-brown and lined inside with a well-developed "stromatic tissue" consisting of
pale cells similar to those which generally form the main mass
of a sclerotium. There are usually no sporophores, the spores
being seated directly on the stroma which may at length re-
solve itself into a mucilage in which the spores are embedded.

By this last character the genus is distinguished from
Plenodomus. But I am convinced that Sclerophoma, like
Plenodomus, is made up chiefly (if not entirely) of species of
Phoma, etc., which have assumed the subsclerotioid state
owing to some influence of the environment. For instance,
Sclerophoma pithyophila is such an abnormal development of
the same fungus which in its normal condition is called *Phoma*
acicola, and a similar statement might be made about other
genera whose names begin with *Sclero-*.

Malus

Sclerophoma Mali Syd. in Ann. Mycol. ix. 146. Died. 280, 902.
Mig. 173. *Cytosporella Mali* Brun. in Bull. Soc. Bot. Fr. 1893, p. 223.
Sacc. Syll. xi. 507. All. vi. 560. *Sclerophoma endogenospora* Laub. in
Gartenflora, lx. 133. *Myxosporium Mali* Bres. in Hedwig. 1897,
p. 382.

Pycnidia densely clustered, at first immersed, then breaking through the periderm, pulvinate, up to 1 mm. broad.
Spores ovoid-ellipsoid, often biguttulate, usually more acute

at one end, 5–10 × 2–4μ; sporophores apparently absent, the spores being set free by the disintegration of the inner subhyaline peridial layers.

On dead twigs of *Malus* and on fruits of *Crataegus*. Cambridge.

Diedicke also (p. 902) records this on *Crataegus*. But see *Phomopsis perniciosa*.

Fr. Germ.

Pinus

Sclerophoma pithya v. Höhn. Fragm. z. Mykol. 1909, no. 402. Died. 280. Mig. 172. Grove, in Journ. Bot. 1918, p. 293, pl. 550, f. 3. *Sphaeropsis pithya* Thüm. Mycoth. Univ. no. 1888. *Phoma pithya* Sacc. Syll. iii. 73, *p.p. Phoma Cembrae* Karst. *Sporonema strobilinum* var. *ramulorum* Vestergr. ? *Sclerophoma Magnusiana* Wils. & Hahn, in T.M.B.S. 1928, xiii. 267, pl. 18 and 19.

Pycnidia scattered or irregularly gregarious, covered by the bark, then semi-erumpent, globose, not papillate, but rounded above and mouthless, up to 500μ diam., at length nearly superficial; contents whitish; peridium thick, solid, parenchymatous, smoky-brown outside, paler within. Spores at first obovoid, 6–7 × 2–2·5μ, then obovate-fusoid, 7–9 × 2·5–3μ, at length distinctly fusoid, acute at one or both ends, 9–12 × 3–4μ (or even 5μ), sometimes guttulate or rather vacuolate, straight or rarely inequilateral, seated directly upon a dense mass of nearly colourless cells that ultimately become reduced to a mucus, which is often faintly tinged with brownish and in which the spores lie embedded.

On small dead branches of *Pinus silvestris*. King's Lynn (Plowright). Cheshire (Ellis). Ayrshire (Boyd). Scotland (Munro). Kew; Birmingham; Sutton Park.   Jan.–Apr.

A much misunderstood and confused species. *Phoma Cembrae* is the young state before the spores assume the fusoid form. The upper part of the pycnidium at length drops out, making it look like *Sporonema strobilinum*, which has similar spores, but that differs in the nature of the pycnidium, and its spores are seated upon long sporophores. Its variety *ramulorum* Vestergr. is, however, merely the Sclerophoma, and it is possible that the Sporonema as a whole may belong to the same life-cycle.

Phomopsis pithya Lind (*q.v.*), is a distinct fungus, being a true parasite (*S. pithya* is not parasitic) and doing great harm to numerous Conifers.

Fr. Holl. Germ. Swed. Ital.

Sclerophoma pithyophila v. Höhn. Fragm. z. Mykol. in Sitz.-ber. Akad. Wiss. Wien, vol. cxviii, 1909, p. 1234. Died. 280. Mig. p. 173, pl. 18, f. 5–8. *Sphaeronema pithyophilum* Corda, Ic. iv. 40, f. 116. *Phoma pithyophila* Sacc. Syll. iii. 101 (*non* Grove, in Journ. Bot. 1886, p. 135). *Sclerotiopsis pithyophila* Oud. Contr. Flor. Myc. Pays-Bas, xvii. 247. *Dothichiza pithyophila* Petrak. *Phoma strobiligena* Desm.

Pycnidia bursting the epidermis, frequently confluent or arranged in a series, irregularly globose or pulvinate, incompletely plurilocellate, up to 400μ wide; peridium thick, sclerotial, dark-brown externally, paler within. Spores immersed in mucus, ovoid-oblong, 5–7 × 2–3·5μ, with no visible sporophores, when old.

On leaves of *Pinus silvestris*. Mickleham, Surrey; Sling Common, Clent, Ws.; Cheshire; Kent; Warwicks.

Agreeing with Corda's figure. The interior of the pycnidium is filled, when young, with a mass of colourless sclerotial cells; in the older pycnidia this has changed into a mucoid mass in which the spores are embedded, but these spores were originally borne on sporophores in the usual way.

This fungus seems to me to be a subsclerotial state of *Phoma acicola* Sacc. (*q.v.*). Moreover, I can see no reason why *Sclerophoma pithyophila* and *S. pithya* should not be, respectively, the *leaf* and *branch* forms of the same species. If so, *P. acicola*, *S. pithyophila*, and *S. pithya* would be advancing states of development, and then Zopf's fungus *Phoma pinicola* Sacc. (*Pycnis pinicola* Zopf) would easily come within the same life-cycle, as von Höhnel and Diedicke have suggested (see Died. p. 280). Finally, *Phoma strobiligena* Desm. (*q.v.*) is merely the cone-scale-inhabiting form of the same fungus.

Sclerophoma pithyella v. Höhn. *l.c.* (*Phoma pithyella* Sacc. Syll. x. 164) is a closely allied form which extends its range to *Larix*. See Died. p. 279, p. 240, f. 8 and Mig. p. 171, pl. 18, f. 1–4.

Holl. Germ. Austr. Denm. Spain, U.S.A.

SPHAERONAEMA Fr. Syst. Myc. ii. 535, 536. (Revised by Saccardo, Syll. iii. 185.)

Pycnidia scattered or occasionally fasciculate, membranaceous, coriaceous, or carbonaceous, dark-coloured or black, immersed or superficial, more or less globose at base, but prolonged upwards into a cylindrical or subulate ostiolar beak; peridium parenchymatous or prosenchymatous, brown or brownish. Spores ovoid or oblong, sometimes elongated,

1-celled, hyaline, often expelled in moist weather and collecting to form a globule at the mouth. (Fig. 10.)

Some species have not a prolonged beak, but the pycnidium itself is elongated, cylindrical or truncate.

Fries coined the name *Sphaeronaema*[1] to signify "the outflowing of a globule" (*l.c.* p. 536), but, since such globules are

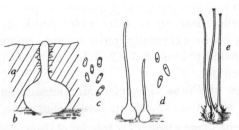

Fig. 10. *Sphaeronaema*: *a*, *S. floccosum*, pycnidium *in situ*, immersed in the outer tissues of a dead stem of *Cirsium arvense*, × 24; *b*, the wood on which it is seated; *c*, the spores, × 600; *d*, *S. mirabile*, two pycnidia, × 24, and three spores, × 600; *e*, *S. cornutum*, three pycnidia, × 24.

formed in a similar manner in many other genera, Saccardo in his Sylloge decided that the chief mark of the genus should be taken to be the elongated beak by which it is distinguished from Phoma and Aposphaeria.

Of the four species included in the genus in Cooke's Handbook, *Sphaeronaema subulatum* = *Eleutheromyces subulatus*, *S. vitrea* = *Melanospora vitrea*, *S. leucoconium* is a Zythia, and *S. epimyces* belongs probably to Hypomyces.

Cirsium

Sphaeronaema floccosum Grove.

Pycnidia immersed in the cortex, arranged ± in rows, black, shining; venter depressed-globose, perfectly glabrous; neck straight, thick, cylindrical, ending above in a very obtuse pore which just pierces the epidermis, fringed all the way up with numerous brown floccose fibres which soon disappear. Spores oblong, obtuse at both ends, biguttulate, 4–5 × 1–1·5μ.

On dead stems of *Cirsium arvense*, Sutton Coldfield, Wk. (Fig. 10 *a–c*.)   Apr.

The fungus is like a long-necked Phoma; venter up to 750μ broad, neck up to 600μ high, 100μ thick. The flocci which clothe the neck

_____

[1] From σφαῖρα and ναῖμα. Not *Sphaeronema*.

seem to be derived from the cortex of the host. Texture of wall of olive-brown oval subpellucid cells.

Corticium

Sphaeronaema epimyces Berk. Outl. 315. Cooke, Handb. 425. Sacc. Syll. iii. 197. All. vi. 424. Mig. 129. *Cytospora epimyces* Ehrenb. Sylv. Myc. Berol. 28 (1818). *Sphaeria epimyces* Fr. Syst. Myc. ii. 499. Sacc. Syll. ii. 425.

Pycnidia gregarious, innate in purple spots, then semi-emergent, globose, smooth, papillate, black; contents gelatinous, colourless. Spores undescribed.

On decaying *Corticium comedens*. Milton, Northants. (Berk.).

Certainly not a Sphaeronaema. Ehrenberg, who first met with this fungus, stated that the contents oozed out in the form of a globule or rough tendril. Jaczewski, who assigned it to Aposphaeria (merely on account of its form), says that it has small ovoid spores. Saccardo more wisely suggests that it is "a sterile *Hypomyces*", or I should rather say a *Hypomyces* like *rosellus* with the asci overlooked.
Germ. Switz. Swed.

Eranthemum

Sphaeronaema deformans Berk. in Gard. Chron. 1850, p. 563. Sacc. Syll. iii. 196. All. vi. 425. *Phyllosticta deformans* Jacz. Monogr. Sphaeronema, 1898, p. 65. Sacc. Syll. xvi. 850.

Pycnidia hypophyllous, superficial, globular, brownish-fuscous, scattered or clustered several together in a pallid pustule, 30–80μ diam., with an elongated ostiole; texture minutely parenchymatous, pale-brownish; ostioles making the surface of the leaf rough. Spores numerous, oblong or ellipsoid, often biguttulate, colourless, 3–4 × 1–1·5μ; sporophores very short; spores oozing out in a pallid globule at the apex.

On living leaves of *Eranthemum pulchellum*. London (Berk.)!

The pycnidia seem to be nearly superficial; Berkeley erred in describing them as "innate". The ostiole is somewhat elongated, but the species might nevertheless be a Phyllosticta. It has not been seen since Berkeley's time; there are specimens (not good) in the Herbaria at Kew, London, and Paris.

Lycopersicum

Sphaeronaema Lycopersici Plowr. Fung. Dis. Tomato, in Gard. Chron. 1881, xvi. 620, fig. 117; Trans. Woolhope Club, 1888, p. 109, f. 1. Sacc. Syll. x. 216. All. vi. 438.

"Pycnidia spherical, about 150μ diam., arranged somewhat concentrically upon the surface of the diseased fruit, at length surmounted by a dingy flesh-coloured globule of spores.

Spores cylindrical or somewhat sausage-shaped, sometimes biguttulate, $10 \times 2-3\mu$."
"On fruits of *Lycopersicum*." King's Lynn (Plowright).

This description is quoted merely as a curious memorial of our distinguished mycologist of King's Lynn. Plowright's idea of placing the fungus in Sphaeronaema arose simply from the globule; his figure shows a globose and immersed peridium with only a short protruding ostiole. See *Ascochyta Lycopersici, infra*, p. 314.

Prunus

Sphaeronaema spurium Sacc. Syll. iii. 186. Phillips, British Discom. 345. Massee, Fung. Flora, iv. 138. Died. p. 289, p. 240, f. 16. Mig. 126. *Ceratostomum spurium* Fr. Obs. ii. 338.

Pycnidia imperfect(?), erumpent, 3 mm. high, very fragile, conico-cylindrical, pulverulent, blackish-fuscous. Spores linear-fusoid, curvulous, hyaline, 1-celled, guttulate, $15 \times 1\cdot5-2\mu$ ($20-30 \times 3-4\mu$, Died.), issuing as a minute terminal grey globule.

On bark of species of *Prunus* (*spinosa*). Shrewsbury (Phillips). Melbourne, Cambs. (F. G. Tutsher).

The pycnidial stage of *Cenangium Prunastri* Fr., in company with which it is found. See Phillips (*l.c.*), pl. 10, f. 66. Diedicke, who gives a slightly different description, records it on other species of *Prunus* also. Phillips, and after him Massee, both described the spores as uniseptate, but Tulasne (Carp. iii. 159) says that they are lunulate, continuous, and $20-23\mu$ long.
Fr. Germ.

Quercus

Sphaeronaema rostratum Fckl. Symb. Myc. 399. Sacc. Syll. iii. 195. All. vi. 439, with fig. Died. 287. Mig. 128.

Pycnidia globose, sunk in the wood half way, gregarious, black, prolonged upwards into a cylindrical beak which is as long as or 3 or 4 times longer than the pycnidium, not fringed at the apex. Spores ovoid, hyaline ($5 \times 2\cdot5\mu$, in the Harlech specimen).

On chips of *Quercus*. Glyn Artro, Harlech (Rhodes). Jan. Germ.

Sphaeronaema glomeratum "Mont." *fide* B. & Br., North Americ. Fung. in Grevill. ii. 179 (perhaps a slip for *S. fasciculatum* Mont. & Fr.). Sacc. Syll. iii. 191.

"Allied to *S. viticola*. Spores minute, shortly oblong; sporophores with a few short branches above" (B. & Br.).

Reported as British, but no locality known. The North American specimen was on twigs of Oak.

Rhamnus

Sphaeronaema versiforme Fr. Scler. Suec. III, no. 102. Massee, Fung. Flor. iv. 123. Phillips, Brit. Discom. 351. *Sphaeria versiformis* A. & S. Consp. Fung. Nisk. p. 52, pl. 9, f. 3.

Pycnidia intermixed with the ascophores, conico-globose, with a minute pore at the apex. Spores elongate-ovoid, straight or slightly curved, continuous, hyaline, about $25 \times 6 \cdot 5\mu$.

On branches of *Rhamnus Frangula*. Shere; Highgate (Cooke, Fung. Brit. no. 310). Not truly a Sphaeronaema.

The pycnidial stage of *Scleroderris Frangulae* Mass., with which it occurs. For figs. see Tulasne in Ann. Sci. Nat. 1853, vol. xx, pl. 16, f. 1–8.

Fr. Germ.

Wood

Sphaeronaema aemulans B. & Br. in Ann. Nat. Hist. 1873, xi. 345, pl. 7, f. 2. Sacc. Syll. iii. 195. All. vi. 440.

"Pycnidia rostrate, arising from a sparse mycelium, 1–1·5 mm. high including the long slender beak which is at least three times as long as the subglobose base; beak composed of parallel hyphae which readily separate so that it becomes ciliate on the summit. Spores very minute, endowed with Brownian motion" (B. & Br.).

On dead wood. Epping Forest (B. & Br.). Liverpool (Travis). Langridge; Scarborough. Jan.–Apr.

Berkeley and Broome say: "Possibly the pycnidial state of some *Melanospora*". In the figure the "spores" look like oil-globules, and Saccardo misrepresents the given size as $2 \cdot 5 – 2 \cdot 7\mu$ (in the original it is printed "·0001–·0003 inch", i.e. $2 \cdot 5 – 7 \cdot 5\mu$). The base of the pycnidium gives off a number of hyphae. Mr Travis's specimens abounded in oil-drops, but they sometimes also contained distinct true ovoid spores, colourless and measuring about $5 \times 2 \cdot 5\mu$. These showed no Brownian motion and, since my specimens of *S. rostratum* have exactly similar spores, it seems likely that the two species are identical. The ciliate apex is never a constant character, since it depends partly upon age.

Sphaeronaema cornutum Preuss, Fung. Hoyersw. no. 144. Sacc. Syll. iii. 195. Grove, in Journ. Bot. 1916, p. 189, pl. 542, f. 10. Mig. 128.

Pycnidia gregarious, immersed, then sometimes becoming superficial, black, $120–200\mu$ diam., subglobose, mostly (when

emergent) provided with a few blackish hairs; neck very long, cylindrical, straight or slightly flexuose, fibrous, penicillate at apex, 500μ or more high. Spores oblong-ovoid, $3-4 \times 2\mu$, immersed in mucus, often congregating together when placed in water to form rounded masses. (Fig. 10 e.)

On soft decayed wood. Everton Cemetery, Liverpool (Travis). Sutton Coldfield; Tanworth-in-Arden; etc.　　Jun.

The spores form a yellowish globule when they ooze out at the apex. Germ. Swed.

Sphaeronaema mirabile Grove.

Pycnidia scattered, subglobose, sunk at the base in the wood, dead-black, somewhat rugulose, $140-160\mu$ diam., tapering upwards suddenly into an exceedingly long black cylindrical gently curving beak, which is less than 20μ wide at the base, 10μ towards the non-ciliate apex, and may reach over 800 (or even 1000) μ in length. Spores elliptic-fusoid, faintly guttulate, colourless, $5-7 \times 1\cdot5-2\mu$. (Fig. 10d.)

On dead friable wood. Middleton and Langley, near Sutton Coldfield.　　Apr.

This species is remarkable for its beak, which was often nearly 80 times longer than its thickness. Similar to *S. rostratum*, but much smaller, and scarcely visible without a lens.

EXCLUDED

Polyopeus Horne, in Journ. Bot. 1920, p. 239. See also Kidd and Beaumont, in T.B.M.S. 1924, x. 105–6.

This genus was founded by Dr Horne to include a number (seven or eight) of forms of *Phoma* which he obtained in cultures made from "spotted" Apples. The pycnidia so produced frequently had numerous papillae attached to a single loculus, thus becoming "multirostrate"; the rostrum was often bent or curved, or even branched. To each freak he gave a separate specific name. *Phoma Lingam* (Tode), which I believe to be only a subsclerotial state of one or more of the Phomas recorded in this book, can show similar curved or bent rostra, though not the other peculiarities. Cf. also *Aposphaeria violacea*, for multirostrate pycnidia. The Petripatellist ought to correlate his museum of freaks with previously known species, before indulging in such a futile orgy of nomenclature.

Mycogala parietinum Sacc. Syll. iii. 185. All. vi. 419. Died. 210. Mig. 122.

This species is recorded as found at King's Cliffe, Hereford, London, etc., on walls, textiles, wood, blotting paper, and other substances, but is by no means common. But all the British specimens I have seen under this name belong to the ascomycetous genus Anixia, some with absolute certainty (the asci being clearly visible), others only with great probability. The asci of Anixia are easily absorbed, as often happens in the Perisporieae. In other respects, both megascopic and microscopic, the specimens agree very closely. By some they have been rashly included among the Myxomycetes.

Fr. Holl. Germ. Ital. Lapland.

Pleosporopsis strobilina (A. & S.) Sacc. Syll. iii. 693.

On cones of Fir, Edinburgh. Belongs to the Uredinales, being the aecidial stage of *Pucciniastrum* (*Thecopsora*) *Padi* (see my British Rust-Fungi, 368).

PHOMOPSIS Sacc. Syll. iii. 66 and in Ann. Mycol. 1905, iii. 166. See also T.B.M.S. 1930, xv. 46–7.

Pycnidia lens-shaped, conical, pustular, or ± globose; peridium several cells thick, below at first pellucid or tinged with olivaceous, but above becoming thicker and darker, brown or blackish towards the outside; provided with a pore or a decided ostiole, occasionally even mouthless; internal cavity divided at times by protrusions of the proliferous layer. Spores hyaline, mostly fusoid with subacute extremities, but sometimes ellipsoid with narrowed ends or even oblong, biguttulate, each guttule generally situated at a small but perceptible distance from the extreme tip; sporophores filiform, linear, or subulate, densely crowded, often curved, ± permanent and longer than the spore. These are called the A-spores.

Besides them, many species produce also B-spores, on sporophores which can be similar to those of the A-spores, though usually shorter and at times very short or papilliform. The B-spores are elongated, filiform, curved, arcuate, S-shaped, or especially hooked at the upper end like a walking-stick (uncinate, hamate). When these have been found by

themselves, they have often been called *Cytosporina* or *Phlyc-taena*, according to the degree of development of the peri-dium. Those species which were
known to produce both kinds were
mistakenly placed by von Höhnel
in a separate genus, *Myxolibertella*.
In a few cases there is also an intermediate kind, the C-spores, which
at times resemble those attributed
to *Septomyxa*; but these spores are
very variable and sometimes hardly
have a definite shape. (Fig. 11.) See Annals Bot. 1930, p. 366.

Fig. 11. Spores of *Phomopsis*: *a*, A-spores; *b*, B-spores; *c*, C-spores; all × 600; *d*, three forms of A-spores, enlarged.

The following British species of Phomopsis have now been observed
to have both A- and B-spores (64 species):

alnea	corticis	incarcerata	perniciosa
ambigua	Cruciferae	japonica	Prunorum
Ampelopsidis	crustosa	Jasmini	pustulata
aquilina	cryptica	Landeghemiae	quercella
Araucariae	decedens	laurella	ramealis
Arctii	var. conjuncta	Leycesteriae	revellens
aucubicola	denigrata	ligulata	Ryckholtii
brachyceras	depressa	Liriodendri	sambucina
Cacti	elliptica	Lonicerae	Sarothamni
Choisyae	eryngiicola	magnoliicola	scobina
cinerascens	Escalloniae	Malvacearum	Sorbariae
Cirsii	Garryae	oblonga	subordinaria
citriodora	Herminierae	occulta	tamicola
coneglanensis	Hyperici	oncostoma	tinea
conorum	hysteriola	padina	Tulasnei
Corni	inaequalis	perexigua	velata
Coronillae			

The following fifteen are suspected of having both kinds, or are so
recorded in other countries:

Achilleae	Dulcamarae	pungens
Asparagi	intermedia	Rhois
Aucubae	linearis	Robergeana
demissa	oblita	Sophorae
Diaporthes-macrostomae	pallida	tamaricaria

It must be remarked that the B-spores are very strongly suspected
of not being real effective spores, but more like paraphyses, chiefly
because they contain no nucleus (Cayley) and seem to be disinclined
for germination. But we know that a somewhat similar idea was
entertained till recently about the pycnidiospores of the Uredinales.

and for the same reason; yet the suspicions so boldly stated in that case are now known to have been false. Moreover both Archer (Ann. Mycol. 1926, p. 22) and Brefeld (Unters. 1891, p. 37) found that B-spores could germinate.

The peridium may seem to be almost absent when very young, but with age it becomes thicker at the vertex and lumpy; when old this upper part often drops out, like a cork, and may leave behind an empty pit or foveola, which while still covered by the spores is whitish, but becomes blackish when they are dispersed. The peridium is thus widely different from that of a typical *Phoma*. (Fig. 12.)

All the species of this form-genus are believed to be pycnidial stages of the ascophorous genus *Diaporthe*. Only a few of them are known to be parasitic, e.g. *subordinaria, aucubicola, corticis*. Several *Diaporthae* have other pycnidial stages

Fig. 12. Diagrammatic sections, showing three stages in the development of the pycnidium of a Phomopsis, enlarged: *a*, when young; *b*, when mature; *c*, when exolete and empty of spores.

(some of them three or four). When the pycnidia form a subvalsoid pustule, as in Fusicoccum, and raise the epidermis convexly without discolouring it, they usually belong to a member of the subgenus *Chorostate* (which preferably should be separated from Diaporthe proper). The Phomopsis pycnidia belonging to the subgenera *Euporthe* and *Tetrastaga* are, in the majority of cases, surrounded each by a brown or blackish stain of the epidermis like a little halo, which afterwards may extend to form a large discoloured patch. By this halo such species may often be recognised as Phomopsis at a glance.

In the present deplorable state of investigations regarding the *Diaporthae*, the following pages must naturally be of value merely as a descriptive list of the observed British forms. As a display of our knowledge (or our ignorance) it will bear comparison with the list of forty or fifty "species" of British *Rubi*, or the 500 (*n'est-ce pas?*) of *Crataegus* reputed to exist in the United States. But I conceive it will be of more advantage to

the future student to leave the list as it is, than to shorten it
by fusing species upon hypothetical bases. Yet I have in a few
cases definitely stated my opinions about such unmade fu-
sions, founding them solely upon a long-continued observation
of the facts of out-door nature.

The species are arranged in the simple alphabetic order of
their host-genera, except that, for greater convenience of
comparison, those belonging to four families are placed under
the family-names, viz: COMPOSITAE, CONIFERAE, ROSACEAE,
and UMBELLIFERAE.

Acer

Phomopsis Platanoidis Died. 242. Grove, in Kew Bull. 1917,
p. 61. *Phoma Platanoidis* Cooke, in Grevill. xiii. 93. Sacc. Syll. x. 151.
All. vi. 173. Mig. 73. (Not *Myxolibertella Aceris* v. Höhn. in Ann.
Mycol. i. 526.)

Pycnidia densely gregarious, unilocular, at first covered, then
erumpent and conical, so that the twigs are rough like a rasp;
texture dark-brown, minutely parenchymatous. Spores fusoid,
rather acute at the ends, biguttulate, 6–8 × 1·5–2·5μ; sporophores crowded, filiform, acute, slightly longer than the spore.

On twigs of *Acer Pseudoplatanus.* Kew Gardens (Cooke).
Bidston, Cheshire (Ellis).   May.

Perhaps the pycnidial stage of *Diaporthe protracta* Nits. Cooke
assigns it to *Calospora Platanoidis* Niessl, with which he says he
found it associated. If so, analogy would lead us to consider Cooke's
pyrenomycete to be as much a Diaporthe as *Calospora Zopfii* Sacc. is;
von Höhnel in fact calls it *Diaporthe Platanoidis. Sclerotiopsis protracta* Died. is probably a subsclerotial form; *Phomopsis pustulata* is
quite different.
Germ.

Phomopsis pustulata Died. in Ann. Mycol. 1911, ix. 28; Pilz.
Brand. 242. Mig. 156. *Phoma pustulata* Sacc. Syll. iii. 91. All. vi. 172.
Myxolibertella Aceris v. Höhn. in Ann. Mycol. i. 526, *p.p. Sclerophoma
pustulata* Petr. in Ann. Mycol. 1919, xvii. 59.

Pycnidia gregarious, immersed, globose-depressed or subconical, 0·5–1 mm. diam., several often included within a
blackish-brown zone, often mouthless, erumpent by the vertex. A-spores oblong or fusoid, rounded at the upper end,
with one, two, or three guttules, 7–10 (or even 13) × 2·5–3·5μ;

sporophores filiform or subulate, about 12μ long: B-spores numerous, filiform, curved or hooked, 15–20 × 1–1·5μ.

On branches of *Acer palmatum*, Kew Gardens (Cooke). On dead branches of *A. Pseudoplatanus*, Ayrshire (Boyd).

Winter

The Ayrshire specimens contained both A- and B-spores, often in the same pycnidium, and were accompanied on the same branches by *Diaporthe pustulata* Sacc. See also *Fusicoccum obtusulum*.

Fr. Holl. Germ. Denm.

Phomopsis Lebiseyi Died. in Ann. Mycol. 1911, ix. 25, pl. 1, f. 12. Died. 242. Mig. 155. Grove in Kew Bull. 1917, p. 58. *Phoma Lebiseyi* Sacc. Syll. iii. 91. All. vi. 173.

Pycnidia gregarious, globose-depressed, up to 500μ diam., pseudolocellate within, long concealed by the epidermis, black. Spores ovoid-fusoid, biguttulate, 8–10 × 3μ; sporophores subulate or filiform, up to half as long again as the spore.

On branches of *Acer Negundo* (*Negundo aceroides*). Kew Gardens. Hadzor, Droitwich. The pycnidial stage of *Diaporthe Lebiseyi* Niessl = *Cryptodiaporthe* Wehm. Apr.

The spores are wider in proportion than in most species of the genus. The pycnidia are rather thick and even papillate toward the mouth, which is at length exposed by the rupture of the epidermis.

Fr. Germ. Denm. Ital. California.

Aesculus

Phomopsis coneglanensis Trav. 257. Died. 244. Mig. 156. *Phoma coneglanensis* Sacc. Syll. iii. 81. All. vi. 174. T.B.M.S. v. 228.

Pycnidia gregarious, oblong or oval-oblong, 300–500μ across, covered by the blackened epidermis which is elevated and ultimately pierced by a small round pore. A-spores oblong-fusoid, biguttulate, 7–8 × 2·5–3μ; sporophores acicular, about 15 × 3μ: B-spores abundant, filiform, curved or hooked, 20–30 × 1μ.

On branches and fallen petioles of *Aesculus Hippocastanum*, accompanied by a Diaporthe without spores (*Tetrastaga*, and therefore probably *D. coneglanensis*). Cheshire (Ellis). Oscott College (Rhodes). Bromsgrove. May, Oct.

On the Continent found on the twigs also. This species is not the same as *Phomopsis Aesculi* Lind, which belongs to *Chorostate*. See *Septomyxa Aesculi*, in Vol. ii.

Fr. Germ. Austr. Ital.

Alnus

Phomopsis alnea v. Höhn. Fragm. z. Mykol. no. 87, p. 33.
Grove, in Journ. Bot. 1918, p. 290, pl. 550, f. 4. Died. 244. Mig. 156.
Phoma alnea Sacc. Syll. iii. 98. All. vi. 178.

Pycnidia scattered or gregarious, globose-depressed, at first
immersed, then bursting the periderm by a short slit, blackish-
grey, 200–380μ diam. A-spores lanceolate-fusoid, acute at
both ends, mostly biguttulate, 7–10 × 2–3μ; sporophores
crowded, subulate, curvulous, 15–20 × 1·5μ, rising from a thick
soft olivaceous-brown stratum: B-spores filiform, hamate,
bent, or curved, 20–26 × 0·75μ, sometimes in the same pycnidia as the A-spores.

On dry dead twigs of *Alnus glutinosa*. Cheshire; Chats-
worth (Ellis). Ayrshire (Boyd).   May–Jun.

The pycnidial stage of *Diaporthe alnea* Fckl.
Fr. Holl. Germ. Austr. Ital.

Aristolochia

Phomopsis Aristolochiae Grove, in Kew Bull. 1917, p. 67.

Pycnidia densely scattered or gregarious, oblong to
roundish, convex, immersed, erumpent at first only by the
ostiole, then somewhat prominent, 250–300μ long, blackish.
Spores elliptic-fusoid, inequilateral or even appearing curved,
rather acute especially at the lower end, biguttulate, 9–10 ×
2·5–2·75μ; sporophores rod-shaped or subulate, crowded,
usually straight, about 12–15 × 1–1·5μ.

On dead stems of *Aristolochia Sipho*. Kew Gardens
(Cooke).   May.

The pycnidium is incomplete, i.e. the basal part which is several
cells thick and is pale olivaceous in colour is merely a proliferous
stratum. At first the pycnidium is entirely hidden beneath the epidermis, then it becomes erumpent by a minute black point (the
ostiole), the rest showing through the translucent epidermis as a convex
blackish mass surrounding the black point; afterwards the whole of
the upper half breaks away and disappears, leaving a wide-mouthed
blackish-brown hollow full of spores. At this stage the fungus looks
very like a Gloeosporium such as *G. nervisequum*, but can easily be
distinguished by its typical spores and sporophores. This account is
given in detail, to show what is characteristic of many species of the
genus. But see *P. Tulasnei*.

Armeria

Phomopsis Armeriae Grove, in Journ. Bot. 1930, p. 270.

Pycnidia imperfectly developed, scattered or two or three close together, immersed, convex, black, at length protruding, often surrounded by a lanceolate black spot which may be as much as 750μ long. Spores oblong-fusoid, biguttulate, pointed only at one end, 6–7 × 1–1·5μ; sporophores crowded, erect, linear-subulate, 15–18 × 1μ.

On dead peduncles of *Armeria maritima*. Polperro, Cornw. Apr.

It was accompanied by the common *Pleospora Armeriae*, but is distinguishable at first sight by the black surrounding area.

Asparagus

Phomopsis Asparagi (Sacc.). *Phoma Asparagi* Sacc. in Mich. i. 257; Syll. iii. 162. All. vi. 333. Died. 120. Mig. 94. *Phlyctaena Asparagi* Fautr. & Roum. Fung. sel. exs. no. 6057 (*non* Died. p. 700).

This species has been said to be a Phomopsis, and some American specimens seem to support the claim. But no good British specimens have yet been seen, nor one of the Phlyctaena. Yet Fautrey's description (*infra*) seems to be that of the B-spores of a Phomopsis, possibly belonging to *Diaporthe Asparagi* Fckl.

Phlyctaena Asparagi F. & R.

"Pycnidia incomplete, erumpent, blackish. Spores numerous, curved, tapering at both ends, but subobtuse, pluriguttulate, 30 × 2μ. On dry stems of *Asparagus officinalis*. France."

Atropa, see *P. hysteriola*

Aucuba

Phomopsis Aucubae Trav. 243. Died. 247. Mig. 157. *Phoma Aucubae* Westd. Exs. no. 1373. Sacc. Syll. iii. 115. *Phoma Aucubae* f. *ramicola* Oud. in Ned. Kr. Arch. ser. 2, vi. 38. Sacc. Syll. xi. 484. *Phoma insularis* Cooke & Mass. in Grevill. xvi. 6 (*non* Speg.). Sacc. Syll. x. 149. *Rhabdospora Aucubae* Brun. Sphaerops. p. 3. Sacc. Syll. x. 397.

Pycnidia numerous, 300–500μ diam., loosely gregarious, immersed, raising the epidermis in a pustule, at length erumpent at the vertex, black, shining, pierced by a pore; contents whitish; frequently two or three pycnidia are surrounded by a black oval patch. Spores ellipsoid or subfusoid, often acute

at the ends, biguttulate, 6–10 × 2–3μ; sporophores cylindric-subulate, straight or curved, 10–20 × 1·5μ.

On fallen leaves and dead twigs of *Aucuba japonica*. Not uncommon, England and Wales. Scotland (Boyd).

The form on the twigs is a true Phomopsis, the pycnidial stage of *Diaporthe Aucubae* Sacc. It is this which is called f. *ramulicola* Sacc. Fung. Venet. v. 201 = *ramicola* Oud. Contr. Fl. Myc. Pays-Bas, xiv. 38, but the form on the leaves seems to be the same species, though with shorter and more obtuse spores. *P. insularis* of Cooke & Massee is only *Phomopsis Aucubae* in which the black line of the ascophorous stage is beginning to be developed. *Rhabdospora Aucubae* Brun. may well represent one of the forms of this species.

Gloeosporium Aucubae Oud. Contr. Fl. Myc. Pays-Bas, xvii. 347 (Sacc. Syll. xvi. 998), has long acicular sporophores and is probably the leaf-form of *Phomopsis Aucubae* or of *Phomopsis aucubicola*. It occupies black patches on the living leaves. Boyd's specimens of the Phomopsis, from Ayrshire, on the leaves, are on distinct spots like those of *Phyllosticta aucubicola* Sacc.

Belg. Holl. Germ. Denm. Ital.

Phomopsis aucubicola Grove, in Kew Bull. 1917, p. 67, pl. 2, f. 31. *Phoma lirelliformis* Sacc. var. *aucubicola* Brun. in Act. Soc. Linn. Bord. 1888, p. 15 (extr.). Sacc. Syll. xiv. 871. Grove, in Journ. Bot. 1916, liv. 187, pl. 542, f. 4.

Pycnidia densely gregarious, black, immersed, then erumpent, of two forms: (1) rounded or oblong, pustular, rather prominent, 500μ diam.; (2) transversely elongated, even lirelliform, up to 3 mm. long, about 160μ wide; texture that of Phomopsis. Spores of two kinds: (1) ovoid-oblong or sub-fusoid, often biguttulate, 7–12 × 2–2·5μ; sporophores densely crowded, 9–15 × 2μ, sometimes longer; (2) filiform, curved or uncinate, 20–30 × 0·75–1μ, with similar sporophores.

On fading or dead branches of *Aucuba japonica*. Botanic Gardens, Edgbaston, with *Diplodia aucubicola* Sacc. Mar.

The lirelliform habit of this seems to distinguish it from *P. Aucubae*. It was distinctly a parasite, appearing first on living and still green twigs, and gradually killing them. Probably a parasitic form of the preceding species.

Buddleia

Phomopsis Buddleiae Grove, in Journ. Bot. 1930, p. 270.

Pycnidia scattered, seated for the most part on whitish areas of the stem, oblong, black, about 600 × 200μ, arranged

more or less in rows, imperfectly formed, papillate, piercing
the epidermis by the protruding ostiole. Spores ellipsoid,
subacute at one or both ends, biguttulate, $6-10 \times 2\mu$; sporophores erect, crowded, filiform, obtuse, granular, colourless,
$20-30 \times 1-1.5\mu$, rising from an olivaceous stratum.

On dead stems of *Buddleia globosa*. Polperro, Cornw.
(Rhodes & Rilstone).   July.

The pycnidia are perfect only in the upper part, which is thick and
black; when this part drops out, an oblong black foveola is left in the
stem.

Buxus

Phomopsis stictica Trav. 276. Died. 249. Mig. 159. *Phoma
stictica* B. & Br. in Ann. Nat. Hist. 1850, v. 370. Cooke, Handb. 420.
Sacc. Syll. iii. 89. All. vi. 183.

Pycnidia somewhat scattered, covered by the epidermis,
which is at length burst above and tends to split longitudinally, convex, blackish-brown, about 250μ diam. Spores elliptic-fusoid, acute at both ends, biguttulate, $7-8 \times 2.5-3.5\mu$;
sporophores linear, about $10 \times 1.5\mu$.

On dead leaves and twigs or branches of *Buxus sempervirens*.
Kew Gardens; Mickleham; Box Hill; Spye Park, Wilts.;
Batheaston; Oscott College; Snitterfield Bushes; Shropshire;
Herefordshire; Coniston; Scarborough; Ayrshire, etc.

Nov.–Apr.

The pycnidial stage of *Diaporthe retecta* Nits.
The spores are broader than in most other species, and are shaped
more like a "tip-cat", i.e. are broadly biconical. Those on the leaves
are exactly the same as on the twigs.
Fr. Holl. Germ. Austr. Ital.

Cactus

Phomopsis Cacti Grove, in Kew Bull. 1917, p. 54, pl. 1, f. 7.
Phoma Cacti Berk. Pl. Port. Welw. 1853, p. 12. Sacc. Syll iii. 138.
All. vi. 276.

Spots roundish or effused. Pycnidia immersed, but somewhat prominent, globose, about 330μ diam., at length bursting the epidermis by the papillate apex. Spores oblong-ellipsoid, subacute at both ends, biguttulate, $6-8 \times 1.5-2\mu$; sporophores cylindrical, crowded, about as long as the spores.

On dead stems of *Cactus*. Lauderdale House, Highgate.

Described from the British specimens. The Portuguese specimens
(Crypt. Lusit. no. 72) are the same, but in them there were also large

numbers of filiform hooked B-spores (18–20 × 0·75μ) in the same pycnidia as the ellipsoid spores. These Berkeley saw and called (*l.c.*) "filiform sporophores". The var. *Opuntiae* Sacc. (*l.c.*) must be different, being seemingly not a Phomopsis.
Port. U.S.A.

Calystegia
Phomopsis Calystegiae Grove, in Kew Bull. 1917, p. 54. Petr. *in litt. apud* Syd. Ann. Mycol. 1932, p. 397. *Phoma Calystegiae* Cooke, in Grevill. xiii. 94. Sacc. Syll. x. 173. All. vi. 277. *Phomopsis convolvulina* Petr. in Hedwig. 1925, p. 292.

Pycnidia gregarious, prominent, about 300μ long, elevating the blackened epidermis, sometimes seated on irregular bleached spots, at first thin and imperfect. Spores sublanceolate, narrowed at each end, biguttulate, 7·5–8 × 2·5μ.

On dead stems of *Calystegia sepium*. Kew Gardens; Highgate; Dartford (Cooke). Worcestershire (Rhodes). Jan.–Mar.

The pycnidium shows the usual changes of a Phomopsis, from the early imperfect to the later fully developed state.

Campanula
Phomopsis minuscula Grove, in Journ. Bot. 1922, p. 44.

Pycnidia scattered, or several aggregated together in dusky spots surrounded by an indistinct black line, oblong, as much as 500μ diam., blackish, covered by the shining darkened epidermis which is at length pierced by a pore; peridium rather thick and fuscous-black around the ostiole, elsewhere thinner. Spores very numerous, oblong-clavate or ellipsoid, obtuse at the apex, biguttulate or vacuolate in the middle, 7–8 × 1·5–2μ; sporophores linear or subulate, erect, colourless, 10–15 × 2μ, rising from a soft olivaceous stratum.

On stems, peduncles, pedicels, and capsules of *Campanula rapunculoides*, Bidford Churchyard. On stems of *C. rhomboidalis*, Edgbaston (Rhodes). Jan.–Mar.

The pycnidial stage of *Diaporthe minuscula* Sacc. & Sp.

Choisya
Phomopsis Choisyae Grove.

Pycnidia densely scattered, globose or oblong, up to 400μ diam., prominent, black, the epidermis also blackened above, opening by a small round pore. A-spores fusoid, acute at both ends, biguttulate, 9–10 × 1·5–2·5μ; sporophores subulate, up

to $15 \times 2.5\mu$: B-spores filiform, curved or hamate, mixed in the same pycnidium, $20\text{–}25 \times 1\mu$.

On old dead stems of *Choisya ternata*. Polperro (Rhodes). Heythrop Park, Oxon. (Rhodes & Grove). Batten Hall, Worcester. Mar.–Jun.

Accompanied by a Diaporthe, on the same stems, in all cases. B-spores seen only at Heythrop Park.

Cistus

Phomopsis cistina Grove, in Kew Bull. 1917, p. 55. *Phoma cistina* Cooke, in Grevill. xiv. 3. Sacc. Syll. x. 153. All. vi. 188.

Pycnidia densely gregarious, immersed, elevating and some-times throwing off the outer layer of the bark, subglobose, black, collapsing when dry; ostiole short and just piercing the surface or "longer and flexuous". Spores cylindric-fusoid, rather obtuse at both ends, biguttulate, $6\text{–}8 \times 2.5\mu$; sporophores cylindrical, about twice as long.

On branches of *Cistus laurifolius*. Kew Gardens (Cooke). May.

Specimens in poor condition; the Phomopsis was accompanied by numerous exolete perithecia, belonging undoubtedly to a Diaporthe, to which the long ostioles and the circumscribing black line referred to by Cooke (*l.c.*) should be assigned.

Clematis

Phomopsis demissa Trav. 234. Grove, in Journ. Bot. 1930, p. 271. *Phoma demissa* Sacc. Fung. Ven. v. 201; Syll. iii. 118. All. vi. 281. Died. 252. Mig. 159.

Pycnidia inserted in the surface of the wood, underneath the bark and not easily visible until the bark peels off, lens-shaped, papillate, black, about 250μ diam., surrounded by a lanceolate blackish halo in the woody tissue, extending more or less in lines, but not gregarious. Spores elliptic-fusoid, obtuse at both ends, biguttulate, $6\text{–}8 \times 2.5\mu$; sporophores sub-ulate, straight, colourless, $15\text{–}20 \times 1.5\mu$.

On dead branches of *Clematis montana*, from which the discoloured bark was peeling off, West Kilbride, Ayrshire (Boyd). July.

The pycnidial stage of *Diaporthe demissa* Sacc.

The situation of this Phomopsis in the wood is most unusual. The "filiform hamate sterigmata, $20 \times 1\mu$", recorded by Saccardo, probably represent B-spores.

Germ.

Colutea

Phomopsis Coluteae Died. in Ann. Mycol. 1911, ix. 22. Grove, in Kew Bull. 1917, p. 69. Mig. 159. *Phoma Coluteae* Sacc. & Roum. Syll. iii. 67. All. vi. 192.

Pycnidia gregarious, lens-shaped, at first covered by the greyish epidermis which is at length ruptured at the vertex, black, about 350μ diam. Spores oblong-fusoid, more or less biguttulate, 7–9 × 2·5–3μ; sporophores oblong-lanceolate, faintly coloured, about as long as the spore.

"On branches of *Colutea arborescens*. Kew Gardens; Dalston. Mar.–Apr." (Cooke). On dead twigs of *Colutea*, Brewood, Staffs. (Rhodes). July.

The description given above is drawn up from French specimens (Roum. no. 911), which are undoubtedly a Phomopsis, though with unusually short sporophores. But Cooke's Kew specimens contain now only a Coniothyrium, with young colourless spores, 5 × 3μ, probably *C. Fuckelii*.

Fr. Germ.

COMPOSITAE

Plurivorous

Phomopsis Achilleae v. Höhn. Fragm. z. Mykol. no. 87, p. 32. Grove, in Kew Bull. 1917, p. 52, pl. 1, f. 1. Died. 243. Mig. p. 156, pl. 15, f. 8. *Phoma Achilleae* Sacc. Syll. iii. 124. All. vi. 261. *Rhabdospora Achilleae* Bres. in Rev. Mycol. 1891, p. 30, pl. 114, f. 9. Sacc. Syll. x. 394. All. vi. 887.

Pycnidia loosely gregarious, sometimes arranged in lines, at first concealed beneath the epidermis, then somewhat projecting, subglobose or oblong, obtuse, black. Spores elliptic-fusoid, bi- or triguttulate, 8–10 × 2·5–3μ; sporophores subulate, 20–26 × 1–1·5μ.

On dead stems of *Achillea Millefolium*. Rather uncommon. Very probably the pycnidial stage of *Diaporthe orthoceras* Nits. Aug.–Nov.

I have seen no B-spores, but they are probably represented by the Rhabdospora, to which Bresadola ascribes spores filiform, arcuate, guttulate, 25–30 × 1·5μ, growing on ampulliform sporophores 10–15 × 4–5μ, and by *Phoma herbarum*, f. *Achilleae*, in Thümen's Fung. Austr. no. 883 (Allesch. vi. 329), which has similar spores.

Traverso records *D. orthoceras* on *Aster, Cichorium, Senecio, Eupatorium, Helianthus*, etc. To the *Phomopsis Achilleae* we may therefore assign:

Var. **Lapsanae.** On *L. communis*. Hartlebury Common (Rhodes).
Var. **Asteris.** On Michaelmas Daisy and *A. Tripolium*. Norfolk
(Rhodes). Polperro (Rilstone).
Var. **Senecionis.** On dead stems of *Senecio Greyii*. Polperro
(Rilstone). Of *Senecio Jacobaea*. Fowcy.
Var. **Tanaceti.** On *Tanacetum vulgare*. Kempsey (Rhodes). Gt.
Haywood, Staffs.
Fr. Holl. Germ. Denm. Latvia, Spain.

Phomopsis albicans Sydow, Mycoth. Germ. no. 1012. Died.
258. Grove, in Kew Bull. 1917, p. 52, pl. 1, f. 2. *Phoma albicans*
Rob. in Ann. Sci. Nat. 1849, xi. 284. Sacc. Syll. iii. 123. All. vi.
280.

Pycnidia abundant, crowded without order on extensive
bleached spots, covered by the epidermis, globose-oblong,
somewhat prominent, 160–200μ diam., brownish-black, papillate, at length piercing the epidermis by the minute ostiole.
Spores elliptic-fusoid, rather acute at the ends, biguttulate,
8–11 × 2–2·5μ; sporophores subulate, frequently curved, up
to 15–16 × 3μ.

On dead peduncles of various ligulate Compositae, especially of *Leontodon*, *Hypochoeris*, and *Tragopogon*. Ayrshire
(Boyd). King's Cliffe; Tottenham; etc. Sept.–Mar.

Stated to be the pycnidial stage of *Pleospora albicans*. But some
error must lie in this, for the fungus is a true Phomopsis, distinguished
by the pycnidia lying on distinctly bleached spots.
Fr. Belg. Holl. Germ. Denm. Ital.

Arctium
Phomopsis Arctii Trav. 226. Died. 246. Mig. 163. Grove, in
Kew Bull. 1917, p. 53, pl. 1, f. 5. *Phoma Arctii* Sacc. Syll. iii. 122.
All. vi. 300. Grove, in Journ. Bot. 1916, liv. 187, pl. 542, f. 5.
Phomopsis immersa v. Höhn. in Sitz. Akad. Wiss. Wien, cxv. 680
(1906).

Pycnidia gregarious, subepidermal, depressed, blackish-
brown, somewhat oblong, about 250μ wide. A-spores elliptic-
lanceolate, rather acute at the ends, often biguttulate, 7–9 ×
2·5–3μ; sporophores crowded, mostly subulate, 20–25 × 1·5μ:
B-spores filiform, curved, 17–23 × 0·75–1μ.

On dead stems of *Arctium Lappa*, which have remained
over from the previous year. England, especially in the

southern counties up to Worcs. and Staffs. The pycnidial stage of *Diaporthe Arctii* Nits. The B-spores will germinate.

Mar.–May.

When young the pycnidium is mainly composed of the blackened epidermis, which covers the proliferous stratum and the abundant A-spores. Diedicke records the intermediate C-spores.
Fr. Germ. Denm.

Artemisia

Phomopsis oblita Sacc. in Ann. Mycol. viii. 343. Died. p. 240, f. 5. p. 247. Mig. p. 157, pl. 17, f. 6, 7.

Pycnidia densely gregarious, occupying large areas on the stem, erumpent, lens-shaped, depressed, up to 500μ wide, 100μ high with a projecting ostiole; peridium thick, dense, dark-brown outside, paler within. Spores fusoid-oblong or sublanceolate, sometimes inequilateral, biguttulate, 8–12 × 2–3μ; sporophores, filiform, 10–12 × 1–1·5μ.

On *Artemisia vulgaris*. Looe, Cornwall (Rilstone). May.

In Germany it occurs on *A. vulgaris* and *A. Absinthium*, and is accompanied by Septoria-like spores, in narrower conical pycnidia; these spores, which are filiform, curved or hamate, 20–26 × 1μ, evidently represent the B-spores.
Germ. Latvia.

Baccharis

Phomopsis Baccharidis Grove.

This is included by Cooke as a form of his *Phoma Coronillae*, which is a Phomopsis, so that one may presume that it too belongs to that genus.

On dead branches of *Baccharis halimifolia*. Kew Gardens (Cooke). *n.v.*

No doubt the pycnidial stage of *Diaporthe Baccharidis* Cooke, in Grevill. vii. 53.
N. America.

Carlina

Phomopsis perexigua Trav. 229. Died. 250. Mig. 159. Grove, in Journ. Bot. 1930, p. 295. *Phoma perexigua* Sacc. Syll. iii. 123. All. vi. 278.

Pycnidia gregarious, arranged more or less in longitudinal series, with two kinds of pycnidia and spores, often separated:

(a) Globose or longitudinally elongated and linear, up to 500μ long, at first covered, then emergent by the upper half, and if linear opening by a slit, black, the epidermis around

them discoloured but not distinctly blackened; texture thick above, paler beneath. A-spores only, elliptic-fusoid, $\pm$ rounded above, sometimes more acute below, biguttulate, $7–8 \times 2–2\cdot5\mu$; sporophores linear-subulate, crowded, $15–20 \times 1\cdot5–2\cdot5\mu$ broad below, $\pm$ straight, rising from a thick olivaceous proliferous stratum.

(b) Globose or oblong, up to 330μ diam., distinctly papillate, at first covered, then emerging by the papilla and at length by the whole convex upper surface, dead-black, stem not blackened around, less completely developed than in (a). B-spores only, filiform, curved or hooked at the summit, very slender, $15–28 \times 1\mu$.

On dead stems of *Carlina vulgaris*. On the cliffs, Polperro, Cornw. (Rhodes & Rilstone). Bolt Head; Prawle Point; Slapton Sands; Devon. Apr.–Jul.

The pycnidial stage of *Diaporthe perexigua*, which accompanied it. There is very little blackening of the surface, except here and there and then only faintly. All previous descriptions of this species call the B-spores "sporophores" or "sterigmata".

Germ. Ital.

Cirsium

Phomopsis Cirsii Grove.

Pycnidia scattered or arranged in short series in the grooves of the stem, oblong, up to $0\cdot5$ mm. in length, blackish, soft and very incomplete, with only a thin proliferous stratum below, but thicker and formed of dense brown cells above, pierced by a pore. A-spores very few, and more especially on the leaves, ellipsoid, biguttulate, $12 \times 3–4\mu$: B-spores very numerous and crowded, filiform, curved, flexuose, but mostly hooked like a walking-stick, hyaline, $20–30 \times 0\cdot7–1\mu$; sporophores very short, ampulliform or obovoid, $3–6 \times 2\mu$.

On dead stems and leaves of *Cirsium eriophorum*, N. Littleton, Ws. (Rhodes). On dead stems of *Cirsium arvense*, Oxwich Bay, Gower. Cf. *P. Achilleae*. Oct.–May.

Matricaria

Phomopsis lirellata Grove. *Phoma lirellata* Sacc. Syll. iii. 118. *Phoma lirelliformis* Sacc. in Mich. ii. 93 (*non* Sacc. in Mich. i. 522).

Pycnidia gregarious, often arranged in lines, immersed, then erumpent, strongly compressed, hardly papillate.

Spores shortly fusoid, 8–10 × 2–3μ; sporophores long and linear.

On stems of *Matricaria salina*. Axmouth (Rhodes). Mar.

Sydow records, on *M. inodora* in Germany, *Phomopsis albicans*, but says that the bleaching of the stem on that host is less evident than on other hosts of *P. albicans*.

Fr. Germ.

Solidago
Phomopsis linearis Trav. 228. Died. 271. Mig. 168. Grove, in Journ. Bot. 1930, p. 274. *Phoma linearis* Sacc. Syll. iii. 124. All. vi. 323. *Phlyctaena arcuata* Berk. in Grevill. ii. 100. Sacc. Syll. iii. 595.

Pycnidia depressed-globose, arranged frequently in short rows of two or three, immersed, erumpent only by the papilla, black, surrounded by a lanceolate blackish stain which is itself bordered by a thin black line. Spores oblong-fusoid, obtuse at both ends, biguttulate, hyaline, 7–8 × 2·5–3μ; sporophores linear, acute at apex, guttulate, colourless, 20 × 1·5–2μ, rising from a pale olivaceous stratum.

On dead stems of *Solidago canadensis*. School House garden, Polperro (Riistone). (In Germany, on *S. virgaurea*.)

Apr.

The pycnidial stage of *Diaporthe linearis* Nits. *Phlyct. arcuata* probably represents the B-spores.

Fr. Germ. N. Amer.

CONIFERAE
Plurivorous
Phomopsis conorum Died. in Ann. Mycol. 1911, ix. 22. Hahn, in T.B.M.S. 1930, xv. 58–60. *Phoma conorum* Sacc. Syll. iii. 150. *Septoria conorum* Oud. in Ned. Krypt. Arch. series 3, ii. 270. *Phomopsis pitya* Lind, Dan. Fung. 1913, p. 421, *p.p.* (not *Phoma pithya* Sacc. which is *Sclerophoma pitya* v. Höhn.).

Pycnidia simple or compound, immersed, ± erumpent, black, carbonaceous, usually subglobose, up to 2 mm. diam. A-spores fusoid, rather acute at both ends, biguttulate, hyaline, 7–12 × 2·5–3·5μ: B-spores filiform, much curved or spiral, rarely hamate or straight, 20–24 × 1μ; sporophores of both persistent, subulate, acute, 6–21 × 1–2·5μ: C-spores rare, intermediate, attenuated at both ends, flexuous, 13–15 × 1·5–2μ; spores exuding as a yellowish tendril.

On cone-scales of *Picea excelsa*, more rarely on leaves of *Pinus*. England, Wales, Scotland.

Its perfect stage is unknown (not *Diaporthe conorum*). This fungus is said to occur also on *Pseudotsuga Douglasii*, etc.
Fr. Holl. Germ. Denm. Ital. Spain.

Phomopsis occulta Trav. 221. Hahn, in T.B.M.S. 1930, xv. 47–52. Mig. 164. *Phoma occulta* Sacc. Syll. iii. 150 (*non* Desm.). All. vi. 195.

Pycnidia occurring by themselves or associated with the ascophorous stage, simple or compound, emerging, carbonaceous, black, ± subglobose or variable, up to 1 mm. long. A-spores ellipsoid-oblong, often tapering below, obtuse above, ± curved in profile, biguttulate, hyaline, $8–11 \times 2–2 \cdot 5\mu$ (6–9 $\times 2–3\mu$, Hahn): B-spores filiform, straight or curved, often hooked like a walking-stick (hamate), acute especially at one end, $20–27 \times 1\mu$: C-spores intermediate, $9–13 \times 1–2\mu$; sporophores ± alike in all, subulate, $6–15 \times 1–3\mu$ (Hahn); spores often exuding as a whitish-yellow tendril.

On fallen cones, dead leaves, and stems of *Picea excelsa*, but also of *Pinus silvestris*, *Abies pectinata*, *Pseudotsuga Douglasii*, *Larix*, etc. England, Wales, Scotland; common.

Undoubtedly the pycnidial stage of *Diaporthe conorum* Niessl (which is *D. occulta* Niṭs. Sacc.).

The descriptions of this species and of the closely allied *Phomopsis conorum* are founded upon the work of Hahn (*l.c.*), but it must be confessed that the conclusions at which he arrives lack somewhat of definiteness and fail to give complete satisfaction. Wehmeyer's account of the *Phomopses* on Conifers (in T.B.M.S. 1933, xvii. 250–1) leaves us also in a maze of doubt. In fact the whole truth is not yet known; it is quite conceivable that *P. conorum* is only a biological modification of *P. occulta* which obstinately declines to proceed to the ascophorous stage, at any rate in our laboratories.

Sclerophoma Magnusiana Wils. & Hahn (*q.v.*), appears to be nothing but a subsclerotial stage of the same fungus, or of one of its allies on *Pinus*.

Var. **ginkgoina** Grove.

A variety of this species occurred on twigs of *Ginkgo biloba* at Cadsleigh, Ivybridge, Devon (Rhodes), Sept. This had all three kinds of spores on the same twig, if not in the same pycnidium; A-spores normal, about $5–8 \times 2\mu$; B-spores straight or curved, rarely hooked, $18–25 \times 1–1 \cdot 5\mu$; C-spores like those of Hahn in T.B.M.S. xv. 55, text-fig. 7.

Var. **Thujae.** *Phomopsis Thujae* Died. 275.
This variety occurs on *Thuja occidentalis* in Germany, and should
also be found in Britain; Hahn records it on *Thuja plicata*. Another
form has been found at Heythrop Park (Grove & Rhodes), in July, on
Taxodium rigescens.
Europe generally, U.S.A.

Phomopsis pithya Lind, Dan. Fung. 1913, p. 421. (Not *Phoma
pithya* Sacc.). See Died. in Ann. Mycol. i. 281, and T.B.M.S. 1928,
xiii. 273. ? *Phomopsis abietina* Grove: see Journ. Bot. 1918, p. 293;
1921, p. 16.

Pycnidia densely scattered, convex, erumpent, black, 200–
350μ broad, usually $\pm$ mouthless, pseudolocellate within;
wall many-layered, dark-brown. Spores oblong-fusoid, subacute below or occasionally at both ends, hardly guttulate,
5–6 × 1·5–2μ; sporophores crowded, linear, tapering, 7–10 ×
1μ, rising from a thick olivaceous stratum.

On dead bark of *Pinus silvestris*. Stevenston, Ayrshire
(Boyd). Reported also on *Abies, Picea*, etc.; a harmful parasite on many Conifers.

Cf. *Dothiorella pithya* Sacc. Syll. iii. 241; Fung. Ital. pl. 1454. Prill.
and Delacr. in Bull. Soc. Myc. Fr. 1890, vi. 98, pl. 15, f. 9–11. Lind's
species presents a similarity to *Sclerophoma pithya*, but the spores are
less fusoid and smaller, and are seated on distinct sporophores longer
than themselves. It inclines also to *Fusicoccum abietinum*, but is
smaller than that and has smaller spores.

Phomopsis Pseudotsugae Wilson, in Trans. Bot. Soc. Edin.
1920, xxviii. 47. T.B.M.S. xiii. 273; xv. 76. *Phomopsis abietina*
Grove, in Journ. Bot. 1921, p. 16 (*non* Hartig).

Pycnidia simple or compound, immersed, partially erumpent, carbonaceous, black, subglobose or irregular, opening in
various ways. A-spores elliptic-fusoid, occasionally ovate or
oblong, acute or $\pm$ obtuse at both ends, usually biguttulate,
5–9 × 2–3μ; sporophores short, broad, acutely pointed above,
5–10 × 1–2·5μ; spores exuding as a whitish tendril.

On trunk, branches, and leaves of *Pseudotsuga Douglasii*.
Great Britain and Ireland.

This species is said to occur also on *Abies, Cedrus, Larix* and *Sequoia*;
but all the species on Conifers have been dreadfully confused, and no
faith can be placed in any of the statements yet made on this subject.
W. Europe.

Araucaria

Phomopsis Araucariae Grove.

Pycnidia incompletely formed, scattered, globose, black, prominent, immersed, then erumpent by a pore or slit, 200–300μ diam. A-spores lanceolate-fusoid, more acute below, biguttulate, 7–9 × 2–2·5μ: B-spores filiform, curvulous, occasionally hooked, 22–25 × 1·5μ, in the same pycnidium with the A-spores.

On both surfaces of the fallen scale-leaves of *Araucaria imbricata*, Foxcote, near Ilmington. Apr.

This Phomopsis was accompanied by the unmistakable signs of a Diaporthe, viz. by the occurrence on the scales, and especially on those of the fallen (immature) fruits, of groups of 1–4 black stromatic rudiments (devoid of asci or spores) on little discoloured oblong, oval, or lanceolate areas, each of which was surrounded by a narrow wavy black line.

Pycnidia like these at Foxcote are found frequently on the fallen scale-leaves of the *Araucaria*, but usually are very imperfectly developed, and the spores which they contain are more like those of an ordinary Phoma. This was so on many of the scales on the ground at Foxcote and elsewhere; these immature states are what has been called *Phoma Araucariae* Trav. (*q.v.*).

Pinus

Phomopsis Strobi Syd. in Ann. Mycol. 1922, xx. 204.

Pycnidia simple or compound, partially erumpent, black, carbonaceous, subglobose. A-spores oblong-ellipsoid, very obtuse at both ends, hyaline, biguttulate, 5–6·5 × 2–2·8μ; sporophores very short, acute, 4–8 × 0·5–1μ.

On branches of *Pinus Strobus*. Also stated to occur on *Pinus montana*.

This species is not certainly known as British. No B-spores or perfect stage yet discovered.

Denm. U.S.A. _____

Cornus

Phomopsis Corni Trav. 268. Died. 252. Mig. 160. Grove, in Kew Bull. 1917, p. 55, pl. 1, f. 11. *Phoma Corni* Fckl. Symb. Myc. 207. Sacc. Syll. iii. 86. All. vi. 201.

Pycnidia somewhat scattered, nestling beneath the epidermis, at length erumpent, about 250μ diam., lens-shaped, papillate, each surrounded by a little halo of the blackened epidermis. A-spores fusoid, rarely oblong, often curved, with

two (rarely three) guttules, 7–10×2–3μ; sporophores subulate, less often linear and pointed, 10–12μ long: B-spores often in the same pycnidium, filiform curved or more often hamate, 20–$30 \times 1\mu$.

On dead twigs of *Cornus alba, C. sanguinea.* Ayrshire (Boyd). Kew Gardens; Heythrop Park, Oxon.; Hadzor Hall, and Besford Court, Worcs.; Dovedale.   Mar.–Nov.

The pycnidial stage of *Diaporthe Corni* Fckl. The reference by Cooke and Massee to *Cornus suecica* is a slip of the pen.

Europe, U.S.A.

Coronilla

Phomopsis Coronillae Trav. 240. Grove, in Kew Bull. 1917, p. 69, pl. 2, f. 32. Mig. 160. *Phoma Coronillae* Westd. Exs. no. 966. Sacc. Syll. iii. 67. All. vi. 202. Cooke, in Grevill. xiv. 25.

"Pycnidia scattered or gregarious, small, subglobose, immersed, then erumpent; contents whitish. Spores ovate-oblong, biguttulate, 7–$8 \times 3\mu$; sporophores filiform, arcuate, $20 \times 1.5\mu$" (Sacc.).

"On dead branches of *Coronilla Emerus.* Kew Gardens" (Cooke). The pycnidial stage of *Diaporthe Coronillae* Sacc.

I can find no fungus answering to this description now on the Kew specimens, although there are, amongst others, a Diplodia and a Hendersonia. The species of Westendorp is a decided Phomopsis, with A-spores fusoid, sporophores acicular and flexuous: the B-spores are represented in Saccardo's Myc. Ven. no. 1210, hooked or arcuate, 15–$16 \times 1\mu$. See *infra*, p. 455.

Fr. Holl. Belg. Germ. Ital. Montenegro, New Zealand.

Corylus

Phomopsis revellens v. Höhn. Fragm. z. Mykol. 1906, no. 87, p. 33. Died. 253. Mig. 160. *Phoma revellens* Sacc. Syll. iii. 99. All. vi. 202. *Phlyctaena Coryli* Lamb. & Fautr. in Bull. Soc. Myc. Fr. 1899, p. 155. Sacc. Syll. xvi. 981. All. vii. 910. *Phoma glandicola*, var. *Coryli-putaminis* Sacc. Syll. iii. 151.

Pycnidia gregarious, convex or globose-depressed, immersed, then erumpent. A-spores oblong-fusoid, biguttulate or at times triguttulate, 6–9×2–3μ; sporophores straight or slightly curved, subulate or sometimes obtuse, 15–20×1.5–2μ, rising from a dusky stratum: B-spores curved or hooked, subacute at both ends or thicker below, 20–28×1–1.5μ, on short sporophores.

On dead twigs and branches, and on nuts of *Corylus Avel-*

lana. Doncaster (Ellis). Ayrshire (Boyd). Botanic Gardens, Edgbaston; Bartley Green, Quinton, Warley, etc., near Birmingham. On nuts of *Corylus*, Bristol (Bayliss Elliott). Feb.–May.

The pycnidial stage of *Diaporthe revellens* Nits. or of *Diap. nucis-Avellanae* Feltgen.
Fr. Holl. Germ. Austr. Ital. Bosnia.

Phomopsis decedens var. **conjuncta** (Nees). See Wehmeyer, in Mycologia, 1927, xix. 174, and T.B.M.S. xvii. 266.

Pycnidia (undescribed). "A-spores elliptic-fusoid, straight, hyaline, $11-15 \times 2-2\cdot5\mu$: B-spores cylindric-filiform, somewhat curved, $8-15 \times 1-1\cdot5$ or 2μ" (Wehm.).
On dead branches of *Corylus Avellana*.

Not found as yet in Britain, but the ascophorous stage, *Diaporthe conjuncta* Fckl. has occurred at Nant Col, Merioneth (Rhodes), and the pycnidial stage, as described by Wehmeyer, will no doubt be discovered on searching for it.

Cruciferae
Phomopsis Cruciferae Grove, in Kew Bull. 1917, p. 68.

Pycnidia scattered, linear-lanceolate, lying parallel to the axis of the stem, covered by the epidermis, then bursting it by a slit, up to 1 mm. long, black. A-spores oblong-fusoid, rather obtuse at the ends, $7-8 \times 2\cdot5\mu$; sporophores cylindrical, straight, $10-12 \times 1\cdot5\mu$: B-spores (on *Brassica, Hesperis* and *Lepidium*) flexuous or hooked, $18-20 \times 1\mu$.

On dead stalks of *Brassica*, Sutton Coldfield. On *Iberis sempervirens*, Harlech. On *Alliaria officinalis*, Martley. On *Arabis perfoliata*, Hartlebury Common. On a Crucifer, Kew. On *Hesperis* and *Lepidium heterophyllum*, Polperrro.

The Sutton specimen may belong to *Diaporthe incrustans* Nits., which is probably *D. coramblycola* B. & Br.

Dianthus
Phomopsis Caryophylli Grove, in Kew Bull. 1917, p. 54, pl. 1, f. 8. *Phoma Caryophylli* Cooke, in Grevill. xiii. 94. Sacc. Syll. x. 176.

Pycnidia gregarious, seated on indefinite bleached spots, oblong, convex, about 300μ long, black, shining, each surrounded by a brown stain or halo. Spores fusoid, somewhat obtuse at the ends, frequently biguttulate, $7-9 \times 2\cdot25-2\cdot5\mu$; sporophores linear, $12-15 \times 2\mu$.

On the calyces, peduncles, and stems of cultivated *Dianthus*.
Twycross; King's Cliffe (Berk.). Shrewsbury (Leighton).
Perranzabuloe Church (Rilstone)! Jan.–Mar.

The dead stems were in parts widely stained with black. Evidently
the pycnidial stage of an unknown Diaporthe.

Dipsacus
Phomopsis Dipsaci Grove, in Kew Bull. 1917, p. 56, pl. 1, f. 12.
Phoma Dipsaci Cooke, in Grevill. xiii. 94. Sacc. Syll. x. 170. All. vi.
289. Died. 138. Mig. 85.

Pycnidia widely gregarious, but not crowded, oblong, about
300μ diam., convex, elevating and at length splitting the epidermis, black. Spores sublanceolate or fusoid, somewhat obtuse at the ends, 8–9 × 2–2·5μ; sporophores linear, crowded,
15–18 × 1·5μ.

On dead stems of *Dipsacus silvestris*. Himbleton, Worcs.
(Rhodes). Kew Gardens (Cooke). Credenhill, Hereford;
Droitwich; Cannon Hill Park, Birmingham. Jan.–Jul.

These pycnidia are often accompanied by what is evidently the beginning of a Diaporthe of the section Tetrastaga.
Denm. Germ.

Epilobium
Phomopsis Epilobii Grove. *Phoma Epilobii* Preuss, Fung.
Hoyersw. no. 282. Sacc. Syll. iii. 134. All. vi. 290. Died. 139. Mig.
96.

Pycnidia (insufficiently described). Spores fusoid, 8–10 ×
2–2·5μ.

On dead stems of *Epilobium angustifolium*. Vize, Micr.
Fungi Brit. no. 591. *n.v.*

The pycnidial stage of *Diaporthe Epilobii* Cooke (*non* Fckl.); see
Sacc. Syll. i. 690. Fuckel's *D. Epilobii* is said to be a Didymella.
A doubtful species, which needs further research; see T.B.M.S. 1933,
xvii. 246.

Escallonia
Phomopsis Escalloniae Grove.

Pycnidia scattered, covered, emerging slowly, blackish,
about 200μ diam. A-spores oval-fusoid, often biguttulate,
6–9 × 1·5–2μ; sporophores subulate, 14–16 × 2μ: B-spores
filiform, curved, 28–30 × 1μ.

On dead twigs of *Escallonia macrantha*. Seamill, Ayrshire
(Boyd). Kemerton, Glos. May, Sept.

Euonymus

Phomopsis ramealis Died. 254. Mig. 161. Grove, in Journ. Bot. 1930, p. 296. *Phoma ramealis* Desm. in Ann. Sci. Nat. 1850, xiv. 113. Sacc. Syll. iii. 71. All. vi. 208. *Phomopsis Celastrinae* Grove, in Kew Bull. 1917, p. 55, pl. 1, f. 9.

Pycnidia thickly crowded for a long distance along the twigs, subepidermal, only at a late stage protruding the pierced vertex, lens-shaped or subconical, about 300μ broad; peridium rather thick. A-spores oblong-fusoid, obtuse at both ends, biguttulate, $7–10 \times 2\cdot5–3\mu$; sporophores filiform, straight or rarely curvulous, hyaline, $15–20 \times 1–2\mu$: B-spores filiform, hooked at the apex, $25–30 \times 1\cdot5\mu$.

On twigs of *Euonymus americanus*, Kew Gardens (Cooke). On thin twigs of *Euonymus europaeus*:—near Park Attwood, Kidderminster (Rhodes). Trench Woods; Sneyd's Coppice, Ws., etc. (Grove & Rhodes). On twigs and leaves of *Eu. japonicus*, Lulworth Cove, Dorset, and Guernsey (Rhodes). Polperro (Rilstone).   May–Sept.

The pycnidial stage of *Diaporthe Laschii* Nits., which occurred in company with the Phomopsis.

There appears to be a *Phoma ramealis*, as well as a *Phomopsis ramealis*, to be found on the *Euonymus*.—It seems that, when old, the pycnidia of the Phomopsis break off at the vertex, and the lower part is left as a honey-comb-like pit, thus making *P. foveolaris* (Sacc.).

Fr. Germ. Austr. Ital.

Phomopsis foveolaris Trav. 257. Died. 253. Mig. 161. *Sphaeria foveolaris* Fr. Syst. Myc. ii. 499. *Phoma foveolaris* Sacc. Syll. iii. 72. All. vi. 209.

"Pycnidia gregarious, immersed, small, depressed, black; contents whitish; when old collapsing, becoming concave and like a honeycomb. Spores ovoid or obovoid, biguttulate, hyaline, $6 \times 3\mu$."

"On dead branches of *Euonymus europaeus*. Kew Gardens (Cooke)." Cooke's specimens, however, are not a Phomopsis.

Fries says: "So crowded that it sometimes covers the branches like a very thin black crust and makes on their surface deeply sunken shining black pits (*foveolae*) by which it can be easily recognised". This phenomenon, after all, is only an exaggeration of what is seen in other Phomopses, and I think *P. foveolaris* is merely an old exolete state of *P. ramealis*, and therefore a pycnidial stage of *Diaporthe*

Laschii Nits. Still, continental specimens seem to have spores less fusoid, and shorter and broader, than is usual in the genus, and the species has been generally accepted as distinct.

Fr. Holl. Germ. Austr. Ital. Denm.

Euphorbia

Phomopsis Euphorbiae Trav. 233. Grove, in Journ. Bot. 1930, p. 272. *Phoma Euphorbiae* Sacc. Syll. iii. 141.

Pycnidia gregarious, subepidermal, oblong, black, not completely formed all round, surrounded by a minute black-brown stain, the shining ostiole emerging through a short slit. Spores ovate-fusoid, subacute at both ends, mostly biguttulate, $7-8 \times 2\cdot5-3\cdot5\mu$; sporophores acicular, fasciculate, a little longer than the spore, rising from an olivaceous basal stratum.

On dead stems of *Euphorbia* (*palustris*, and *amygdaloides* = *silvatica*) in a garden at Edgbaston, Birmingham (Rhodes). Ockeridge Wood and Monk Wood, Ws. On *Euphorbia Paralias*, and *E. Cyparissias*, Borth. Apr.–Jun.

The pycnidial stage of *Diaporthe Euphorbiae* Cooke, in Grevill. iii. 67, which occurred with it at Ockeridge Wood (on *Euph. silvatica*, and not, as Saccardo says in Syll. i. 655, "*in caule Euphorbiarum silvaticarum*").

Fr. Ital.

Fagus

Phomopsis Diaporthes-macrostomae Trav. 280.

This I have not seen. The Diaporthe is recorded on *Fagus* by Wehmeyer, *l.c.* 261, from a collection made by Currey at Eltham Grove, Oct. 1856. Nitschke describes his *Diaporthe macrostoma* as having A-spores fusoid, $8-9 \times 3\mu$, and B-spores filiform, hamate, $32\ 36 \times 1\mu$, but it is not known that these pycnidial spores have yet been seen in Britain.

Germ. Ital.

Ficus

Phomopsis cinerascens Trav. 278. Grove, in Journ. Bot. 1917, p. 55, pl. 1, f. 10. Mig. 161. *Phoma cinerascens* Sacc. Syll. iii. 96. All. vi. 210. Wormald, in Ann. Appl. Biol. 1916, iii. 1, plates I, II. *P. Ficus* Cast. in Klotzsch, Herb. Mycol. no. 1870. Sacc. Syll. xi. 486. *Libertella ulcerata* Mass. in Gardeners' Mag. 1898, p. 475, f. 1–3.

Pycnidia gregarious, immersed in the bark, globose-depressed, $250-500\mu$ diam., blackish, at length emerging by the ostiole. A-spores elliptic-fusoid, somewhat obtuse at one or both ends, often biguttulate, $6-9 \times 2-2\cdot5\mu$, sometimes exuding

as a pallid globule; sporophores crowded, filiform-subulate, nearly straight, faintly coloured at base, 15–$20 \times 1 \cdot 5$–2μ: B-spores filiform, mostly hooked, 20–$25 \times 1\mu$, on short pedicels, with occasional A-spores intermixed.

On living and dead branches of *Ficus Carica*. Kew Gardens; Highgate; Sompting; Wisley; Reading; Shinfield, Bucks.; Sussex; Wiltshire; Kidderminster; Ayrshire; Anglesey; etc. Spring, summer.

The pycnidial stage of *Diaporthe cinerascens* Sacc.

A very typical Phomopsis in structure; pycnidium often incomplete. It is a wound-parasite, and occurs on the bare wood as well as in the bark, causing a "canker". The length of the sporophores of the A-spores, given by Allescher, Diedicke, and Migula (7–8μ), is wrong; it is copied from Saccardo, and may be a misprint for "17–18μ". Massee assigned to his *Libertella ulcerata* (the type specimen of which in the Kew Herbarium is exactly *Phomopsis cinerascens*) spores 55–$60 \times 4\mu$; these are now known to have been accidental intruders, having been found again, but only in very old material, by Mr Buddin and Miss Wakefield at Shinfield, and by myself at Kidderminster. They become ultimately septate and certainly belong to *Fusarium Urticearum* (Corda) Sacc., which grows habitually on *Ficus* and *Morus* in this country.

In Denmark this species of Phomopsis is recorded by Lind on *Ficus elastica* as well as on *F. Carica*; it is probably the same as *Phomopsis elastica* Petrak, which has A- and B-spores, and is otherwise similar.

Europe, from Denmark to Sardinia.

Forsythia

Phomopsis Dominici Trav. in Ann. Mycol. 1903, i. 229. Sacc. Syll. xviii. 266.

Pycnidia erumpent, gregarious, sometimes even confluent, depressed, irregular, mostly lenticular and obtusely papillate, brownish, 350–600μ diam. Spores cylindric-ellipsoid, hyaline, biguttulate, 6–$8 \times 2 \cdot 5$–3μ; sporophores linear, at length hooked, separating very easily, up to $25 \times 1\mu$.

On *Forsythia* sp. School House, Polperro (Rilstone & Rhodes). Kew Gardens. Apr.–Jun.

Fraxinus

Phomopsis controversa Trav. 273. Died. 255. Mig. 161. *Phoma controversa* Sacc. Syll. iii. 81. All. vi. 211.

Pycnidia widely gregarious, often confluent, hemispherical or conical, occasionally oblong, at first covered, then raising

the epidermis and erumpent, 200–300μ diam.; peridium rather
thick. Spores fusoid, biguttulate, colourless, 7–8 × 2–3μ;
sporophores filiform-subulate, curved or nearly straight,
about 20 × 1·5μ.

On dry branches of *Fraxinus excelsior*. Rather uncommon.

The pycnidial stage of *Diaporthe controversa* Nits. in *litt. apud* Fckl.
(1871).

Phomopsis scobina Cooke and *P. pterophila* Died. (*qq.v.*) are almost
certainly the same species as this.

Fr. Germ.

Phomopsis scobina v. Höhn. *l.c.* p. 33. Grove, in Kew Bull. 1917,
p. 64, pl. 2, f. 27. Died. 255. Mig. 161. *Phoma scobina* Cooke, in
Grevill. xiii. 92. Sacc. Syll. x. 147. All. vi. 212. *Myxolibertella scobina*
v. Höhn. in Ann. Mycol. i. 526. *Phlyctaena Fraxini* J. W. Ellis, in
Herb.

Pycnidia scattered or gregarious, often clustered near the
nodes, long remaining covered, hidden beneath the epidermis,
at length bursting it by a round or elongated opening, globose-
depressed, black, 250–500μ diam. A-spores elliptic-fusoid,
sometimes subclavate, acute at both ends, uni- or often biguttulate, 7–10 × 2–2·5μ; sporophores subulate or cylindrical,
occasionally curved or bent, 10–12 × 1·5μ (up to 18 × 1μ,
Ellis): B-spores filiform, curved or uncinate, 20–25 × 1μ;
sporophores up to 5μ long.

On twigs and petioles of *Fraxinus excelsior*, *F. Ornus*.
Rather common. England, Scotland.   Mar.–Jul.

The pycnidial stage of *Diaporthe scobina* Nits. (1870), which frequently accompanies it. *P. pterophila* Died. is certainly, and *P. controversa* Trav. is probably, the same species as this, although attempts
are made to distinguish *P. scobina* by assigning to it longer A-spores;
Cooke said in his original diagnosis (*l.c.*) that they measure 10–12 ×
3–3·5μ; but I fear that was an error. It seems likely that *Cytospora
Fraxini* Delacr. in Bull. Soc. Myc. Fr. 1890, p. 184, pl. 20, f. 5 (Sacc.
Syll. x. 245; All. vi. 582; Mig. 197) is merely a more complex (plurilocellate) form of this species.

Europe generally.

Phomopsis pterophila Died. 255. Mig. 161. Grove, in Kew Bull.
1917, p. 61, pl. 2, f. 23. *Sphaeria pterophila* Nits. *in litt. apud* Fckl.
Phoma pterophila Fckl. Symb. Myc. 377. Sacc. Syll. iii. 153. All. vi. 213.

Pycnidia scattered, about 300μ diam., subglobose, papillate, black, prominent, bursting the raised epidermis which

often forms a whitish spot over the papilla, each pycnidium surrounded by a faint brown halo. Spores ellipsoid, subacute at the ends, biguttulate, 7–8 × 2·5μ; sporophores subulate or filiform, curved or straight, 11–13 × 1–1·5μ: B-spores as above.

On samaras of *Fraxinus excelsior*, but only on the thick part containing the seed, not on the wing. Common.

The pycnidial stage of *Diaporthe samaricola* Ph. & Pl. But there is not the slightest doubt that it is the same as *Phomopsis scobina* v. Höhn. *Phoma samararum* occurs on the wing of the fruit, but is at once distinguished by its smaller size and want of halo.

Galium

Phomopsis elliptica Grove. *Phoma elliptica* Peck, in 27th Rep. N.Y. State Mus. 1875, p. 101. Sacc. Syll. iii. 137. Cf. *Phomopsis mazzantioides* Petr. in Ann. Mycol. xix. 52.

Pycnidia thinly scattered, immersed, subglobose, up to 120μ diam., imperfectly formed, black, soon emerging, not surrounded by a black zone or line. A-spores oblong-lanceolate, mostly obtuse at both ends, biguttulate in the usual fashion, 9–10 × 2·5–3μ; sporophores crowded, subulate, very acute, 15–18 × 2·5–3μ, rising from a pale-brownish basal stratum: B-spores intermixed within the same peridium, flexuous or (mostly) hooked, 18–20 × 0·5μ.

On dead stems of *Galium Mollugo*, Polperro, Cornwall (Rilstone & Rhodes); Fowey. On *G. Aparine*, North Littleton and Hartlebury Common, Ws. (Rhodes).   Jan.–Apr.

Possibly the pycnidial stage of *Diaporthe mazzantioides* Sacc. & Sp. I have put this under Peck's name with a little hesitation, having seen no American specimen. His was on *G. boreale*, and he says of it: "The pycnidia are rather large, and when broken from the matrix leave a whitish spot surrounded by a black line". The spores he describes as "oblong-ellipsoid, 8–9 × 4μ".
U.S.A.

Garrya

Phomopsis Garryae Grove, in Journ. Bot. 1922, p. 43; 1933, p. 255.

Pycnidia incomplete above, crowded, about 200μ diam., conical, pallid, long covered by the epidermis, at length black. A-spores elliptic-fusoid, often biguttulate, acute at both ends, 5·5–7 × 2–2·5μ; sporophores linear-subulate, generally curved, 15–20 × 1·5μ: B-spores filiform, hooked, about 25 × 1μ:

C-spores intermixed, linear or narrow-fusoid, acuminate at both ends, 15–17 × 0·75–1μ; sporophores not seen.

On dead twigs of *Garrya elliptica*, always in association with the Diaporthe. West Kilbride, Ayrshire (Boyd). Heythrop Park, Oxon.   Jun.–Aug.

The pycnidial stage of *Diaporthe Garryae* Grove, in Journ. Bot. 1933, p. 255.

Hedera

Phomopsis pulla Trav. 244. Died. 256. Mig. 161. Grove, in Kew Bull. 1917, p. 62. *Phoma pulla* Sacc. Syll. iii. 87. All. vi. 215. *Phoma Hederae* Fckl. Symb. Myc. 211!

Pycnidia densely gregarious, flat or hardly projecting, concealed by the somotimes discoloured epidermis, black. Spores oblong or ellipsoid, obtuse at both ends, biguttulate, 7–8 × 2–3μ; sporophores curved, 12–16 × 1μ.

On dead twigs of *Hedera Helix*. Neatishead (Cooke). Aberdeen (Trail). Ayrshire (Boyd). Harvington Hall; Polperro (Rhodes). Kew Gardens; Wixford; Ledbury; Barmouth, etc.
                                                                          Apr.–Aug.

The pycnidial stage of *Diaporthe pulla* Nits. by which it is often accompanied; the inky black stain of the wood is frequently to be seen on old stems or shoots of Ivy, growing on ancient walls, castles, etc. W. and S. Europe.

Herminiera

Phomopsis Herminierae Grove, in Kew Bull. 1917, p. 57, pl. 1, f. 14. *Phoma Herminierae* Cooke, in Grevill. xiii. 93. Sacc. Syll. x. 139.

Pycnidia widely but closely distributed, nestling in the cortex, about 250μ diam., depressed, black, at first covered by the epidermis, then splitting it in a substellate manner. A-spores lanceolate, somewhat rounded above, acute below, biguttulate, 7–8 × 2μ; sporophores subulate, 12–15 × 3μ: B-spores filiform, flexuous, on short sporophores, mingled in the same pycnidia.

In bark of *Herminiera Elaphroxylon*. Kew Gardens (Cooke).

A typical *Phomopsis*, evidently introduced with the host from tropical Africa. Cooke wrongly gives the size of the fusoid spores as 10 × 3·5μ.

Hibiscus
Phomopsis Ophites Trav. 254. *Phoma Ophites* Sacc. Syll. iii. 89.
All. vi. 216.

"Pycnidia subepidermal, globose-depressed, olivaceous-black, at length surrounded by a blackish subcortical line arising from the stroma; ostiole obtuse, erumpent. Spores acutely fusoid, straight, biguttulate, hyaline, 8–10 × 2μ; sporophores acicular, crowded, hyaline, 15 × 1·5μ."

"On dead stems of *Hibiscus syriacus*. Kew Gardens" (Cooke).

The pycnidial stage of *Diaporthe Ophites* Sacc., or possibly it is merely a form of *Phomopsis Malvacearum*.

The French specimens are a typical Phomopsis, having spores as described above. The pycnidium resembles that of *Phomopsis Arctii*, and is immersed wholly in the wood. But on Cooke's specimens there is now nothing in the remotest degree resembling this.

Fr. Ital.

Humulus
[**Phomopsis sarmentella** Trav. 277. Died. 256. Mig. 162.
Phoma sarmentella Sacc. Syll. iii. 140. All. vi. 297.

"Pycnidia gregarious, subepidermal, oblong, black. Spores cylindric-fusoid, curvulous, obtuse, 5–6 × 2–3μ; sporophores rod-shaped, almost twice as long as the spore."

"On Hop-bines (*Humulus Lupulus*). Isleworth" (Cooke).]

The Phomopsis is considered to be the pycnidial stage of *Diaporthe sarmenticia* Sacc. On the specimen from Isleworth in Herb. Kew, however, there is no Phomopsis, only *Phoma herbarum*, f. *Humuli*, and two fungi belonging to other genera.

Fr.

Hypericum
Phomopsis Hyperici Grove, in Journ. Bot. 1922, p. 43. *Phlyctaena Hyperici* Hollós, in Ann. Mus. Nat. Hung. 1906, iv. 353, pl. 8, f. 17. Sacc. Syll. xxii. 1125.

Pycnidia scattered or subgregarious, in irregular rows, long covered by the epidermis which is elevated into a convex pustule, at length slightly erumpent at the vertex, oblong, up to 400μ broad; peridium thick and smoky-brown. A-spores fusoid, acute at both ends, biguttulate, 7–8 × 1·5–2μ; sporophores linear-subulate, of about the same length, rising from a thick olivaceous stratum: B-spores filiform, curved, usually

hooked, 25–30 × 1–1·5μ, mixed with the A-spores but on shorter sporophores.

On dead stems of *Hypericum* (*Androsaemum, perforatum*). West Kilbride, Ayrshire (Boyd). Anglesey (Rhodes).

Jul.–Sept.

Both kinds of spores grew intermixed in the same pycnidia. The B-spores were evidently the Phlyctaena of Hollós.
Hung.

Phomopsis picea v. Höhn. in Sitz. Ber. Acad. Wiss. Wien, 1906, p. 681. Died. 277. Mig. 157. *Sphaeria picea* Pers. Syn. 31. *Phoma picea* Sacc. Syll. iii. 140. *Sphaeropsis picea* Fr. Summ. Veg. Scand. 419. Fckl. Symb. Myc. 397.

"Stromata elongated, unequal, pitch-black. Pycnidia scattered, somewhat depressed, covered by the epidermis, at first mouthless, then pierced at the summit. Spores subfusoid or ellipsoid, acute at both ends, biguttulate, hyaline, 8–10 × 2·5–3μ."

On dead stems of *Hypericum hirsutum*. Hadzor, Worcs. (Rhodes).   July.

Forma **Obiones** Grove.

Pycnidia gregarious, black, soft, subglobose but lumpy and irregular, covered, then erumpent by the vertex, each surrounded by a blackish zone or halo which afterwards becomes effused as a black patch, dotted over with pitch-black points. Spores numerous, oblong-ellipsoid or lanceolate-fusoid, acute at one or both ends, faintly guttulate, 7–8 × 2·5–3μ; sporophores crowded, erect, filiform, up to twice as long as the spore or more, rising from a soft cinereous stratum: no B-spores seen.

On dead stems of *Obione portulacoides*. Seaton, Devon (Rhodes).   Sept.

Phomopsis picea is a composite species, and is recorded abroad on other hosts also (*Atriplex, Artemisia, Verbena*, etc.). Saccardo (*l.c.*) suggests that it is the pycnidial stage of his *Diaporthe picea*.
Germ. Swed. Siberia.

Ilex

Phomopsis crustosa Trav. 256 (1906). Died. in Ann. Mycol. ix. 22; Pilz. Brand. 256. Grove, in Journ. Bot. 1922, p. 43. Mig. 162.

Phoma crustosa Bomm. Rouss. & Sacc. in Bull. Soc. Bot. Belg. 1887, xxvi. 214. Sacc. Syll. x. 149. All. vi. 217. *Phomopsis Ilicis* v. Höhn. in Hedwig. 1918, lx. 206. (Not *Sphaeropsis ilicicola* Cooke & Ellis, in Grevill. vi. 3.)

Pycnidia somewhat scattered, a few occasionally clustered together, conical-depressed, up to 500μ diam., shining-black, long covered by the epidermis which is at length elevated and whitish in the centre, surrounded by a blackish-brown halo, sometimes several occupying a common blackish area which is bounded by a distinct narrow black Diaporthe-like line; ostiole minute, black, emerging; peridium everywhere thick, of dark squarish olive-brown parenchyma. A-spores fusoid, often irregular, sometimes more obtuse above, biguttulate, $7-9 \times 2 \cdot 5-3\mu$; sporophores subulate, acuminate, rather granular towards the base, $12-22 \times 1 \cdot 5-2\mu$: with these a few B-spores, lunate, acuminate, rarely hooked, $20 \times 1\mu$.

On dead twigs and leaves of *Ilex Aquifolium*. West Kilbride, etc. Ayrshire (Boyd). Kew Gardens; Middleton, Warwicks.; Portishead; Wales; etc.

The B-spores are doubtful, and might be elongated sporophores. The pycnidial stage of *Diaporthe crustosa* Sacc. & Roum. = *D. ilicina* Cooke (1890).

Von Höhnel mistakenly confused this with *Phoma Ilicis* Desm., and therefore renamed it *Phomopsis Ilicis* v. Höhn.; but the spores of *Phoma Ilicis* are more like those of *Macrophoma cylindrospora*. On an old branch of Holly, at Cil-y-Cwm, Carmarthenshire, in May, among some old but typical pustules of *P. crustosa*, I found a quantity of immature asci and spores of *Diaporthe crustosa*, with the black line well marked.

Belg. Holl. Germ. Ital.

Jasminum

Phomopsis Jasmini Petr. in Ann. Mycol. 1916, xiv. 170. Grove, in Journ. Bot. 1930, p. 273. *Phoma Jasmini* Cooke, in Grevill. xiv. 2. Sacc. Syll. x. 146. All. vi. 217. Mig. 96.

Pycnidia rather closely scattered, often in rows, convex, papillate, covered by the epidermis which is at length torn irregularly at the vertex, opening by a pore, blackish-brown, 200–300μ diam. A-spores subfusoid, biguttulate, $8-9 \times 2 \cdot 5-3\mu$; sporophores linear-subulate, $12-15\mu$ long, granular, rising from a thickish pale-olivaceous stratum: B-spores filiform, flexuose or hamate, $18-20 \times 0 \cdot 75-1\mu$.

On dead branches of *Jasminum officinale*, *J. nudiflorum*.
Kew Gardens (Cooke). West Kilbride, Ayrshire (Boyd).
School House, Polperro; also with B-spores in the same pyc-
nidia, at Landeviddy, Cornw. Apr.–Sept.

The pycnidial stage of *Diaporthe culta* S. & S., which occurred on
the same plant at Polperro.

Cooke's specimens were associated with *Phoma domestica*, which is
smaller and less prominent. Petrak also found B-spores on *Jasminum
Sambac*, exactly similar to the Polperro ones; his "intermediate"
spores seem to be merely the loose sporophores of the A-spores.

Fr. Germ. Moravia.

Juglans
Phomopsis juglandina v. Höhn. Fragm. z. Mykol. 1906, no. 87,
p. 32. Died. 257. Mig. 162. Grove, in Kew Bull. 1917, p. 57. *Phoma
juglandina* Sacc. Syll. iii. 90. All. vi. 217.

Pycnidia covered by the epidermis, globose-depressed,
greyish-black. Spores fusoid, $8–12 \times 2\cdot5–3\cdot5\mu$; sporophores
filiform, curvulous, $15–25 \times 1–1\cdot5\mu$.

On bark of branches of *Juglans regia*. Kew Gardens; Hereford; N. Wales; Anglesey; etc. Aug.

The pycnidial stage of *Diaporthe juglandina* Nits.
The Kew specimens are rather imperfect, but seem to belong to this
species, at least in part. *Phoma Juglandis* Sacc. Syll. iii. 152, seems to
be the same; it is on the fruits, but no specimens have been seen.
Fr. Germ. Austr. Denm. Ital.

Laburnum
Phomopsis rudis v. Höhn. Fragm. z. Mykol. 1906, no. 87, p. 32.
Died. in Ann. Mycol. 1911, ix. 29, pl. 2, f. 2; Pilz. Brand. 253.
Mig. p. 160, pl. 16, f. 6. Grove, in Kew Bull. 1917, p. 63. *Phoma rudis*
Sacc. Syll. iii. 68. All. vi. 203. *Rabenhorstia rudis* Died. et Auct. plur.
(*non* Fr.).

Pycnidia gregarious, very numerous, subglobose, about
500μ wide, black, at first concealed by the epidermis, at
length emerging at the summit; wall thick and firm, olivaceous-black. Spores elliptic-fusoid, subacute at the ends,
not always biguttulate, $7–9 \times 2–2\cdot5\mu$, sometimes emerging in
yellowish tendrils; sporophores densely crowded, filiform,
usually straight, $20–24 \times 1–1\cdot5\mu$.

On dead twigs of *Laburnum vulgare*, *L. alpinum*. Cheshire
(Ellis). Ayrshire (Boyd). Brewood, Staffs. (Rhodes). Kew;
Cambridgeshire; etc. Apr. May.

The pycnidial stage of *Diaporthe rudis* Nits.

The pycnidia are not depressed, but somewhat conical, and raise the epidermis considerably before bursting it open. It seems not to be connected with the true Rabenhorstia of Fries as Saccardo suggested (Syll. iii. 244), since the pustules apparently remain unilocular. See Ann. Mycol. 1923, xxi. 356.

Fr. Holl. Germ. Denm. Ital.

Lathyrus

Phomopsis lathyrina Grove, in Kew Bull. 1919, p. 433. *Phoma lathyrina* Sacc. Syll. iii. 147; Mycoth. Venet. no. 1542! *Phoma Salweii* Berk. in Herb.

Pycnidia gregarious, orbicular, convex or globose-depressed, covered but rather prominent, black, somewhat shining, up to 400μ diam., surrounded by a dull blackish halo, and sometimes two or three enclosed by a sinuous Diaporthe-like line, at length dropping out and leaving a pale-coloured pit: peridium thick above, blackish-brown. Spores oblong-ellipsoid, subobtuse at both ends, often biguttulate, sometimes inequilateral, $8–10 \times 2–2·5\mu$; sporophores crowded, erect, acicular, $16–20 \times 1–1·5\mu$, rising from a thick brownish stratum.

On dead stems of *Lathyrus silvestris*, Par, Cornw. (Rilstone)!
On leaves of *Lathyrus latifolius*, Guernsey (Salwey).

Aug. Sept.

Saccardo's specimen was on dead pods of *L. latifolius*.
Ital.

Laurus

Phomopsis laurella Trav. 276 (1906). Grove, in Journ. Bot. 1922, p. 44. *Phoma laurella* Sacc. Syll. iii. 82. All. vi. 219. *Phoma nobilis* Sacc. in Mich. ii. 616 (*non* Thüm.). *Phomopsis laurina* Petrak, in Ann. Mycol. xiv. 173 (1916).

Pycnidia very numerous, gregarious but hardly crowded, incomplete, roundish, depressed or conical, $250–300\mu$ diam., becoming pallid, at length elevating and piercing the epidermis by a minute pore. A-spores fusoid, nearly straight, indistinctly guttulate, $8–10 \times 2·5–3\mu$; sporophores subulate, $8–12 \times 1·5\mu$, rising from a thickish yellow-fuliginous fertile stratum: B-spores linear, mostly curved or hooked, $16–18 \times 1\mu$.

On bark of twigs, and also on the fading leaves, of *Laurus*

nobilis. Kew Gardens (Cooke). Balbriggan, Dublin (Scriven). West Kilbride, Ayrshire (Boyd). Polperro, Cornwall.

Apr.–Sept.

The pycnidial stage of *Diaporthe nobilis* S. & S. In the Irish specimens the fungus appeared to be gradually killing the twigs backwards, beginning at the tips, exactly as *P. aucubicola* does. In Mr Boyd's specimens A- and B-spores occurred together in the same pycnidia on the twigs; the A-spores alone were found on the leaves, and these were often smaller than on the twigs. These latter may possibly be *Phyllosticta Lauri* Westd., since they were thickly spread over the upper surface of large, brown, dry, darker-margined spots, like a normal Phyllosticta.

Fr. Germ. Moravia.

Leycesteria

Phomopsis Leycesteriae Grove, in Journ. Bot. 1930, p. 274.

Pycnidia rather densely scattered, sometimes covering large areas of the stem, black, depressed, each surrounded by a very conspicuous cinereous halo, which can reach a diameter of 500μ and is itself at length surrounded by a narrow black line, soon raising the epidermis and bursting it or piercing it by the faintly papillate ostiole which is pierced by a rather wide pore, round or oval, $200–300\mu$ diam.; peridium thick and fuscous-black above, but below brownish, subtranslucent. A-spores ovate-fusoid, acute at one end, biguttulate, $5–7 \times 2–2\cdot5\mu$; sporophores crowded, subulate, as long as the spore or rather longer: B-spores in separate pycnidia, filiform-linear, usually somewhat curved or flexuous, mostly distinctly hamate, $20–28 \times 1\mu$.

On dead stems of *Leycesteria formosa.* West Kilbride, Ayrshire (Boyd). Polperro, Cornwall (Rilstone & Rhodes). Heythrop Park (Grove & Rhodes).

Jun. Jul.

The pycnidial stage of *Diaporthe Leycesteriae* Grove (in Journ. Bot. *ibid.* p. 274), which occurred on older and thicker stems of the same tree at Polperro. The B-spores were found on the Polperro specimens. The Scottish specimens were accompanied by immature states of the Diaporthe.

Ligustrum

Phomopsis brachyceras Grove.

Pycnidia widely and irregularly scattered, at first and for a long time covered, at last erumpent by a roundish torn pore in the epidermis, globose, not blackened above or around,

300–400μ diam. A-spores acutely lanceolate-fusoid, almost tip-cat-shaped, biguttulate, often slightly bent or curved, 7–9 × 1·5–2μ, broadest in the middle; sporophores linear, straight, 15–20 × 1·5μ: B-spores abundant, filiform, curved or flexuous, rarely hooked, 20–24 × 1μ.

On dead twigs of *Ligustrum vulgare*. Seamill and West Kilbride, Ayrshire (Boyd). Hanbury, Ws. (Rhodes). Fowey (Rilstone). May–Jul.

Accompanied by *Diaporthe brachyceras* Sacc. (Syll. i. 643) on the same twigs, and by a Cytospora and a Valsa.

Lippia

Phomopsis citriodora Grove, in Journ. Bot. 1930, p. 270.

Pycnidia scattered over a whitish spot, black, immersed in the soft cortex, 150–180μ diam., often imperfectly developed, formed of a somewhat parenchymatous texture. A-spores ellipsoid-lanceolate, pointed at both ends or with one end rather obtuse, biguttulate, hyaline, 9–12 × 2–2·5μ; sporophores erect: B-spores filiform, curved or often hooked at one end, 20–22 × 1μ.

On dead stems of *Lippia* (*Aloysia*) *citriodora*. Lansallos, near Polperro (Rhodes). Lambourne Hill, Cornw. (Rilstone).

Jun. Jul.

Pycnidia round or oval-lanceolate; both kinds of spores could be found in the same pycnidium, although they were more often separate. Indications of a Diaporthe were found on another branch of the same bush in the following March, but no mature perithecia were formed. A very typical Phomopsis.

Liriodendron

Phomopsis Liriodendri Grove, in Journ. Bot. 1930, p. 275.

Pycnidia scattered, 200–400μ diam., globose-depressed, black, long covered by the periderm, which is raised and at length perforated by the minute shining papilla (the cortex round the papilla becoming whitish and often surrounded by a rather broad bright-brown zone); peridium thick and opaque above, paler below. A-spores ellipsoid, rounded above, hardly attenuated below, biguttulate, 7–9 × 2μ; sporophores generally at first oblong and shorter than the spore, but at length subulate and longer, 15–20μ, rising from a pallid olivaceous stratum: "B-spores hamate, 20 × 1μ" (Rhodes).

On dead branches of *Liriodendron tulipifera*, Polperro (Rhodes), July, 1929. At the same place (Rilstone), March, 1930. Heythrop Park (Grove & Rhodes), June, 1932.

The March specimens were filled with A-spores only; the July ones had them accompanied by a Diaporthe with clavate asci, about $50 \times 8\mu$, containing biseriate spores, fusoid, very acute at both ends, not visibly septate, 4-guttulate, 14–$15 \times 2 \cdot 5$–3μ, doubtless belonging to *Diaporthe delitescens* B. R. & S.

Lonicera

Phomopsis cryptica v. Höhn. Fragm. z. Mykol. 1906, no. 87, p. 32. Died. 259. Mig. 163. *Phoma cryptica* Sacc. Syll. iii. 69. All. vi. 221.

Pycnidia gregarious, subepidermal, depressed-globose, obtuse, greyish-black. Spores oblong-fusoid, biguttulate, 7–$9 \times 2 \cdot 5$–3μ; sporophores filiform-subulate, curved, 13–20×1 $1 \cdot 5\mu$.

On living stems of *Lonicera Periclymenum*. Several places in Cheshire (Ellis). Ockeridge Wood, etc., Worcs. Red Wharf Bay, Anglesey, with B-spores 30–$33 \times 1\mu$.   Jan.–Apr.

The pycnidial stage of *Diaporthe cryptica* Nits. The pycnidium is, as usual, often imperfectly formed. The Kent specimens assigned to this species by Cooke were found, on examination, to be on *Tamus communis*, and therefore to be *Phomopsis Tami*. On the continent *P. cryptica* is recorded on *L. Caprifolium* and other species of the genus. Diedicke found B-spores, filiform, bent or hamate, 20–$30 \times 1\mu$, in *P. cryptica*, but on *dead* branches; cf. *Phomopsis Lonicerae*. Fr. Holl. Germ. Ital. N. Amer.

Phomopsis Lonicerae Grove, in Kew Bull. 1917, p. 58, pl. 1, f. 16. *Phoma Lonicerae* Cooke, in Grevill. vi. 83 (1878); Fung. Brit. i. 616. Sacc. Syll. iii. 70.

Pycnidia scattered or gregarious, immersed in the cortex with the base seated on the wood, completely covered by the epidermis which is raised in a slight pustule but not discoloured and is at length pierced by a minute opening at the summit, oblong or hemispherical, truncate, black, 250–330μ long. A-spores fusoid or elliptic-fusoid, acute at both ends, biguttulate, 8–$10 \times 2 \cdot 5\mu$; sporophores subulate, 15×2–$2 \cdot 5\mu$: B-spores filiform, hooked, 25–30μ long, on shorter sporophores.

On old stems of *Lonicera.* Irstead (Fung. Brit., *l.c.*); Neatishead (Cooke).

A most typical Phomopsis, but apparently different from *P. cryptica* v. Höhn., as that is represented in Sydow's Mycothec. German. no. 808, where the pycnidia are not seated on the wood. In some of the pycnidia A-spores and B-spores were found mixed together, *in situ*, in the same pycnidium. The wood is frequently stained black round the base of the pycnidia, which leave a whitish pit when they fall away. But it seems as if *P. Lonicerae* stood to *P. cryptica* much in the same way as *P. foveolaris* does to *P. ramealis.*

Lupinus

Phomopsis leptostromiformis Bubák, Exs. no. 660. Lind, Dan. Fungi, 422. *Cryptosporium leptostromiforme* Kühn, in Ber. aus physiol. Lab. Landsw. Inst. Halle, 1880, p. 121.

Pycnidia scattered, black, 100–200μ diam., subglobose, papillate, just piercing the epidermis with the papilla, surrounded by a distinct oval blackish stain which afterwards becomes effused. A-spores oval-lanceolate, biguttulate in the usual manner, acute below, 8–9 × 2–2·5μ; sporophores filiform, straight, acute, as long as the spore, or 15–20 × 1·5μ.

On dead petioles of *Lupinus polyphyllus*, King's Norton (Chesters). On dead stems of the same, Rednal, Ws., and of *L. arboreus*, Talland Bay, Cornw.　　　　　Feb.–Apr.

Bubák describes the spores as "cylindrical, straight, rounded at both ends, hyaline, 8–10 × 1·5–2μ". See Rostrup, Plantepatologi, p. 597. There is a *Diaporthe* (*Tetr.*) *Lupini* Harkn. (Sacc. Syll. ix. 722), on *L. arboreus*, from California, to which this Phomopsis may belong. Germ. Denm.

Lycium

Phomopsis importata Died. in Ann. Mycol. 1911, ix. 24; Pilz. Brand. 259. Mig. 163. *Phoma importata* Sacc. iii. 127. All. vi. 223.

Pycnidia gregarious, somewhat conical, erumpent, but not much protruding, blackish. Spores cylindric-fusoid, rather obtuse at both ends, biguttulate, 7–10 × 2·5–3μ; sporophores filiform, 18–20 × 1·5–2μ.

On dry branches of *Lycium barbarum*. Budleigh Salterton, Devon; Lulworth Cove, Dorset (Rhodes).　　　　Mar.–May.

The pycnidial stage of *Diaporthe importata* Nits. Germ. Ital.

                                                            Lysimachia
Phomopsis Lysimachiae Grove, in Kew Bull. 1917, p. 58. *Phoma Lysimachiae* Cooke, in Grevill. xiii. 94. Sacc. Syll. x. 171. All. vi. 303.

Pycnidia scattered, convex or depressed-oblong, black, 250µ long, covered by and slightly elevating the blackened epidermis, which is at length pierced by the ostiole. Spores broadly lanceolate, biguttulate, 7–9 × 2·5–3µ; sporophores linear, straight, a little longer than the spore.

On stems of *Lysimachia vulgaris*. Kew Gardens.   Apr.

Presumably the pycnidium of a Diaporthe, since it has the true Phomopsis characters.

                                                            Maclura
Phomopsis exul Grove, in Kew Bull. 1917, p. 56. *Phoma exul* Sacc. Syll. iii. 89. All. vi. 224.

Pycnidia gregarious, covered by the epidermis, occasionally joined together by a black stroma-like layer, conico-truncate, piercing the epidermis at the summit, at first grey, then blackish. Spores fusoid or cylindric-fusoid, subacute at both ends, biguttulate, 7–10 × 2–2·5µ; sporophores very crowded, subulate, slightly curved, 12–18 × 2µ.

On twigs of *Maclura aurantiaca*. Kew Gardens (Cooke).

The pycnidial stage of an unknown Diaporthe.   Fr.

                                                            Magnolia
Phomopsis magnoliicola Died. 260. Mig. 163. Grove, in Journ. Bot. 1930, p. 293. *Phoma magnoliicola* Syd. in Hedwig. 1900, p. (2). Sacc. Syll. xvi. 857. All. vii. 812. *Phomopsis viridarii* Grove, in Kew Bull. 1917, p. 67.

Pycnidia scattered or gregarious, elevating the epidermis and then piercing it, globose, black, 200–250µ diam., pierced by a pore; texture thick and dark. A-spores oblong-ellipsoid, boat-shaped or even oblanceolate, somewhat acute at both ends, biguttulate, 8–12 × 2–3µ; sporophores ± straight, linear or subulate, 15–20 × 1–2µ: B-spores filiform, hooked, 15–20 × 1µ.

On dead branches of *Magnolia Soulangeana*, Harborne Hall, near Birmingham (Rhodes). On twigs and on dry fallen leaves of *Magnolia grandiflora* (on lamina, nerves, and petioles), Kew Gardens; Hadzor Hall, Worcs.   Feb.–Aug.

The pycnidial stage of *Diaporthe americana* Speg., which occurred with it at Hadzor. See especially Journ. Bot. 1930, p. 294.
Fr. Germ. Ital.

Mahonia
Phomopsis Mahoniae Grove, in Journ. Bot. 1930, p. 294.

Pycnidia scattered or subgregarious, immersed, globose, depressed, black, up to 300μ diam., piercing the epidermis by the very black shining papillate ostiole, which is surrounded by a cinereous-black halo (up to 750μ diam.) that is itself at length bounded by a thin black line, the line sometimes including two or three pycnidia. Spores oval-lanceolate, subacute at one end, biguttulate, 6–$8 \times 1 \cdot 5$–$2 \cdot 5 \mu$; sporophores subulate, at times reaching a length of 14–15μ.

On fallen leaves of *Mahonia japonica*, Hadzor Hall, near Droitwich (Grove & Rhodes).   Jan.

With these A-spores were a few filiform faintly curved B-spores(?), about $20 \times 1 \mu$. On the ground, on other leaves fallen from the same shrubs, was *Diaporthe Mahoniae* Speg. Cf. also *D. hypospilina* Sacc. & Flag. in Grevill. xxi. 65.

Malvaceae
Phomopsis Malvacearum Grove, in Kew Bull. 1917, p. 58. *Phoma Malvacearum* Westd. Exs. no. 1232. Sacc. Syll. iii. 122. All. vi. 263. *P. Lavaterae* Westd. Not. vi. 22. Sacc. Syll. iii. 122. All. vi. 301.

Pycnidia gregarious, oblong, blackish-brown, 500μ long or more, covered at first by the blackened epidermis, at length erumpent by a slit. A-spores elliptic fusoid, somewhat obtuse at both ends, biguttulate, 7–10×2–3μ; sporophores filiform, densely crowded, 15–$18 \times 1 \cdot 5 \mu$: B-spores filiform, curved, arcuate, or hooked, $15 \times 0 \cdot 75 \mu$.

On stems of *Malva moschata*, Kew Gardens. On stems of *Lavatera arborea*, both A- and B-spores, Guernsey (Rhodes). On *Althaea officinalis* and *Sidalcea*, Polperro (Rilstone). Also at Leatherhead; Hendon; etc.   Jul.–Sept.

Recorded abroad on *Malva silvestris* and other Malvaceae. It may not be different from *P. Ophites* Trav. (*q.v.* p. 191). It is not, as Allescher asserts, the same as *Phoma nebulosa* Berk.
Europe, Siberia, N. Africa.

Melilotus

Phomopsis Meliloti Grove, in Journ. Bot. 1930, p. 294.

Pycnidia scattered, not at all in contact but sometimes arranged in rows, oblong, convex, imperfectly developed, black, about 500μ long, pierced by a round pore and surrounded by a pale-fuscous halo. Spores oblong-ellipsoid, obtusely rounded above, somewhat pointed below, biguttulate, about 7 × 3μ; sporophores subulate, less crowded than is usual, straight or nearly so, faintly olivaceous, 16–20μ long, rising from a soft pale-olivaceous proliferous stratum.

On stems of *Melilotus*, by the roadside near Trench Woods, Droitwich (Rhodes).   Nov.

Presumably the pycnidial stage of *Diaporthe Meliloti* Trav. (p. 223), but Traverso does not mention the Phomopsis stage.

Menispermum

Phomopsis Menispermi Grove, in Kew Bull. 1917, p. 59, pl. 2, f. 17. *Phoma Menispermi* Peck, in 24th Rep. State Mus. New York, 1872, p. 85. *P. sarmenticia* Sacc. in Mich. ii. 94 (1880); Syll. iii. 136. All. vi. 307. Cooke, in Grevill. xiv. 31.

Pycnidia subgregarious or scattered, at first covered by the discoloured epidermis, which is at length elevated and burst by a short slit, oblong, prominent, 200–250μ long, blackish, somewhat shining; contents colourless. Spores oblong-fusoid, subacute at the ends, biguttulate, 7–10 × 2–2·25μ; sporophores crowded, subulate, 20–25 × 1–1·5μ.

On dead branches of *Menispermum canadense*. Kew Gardens (Cooke).

The pycnidial stage, undoubtedly, of an unknown *Diaporthe*.

A comparison of the Kew specimens with those of *Phoma Menispermi* (Roumeguère, no. 4461) from Portugal makes it as certain as one can be without seeing Peck's original specimens that *P. sarmenticia* Sacc. is the same as *P. Menispermi* Peck. The agreement with Peck's short description is exact; his statement that the pycnidia, on falling out, leave little white pits is just what takes place, and what would be expected with a Phomopsis where the pycnidium is deeply seated, thick above and imperfectly formed below. The discoloured epidermis forms a little halo; the sporophores are unusually long even for a Phomopsis, reaching sometimes as much as 35μ. Cooke's statement (*l.c.*), that the same species occurred on *Cocculus carolinianus* is improbable; a Phomopsis on that host is likely to be *P. Cocculi* Maffei (in Atti Ist. Bot. Pav. 1916, p. 236).

Fr. Germ. Port. U.S.A.

Morus

Phomopsis moricola Grove, in Kew Bull. 1917, p. 59, pl. 2, f. 18.
Phoma moricola Sacc. Syll. iii. 95. All. vi. 225.

Pycnidia scattered or subgregarious, nestling in the cortex, globose-depressed or irregular, dark-grey, 300–500μ across, imperfectly developed and at length opening like a cup. Spores oblong-ellipsoid, slightly tapering below, at times somewhat curved, biguttulate, 8–9 × 2–2·5μ; sporophores cylindrical, very crowded, curvulous, 10–12 × 1·5μ, rising from a brownish basal stratum.

On dead twigs of *Morus nigra*. Lostwithiel, Cornw. (Rhodes). Kew Gardens; Hadzor Hall, Droitwich. Jan.–Jul.

Possibly the pycnidial stage of *Diaporthe Mori* Berl. The peridium is that of a typical Phomopsis. When the bark falls off with age, the pycnidia are seen attached to the wood.
Fr. Germ.

Myrica

Phomopsis incommoda Grove. *Phoma incommoda* Trail, in Scot. Nat. 1889, new ser., iv. 70. Sacc. Syll. x. 154.

Pycnidia punctiform, somewhat prominent, gregarious, black, imperfectly separated from the mesophyll of the leaf; ostiole somewhat papillate. Spores elongate-ellipsoid, 8–10 × 2–2·5μ; sporophores densely crowded, 20 × 2μ.

On dead leaves of *Myrica Gale*, near Loch Awe (Trail). On dead branches of the same, Glen Falloch, Perthshire (Boyd). Brecknockshire (Rhodes).   July.

The pycnidial stage of *Diaporthe Wibbei* Nits.

Olearia

Phomopsis Oleariae Grove, in Kew Bull. 1922, p. 44.

Pycnidia incomplete above, scattered, 250–500μ diam., black, erumpent, surrounded by a pale-brownish halo. Spores elliptic-fusoid, curved and subclavate in profile, rather acute below, seldom guttulate, 7–8 × 2μ; sporophores subulate, a little shorter than the spore, rising from a blackish-olive proliferous stratum.

On twigs of *Olearia Haaslii*. West Kilbride, Ayrshire (Boyd). Polperro (Rilstone & Rhodes). Hednesford, Staffs. (Grove & Rhodes).   Jul.–Sept.

Some of the pycnidia were seated on blackish patches, reminiscent of a Diaporthe.

Orobanche

Phomopsis Orobanches Grove, in Journ. Bot. 1933, p. 257.

Pycnidia scattered, very minute, immersed, imperfectly formed and scarcely visible, because the brown epidermis above them is hardly elevated and is stained only by a faintly browner mark. Spores elliptic-fusoid, rather obtuse at both ends or sometimes acute at one end, colourless, biguttulate, 8–9 × 1·5–2μ; sporophores not seen.

On dead peduncles of *Orobanche elatior* (? *major*). Warminster, S. Wilts. (Rhodes).   May.

On the lower part of the same dead flowering stems was the corresponding *Diaporthe Orobanches* Berl., but Berlese does not record the Phomopsis in its company in Italy.

Ital.

Papaver

Phomopsis morphaea Grove, in Kew Bulletin. 1917. p. 70; and in Journ. Bot. 1930, p. 294. *Phoma morphaea* Sacc. Syll. iii. 154.

Pycnidia somewhat gregarious, subcutaneous, then erumpent, globose-depressed, 150–200μ diam., black, at length surrounded by a distinct dusky halo, mostly imperfectly formed, but projecting slightly with a minute papilla; peridium soft, indistinct, minutely parenchymatous, fuliginous. Spores oblong-ellipsoid, obtuse at the ends, 7–8 × 2·5–3μ, occasionally lop-sided, hyaline, biguttulate, sometimes with only a central guttule; sporophores crowded, subulate, soft but persistent, nearly colourless, 15–20 × 2–3μ.

On dead capsules of Garden Poppy (*Papaver*), Oscott College (Rhodes). On dead stem of *Papaver orientale*, Polperro (Rilstone).   Nov. Dec.

Cooke's record, in Grevill. xiv. 32, "on stems and capsules of *Papaver*" *orientale* (not *somniferum*, as he states) "Kew Gardens", is doubtful, since nothing answering to the description can now be found on his specimens, although there is a Diplodina which might have been mistaken for the Phomopsis.

Ital.

Phaseolus

Phomopsis Phaseoli Grove, in Kew Bull. 1917, p. 60, pl. 2, f. 20. ?*Phoma Phaseoli* Desm. in Ann. Sci. Nat. 1836, vi. 247. Sacc. Syll. iii. 120. All. vi. 312. Died. 158. Mig. 92.

Pycnidia gregarious, arranged ± in rows, lanceolate or oblong, convex, 300–500μ long, black, covered by the epidermis,

which is raised and at length pierced by the obtuse apex, surrounded by a blackish-brown halo. Spores elliptic-oblong or even subclavate-fusoid, subacute at the ends, bi-triguttulate, $7-9 \times 2 \cdot 5-3\mu$; sporophores cylindric-subulate, up to $15 \times 2 \cdot 5\mu$. On old stems of *Phaseolus*. Highgate (Cooke).   Feb.

The pycnidial stage of a *Diaporthe* (? *Phaseolorum* C. & E.). Desmazières' specimens (Pl. crypt. no. 843) are a Phomopsis, but young; Saccardo's f. *Lepidii* is different.

S. Europe, U.S.A.

Philadelphus

Phomopsis Landeghemiae v. Höhn. Fragm. z. Mykol. 1906, no. 87, p. 33. Died. 261. Mig. 164. Grove, in Journ. Bot. 1917, p. 57, pl. 1, f. 15. *Phoma Landeghemiae* Sacc. Syll. iii. 71. All. vi. 230.

Pycnidia very minute, buried in the inner bark, scarcely erumpent, subglobose, pierced by a pore. A-spores oblong or subfusoid, nearly always straight, biguttulate, $5-8 \times 2-2 \cdot 5\mu$; sporophores densely crowded, linear, straight, $12-13 \times 1 \cdot 5\mu$: B-spores filiform, flexuous, rarely hooked, guttulate, $17-25 \times 0 \cdot 8-1\mu$ ($30-40 \times 1 \cdot 5-2\mu$), on short papilliform sporophores.

On dead twigs of *Philadelphus coronarius*. Kew Gardens (Cooke). Clyde (Trail). Cheltenham; Polperro.   Mar.–May.

The pycnidial stage of *Diaporthe Landeghemiae* Nits. What is probably the same species has occurred near Birmingham on *Deutzia crenata*. Belg. Holl. Germ. Ital.

Phlomis

Phomopsis Desmazieri Grove, in Journ. Bot. 1930, p. 272. Var. **Phlomidis** Grove, *ibid.*

Pycnidia imperfectly developed, thick and dark-fuscous above, pallid-olivaceous below, oblong, black, about 400μ long, each surrounded by a pale-coloured lanceolate spot, and aggregated on an oblong or irregular (up to 1 cm. long) patch of the epidermis which is pale-cinereous and is itself surrounded by a thin flexuous black line. Spores lanceolate or elliptic-fusoid, subacute at both ends or acuminate at one end only, hyaline, biguttulate, $8-10 \times 2-2 \cdot 5\mu$; sporophores erect, very crowded, acuminate-subulate, microguttulate, $15-20 \times 1-1 \cdot 5\mu$, rising from a fusco-olivaceous stratum.

On dead stems of *Phlomis fruticosa*. Polperro.   Apr.

One of the forms of the pycnidial stage of *Diaporthe Desmazieri* Niessl, but perhaps worthy of being considered a distinct species. Cf. *P. denigrata*.

Plantago
Phomopsis subordinaria Trav. 232. Died. in Ann. Mycol.
ix. 31, pl. 2, f. 7; Pilz. Brand. 262. Grove, in Kew Bull. 1917, pp. 65–6;
in Journ. Bot. 1918, p. 292. Mig. 164. *Phoma subordinaria* Desm. in
Ann. Sci. Nat. 1849, xi. 284. Sacc. Syll. iii. 136. All. vi. 313. *Phlyc-*
taena Plantaginis Lamb. & Fautr. in Rev. Mycol. 1896, p. 70. All. vi.
940. Sacc. Syll. xiv. 987. *Rhabdospora pachyderma* Kab. & Bub.
(C-spores), in Hedwig. 1904, p. 420.

Pycnidia numerous, arranged ± in lines, covered by the
discoloured (blackish-brown) epidermis, lens-shaped, 250–
500μ diam., oblong, thicker above where there is often a short
papillate ostiole, whitish within. A-spores oblong-fusoid,
rather blunt at the ends, often curvulous, sometimes subclavate, 7–12 × 2–2·5μ; sporophores rather short, but reaching up to 12 × 1·5μ: B-spores straight, curved, flexuous, bent,
or hooked, 20–23 × 0·75–1μ.

On living and dead scapes and occasionally on the lower
bracts of *Plantago lanceolata*. King's Lynn (Plowright). Ayrshire (Boyd). Aberdeen (Trail). Cornwall; Barmouth;
Guernsey (Rhodes). Warwickshire, etc. Not uncommon in the
south of England.   Jun.–Nov.

On the Continent it is said to be found also on *P. major*, *P. media*,
P. arenaria. It is the pycnidial stage of *Diaporthe adunca* Niessl.

There is at first no pycnidium, merely the discoloured epidermis;
but later there arises around the pore a thick smoky-brown sclerotioid
tissue, which is at length deciduous.

This species is a true parasite, attacking the upper part of the green
scapes, where it causes a sharp downward curvature by which they
can easily be recognised. A true Phoma, with a complete all-round
parenchymatous peridium, can be found on the same host.

The species seems not to occur every year in the Midlands; I have
looked for it in vain many times, but at Earlswood Lakes in 1917 it
was found in large quantity, the B-spores occurring in the same
pycnidia with the A-spores and in greater numbers.

Fr. Belg. Germ. Austr. Denm. Ital. Bosnia.

Platanus
Phomopsis Radula Grove, in Kew Bull. 1917, p. 62, pl. 2, f. 25.
Phoma Radula B. & Br. in Ann. Nat. Hist. 1850, v. 369. Cooke,
Handb. 419. Sacc. Syll. iii. 94. All. vi. 233. *Phomopsis scabra* Trav.
279.

Pycnidia uniformly distributed, immersed, then erumpent,
broadly conical, 330–500μ diam., black; texture rather soft
and loose. Spores elliptic-fusoid, subacute at the ends, with

two (rarely three) guttules, 9–10 × 2–3μ; sporophores acicular, 15–20 × 2μ.

On dead twigs of *Platanus*. Batheaston, Wilts. (Broome).
Jan. Feb.

A true Phomopsis, but probably identical with *Phomopsis scabra* Trav. and therefore the pycnidial stage of *Diaporthe scabra* Nits. "Closely sprinkled over the twigs, which it makes rough like a little rasp or grater; the epidermis splits over each pycnidium" (B. & Br.). Holl. Germ. U.S.A.

Podophyllum
Phomopsis Podophylli Grove, in Kew Bull. 1917, p. 61, pl. 2, f. 22. *Phoma Podophylli* Cooke, in Grevill. xv. 108. Sacc. Syll. x. 172.

Pycnidia epiphyllous, seated on dead brown spots of the decaying leaves, rather scattered, punctiform, black, 400–500μ diam., convex and somewhat prominent. Spores elliptic-fusoid, frequently biguttulate, 7–10 × 2·5–3μ; sporophores linear, straight, 15–20 × 1·5–2μ.

On fading leaves of *Podophyllum*. Kew Gardens (Cooke).

No doubt the pycnidial stage of an unknown Diaporthe. Other species of Diaporthe occur on leaves, though such a habitat is rare. This species has not a true complete pycnidial wall.

Polygonatum
Phomopsis Convallariae Grove, in Kew Bull. 1921, p. 138. *Phoma Convallariae* Westd. in Bull. Acad. Roy. Belg. 1852, xix. 50. *Phoma polygonatea* Sacc. Syll. iii. 161. Roum. Fung. Gall. exs. no. 3674. *Phomopsis pardalota* Died. 263 (1912).

Pycnidia scattered or several together seated on an elongated spot sharply margined by a thin brownish line, oblong, blackish, up to 1 mm. long, but not so wide, covered by the epidermis, but showing through it, and at length splitting it, mostly imperfectly formed, frequently surrounded by a small halo or by a narrow oval black line. Spores elliptic-fusoid, usually acute at the ends, biguttulate, sometimes pseudo-septate, 7–9 × 1·2–2·5μ; sporophores linear-subulate, 12–18 × 1·5μ, rising from a soft brown parenchymatous layer.

On dry dead stems of *Polygonatum multiflorum* (= *Convallaria multiflora* Flor. Dan.). Polperro (Rilstone). Mar.

See also Cooke's Fung. Brit. ii. 687; Berk. Brit. Fung. iii. 175; Currey, in Linn. Trans. xxii. 285; and Cooke, Handb. 895. The

pycnidial stage of *Diaporthe pardalota* Nits. the early stages of which accompanied it at Polperro.

Fr. Belg.

Polygonum

Phomopsis Polygonorum Grove, in Kew Bull. 1917, p. 61.
Phoma Polygonorum Cooke, in Grevill. xiv. 3. Sacc. Syll. x. 179.
All. vi. 315.

Pycnidiä loosely gregarious, oblong, black, 300–500μ long, elevating the epidermis, which is discoloured above them, and is at length pierced by a round pore that elongates into a longitudinal fissure. Spores ellipsoid, often somewhat obtuse at the ends, but sometimes fusoid, biguttulate, 6–9·5 × 2·5–3μ; sporophores acicular, 10–15 × 1·5–2μ.

On dead stems of *Polygonum* (*cuspidatum, Baldschuanicum, sachalinense*). Kew Gardens (Cooke). Ayrshire (Boyd). Harvington (Rhodes). Edgbaston; Heythrop Park, Oxon.; Cornwall; Argyll. May–Aug.

The pycnidial stage of *Diaporthe discors*, f. *Polygoni* Grove.
Cooke wrongly describes the spores of his specimens as 12μ long. Very similar to *P. Durandiana* and perhaps identical. The form on *P. sachalinense* seems, however, to be different from that on *P. cuspidatum*.

Populus

Phomopsis pallida Sacc. & D. Sacc. Syll. xviii. 264. *Libertella pallida* Fckl. Symb. Myc. 398. Sacc. Syll. iii. 746. All. vii. 739.
Myxolibertella pallida v. Höhn. in Ann. Mycol. i. 526. *Septomyxa Salicis* C. & M. in Herb. *ined.* (*non* Grove, 1922, *q.v.*).

"Pustules gregarious. Spores cylindrical, short, nearly straight, mixed with others which are very long, exuding as very slender flexuous pallid tendrils."

On branches of *Populus nigra*. Kew Gardens; Stokesley, Yorks. (Cooke). *n.v.*

Fuckel found his *Libertella pallida* on the bark of *Salix*; his specimens (no. 637) have the A-spores elliptic-fusoid, 9–10 × 2–2·5μ. Von Höhnel found his specimens on old bark of *Salix* in Bosnia; A-spores linear or fusoid, 10–12 × 2–3μ; B-spores filiform, curved, 25–30 × 1μ.
Germ. Bosnia.

Phomopsis putator v. Höhn. Fragm. z. Mykol. no. 87, p. 33.
Phoma putator Sacc. Syll. iii. 97. All. vi. 233. Died. 263. Mig. 165.

Pycnidia scattered or gregarious, covered by the bark, then erumpent by a minute slit, ± conical or subglobose, black.

Spores fusoid, pointed at both ends, biguttulate in the usual way, $9-11 \times 2 \cdot 5\mu$; sporophores shorter than is customary, crowded, straight, filiform, $8-13 \times 1 \cdot 5\mu$.

On dead twigs of *Populus canescens*. Heythrop Park, Oxon. (Grove & Rhodes). June.

The pycnidial stage of *Diaporthe putator* Nits. Fr. Germ. Ital. Thuringia.

Prunella

Phomopsis denigrata Trav. 230. Grove, in Journ. Bot. 1930, p. 272; in Kew Bull. 1920, p. 428, f. 1*b*. *Phoma denigrata* Rob. & Desm. in Ann. Sci. Nat. 1853, xx. 218. Sacc. Syll. iii. 130.

Pycnidia rather large, scattered, convex, black, covered by the blackened epidermis, then erumpent; ostiole papillate, black, at length becoming circumscissile and falling off. A-spores fusoid, biguttulate, $10-12 \times 3 \cdot 5-4\mu$: B-spores filiform, hamate, $20-24 \times 1\mu$: C-spores (not in Britain) fishshaped, $12-15 \times 3 \cdot 5-4\mu$.

On blackened and dead stems and peduncles of *Prunella vulgaris*. Kilwinning, Ayrshire (Boyd). Leamington and Harbury (Rhodes). Hay Bridge, Brecon; Kidderminster.

May.

The pycnidial stage of *Diaporthe Desmazieri* Niessl, which is often found in company with it. For the leaf-form see Kew Bull. *l.c.* p. 429, and cf. *Phomopsis Desmazieri, supra,* p. 205.

Desmazières' specimens (Crypt. Fr. no. 353) make an extensive black stain all over the stems of *Prunella*. This species is considered to occur also on *Melampyrum, Euphrasia,* and *Bartsia,* and a similar form has been found in Devon by Dr Rhodes, on *Lithospermum*.

Fr. Holl. Germ. Austr. Ital. Swed. N. America.

Pteridium

Phomopsis aquilina Petr. in Ann. Mycol. xix. 204. See Cooke, Handb. 895, and Currey, in Linn. Trans. xxii. 285.

Pycnidia very incompletely formed, gregarious, lirelliform, Leptostroma-like, making short linear blackish slightly raised streaks, 1-3 mm. long, lying longitudinally on the stem. A-spores narrowly ellipsoid, faintly guttulate, $8-10 \times 2\mu$, on sporophores hardly longer than themselves: B-spores abundant, standing in crowded ranks, filiform, curved or flexuous, rarely hooked, $20-26 \times 0 \cdot 5\mu$, on very short sporophores; often both kinds in the same pycnidium.

On dead "stems" (petioles) of *Pteridium aquilinum*, in company with *Diaporthe pantherina* Cooke. Harlech; Herm (north end), Channel Is. (Rhodes). Aug. Sept.

A very remarkable species. The ascophorous stage, which accompanied it, was named *Sphaeria pantherina* by Berkeley in Mag. Zool. and Bot. 1837, i. 47; the oval enclosing line around the perithecia is well marked. See Grevill. vii. 83.

Bosnia, Spain.

Quercus

Phomopsis quercella Died. in Ann. Mycol. 1911, ix. 28. Grove, in Kew Bull. 1917, p. 62, pl. 2, f. 24. *Phoma quercella* Sacc. Syll. iii. 96. All. vi. 235. Probably it is the same as *P. quercina*.

Pycnidia loosely gregarious, immersed, then erumpent by a longitudinal slit, globose-depressed, shortly papillate, black; texture parenchymatous, dusky-olive. A-spores fusoid, acute at both ends, but more so below, biguttulate, $8–12 \times 2–3\mu$; sporophores acicular or linear, $10–15 \times 1·5–2\mu$: B-spores filiform sometimes slightly thicker in the middle, curved or hooked, $20–30 \times 1·5–2\mu$; sporophores short, papilliform.

On twigs of *Quercus rubra*, Kew Gardens (Cooke). On twigs of Oak, Cheshire (Ellis). On dead twigs of *Quercus Cerris*, Ayrshire (Boyd). Dec.

In Mr Boyd's specimens A- and B-spores occurred in the same pycnidium. The fungus recorded as *Phoma quercella*, on slender twigs of *Q. coccinea* in Kew Gardens, by Cooke is not a Phomopsis.

Phomopsis quercina v. Höhn. Fragm. z. Mykol. 1906, no. 87, p. 33. Died. in Ann. Mycol. 1911, ix. 28, pl. 3, f. 2; Pilz. Brand. 264. Mig. p. 166, pl. 17, f. 3–5. Grove, in Kew Bull. 1917, p. 62.

Pycnidia irregular, flattened. Spores cylindric-fusoid, gently curved, $7–10 \times 1·5–2\mu$; sporophores linear, a little shorter than the spore.

On dead branches of *Quercus Robur*. Malvern (Ellis).

These are the smaller pycnidial spores assigned by Fuckel to his *Cryptospora leiphaemia* (Symb. Myc. 194), which is *Diaporthe leiphaemia* Sacc. For the larger spores see *Fusicoccum quercinum*, but all the intermediate sizes of spores occur in company with these; see Grove, *l.c.*

Europe, N. Amer.

Phomopsis glandicola Grove, in Kew Bull. 1917, p. 57, pl. 1, f. 13. *Phoma glandicola* Lév. in Ann. Sci. Nat. 1846, v. 281. Cooke,

Handb. 421. Sacc. Syll. iii. 151. All. vi. 236. Died. 167. Mig. 86.
Sporonema glandicola Desm. in Ann. Sci. Nat. 1852, xviii. 367.

Pycnidia gregarious, arranged ± in lines, linear-oblong, pustular, covered, then erumpent and surrounded by the burst epidermis, subglobose or hemispherical, smooth, shining, black, with an indistinct ostiole. Spores oblong or oblong-fusoid, $6-7 \times 1\cdot75-2\mu$; sporophores simple, obclavate (ampulliform) or subulate, $8-14 \times 2\cdot5\mu$, rising from a smoke-coloured proliferous stratum.

On fallen Acorns (of *Quercus Robur*, *Q. Ilex*) and on Oak-galls (marble-galls). Kew Gardens; Hampstead; Dartford; Woolwich; Worcs.; Cheshire; Yorkshire; Ayrshire. Probably not uncommon; it is possibly a form of *Phomopsis quercina*.

There are two forms of this species, frequently occurring together. In one, the pycnidia are solitary, and the spores as described above; in the other (f. *major*) the pycnidia are clustered, three or four together, almost as in a stroma, and the spores are larger, $11-12 \times 2\cdot5-3\mu$. The latter is not a typical Phomopsis but more like a Sporonema; it has been found in Kew Gardens and at Upton Warren. Saccardo gives two other forms, *cupulae* (on the acorn-cup) and *Coryli-putaminis* (on Hazel), both with longer filiform and sometimes forked sporophores: for the latter see *Phomopsis revellens*.

Europe, Algeria, U.S.A.

Rhus

Phomopsis Rhois Trav. 258. Died. 266. Mig. 166. Grove, in Kew Bull. 1917, p. 63. *Phoma Rhois* Sacc. Syll. iii. 85. All. vi. 238. *Phoma rhoina* Cooke, in Grevill. xiv. 27 (*ex errore calami, vice P. Rhois*).

Pycnidia somewhat gregarious, immersed, then erumpent at the apex, conico-truncate, black, 500μ diam. Spores elliptic-fusoid or oblong-fusoid, rather obtuse at the upper end, biguttulate, $7-10 \times 2-2\cdot5\mu$; sporophores subulate, $12-15 \times 1\cdot5-2\mu$.

On dead branches and peduncles of *Rhus typhina*, *R. radicans*. Kew Gardens; Whitehall; Swanscombe; Heythrop Park, Oxon. Dec.–Apr.

The pycnidial stage of *Diaporthe Rhois* Nits., which sometimes accompanied it.

The hooked so-called "basidia" of Saccardo, $25 \times 1\mu$, no doubt represent B-spores, but no such spores were seen.

Fr. Germ.

Ribes

Phomopsis pungens Grove. *Phoma pungens* Sacc. in Mich. i. 520
(1879). *Phomopsis ribesia* Died. 266. Mig. 166. *Phoma ribesia* Sacc.
Syll. iii. 88 (1884). All. vi. 238.

Pycnidia gregarious, covered, then erumpent, globose, depressed, thickened above; texture dense and indistinct.
Spores oblong-fusoid, inequilateral, biguttulate, 6–10 × 2·5–
3·5μ, sometimes acute above; sporophores subulate, fasciculate, 10–13 × 1–2μ.

On stems of *Ribes Grossularia*. Near Ockeridge Wood, Ws.
(Rhodes). Faversham; Evesham. Recorded abroad on
Ribes rubrum also.   Jan.–Apr.

The pycnidial stage of *Diaporthe pungens* Nits., but cf. *D. strumella*
Fckl. which is probably identical. The B-spores may be represented
by *Cytosporina Ribis* Magn. and/or *Libertella Ribis* Smith.
Germ.

Robinia

Phomopsis oncostoma v. Höhn. in Sitz. Akad. Wiss. Wien, 1906,
cxv. 33. Died. 267. Mig. 167. *Phoma oncostoma* Thüm. Mycoth.
Univ. no. 877. Sacc. Syll. iii. 69. *Phoma petiolorum* Desm. in Ann.
Sci. Nat. 1847, viii. 16, *p.p.* See also *Phomopsis Pseudacaciae*.

Pycnidia gregarious or arranged in series, pustular, covered,
raising the epidermis considerably and at length bursting it
by the broad obtuse dark-grey discoid vertex, blackish, up to
500μ diam.; texture thick, dark-olivaceous. A-spores fusoid
or elliptic-fusoid, acute at both ends, mostly biguttulate,
8–10 × 2–2·5μ; sporophores subulate, about twice as long: B-
spores filiform, flexuous or hooked, 18–30 × 1μ; sporophores
short.

On bark of petioles, twigs, and branches of *Robinia Pseudacacia*. Not uncommon; Peaslake; Swanscombe; Broadway;
Polperro; etc.   Jan.–Jul.

The pycnidial stage of *Diaporthe oncostoma* Fckl.
In the Peaslake specimen the disc of the stroma is large, ochreous-
whitish and very prominent, up to 1 mm. diam., and pierced in the
centre by a single black ostiole; the B-spores are present in enormous
numbers without any A-spores. A specimen in Sydow, Mycoth. germ.
no. 1014, contains both A- and B-spores growing in the same pycnidium. It is worthy of notice that Charles Tulasne (Sel. Fung. Carp.
vol. ii, pl. 20, f. 6) gives a beautiful figure of a vertical section of a
pycnidium, no doubt of this species (though he calls it *Aglaospora
profusa*), showing the two kinds of spores growing side by side, exactly

as they do. No one else has ever drawn such an accurate picture of
them, either before or since.
Europe, U.S.A.

Phomopsis Pseudacaciae v. Höhn. Fragm. z. Mykol. 1917, p. 42.
Died. 267. Mig. p. 167, pl. 15, f. 5. *Phoma Pseudacaciae* Sacc. Syll.
iii. 69. All. vi. 240. *Phoma Robiniae* Sacc. Syll. iii. 69. Mig. 92.

"Pycnidia between the fibres of decorticated wood or in the
bark, erumpent in rows, crowded or solitary, black, up to
1 mm. wide, flatly conical; texture thick, especially at the
vertex. A-spores fusoid, acute at both ends, straight, with
2–4 guttules, $10–16 \times 2 \cdot 5–3\mu$; sporophores subulate, a little
longer than the spore: B-spores fasciculate, filiform, 15–20 or
longer $\times 1–1 \cdot 5\mu$."

On branches of *Robinia Pseudacacia*. Dartford; Oscott
College; Ayrshire.

The forms of Phomopsis on *Robinia* have been unusually confused;
the present one is assigned to *Diaporthe fasciculata* Nits., which is said
to be the same as *D. oncostoma* Fckl.; in that case the two Phomopses
must be identical, as I believe they are.
Germ. Austr.

Phomopsis petiolorum Grove, in Kew Bull. 1917, p. 60, pl. 2,
f. 19. *Phoma petiolorum* Desm. in Ann. Sci. Nat. 1847, viii. 16. Cooke,
Handb. 421. Sacc. Syll. iii. 103. All. vi. 241.

This "species" is made up of the forms of Phomopsis occurring in
various countries on the petioles of the respective hosts, which are
given as *Robinia, Sophora, Cytisus, Fraxinus,* and *Gleditschia.* But
these petiolar fungi do not differ from the forms which are found on
the twigs and branches of those same hosts, except in being smaller,
as would naturally be expected. There is no distinct species of Phomopsis confined to petioles.

Sometimes, however, a fungus with a true Phoma-like peridium can
be found, especially on petioles of *Robinia,* mingled with the Phomopsis, and this (which belongs to a Pleospora) has been called *Phoma
petiolorum* (*q.v. supra,* p. 64).

ROSACEAE
Plurivorous
Phomopsis ambigua Trav. 266. Grove, in Kew Bull. 1917, p. 53,
pl. 1, f. 3. Died. 261. Mig. 164. *Phoma ambigua* Sacc. in Mich. i. 520
(1879); Syll. iii. 75. All. vi. 231. ? *Phoma Mali* Sch. & Sacc. in Hedwig. 1884, xxiii. 91; Syll. iii. 75.

Pycnidia gregarious, somewhat laterally compressed,
broadly conical, for a long time covered by the raised epi-

dermis, at length erumpent by a fissure, slightly papillate, black, 250–350μ diam.; texture olivaceous, rather indistinct. A-spores fusoid, often more acute at the lower end, usually biguttulate, 8–10 × 2–3μ; sporophores filiform-subulate, 12–20 × 1–1·5μ: B-spores curved or hamate, 28–40 × 1μ.

On twigs of *Pyrus communis*; reported also on *P. Malus*, *P. torminalis*, and on fruits of *Mespilus*. Common. The pycnidial stage of *Diaporthe ambigua* Nits.

The description given above refers especially to the form on *Pyrus communis*. Diedicke distinguishes the form on *Malus*, *l.c.* p. 261, by a difference in the shape of the pycnidium, to which he assigns a kind of conical columella and B-spores 15–25 × 1–1·5μ.

Fr. Germ. Denm. Austr. New Zealand.

Phomopsis Amelanchieris Grove, in Kew Bull. 1917, p. 53, pl. 1, f. 4. *Phoma Amelanchieris* Cooke, in Grevill. xiii. 93. Sacc. Syll. x. 142. All. vi. 178.

Pycnidia subgregarious, immersed in the bark, black, globose, elevating and cracking the epidermis, about 330μ diam. Spores subfusoid, obtuse at the apex, biguttulate, 8–9 × 2–2·5μ; sporophores subulate, curved, 15–20μ long.

On branches of *Amelanchier*. Kew Gardens (Cooke). Apr.

It is probable that this is merely a form of *P. ambigua* Trav. Germ.

Phomopsis perniciosa Grove; see *Diaporthe perniciosa* Marchal, in Bull. Soc. Roy. Bot. Belg. 1921, liv. 117. Cayley, in Ann. Appl. Biol. 1923, x. 260, pl. 13, f. 1, 2, 6, 7. Kidd & Beaum. in T.B.M.S. x. 101–4. *Fusicoccum Malorum* Oud. Contr. Flor. Myc. Pays-Bas, xi. 29, *p.p.* Sacc. Syll. x. 239. *Aposphaeria Pomi* Sacc. & Sch. Syll. iii. 177. *Myxosporium Mali* Bres. in Hedwig. 1897, p. 382. *Fusicoccum pyrorum* Ch. & Cl. Phytopath. 1923, xiii. 228.

Pycnidia scattered or in clusters, at first immersed, then semi-erumpent or becoming superficial, subglobose or hemispherical, rarely globose-conical, black, surrounded at base by dusky often torulose hyphae, 1–plurilocular; loculi incomplete, more or less radiating, opening by a common pore. A-spores oblong-fusoid, subobtuse at both ends, hyaline, continuous, usually biguttulate, 7–9 × 2–3μ; sporophores linear, simple, cylindrical or subulate, 15–18μ long: B-spores filiform, hyaline, hooked at one end, 25–30 × 1–1·5μ; sporophores short

and subulate; both spores issuing as yellowish or pinkish tendrils.

On branches and fruits of *Pyrus, Malus, Prunus, Cerasus,* and ? *Persica* (according to Miss Cayley) and of *Mespilus.* Many counties of Wales and of the Midlands and S. England, causing a canker or so-called "die back".

It is likely that the following three names were given by their authors to more or less sclerotial states of this fungus:
Sclerophoma Mali Syd. in Ann. Mycol. ix. 146. Died. 280. *Cytosporella Mali* Brun. in Bull. Soc. Bot. Fr. 1893, p. 223. Sacc. Syll. xi. 507. *Sclerophoma endogenospora* Laub. in Gartenfl. lx. 133; see p. 155.

There can be little doubt, I think, that *Phomopsis perniciosa* is a form of one (or more) of previously known species, perhaps one which suddenly developed a more parasitic tendency. It is up to the Phytopathologists to decide this question, but not to talk of "die back" as a disease.

Fr. Belg. Holl. Germ.

Kerria

Phomopsis japonica Trav. 241. Died. 257. Mig. 162. *Phoma japonica* Sacc. Syll. iii. 78. All. vi. 218. *Phlyctaena Kerriae* Karst. in Rev. Mycol. 1887, p. 11. All. vi. 939.

Pycnidia scattered, covered by the epidermis, very minute, black, oblong or globose-depressed, sometimes surrounded by a blackish stain. Spores fusoid, biguttulate, $6–10 \times 2–3\mu$; sporophores filiform, flexuous, $15–20 \times 1·5\mu$: B-spores hamate, $18–26 \times 1\mu$.

On twigs of *Kerria japonica*. Thringstone (Cooke). Heythrop Park (Rhodes & Grove).   Sept.–Jun.

The pycnidial stage of *Diaporthe japonica* Sacc.
The black line, mentioned by Saccardo as sometimes bordering groups of pycnidia, belongs to the ascophorous stage. Cf. also *Phomopsis striaeformis*, which is probably a form of the same species.
Fr. Germ. Ital.

Phomopsis striaeformis Grove, in Kew Bull. 1917, p. 65, pl. 2, f. 29. *Phoma striaeformis* Dur. & Mont. Flor. Alg. p. 603. Sacc. Syll. iii. 131. All. vi. 246.

Pycnidia ovoid, elongated, ± arranged in rows, black, opaque, immersed in the cortex, then erumpent, with a short ostiole or simply pierced by a pore. Spores elliptic-fusoid, at times slightly clavate, often biguttulate, $7–9 \times 2–2·5\mu$; sporophores rod-shaped or often curved, $15–18 \times 2\mu$.

On twigs of *Kerria japonica*. Neatishead (Cooke). Polperro.

It is recorded on the same host from Belgium. The records on *Cytisus* and *Sambucus* are probably in error. It forms short linear black flecks, arranged longitudinally on the stems, about 1 mm. long, but sometimes shorter or longer. The statement in the descriptions that the sporophores are "very short" is not in accordance with the specimens issued by Desmazières (ser. ii, no. 59).

Fr. Belg. Holl.

Prunus

Phomopsis padina Died. 264. Grove, in Journ. Bot. 1930, p. 295; in Kew Bull. 1919, pp. 181–2, f. 4. *Phoma padina* Sacc. Syll. i. 619; iii. 74. All. vi. 234.

Pycnidia gregarious, but not crowded, up to 1 mm. diam., covered, then protruding in a distinctly conical form with the periderm still intact, at length opening by a short slit at the vertex, and surrounded by the laciniae of the bark which is not at all discoloured. A-spores lanceolate-fusoid, very acute at the base, $9–12 \times 2–2 \cdot 5\mu$, indistinctly guttulate (biguttulate, Died.); sporophores subulate, up to 20μ long: B-spores mixed with the A-spores in the same pycnidia, flexuose or hamate, $23–30 \times 1\mu$; sporophores somewhat papilliform: C-spores fusoid, acute at both ends, curved, $20–22 \times 2 \cdot 5–3\mu$.

On dead branches of *Prunus Padus*. Whiting Bay, Isle of Arran (Boyd), A- and B-spores only.   June, 1919.

The pycnidial stage of *Diaporthe decorticans* S. & R.
A very distinct Phomopsis, differing from all the others in external appearance. The C-spores (which were found only in Roumeguère's exsiccatum, Fung. Gall. sel. no. 493) were borne on linear fasciculate sporophores $20–25 \times 1\mu$; see Kew Bull. *l.c.*

Fr. Germ.

Phomopsis Prunorum Grove, in Kew Bull. 1917, p. 61. *Phoma Prunorum* Cooke, in Grevill. xiii. 92. Sacc. Syll. x. 142. All. vi. 235. *Phoma Pruni-lusitanicae* Cooke, *l.c.* p. 93. Sacc. Syll. x. 141. All. vi. 234. *P. Pruni* Peck, in 38th Rep. State Mus. p. 95. Sacc. Syll. x. 142.

Pycnidia gregarious, collected about the extremities of slender twigs, hemispherical, $250–500\mu$ diam., elevating but scarcely discolouring the epidermis, which is split by the minute ostiole. Spores fusoid, subacute at the ends, unibiguttulate, $8–9 \times 2–2 \cdot 5\mu$ ($10 \times 4 \cdot 5\mu$, Cooke; $8–9 \times 3–4\mu$, Ellis); sporophores linear, $12–15 \times 2\mu$: B-spores filiform, hooked, $30 \times 1\mu$.

On twigs of *Prunus Laurocerasus, P. lusitanica.* Kew Gardens (Cooke)! Bidston, Cheshire (Ellis). Par, Cornwall.

Mar.–May.

Apparently the pycnidial stage of *Diaporthe viridarii* Sacc.
When the twigs of *P. lusitanica* are dry, the epidermis around the pycnidia retains its colour; on *P. Laurocerasus* it does not. There is no other difference. Cf. *Phomopsis padina.*
Holl. Germ. U.S.A.

Pyrus
Phomopsis stictostoma Grove, in Kew Bull. 1923, p. 27.
Cytospora stictostoma Grove, in Journ. Bot. 1916, p. 190.

Pycnidia densely gregarious, immersed in the periderm and adnate to it, pustular, protuberant, conical on a rounded base, black, pseudolocellate within, 250–300 μ diam.; texture somewhat waxy; disc emergent, truncate, powdered with white, generally perforated by a single black central ostiole. Spores elliptic-fusoid, subobtuse at both ends or acute at base, biguttulate, 8–10 × 2–2·5 μ, when seen in profile curved; sporophores subulate, crowded, straight, often faintly guttulate, 12–15 × 1·5 μ, rising from a dusky stratum of square-celled parenchyma.

On branches of *Pyrus Malus*, originally prepared for grafting, Bristol (Cotton). It occurred chiefly on the upper part, and was accompanied at the base by *Diaporthe stictostoma* Sacc. on almost every stick.   Oct.

It was inevitable that the two fungi should be supposed to be genetically connected. See Journ. Bot. *l.c.* p. 185. The branches were pervaded with both forms, and had been killed by them and laid aside. The pycnidia resembled the perithecia in size, shape, and arrangement, but were less perfectly formed. The pycnospores had usually two guttules, but a few had three, and some (but none on the sporophores) had four; seen in profile, they could be mistaken for those of *Cytospora*. In making such an error, I had the melancholy pleasure of doing, without knowing it at the time, what had been done for other species by Berkeley & Curtis (*C. abnormis* and *C. orthospora*) and by Schweinitz (*C. Robiniae*).
U.S.A.

Rosa
Phomopsis incarcerata v. Höhn. Fragm. z. Mykol. 1906, no. 87, p. 33. Grove, in Kew Bull. 1917, p. 57. Died. 268. Mig. 167. *Phoma*

incarcerata Sacc. Syll. iii. 77. All. vi. 243. *Phoma Rosae* Sch. & Sacc. Syll. iii. 76. *Phomopsis Rosae* Grove, in Kew Bull. 1917, p. 63.

Pycnidia gregarious or densely and widely scattered, subepidermal, 0·5–1 mm. diam., globose-depressed, then somewhat prominent, at length erumpent and black. A-spores elliptic-fusoid, straight, generally obtuse at the ends, biguttulate, 8–10 × 2–3μ; sporophores ± arcuate or at times parallel and straight, often obtuse at the apex, 15–20 × 1–2μ: B-spores filiform, flexuous or hamate, 24–30 × 1μ, supported on digitaliform sporophores 8–10μ long.

On dead branches and prickles of *Rosa canina* and various cultivated Roses. Kew Gardens; Reading; Wiltshire; Birmingham; Worcestershire; Hereford; Glamorganshire; Pembrokeshire; Ayrshire; etc.   Winter and spring.

The pycnidial stage of *Diaporthe incarcerata* Nits.

On the stems the masses of spores remain for a long time hidden by the epidermis ("incarcerata"). On the prickles the pycnidia are, of course, smaller, and the A-spores (which alone have been found on them = *P. Rosae*) are generally somewhat shorter, but not always; in other respects the two supposed species are identical. The B-spores seem to be the earlier, appearing in winter, and the A-spores succeed them in spring, at first in the same, afterwards in separate pycnidia. Fr. Holl. Germ. Austr. Ital.

Phomopsis piccata Grove, in Kew Bull. 1917, p. 60, pl. 2, f. 21. *Phoma piccata* Sacc. Syll. iii. 107. *Phoma picea* B. & Br. in Ann. Nat. Hist. 1850, v. 370 (*non* Pers.). Cooke, Handb. 420.

Pycnidia hypophyllous, scattered, convex, at length papillate, projecting, brownish-black, 200μ diam., at first adnate to the epidermis which is at length burst above. Spores oblong-ellipsoid, subacute at the ends, straight or faintly curved, often irregular, biguttulate, 7–9 × 2–2·5μ; sporophores linear, straight, 15–18 × 2μ.

On the under surface of dead Rose-leaves. King's Cliffe (Berk.).   Feb.

The measurements are taken from Berkeley's original specimen.

"Scattered. Pustules conspicuous, convex, pitch-brown, epidermis closely connected with the spurious pycnidia. Externally resembling *Cytospora foliicola*, but differing greatly in structure. *Ceuthospora concava*, which also grows on Rose-leaves, in France, is much bigger" (B. & Br. *l.c.*).

Ceuthospora concava Desm. (in Ann. Sci. Nat. 1847, viii. 17) is about

500μ diam., concave, and shining. It has curved eguttulate spores of about the same size as those of *P. piceata*, but more acute at the ends. The spores of *Phomopsis piceata* were often seen constricted in the middle, as if about to become 1-septate, although they never became so. *P. picea* (Pers.) is also a Phomopsis, therefore Berkeley's specific name cannot stand; see under *Hypericum*.

Rubus

Phomopsis vepris v. Höhn. Fragm. z. Mykol. 1906, no. 87, p. 33. Died. 268. Mig. 167. Grove, in Journ. Bot. 1918, p. 292. *Phoma vepris* Sacc. Syll. iii. 76. All. vi. 244. (Not *Phoma corticis* Fckl.)

Pycnidia gregarious, small, round, immersed, globose-depressed, blackish, at length just piercing the epidermis, about 200μ diam. Spores cylindric-fusoid or ellipsoid, 5–7 × 1–1·5μ (4–7 × 1–2μ, Wehmeyer); sporophores crowded, linear, erect, hardly longer than the spore, rising from a pale yellowish stratum.

On dead stems of *Rubus*. Common. Cheshire (Ellis). Tal-y-bont, Merioneth.; etc. The pycnidial stage of *Diaporthe vepris* Fckl. = *Apioporthe vepris* Wehm.

Fuckel's exsiccatum, no. 1943, does not agree with his description in the example I have seen. There seems to have been some confusion with *Septoria ramealis* Rob. & Desm. or *Rhabdospora ramealis* Sacc. var. *crassiuscula* Berl.

In his article on Diaporthe, in T.B.M.S. 1933, xvii. 289, Wehmeyer includes a large number of described Pyrenomycetes under this head.

Europe, N. America.

Phomopsis Mulleri Grove, in Kew Bull. 1917, p. 59. *Phoma. Mulleri* Cooke, in Grevill. viii. 8 (1879). Sacc. Syll. iii. 76. Cf. *Phomopsis insignis* Trav. 264.

Pycnidia scattered, roundish or oblong, immersed in the cortex, covered by the epidermis, which is elevated but not darkened and is at length ruptured at the summit by the minute ostiole, blackish, about 300μ diam. Spores narrowly ellipsoid, subacute at the ends, often curved, biguttulate, 8–10 × 2–3μ; sporophores crowded, acicular, curvulous, about 15 × 1μ.

On branches of *Rubus fruticosus*, *R. idaeus*. Eastbourne (C. J. Muller). Hampstead (Cooke). Clyde (Trail). Hereford; Borth. (On *R. fruticosus*, in Spain also.)

The spores and sporophores are much longer than in *P. vepris*. Does this belong to *Diaporthe insignis* Fckl. ?

Phomopsis corticis Grove. *Phoma corticis* Fckl. Symb. Myc. 378
(1871); Fung. Rhen. no. 1943! Sacc. Syll. iii. 76. ? *Macrophoma
corticis* B. & V. in Syll. Addit. 312. Sacc. Syll. x. 201. All. vi. 373.
Died. 192 ? Mig. 112. ? *Rhabdospora ramealis* Sacc. var. *crassiuscula*
Berl. Pug. Fungh. Fior. 85. Sacc. Syll. x. 338.

Pycnidia oblong, very convex, placed longitudinally, up to
500μ long, covered by the epidermis, which is raised, becomes
whitish at the summit and at length burst by the thick
ostiole, each surrounded by a deep-black shining stain. A-
spores fusoid, 6–7 × 1·5μ; sporophores long, crowded, subulate, curvulous: B-spores linear, straight or bent, subobtuse
at the ends, 20–25 × 1–1·5μ, on shorter sporophores.

On dead stems of *Rubus fruticosus*. Meols and Storeton,
Cheshire (Ellis). Polperro (Rhodes & Rilstone). Jan.–Apr.

This is not, I think, merely a form of *Phomopsis vepris* (Sacc.) v.
Höhn. The pycnidium was often incompletely formed, as usual. The
Cheshire specimens yielded only A-spores, but the pycnidia of Fuckel's
no. 1943, which are exactly the same in appearance, contained the
B-spores. *Rhabdospora ramealis* (R. & D.) Sacc. (*q.v.*) has spores somewhat similar to these latter, but its pycnidia are situated on large
purple spots on living stems. There are no "spots" in Fuckel's specimens of *P. corticis*; *Macrophoma corticis* Died. is not the same as
Fuckel's species.

Fr. Germ. Ital.

Sorbus

Phomopsis sorbicola Grove, in Journ. Bot. 1930, p. 296.

Pycnidia gregarious, covered by the bark, raising it in a
conical or convex pustule and at length bursting it, unilocular;
mass of spores colourless. Spores abundant, elliptic-fusoid,
somewhat inequilateral, subacute at one or both ends, hyaline, biguttulate, 9–12 (or even rarely 14) × 2–2·5μ; sporophores crowded, linear, slightly tapering upwards but not
acute, microguttulate, 20–25 × 2·5–3μ, sometimes shorter.

On dead twigs of *Sorbus Aucuparia*. Ayrshire (Boyd).
Oscott College (Rhodes). Foxcote, near Ilmington. June.

The pycnidial stage of *Diaporthe sorbicola* (Nits.) v. Höhn. = *D. im-
pulsa* Sacc. = *D. patria* Speg. No B-spores were seen.

Spiraea

Phomopsis Spiraeae Grove, in Kew Bull. 1920, p. 429, f. 2 *a*.
Phoma Spiraeae Desm. Obs. Crypt. 1830, p. 13; Pl. Crypt. no. 481.
Sacc. Syll. iii. 132. All. vi. 324. Died. 175, *p.p.* Mig. 100.

Pycnidia gregarious, arranged longitudinally on the stem, oval, imperfectly formed, black, shining, $250-500\mu$ long, immersed, not prominent, at length opening by an impressed pore, each surrounded by a brownish halo and sometimes situated on an effused blackish Diaporthe-like stain. Spores oval-oblong or even subcylindric, but often strictly fusoid, mostly acute at both ends, occasionally rounded above, biguttulate, $8-10 \times 2 \cdot 5-3\mu$; sporophores subulate, pointed, 12–15μ long, with a base $2 \cdot 5-3\mu$ wide, rising from a dark-olivaceous stratum.

On dead stems of *Spiraea Aruncus*. The pycnidial stage of *Diaporthe Lirella* Fckl.

Not yet found in Britain for certain, since the specimens recorded under the name *Phoma Spiraeae* by Cooke, from Kew Gardens, are not a Phomopsis; the description given above is taken from Desmazières' own specimens, no. 481. The sporophores seem to lengthen after they have shed their spores, and may easily be mistaken for paraphyses. The upper part of the pycnidium disappears with age. *Phomopsis Spiraeae* is not the same as *Leptostroma spiraeinum*, on *Spiraea Ulmaria*; there seem to be five or six different forms of Phoma-like fungi which pass under the name of *P. Spiraeae* in herbaria.

Fr. Germ. Ital.

Phomopsis Sorbariae v. Höhn. Fragm. z. Mykol. 1906, no. 87, p. 32. Grove, in Kew Bull. 1917, p. 64, pl. 2, f. 28. Died. 272. Mig. 169. *Phoma Sorbariae* Sacc. Syll. iii. 75. All. vi. 248. *Phoma Opulifoliae* Cooke, in Grevill. xiv. 2 (a young state).

Pycnidia loosely gregarious on paler spots or scattered, covered, seated deeply in the cortex, and therefore remaining immersed when the epidermis falls off, globose-depressed, about 330μ diam., blackish above. Spores oblong-fusoid, often rather blunt at the ends, biguttulate, $7-9 \times 2 \cdot 5\mu$; sporophores linear, up to twice as long as the spore: B-spores filiform, flexuous or hooked, $20-25 \times 1\mu$, contained within the same pycnidia in abundance.

On dead branches of *Spiraea callosa*, and *Neillia opulifolia*, Kew Gardens. On *Spiraea Lindleiana*, Heythrop Park. On *S. (californica?)*, Polperro (Rilstone & Rhodes).   Apr.–Jul.

The pycnidial stage of *Diaporthe Sorbariae* Nits. Germ.

Rumex
Phomopsis Durandiana Died. in Ann. Mycol. 1911, ix. 24; Pilz.
Brand. 268. Mig. 167. *Phoma Durandiana* Sacc. & Roum. in Rev.
Mycol. 1884, p. 29, pl. 45, f. 37. Sacc. Syll. iii. 140. All. vi. 318.

Pycnidia gregarious, each covered by a small black spot of
the epidermis, globose-depressed, about 500μ diam., obtuse,
only just emerging by the vertex, black. Spores oblong-
fusoid, usually biguttulate, obtuse above, sometimes pointed
below, 7–10 × 2–3μ; sporophores linear-subulate, crowded, up
to 15 or 20μ long.

On dead stems of *Rumex* (chiefly *obtusifolius*). Kew Gardens; Dartford; Tunbridge Wells; Totteridge; Dunhamstead;
King's Norton; Shustoke; Ayrshire; Argyllshire; etc.

May.–Aug.

The pycnidial stage of *Diaporthe discors* Sacc., which occurs with it.
The epidermis is stained in a small black area over each spore-mass,
but there is little of a true pycnidial wall, only an olivaceous proliferous stratum below and the discoloured epidermis above. When old,
the mass drops out, leaving a whitish pit surrounded by a black
margin.
Saccardo and Diedicke both say that this Phomopsis is the pycnidial stage of *D. maculosa* S. & Sp., but the ascophorous stage which is
intimately mixed with the earlier stage in Boyd's Ayrshire specimens
accords best with *D. discors* Sacc. (which is *D. Rumicis* Plowr.),
having ascospores which measure 17–18 × 4μ. Nevertheless I believe
D. discors and *D. maculosa* are the same species.
Fr. Holl. Germ. Denm.

Ruscus
Phomopsis Rusci Grove. *Phoma Rusci* Westd. in Bull. Acad.
Belg. ser. 2, vol. 7, no. 5. Sacc. Syll. iii. 162.

Pycnidia gregarious, flat, unilocular, imperfectly formed,
immersed, black, up to 500μ diam. or more, piercing the epidermis by the minute pore and showing through it. Spores
ovate-fusoid, acute at both ends or only below, biguttulate as
usual, 6–9 × 2–3μ; sporophores crowded, linear, twice as long
as the spore or longer, rising from a pale-olivaceous stratum.

On old and decaying cladodes of *Ruscus aculeatus*. Jer-
bourg Point, Guernsey (Rhodes).   Sept.

A rudimentary Phomopsis, surely.
Belg. Port.

Salix

Phomopsis salicina Died. in Ann. Mycol. 1911, ix. 30; Pilz. Brand. 269. Mig. 167. *Phoma salicina* Westd. Crypt. Cl. App. *ex* Sacc. Syll. iii. 97. All. vi. 245. (Not *Phoma Salicis* Sacc.)

Pycnidia rather densely gregarious, subepidermal, globose or conically emergent, 200–300μ diam., imperfectly locellate; texture thick and black above. Spores elliptic-oblong, subobtuse at the ends when mature, biguttulate in the usual way, 6–8 × 2–3μ; sporophores densely crowded, about as long as the spore.

On dead twigs and branches of *Salix* (*alba, babylonica, Caprea, viminalis*, etc.). Kew Gardens (Cooke). Cheshire (Ellis). Rednal, Ws.! Nov.–May.

Supposed to be the pycnidial stage of a Diaporthe. There are both a Phoma and a Phomopsis to be found on the twigs, and most of the British specimens I have seen under the name *P. salicina* belong rather to the former genus.
Fr. Germ. Bohemia.

Sambucus

Phomopsis ebulina Grove. *Phoma ebulina* Sacc. & Sch. Micr. Slav. no. 40. Sacc. Syll. iii. 132.

Pycnidia imperfectly formed, gregarious, minute, immersed, scarcely erumpent, depressed-globose, up to 120μ diam. Spores oblong-ellipsoid, rather obtuse at both ends, faintly biguttulate, hyaline, mostly 6–8 × 2–2·5μ; no sporophores seen.

On stems of *Sambucus Ebulus*. Pickering, Yorks. (F. A. Mason). June.

The spores were very variable. Some spores were seen which were longer (14 × 2μ), uniseptate and 4-guttulate; these looked very like the ascospores of a Diaporthe.
Slavonia.

Phomopsis sambucella Trav. 244. Died. 268. Mig. 167. *Phoma sambucella* Sacc. Syll. iii. 71. All. vi. 245.

"Pycnidia subepidermal, erumpent, gregarious, depressedglobose. Spores ovate-oblong, biguttulate, hyaline, 8 × 3–4μ. On dead branches of *Sambucus nigra*. Kew Gardens."

Said to be the pycnidial stage of *Diaporthe spiculosa* Nits., and considered by Lind to be a true parasite in Denmark. But none of the British specimens seen, including those of J. W. Ellis from Cheshire,

answer to the description; the latter are distinctly not a Phomopsis.
Probably the two *Diaporthae* (and the *Phomopses*) on *Sambucus nigra*
are identical.
Fr. Holl. Denm. Germ. Ital.

Phomopsis sambucina Trav. 269. Grove, in Kew Bull. 1917,
p. 64, pl. 2, f. 26. Died. 269. Mig. 168. *Phoma sambucina* Sacc. Syll.
iii. 71. All. vi. 245.

Pycnidia gregarious, up to 500μ diam., at first concealed by
the epidermis, then raising it in a pustule and emerging by a
torn opening, globose-depressed, then oblong-conical, truncate, greyish-black, with a thick ostiole. Spores oblong-fusoid,
subacute at both ends, biguttulate, 5–9 × 2·5–3μ; sporophores
acicular or subulate, 15–20 × 1·5–2μ: B-spores filiform, bent,
curved or hooked, 16–23 × 0·75–1μ, in the same pycnidium.

On dead twigs of *Sambucus nigra*. Kew Gardens; Whitehall; Cheltenham; Gloucester; Liverpool; Cheshire; Worcestershire; Ayrshire. Oct.–Jul.

The pycnidial stage of *Diaporthe circumscripta* Otth.
The little groups of pycnidia, when older, become surrounded by
a ± circular, Diaporthe-like, black line, but before any perithecia are
developed. The tissue of the upper part of the pycnidium is several
cells thick, cells minute, dark-fuscous; cells of the basal stratum the
same size, but only pallid in colour.
Fr. Holl. Germ. Ital. U.S.A.

Phomopsis vicina Grove, in Kew Bull. 1917, p. 71. *Phoma vicina*
Desm. Exs. ser. 2, no. 352! (*non* Sacc. Syll. iii. 71, which is *Phoma
sambuciphila* Oud. Cat. Rais. Champ. Pays-Bas, p. 415).

Desmazières' species on *Sambucus* (*l.c.*), which I have examined, is
a true Phomopsis, with subfusoid biguttulate spores, 7–10 × 2–2·5μ,
on linear or subulate, straight or curved sporophores, 15–25 × 1·5μ.
This may very well be nothing but *Phomopsis sambucina*. But
Cooke's Ascot specimens, under this name in Grevill. xiv. 26, are
Phoma sambuciphila Oud. (*q.v.*).
Fr. Holl. Germ.

Saponaria
Phomopsis intermedia Grove, in Journ. Bot. 1930, p. 273.
Phoma intermedia Sacc. Syll. iii. 131. All. vi. 319.

Pycnidia scattered or arranged more or less in short series,
often included within a thin black line which marks off a
pallid lanceolate or irregular area, black and convex above,
but below having only a proliferous stratum, roundish or ob-

long-lanceolate, about 250µ diam. Spores oblong-fusoid, more or less acute at the ends, 5–6 × 2–2·5µ, each containing a large conspicuous guttule near each extremity; sporophores densely clustered, persistent, subulate, colourless, often guttulate, 15–16 (or even 20) × 1–1·5µ.

On dead stems of *Saponaria officinalis*. By the river side, Ribbesford, Worcs. (Grove & Rhodes). Perrancoombe, Cornw. (Rilstone). Mar. Apr.

No B-spores were seen, but Saccardo's "hamate basidia, 20 × 0·5µ", are doubtless such. The pycnidial stage of *Diaporthe intermedia* Sacc.

Germ. Ital.

Sarothamnus

Phomopsis Sarothamni v. Höhn. Fragm. z. Mykol. 1906, no. 87, p. 33. Died. in Ann. Mycol. ix. 30, pl. 2, f. 4; Pilz. Brand. 272. Grove, in Journ. Bot. 1930, p. 296. *Phoma Sarothamni* Sacc. Syll. iii. **68**. All. vi. 247. *Phoma Spartii* Sacc. Syll. iii. 67. All. vi. 248. *Phomopsis Spartii* Died. in Ann. Mycol. ix. 30, pl. 2, f. 5; Pilz. Brand. p. 272, p. 240, f. 6.

Pycnidia more or less aggregated or arranged in series, immersed, then raising the bark in a convex pustule which bursts at the apex by a roundish or transversely elongated opening, oblong or subglobose, black, irregular, thickened above, 300–600µ diam. A-spores oblong-fusoid, acute at lower end, usually biguttulate, 8–12 × 2–2·5µ; sporophores filiform-subulate, curvulous, 15–20 × 1–1·5µ: B-spores in the same pycnidia, hamate, 18 × 1µ.

On dry branches of *Sarothamnus scoparius*, Swanscombe (Cooke). Cheshire (Ellis). Ayrshire (Boyd). Near Brecon (Rhodes). Worcestershire; Polperro. Dec.–Mar.

The pycnidial stage of *Diaporthe Sarothamni* Nits.
When fully formed this is very conspicuous. Dr Rhodes has found at Polperro *Phomopsis Spartii* Died. on *Spartium junceum*; it seems not to differ in any respect from *P. Sarothamni*.

Fr. Holl. Germ. Austr. Denm. U.S.A.

Scrophularia

Phomopsis nitidula Grove, in Kew Bull. 1917, p. 59. *Phoma nitidula* Sacc. Syll. iii. 128. All. vi. 320.

Pycnidia gregarious, oblong-depressed, 200–400µ long, covered by the shining epidermis, which is stained round each by a blackish-brown halo, and is at length elevated and

pierced by the small papilla. Spores broadly elliptic-fusoid, subacute at both ends, biguttulate, $7-9 \times 2\mu$ ($10-11 \times 2-2\cdot5\mu$, Sacc.); sporophores filiform, about $15 \times 1\cdot5\mu$, rising from a soft and fuliginous stratum, exactly as in *P. Tulasnei*.

On dead stems of *Scrophularia nodosa*. Neatishead, Norfolk (Cooke). Coleshill, Warwicks.   Feb.–Jun.

The pycnidial stage of an unknown Diaporthe (? *D. Tulasnei*). The spores of the Coleshill specimen measured $8-10 \times 2\cdot5-3\mu$. Fr.

Skimmia

Phomopsis Skimmiae Grove, in Journ. Bot. 1933, p. 258.

Pycnidia scattered, blackish, up to 500μ wide, at first covered and raising the epidermis in a conical fashion, at length bursting it irregularly. Spores oblong-ellipsoid, rarely somewhat acute at one end, hyaline, biguttulate, $7-9 \times 2-3\mu$; sporophores subulate, microguttulate, acute, $10-18\mu$ long.

On branches of *Skimmia japonica*. Harborne Hall, near Birmingham (Grove & Rhodes). Heythrop Park, Oxon. (Rhodes).   Mar.–Jun.

In both localities it was accompanied by *Diaporthe Skimmiae* Grove, in Journ. Bot. 1933, p. 257, and the bushes seemed to have been killed by its action.

Solanum

Phomopsis Dulcamarae Trav. 246. Died. 270. Mig. 168. *Phoma Dulcamarae* Sacc. Syll. iii. 127. All. vi. 322.

Pycnidia gregarious, subepidermal, pustular, black, at length bursting the epidermis. Spores fusoid, biguttulate, $8-10 \times 2-2\cdot5\mu$; sporophores subulate, more or less curved, $12-15 \times 2\mu$.

On dry stems of *Solanum Dulcamara*. Perranzabuloe Church, Cornw. (Rilstone). Kew Gardens.   May.

The pycnidial stage of *Diaporthe Dulcamarae* Nits.
Saccardo says (*l.c.*) "basidiis filiformi-hamatis, $25 \times 1\cdot5\mu$"; no doubt these were B-spores, as Diedicke remarks.
Fr. Germ. Holl. Denm. Ital.

Phomopsis Tulasnei Sacc. in Ann. Mycol. 1903, i. 27 (*non* v. Höhn. in 1906, p. 33, which is a Septomyxa). *Phlyctaena maculans* Fautr. in Rev. Mycol. 1896, p. 70. Sacc. Syll. xiv. 987.

Pycnidia densely scattered, immersed, each surrounded by a small blackish halo, scarcely erumpent, globose-depressed

or oblong, about 200μ diam. A-spores ovate-oblong, sub-obtuse at both ends, especially above, 7–9 × 2·5–3μ; sporo-phores linear-acute, at length curved, 15–18 × 1·5μ: B-spores filiform, curved or hamate, faintly multiguttulate, 20–27 × 1μ, on short sporophores, rising from a thick brownish stratum. On dead stems of *Solanum tuberosum*. Evesham (Rhodes). Botley, Hants. (Cotton). On dead stems of *Urtica dioica*; Hereford; Forhill, Worcs.   Jan.–Apr.

The "walking-stick" spores of this, on *Solanum*, are evidently *Phlyctaena maculans* Fautr. A- and B-spores often in the same pycnïdium.

This species has been recorded on many other hosts—*Aristolochia*, *Calamintha*, *Chenopodium*, *Galeopsis*, *Gentiana*, *Hesperis*, *Lamium*, *Medicago*, *Mentha*, *Salvia*, *Scrophularia*, *Verbascum*, etc. It is a use-less composite title, unless it is restricted entirely to the cases where it is accompanied by *Diaporthe Tulasnei* Nits.; this would make it a good name to embrace many of the hardly distinguishable species which infest the dead stems of herbaceous perennials, and which are probably going to be proved by future persistent pathologists to be forms of a highly plurivorous fungus.

Fr. Ital. Spain.

Sophora
Phomopsis Sophorae Trav. 260. Died. in Ann. Mycol. ix. 31, pl. 2, f. 6; Pilz. Brand. p. 271, p. 240, f. 7. Mig. 168. *Phoma Sophorae* Sacc. Syll. iii. 67. All. vi. 247.

Pycnidia scattered, nestling beneath the epidermis which is raised and at length irregularly torn at the vertex, lenticular, slightly papillate, black, 200–400μ diam. Spores oblong-fusoid, sometimes curved, often somewhat clavulate, bigut-tulate, 8–11 × 2–2·5μ; sporophores cylindrical, rather obtuse, 15–20 × 2μ.

On dead twigs of *Sophora japonica*. Kew Gardens (Cooke). Arundel (Wakefield).   May.

The pycnidial stage of *Diaporthe Sophorae* Sacc.
The pycnidia are sometimes arranged in little groups, surrounded by a narrow sinuous black line significant of a Diaporthe, but this is not always present. The width of the spores is given by Saccardo as 3·5–4μ, and the sporophores are said to be hooked, 25 × 0·5μ; these latter, however, no doubt represent B-spores, such as Diedicke found in the larger pycnidia, but of which no trace was seen in the many (British and foreign) specimens examined.

Saccardo issued (Mycoth. Ven. no. 1547) a remarkable form of this

(var. *libricola* Sacc.), which has the pycnidia arranged in lines, immersed in the bark of the trunk, and each surrounded by a black stain; the spores and sporophores, however, are as described above. Fr. Germ. Denm. Austr. Ital.

Staphylea

Phomopsis Staphyleae Grove, in Kew Bull. 1917, p. 71. *Phoma Staphyleae* Cooke, in Grevill. xiv. 2 (1885). All. vi. 249. Sacc. x. 150.

Pycnidia gregarious, punctiform, covered by the epidermis which is at length blackened, rather prominent, but seldom emerging completely. Spores elliptic-fusoid, often acute at the lower end, $8-10 \times 2 \cdot 5-3\mu$; sporophores linear, about 10μ long.

On thin twigs of *Staphylea colchica, S. pinnata, S. trifoliata,* Kew Gardens (Cooke). On *S. pinnata,* Heythrop Park, Oxon.

June.

These specimens appear to be a Phomopsis, but the sporophores are not, as Cooke stated, "indistinct". It is probable, however, that Cooke's fungus is nothing but a younger state of *P. Robergeana* Died.

Phomopsis Robergeana Died. in Ann. Mycol. 1911, ix. 29; Pilz. Brand. 273. Mig. 169. Grove, in Kew Bull. 1917, p. 63. *Phoma Robergeana* Sacc. in Mich. i. 520 (1879); Syll. iii. 89. All. vi. 249.

"Pycnidia gregarious, immersed, then erumpent, depressed-globose, scarcely pierced at the vertex. Spores fusoid or lanceolate, straight or somewhat curved, often without guttules, $9 \times 2\mu$; sporophores filiform, $25-30 \times 1 \cdot 5\mu$" (Sacc.).

On twigs of species of *Staphylea.* Kew Gardens (Cooke). *n.v.*

The pycnidial stage of *Diaporthe Robergeana* Niessl.

The specimens just previously described under the name *Phomopsis Staphyleae* seem to be smaller and younger forms of the above little known species. But, as they have sporophores only about 10μ long, it appears likely that the long filiform sporophores mentioned by Saccardo (*l.c.*) are really B-spores.

Fr. Belg. Germ.

Symphoricarpus

Phomopsis Ryckholtii v. Höhn. Fragm. z. Mykol. 1906, no. 87, p. 33. Died. 273. Mig. 169. *Phoma Ryckholtii* Sacc. Syll. iii. 70. All. vi. 250. *Phlyctaena phomatella,* var. *Symphoricarpi-racemosae* Sacc. Syll. iii. 594. All. vi. 942.

Pycnidia gregarious, subepidermal, globose-depressed, 250μ diam. A-spores obtusely fusoid, biguttulate, $5-9 \times 2 \cdot 5-3\mu$;

sporophores rather long: B-spores filiform, hooked, 20–22 × 1μ; sporophores short, 8–10 × 1μ.

On branches of *Symphoricarpus racemosus*. Kew Gardens; Monsal Date, etc., Derbyshire; Staffordshire; Shelsey Walsh; Polperro; Aberdeen; Ayrshire.   Jun.–Aug.

The pycnidial stage of *Diaporthe Ryckholtii* Nits.
Belg. Holl. Germ. Ital.

Syringa

Phomopsis depressa Trav. 272. Died. 273. Mig. 169. *Sphaeropsis depressa* Lév. Descr. Champ. Mus. Paris, 1846, p. 295. *Phoma depressa* Sacc. Syll. iii. 82. All. vi. 251. (Not *P. depressa* B. & Br. for which see *Fusicoccum depressum* Gr.).

Pycnidia numerous, subepidermal, then erumpent, black, globose or oblong or even linear, at length depressed, slightly prominent, pierced by a narrow pore. A-spores lanceolate-fusoid, biguttulate, 8–10 × 2·5μ; sporophores linear, 6–12μ long: B-spores filiform-arcuate, 20–28 × 1·5μ.

On dead twigs of *Syringa vulgaris*. Ayrshire (Boyd). Kew Gardens; Lostwithiel; Kidderminster; Hanbury and Piper's Hill Wood, Ws.; etc.   May, Jun.

The pycnidial stage of *Diaporthe resecans* Nits., which often accompanies it.
Sometimes there is hardly a trace of a pycnidium. A var. *fructicola* is recorded abroad on the fruits.
W. Europe.

Tamarix

Phomopsis tamaricaria Grove. *Phoma tamaricaria* Sacc. Syll. iii. 93. Mig. 104.

Pycnidia subgregarious, covered by the epidermis, at length erumpent by the vertex, blackish, globose-depressed, up to 600μ diam. A-spores fusoid, nearly straight, acute at both ends, biguttulate in the usual way, hyaline, 8–9 × 2–2·5μ; sporophores oblong, crowded, straight, 14–18 × 2–4μ.

On twigs of *Tamarix*. Polperro, Cornw. (Rilstone & Rhodes)!   July.

The pycnidial stage of *Diaporthe tamaricina* Sacc. & Flag. (Syll. xvii. 672), which occurred with it. Only the A-spores were seen, but Saccardo's "uncinate basidia, 30 × 1μ" must be the B-spores.
Fr. Germ.

Tamus

Phomopsis tamicola Trav. 233. Grove, in Kew Bull. 1917, p. 66.
Phoma tamicola Cooke, in Grevill. xiii. 95. Sacc. Syll. x. 183. *Phlyctaena vagabunda* Desm. in Ann. Sci. Nat. 1847, viii. 16, var. *Tami.*
All. vi. 940.

Pycnidia gregarious, subglobose or oblong, depressed, covered by the discoloured epidermis which is at length pierced at the summit by a rather large round pore, black, about 300–500μ diam. when mature, surrounded when young by a brown halo. A-spores rather obtuse at the ends, often biguttulate, 8–9 × 2·5–3μ, sporophores linear-subulate, crowded, about 15 × 1–1·5μ: B-spores $\pm$ arcuate, seldom hamate, 20–25 × 1–1·5μ, shorter in very young pycnidia.

On dry dead stems of *Tamus communis*, hanging in the hedges. Common, especially in the Midlands, wherever *Tamus* grows. Feb.–May.

The pycnidial stage of *Diaporthe scandens* S. & S., which has been found, so far, in only one place in Britain (Ockeridge Wood). See Grove, in Journ. Bot. 1930, p. 70.

There cannot be the slightest doubt that the Phlyctaena is merely the earlier state of the Phomopsis, before the pycnidial wall is fully developed, and when the filiform spores alone are being produced. I have not succeeded, however, in finding both forms of spores in the same pycnidium. The ascophorous stage is very rare, and has not been found earlier than the end of March. The halo which is characteristic of many species of Phomopsis seems to be most fully exhibited in this species. There is a true Phoma (allied to *P. oleracea*) sometimes to be found on the same dead *Tamus* stems.

Fr. Belg.

Tecoma

[**Phomopsis Tecomae** Grove, in Kew Bull. 1917, p. 71. *Phoma Tecomae* Sacc. Syll. iii. 91. All. vi. 254.

Recorded on *Tecoma radicans*, for Kew Gardens, in Grevill. xiv. 28, under the name *Phoma Tecomae*.]

But in the specimens preserved in Kew Herbarium there is nothing at all resembling Saccardo's description, which is that of a true Phomopsis.

Fr. Ital.

Tilia

Phomopsis velata v. Höhn. Fragm. z. Mykol. 1906, no. 87, p. 33. Died. 275. Mig. 170. *Phoma velata* Sacc. Syll. iii. 92. All. vi. 255.

Forma **minor** Sacc. *l.c.* Grove, in Kew Bull. 1917, p. 66, pl. 2, f. 30, including *Phoma communis* Rob. in Herb. Desm. ser. II, no. 693.

Pycnidia scattered or in little groups of 2 or 3, immersed in
the cortex, subglobose, covered by the epidermis which is at
length burst above, then falling out and leaving a little pit in
the cortex; texture thick above and olivaceous. A-spores oblong-fusoid, obtuse at the ends, biguttulate, $7–8 \times 2–2·5\mu$;
sporophores linear, up to $14 \times 1·5\mu$: B-spores filiform, flexuous
or hooked, $16–20 \times 1\mu$: sporophores short, papilliform.

On branches of *Tilia*. Kew Gardens; Blackheath; Shrawley
Wood; Heythrop Park; Cheshire; Scarborough; Oscott; Brewood; Ayrshire.   Summer.

The pycnidial stage of *Diaporthe velata* Nits.
The typical form has longer spores ($10–12\mu$) and sporophores (20μ).
Phoma communis Rob. is a smaller form on the twigs and on petioles
and mid-ribs of the leaves. In Desmazières' no. 693 I found the
B-spores in great abundance.
Fr. Holl. Germ. Austr. Bosnia.

Phomopsis ligulata Grove.   **Ulex**

Pycnidia often large, pulvinate, surrounded by the much
blackened surface of the matrix, greyish, then black above;
loculi irregular, often compound, flattened. A-spores oblong
to ellipsoid-oblong, rather variable, faintly biguttulate, $6–8 \times$
$1·7–2·5\mu$; sporophores linear, straight, $10–15 \times 1\mu$: B-spores
scarce, hamate or curved, $10–21 \times 1\mu$.

On dead stems of *Ulex europaeus*. Ayrshire (Boyd). Polperro (Rilstone & Rhodes). Powick, near Worcester (Rhodes).
Malvern (Ellis). Ham Common (E. W. Mason). Esher; Sussex; etc.   Mar.–Jun.

The pycnidial stage of *Diaporthe ligulata* Nits. = *D. nucleata* Sacc.
B-spores were seen only in the Ayrshire specimens.
Europe (near the Atlantic).

Phomopsis inaequalis Trav. 259. *Phoma inaequalis* Speg. Fung.
Arg. II. 128. Sacc. Syll. iii. 67.

Pycnidia small, scattered, seated on the wood, covered by
the epidermis, occasionally surrounded by a Diaporthe-like
line. A-spores elongate-ellipsoid, inequilateral, biguttulate,
tapering but rounded at both ends, $7–10 \times 2–3\mu$: B-spores
filiform, curved, "$21–27 \times 2\mu$" (Nitschke).

On dead branches and spines of *Ulex europaeus*. Lulworth Cove, Dorset (Rhodes). No other certain British specimens seen.

It is said to occur on *Cytisus* also, and is considered to be the pycnidial stage of *Diaporthe inaequalis* Nits., which differs from *D. ligulata* in its much larger ascospores, etc.

When the bark scales off, extensive but interrupted blackened areas are seen on the wood. *Phoma Ulicis* Syd. may often be found on the dead spines, but the Phomopsis on them seems to be nearly always badly or only partially developed, as I have found at Worms Head, Gower, etc. Is the Phoma a state of the Phomopsis?

Germ. Spain, Argentina.

Ulmus

Phomopsis oblonga Trav. 248. Died. 275. Mig. 170. *Phoma oblonga* Desm. in Ann. Sci. Nat. 1853, xx. 218. Sacc. Syll. iii. 99. *Phomopsis Eres* Grove, in Journ. Bot. 1918, p. 291. *Phoma Eres* Sacc. in Mich. i. 521 (1879); see also Syll. i. 631 and iii. 99. All. vi. 256. Cf. *Phlyctaona phomatella* Saac. Syll. iii. 504 (B sporos).

Pycnidia scattered or somewhat gregarious, conico-convex, oblong, blackish, 250–300μ diam., long covered by the periderm, only after a long time erumpent by a longitudinal slit or an irregular pore; contents greyish. A-spores oblong or fusoid, rarely subacute, biguttulate, 9–10 × 2·5–3μ; sporophores linear or subulate, straight or curved, simple or rarely forked, crowded, 18–20 × 2μ: with them were sometimes found uncinate B-spores, 25–30 × 1μ or sometimes shorter.

On dead twigs of *Ulmus campestris*, *U. montana*. Oscott College and Harvington (Rhodes). Ayrshire (Boyd). Kew Gardens; Walmley, near Sutton Coldfield; etc.   Dec.–Jun.

The pycnidial stage of *Diaporthe Eres* Nits. A black line below the fungus penetrates deeply into the wood.

Fr. Germ. Ital.

UMBELLIFERAE

Plurivorous

Phomopsis hysteriola, comb. nov. *Phoma striaeformis* var. *hysteriola* Sacc. Syll. iii. 132. Grove, in Journ. Bot. 1916, p. 188. *Phoma hysteriola* All. vi. 288. Mig. 85.

Pycnidia collected 2–5 together in short black rows or sometimes standing singly, ± globose, immersed between the woody fibres of the stem, and protruding in a Hysterium-like manner when the epidermis has vanished, with the short ostiole projecting slightly. A-spores oblong-lanceolate, tapering at the base or even acute, biguttulate or occasionally with

3 or 4 guttules, 6–9 × 2·5–3μ; sporophores densely crowded, simple, subulate, as long as or a little longer than the spore, springing from a thick olive-brown stratum: B-spores filiform, uncinate, 28–30 × 1·5μ.

On dead stems of *Chaerophyllum temulum* (especially on the swollen part). Cheshire (Ellis). Gower; Evesham. On *Heracleum*, Hereford; Wixford. On *Atropa Belladonna*, Hereford (but ?). On *Sison Amomum*, Looe (Rilstone).

Allescher, who appears not to have seen either *striaeformis* or the variety, makes the var. distinct because he thought (wrongly) that the former had short sporophores.

Fr. Germ. Port. Alger.

Phomopsis caulographa Grove, in Kew Bull. 1917, p. 54. *Phoma caulographa* Dur. & Mont. Flor. Alg. *ex* Sacc. Syll. iii. 126. All. vi. 280.

Pycnidia ± imperfect, pustular, up to 500μ long, arranged in short linear series on lanceolate black or blackish spots which are at length confluent, surrounded by a black line which penetrates the stem. Spores oblong-fusoid, often in-equilateral, rounded above, acute below, frequently with one or two guttules, 7–8 × 2–2·5μ; sporophores densely crowded, subulate, 10–12 × 1·5–2μ, rising from a very pale proliferous stratum.

On dead stems of *Chaerophyllum temulum*, Lapworth and Shustoke, Warwicks.; Droitwich and Bromsgrove, Worcs. On *C. aromaticum*, Cannon Hill Park, Birmingham. On *Angelica silvestris*, Murlough Bay, Antrim.   Jan.–May.

Distinguished from *Phomopsis hysteriola* in being situated on blackish spots and by not being erumpent by a slit. It is quite possible that all the specimens recorded here under *P. caulographa* are only later states or developments of *P. Asteriscus*.

The Yorkshire specimens, recorded in the "Naturalist", 1904, p. 6, under this name, are evidently *Phoma complanata*.

Fr. (on *Chaerophyllum*), Holl. (on *Anthriscus*), Alg. (on *Smyrnium*), Germ.

Phomopsis Asteriscus Grove, in Kew Bull. 1917, p. 53, pl. 1, f. 6. *Phoma Asteriscus* Berk. in Ann. Nat. Hist. 1850, v. 368. Cooke, Handb. 418. Sacc. Syll. iii. 126. All. vi. 296.

"Unilocular, forming little pitch-brown rather convex dots with a paler cloudy narrow border. Mass of spores surrounded

by a dark cellular stratum, consisting of hexagonal cells confused with the matrix, but scarcely presenting a definite perithecium. Spores narrow, oblong, subelliptic, but by no means filiform" (Berk. *l.c.*).

On dead stems of *Angelica silvestris, Chaerophyllum aromaticum, C. temulum, Peucedanum officinale*, and above all of *Heracleum Sphondylium*. Highgate; Surrey; East Bergholt; Worcestershire; Warwickshire; Yorkshire; Lancashire; Guernsey; Jedburgh; Ayrshire; Aberdeen; Leinster; etc.

Jul.–Apr.

This is a very interesting species, being the first recognised to possess the characters which now constitute the genus Phomopsis. For this reason Berkeley's description is quoted above unaltered. It shows perfectly the acute perception and easy power of expressing facts which placed Berkeley so high among the mycologists of his time.

A few particulars may be added, derived from Berkeley's original specimen (Guernsey, Rev. T. Salwey) on *Heracleum Sphondylium*.

Pycnidia gregarious, often scarcely prominent, oblong, up to 600μ long, with a minute papilla which just pierces the epidermis, usually surrounded by a cloudy brown aureole. Spores oblong-ellipsoid, when young scarcely acute at the ends, bi-triguttulate, $7–10 \times 2–2\cdot5\mu$; sporophores crowded, filiform-arcuate, $15–20 \times 1–1\cdot5\mu$. Some of the spores were constricted in the middle and even faintly pseudoseptate, as if aping the form of a Diaporthe spore.

The specimens on *C. aromaticum* in the Students' Garden at Cannon Hill Park, Birmingham, yielded both A- and B-spores: A-spores $9–12 \times 2\cdot5–3\mu$; B-spores filiform, curved or hamate, $20–30 \times 0\cdot7–1\mu$, on short conical or ampulliform sporophores about $4–5 \times 2\mu$. Similar B-spores were found by Dr Rhodes on *Heracleum Sphondylium*, in Guernsey, Sept. 1931. This species is accompanied at times by the beginnings of *Diaporthe Berkeleyi* Nits. (which is *Diaporthopsis Angelicae* according to Wehmeyer).

Conium

Phomopsis Conii Died. 901. Grove, in Journ. Bot. 1930, p. 271.

Pycnidia irregularly gregarious, extending for some distance along the stem, subepidermal, lens-shaped, flatly conical or subhemispherical, black, surrounded by a faint blackish halo, rather thick above and olive-brown, paler below, indistinctly ostiolate, 200–250μ diam. Spores fusoid, not very acute at the ends, biguttulate, $6–8 \times 2–3\mu$; sporophores filiform, crowded, $12–18 \times 1\cdot5\mu$. No B-spores seen.

On dead stems of *Conium maculatum*. Ham Bridge, Worcs. (Rhodes). ? Pycnidial stage of *Diaporthe inquilina* Nits.

Nov.

The wall of the pycnidium is often very imperfectly formed and reminds one of that found in some of the Leptostromataceae; but the spores and sporophores are exactly those of Phomopsis. Germ.

Eryngium

Phomopsis eryngiicola Trav. 251. Died. 245. Mig. 160. *Phoma eryngiicola* Brun. Champ. Saint. in Bull. Soc. Bot. Fr. 1889, p. 337. Sacc. Syll. x. 176. All. vi. 292. *Phoma Bloxami* Berk. in Herb. Kew. *Phomopsis Bloxami* Grove, in Kew Bull. 1917, p. 68. *Vermicularia Eryngii* Cooke, in Grevill. xiv. 35 (*non* Fckl.). *Rhabdospora Eryngii* Syd. in Hedwig. 1900, p. 129. *Phoma nigrella* Magn. *apud* All. vi. 292.

Pycnidia densely congregated, innate, glabrous, 160–300μ diam., black, the epidermis around the minute ostiole being smooth and black; peridium thin, parenchymatous, fuliginous. Spores fusoid or subcylindrical, mostly acute at both ends, rarely curvulous, hardly ever guttulate, 10–12 × 1·5–2μ (rarely 2·5μ broad): B-spores filiform, curved and hooked, 20–27 × 1·5μ.

On dead stems and leaves of *Eryngium maritimum*. Fleetwood (Bloxam). Scotland (Greville). Tenby; Herm; Alderney; Guernsey (Rhodes).   Jun.–Sept.

The shining inky-black patches of the epidermis, just pierced by the minute ostioles, are very large and conspicuous, and very different from what is seen on other Umbellifers. It is recorded also, abroad, on *E. campestre*, and (but wrongly) on *Anthriscus silvestris*. It is the pycnidial stage of *Diaporthopsis nigrella* Fabre. Holl. Germ. Thuringia.

Veronica

Phomopsis Veronicae-speciosae Died. 276. Mig. 170. Grove, in Journ. Bot. 1930, p. 296. *Phoma Veronicae-speciosae* Henn. in Verh. Bot. Ver. Prov. Brandenb. xl. 166. Sacc. Syll. xvi. 871. All. vii. 831.

Pycnidia scattered or gregarious, covered, then bursting the epidermis by a slit or pore, convex, round or mostly linear, at length multilocellate, confluent, and up to 700μ or more long; peridium thick, dark-brown above, paler below. Spores fusoid, acute at one end at least, biguttulate, 7–10 × 2–2·5μ; sporophores subulate, longer than the spore.

On dead stems of a large-flowered shrubby Veronica (a

hybrid of *V. speciosa*), Polperro (Rhodes & Rilstone). On a red-flowered form of the same, Lambourne Hill, W. Cornwall (Rilstone).   May–Jul.

The pycnidial stage of *Diaporthe Veronicae-speciosae* Rehm, which has occurred on *Veronica Traversii* at Heythrop Park, Oxon. (Grove & Rhodes).
Germ. Moravia.

Viburnum

Phomopsis tinea v. Höhn. Fragm. z. Mykol. no. 87. Died. 276. Mig. 170. *Phoma tinea* Sacc. in Mich. i. 521 (1879); Syll. iii. 87. All. vi. 257. *Phomopsis Beckhausii* Trav. 270. *Phoma Beckhausii* Cooke, in Grevill. xiii. 91 (1885). Sacc. Syll. x. 144.

Pycnidia scattered or rarely aggregated, subglobose, immersed in the bark which is slightly elevated, then after a time erumpent, at length collapsed and surrounded by a cushion of the hypertrophied cortex. A-spores oblong-fusoid or sublanceolate, usually biguttulate, $8–10 \times 2–2·5\mu$; sporophores filiform, acute, $15 \times 1·5\mu$: B-spores filiform, curved and hooked, $18–20 \times 1·5\mu$.

On dead branches of *Viburnum Lantana*, *V. Tinus*. Ayrshire (Boyd). Kew; Dartford; Oxfordshire; Cheshire; Yorkshire; Worcestershire; Devon.   Apr. May.

It is frequently found in company with young *Diaporthe Beckhausii* Nits. The B-spores have been seen only on *V. Lantana*, near Torquay (Rhodes), but there they were in great abundance.

Vinca

Phomopsis Lirella Grove, in Kew Bull. 1917, p. 58. *Phoma Lirella* Desm. in Ann. Sci. Nat. 1849, xi. 281. Sacc. Syll. iii. 139. All. vi. 328.

Pycnidia linear-oblong, narrow ($250–330\mu$ in breadth), $500–750\mu$ long or even 1 mm. long, arranged 3–5 or more in a row parallel to the axis, covered by the unchanged epidermis, then erumpent by an elongated fissure, black, pierced by a pore. Spores elliptic-fusoid, subacute at the ends, biguttulate, $7–8 \times 2–2·5\mu$; sporophores crowded, $\pm$ cylindrical, $12–15 \times 1\mu$.

On dry decorticated stems of *Vinca* (*minor, major*). Swanscombe, Kent (Cooke). Pwllcrochan, Pemb. (Rhodes).

Externally exactly like a species of Leptostroma. The pycnidium of *Diaporthe Vincae* Cooke, in Grevill. v. 63 (1876)=*D. eumorpha* Maire (1917).
Fr. Germ.

Vitis
Phomopsis Ampelopsidis Petr. in Ann. Mycol. 1916, xiv. 441.
Phoma nidulans Grogn. *apud* Sacc. in Mich. ii. 341; Syll. iii. 80.

Pycnidia widely dispersed, nestling in the bark, covered, then emerging slightly, subglobose, brownish-black, up to 1 mm. long, with a short conical ostiole. A-spores linear or subfusoid, bluntly attenuated at both ends, 2- or 3-guttulate, nearly straight, 6–11 × 2–3μ; sporophores not seen: "B-spores cylindric, curved or hamate, 16–20 × 1–1·5μ" (Wehmeyer, in culture).

On dead branches of *Vitis* (*Ampelopsis*) *quinquefolia*. Ayrshire (Boyd). Polperro (Rilstone).   May.

The pycnidial stage of *Diaporthe Ampelopsidis* E. & E.
Probably merely a form of *P. viticola*, namely var. *Ampelopsidis* Grove, in Kew Bull. 1919, pp. 183–4, though certain small differences between them may be observed.
Europe, U.S.A.

Phomopsis viticola Sacc. in Ann. Mycol. 1915, xiii. 118. *Phoma viticola* Sacc. in Mich. ii. 92 (1880); Syll. iii. 79. *Phoma viniferae* Cooke, in Grevill. xiii. 92 (1885). Sacc. Syll. x. 152. All. vi. 258. *Phoma cordifolia* Brun. Champ. Saint. vii. 4. (Not *P. viticola* Sacc. Syll. iii. 110 = *Sphaeropsis viticola* Cooke, in Grevill. xii. 22 = *P. vitea* Sacc. Syll. iii. 860.)

Pycnidia scattered, covered by the epidermis, globose-oblong, blackish, up to 400μ long, at length erumpent at the apex; texture above thick, sooty-olive. Spores elliptic-fusoid, subacute at the ends, usually straight, with 1 or 2 guttules, 7–10 × 2–2·5μ; sporophores subulate, 10–12 × 2·5μ.

On dead branches of *Vitis vinifera*. Not common; Kew; Polperro, etc. The pycnidial stage of *Diaporthe viticola* Nits.
Apr.–Jul.

Phoma Vitis Bon. may occur on the same rods. *Phoma lenticularis* Cav. is said to have longer sporophores, 20–22μ long; also cf. *Phoma desciscens* Oud. in Hedwig. 1898, xxxviii. 314, which is evidently a Phomopsis, and differs chiefly in having its pycnidia 2–4 together, seated on a blackish lanceolate patch which signifies the beginning of the ascophorous stage.

DOTHIORELLA Sacc. in Mich. ii. 5.

Pycnidia erumpent, for the most part aggregated in botryoid clusters on a basal stroma or occasionally immersed in a pulvinate stroma, more or less globose, often papillate; wall rather thick. Spores ovoid or oblong, continuous, hyaline; sporophores usually evident, though short sometimes. (Fig. 13.)

Dothiopsis Karst. is the same thing as Dothiorella when the stroma is reduced or even altogether wanting. The two extreme states, with all the intermediate states, can be seen on the same branch or twig, without any other distinction. Occasionally the pycnidia may stand singly or two together; then they can hardly be distinguished from a Phoma. Haplosporella also is easily confounded with Dothiorella. Some of these fungi are young states of Botryodiplodia; some are pycnidial stages of Botryosphaeria, but others belong to widely different life-cycles.

Plurivorous

Dothiorella pyrenophora Sacc. Syll. iii. 238. ? *Dothidea pyrenophora* Fr. Syst. Myc. ii. 552, *p.p. Dothiora pyrenophora* Karst. Symb. Myc. Fenn. xiii. 9. *Dothiopsis pyrenophora* All. vi. 516. Died. p. 238, p. 240, f. 2. Mig. 174. *Dothichiza Sorbi* Lib. in Rev. Mycol. ii. 17.

Pycnidia single or a few (2–8) together, immersed in a stroma, or seated on a thin blackish stroma, or stroma altogether wanting, subglobose, black, 0·5–1 mm. diam., erumpent and surrounded by the torn epidermis, sometimes con-

Fig. 13. *Dothiorella pyrenophora*: *a*, pycnidia on *Sorbus Aucuparia*, × 12; *b*, spores of var. *Salicis*, and *c*, spores of var. *Mespili*, both × 600.

vex, at others provided with a broad black papilla; contents white. Spores very numerous, elliptic-ovoid, continuous, eguttulate, about 5–6 × 2–2·5μ (3–5 × 1·5–2μ, Karst.). (Fig. 13 *a*.)

On dead twigs and branches of *Sorbus Aucuparia*. West Kilbride, Ayrshire (Boyd). Harborne, Birmingham.

Feb.–Apr.

The type of the species in Finland was densely pulvinato-caespitose, but here, as in other species of the genus, the pycnidia tend to occur quite singly, in which case it may look almost exactly like a Phoma. Finl. Lapl. Denm. Germ.

Var. **Mali** Karst. *l.c.*

Pycnidia densely pulvinate-caespitose, on a thin stroma-like base, each covered by the thin whitish epidermis, then erumpent (often singly) by a torn orifice, dull-black, ± globose, unequal; texture thick, parenchymatous, dark-brown. Spores oval, $6-10 \times 3-4\mu$.

On dead twigs of *Pyrus Malus*, Forden (Vize); Kent (Brooks). On *P. communis*, Ayrshire (Boyd), spores only 4–$5 \times 2\mu$.   May, Sept.

No doubt common, but I have seen no other unmistakable specimens; it was confused by the earlier mycologists with *Botryodiplodia pyrenophora* (*q.v.*), of which it is doubtless an immature form.

Var. **Mespili**.

Ayrshire (Boyd), on fruits of *Mespilus*, with acute-ended spores, about $4 \times 2-3\mu$, on linear sporophores $5-8\mu$ long. (Fig. 13 *c*.)

Var. **Salicis** Karst. *l.c.*

On twigs of *Salix*. King's Norton; Halesowen; Edgbaston; Heythrop Park, Oxon.; etc. Spores $4-8 \times 2-3\mu$. (Fig. 13 *b*.)

The specimens on *Salix* from King's Norton, which I attribute to this variety, have dull-black rugulose pycnidia, crowded several (2–12) together on a thin black stroma, which is surrounded as a whole by the margin of the ruptured epidermis. The spores measure $5-7 \times 2-3\mu$ ($7-9 \times 3-4\mu$), and are very variable; mostly oval or oblong, full of refringent contents but without distinct guttules or with one only in the centre. They are exactly like those of the var. *Mali*; in both they are supported on a whitish mass of subsclerotial cells.

Other varieties have been recorded on *Betula* and on the fruits of *Juniperus*, all differing merely in size; Miss Cayley met with a form (var. *Pruni*), in bark of Plum, at Merton, Surrey, in company with *Cytospora microstoma*.

Fraxinus

Dothiorella fraxinea Sacc. & Roum. Rel. Lib. iv. 90, f. 43. Sacc. Syll. iii. 236. All. vi. 521, with fig. Mig. 215.

Pycnidia subglobose, clustered, erumpent, subconfluent, the mass often flattened, or convex, or mamillate with the

indistinct ostioles, black, up to 500μ diam., closely surrounded by the laciniae of the bark; contents whitish. Spores oblong-ellipsoid or subclavate, sometimes inequilateral, frequently tapering at the ends, rarely with an indistinct guttule, $8-10 \times 2-2\cdot5\mu$ ($12 \times 5\mu$, Sacc.); sporophores not seen.

On bark of *Fraxinus*. Lichfield. Feb.

Externally it exactly resembles *Botryodiplodia Fraxini*, of which it is the early stage. In fact, *Dothiorella fraxinea* stands to *Botryodiplodia Fraxini* exactly as *D. pyrenophora* does to *B. pyrenophora*.

Picea, etc.

Dothiorella pithya Sacc. Syll. iii. 241. All. vi. 519, with fig. Died. 295. Cf. *infra*, p. 249, and see also p. 180.

On seedlings of Douglas Fir, brought over from Germany (Journ. Board Agric. 1910, p. 216). *n.v.* Also, Mar. 1935, at the Ben More Forestry Reserve, on fallen cones of *Picea excelsa*; oval spores, granular within, on long pedicels and measuring $18-20 \times 5-6 \mu$ (i.e. the spores of *D. pithya* Sacc.), reminding one strongly of Fusicoccum, could be seen mixed with others like those of *Discella strobilina* Died., side by side in the *same* pycnidia and on the *same* proliferous stratum.

Salix

Dothiorella gregaria Sacc. Syll. iii. 236. All. vi. 520.

Pycnidia subcutaneous, then erumpent, gregarious or gathered here and there into clusters, pallid within. Spores oblong-fusoid, $18-22 \times 6-6\cdot5\mu$, clouded, hyaline; sporophores acicular, $25-30 \times 3\mu$.

On bark of branches of *Salix*. A pycnidial stage of *Physalospora gregaria*. Also recorded on *Cornus* and *Populus*, abroad.

No certain British specimens seen, but see *Diplodina salicicola* S. & T., *infra*, p. 337.

Fr. Ital.

PLACOSPHAERIA Sacc. in Mich. ii. 115.

Stroma flat or convex, $\pm$ effused, often deeply concrete with the substratum, covered by the epidermis or transforming it into a black crust roofed only by the cuticle, hyaline within. Loculi arising as hollows within the stroma, dehiscing above by pores or often by fissures. Spores ovoid or cylindrical, 1-celled, hyaline; sporophores linear or filiform. (Fig. 14.)

The effused black stroma, concrete with the leaf or stem, is the mark of this genus.

Plurivorous
Placosphaeria corrugata Sacc. Syll. iii. 246. All. vi. 537. Mig.
220. *Lecidea corrugata* Ach. Syn. Lichen. 1814, p. 18. *Rhytismella*
corrugata Karst. in Hedwig. 1884, p. 60. *Cliostomum corrugatum* Fr.
Sum. Veg. Sc. 121. Leighton, Angioc. Lich. p. 69, pl. 30, f. 1.

Gregarious, quite superficial, rugose-plicate, rather flat,
sometimes subspheroid or depressed-concave, horny, black,
fragile, with few loculi which dehisce by flexuous fissures,
0·5–2 mm. diam. Spores elongate or sausage-shaped, straight
or curvulous, $3 \times 0·5\mu$.

On hard bark of *Cedrus*, Mt. Stewart, Isle of Bute (W. H.
Wilkinson), Oct.; this is the spermogone of a Lichen, viz. it
is said *Biatorina Ehrhartiana* Ach. On the husks of a ger-
minating acorn, Hebden Bridge, Yorks. Fung. Fl. p. 370. On
hard wood (Cooke). A dubious fungus, often mistakenly recorded. See Keissler, Flechten-Parasiten, 580.

Fr. Germ. Swed. Ital.

Galium
Placosphaeria Galii Sacc. Syll. iii. 245. All. vi. 540. Died. 302.
Mig. 221.

Stromata at first covered by the epidermis which is at
length broken and pierced, lying lengthwise on the stem,
somewhat convex, dark-brown outside, colourless within, the
tissue full of hyaline oil-drops; loculi under the brown layer,
elongated, narrow. Spores erect, parallel to one another,
cylindrical, mostly straight, with a few oil-guttules, hyaline,
$8–10 \times 2–3 \mu$; sporophores inconspicuous.

On stems of *Galium Aparine, G. Mollugo*. Polperro (Rhodes).
Gower peninsula, Wales. It is said to be the spermogone of
Mazzantia Galii Mont. Jul. Aug.

Germ.

Placosphaeria punctiformis Sacc. Syll. viii. 726. All. vi. 540,
with fig. Died. p. 303, p. 240, f. 22. Mig. p. 221, pl. 29, f. 1–3.
Phyllachora punctiformis Fckl. Symb. Myc. 219; Nachtr. ii, 52. Sacc.
Syll. ii. 615.

Pycnidia very minute, hypophyllous, arranged six or eight
together in a circle about 0·5 mm. diam., confluent, situated
on pale scattered spots, black. Spores cylindrical, almost

straight, hyaline, 6 × 1·5µ, issuing in golden-yellow tendrils; sporophores filiform, 1µ thick, somewhat longer than the spore.

On living or fading leaves of *Galium saxatile*, less often on the stems; Cheshire, and Gower peninsula, Wales (Ellis). On *Galium Mollugo*, Cropthorne, Ws. and Bickleigh, S. Devon (Rhodes).   Jul.–Oct.

It may occur on other species of *Galium*, and also on *Asperula* and *Sherardia*; it is said to be a spermogonial stage of *Pseudopeziza repanda* (Fr.) Karst.
Germ. Holl. Denm. Canada.

Placosphaeria stellatarum Sacc. Syll. iii. 245. Massee, Fungus Flora, iv. 194. All. vi. 540.

Stromata amphigenous, minute, subcircular, 500µ diam., black, plurilocellate within, surrounded at the base with short fuscous hyphae; texture parenchymatous, fuliginous. Spores cylindric, rather obtuse at both ends, 5–6-guttulate, hyaline, 30–40 × 1·5–2µ.

On fading leaves of *Galium* or *Sherardia*. *n.v.*

This may be another spermogonial stage of *Pseudopeziza repanda*, like *P. punctiformis*. See Massee, Fung. Flor. iv. 194.
Fr.

                                                                    Gramineae
Placosphaeria graminis Sacc. & Roum. Syll. iii. 246. Mig. 222. All. vi. 536.

Stromata oblong, mostly hypophyllous, flattened, black, shining, subinnate. Spores oblong, subfusoid, curvulous, bi-triguttulate, colourless, 25–28 × 5–6µ.

On fading leaves of Grasses, e.g. *Agrostis*. Perhaps the spermogone of *Phyllachora Agrostidis* Fckl.

Saccardo also records a var. *anceps*, with slightly smaller spores, 20–24 × 4µ, which are at length biseptate, supported on subcylindrical sporophores. This variety was found by Madame Libert in the Ardennes on the leaves of various grasses. It has the habit of a Phyllachora.
Germ.

                                                                    Juncus
Placosphaeria Junci Bubák, in Ann. Mycol. 1906, iv. 113, with fig. Sacc. Syll. xxii. 948.

Stromata scattered, roundish or elongated, 0·25–1 mm. long, up to 0·5 mm. broad, immersed, covered by the epi-

dermis, dull-black, convex, divided into many incomplete loculi, mostly opening by a slit; texture parenchymatous, dusky-brown. Spores globose or sub-ovoid, hyaline, 2–2·5μ wide; sporo-phores straight or curvulous, often swollen below, acute above, almost flask-shaped, sometimes branched be-low, 15–25μ long, about 2μ broad at base. (Fig. 14.)

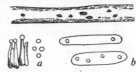

Fig. 14. *Placosphaeria Junci*, on culms of *Juncus*, ×2·5; *a*, spores and sporophores of the same, ×600; *b*, spores of *Placosphaeria Ulmi*, ×600.

On culms of *Juncus communis*, mountain bogs, near Foel, Mont-gomeryshire (Rhodes), and other places in Wales. On *Juncus effusus*, Henley-in-Arden, Wk. (Rhodes); Lady Wood, Worcs. On *J. conglomeratus*, Defford Common, Worcs. (Rhodes). Jul. Aug.

Bubák remarks that it is parasitic in *J. filiformis*, and that the parts attacked (culms and bracts) are killed and can be easily recognised by their leather-yellow colour. He discovered it in mountain bogs in June, 1904. Bohemia.

Onobrychis

Placosphaeria Onobrychidis Sacc. Syll. iii. 245. All. vi. p. 541, p. 536, fig. Died. p. 303, p. 240, f. 21. Mig. p. 222, pl. 28, f. 5–7. *Rhytisma Onobrychidis* DC. in Mém. Mus. iii. 324.

Stromata innate in the leaf, amphigenous, flattened, black, oblong, indefinite, 8–12 × 3–5 mm., obscurely plurilocular within, dehiscing by wide irregular slits. Spores abundant, obovoid or subfusoid, 8–10 × 2–2·5μ, prolonged downwards into a filiform tail (the ± persistent sporophore) 15–18 × 1μ.

On living leaves, or even on the stems, of *Lathyrus*. Kew Gardens. Recorded abroad on *Onobrychis sativa* also.

The English specimens which I have seen, though no doubt be-longing to this species, seem to be mostly imperfect. The spores vary much; in a Russian specimen they measured 5–10 × 1·5–2μ, and a variety is recorded with spores 7–8 × 4–5μ. The perfect stage is said to be *Diachora Onobrychidis* J. Müller.

Fr. Germ. Hung. Ital. Russ.

Ulmus

Placosphaeria Ulmi Grove, in Journ. Bot. 1922, p. 42, pl. 563, f. 11.

Stromata round, convex, blackish, covered only by the cuticle, thick, dark-brown within, divided into many globose

loculi which dehisce by slightly protruding ostioles. Spores cylindric-oblong, rounded at both ends, hyaline, with two or more guttules, $17-25 \times 4 \cdot 5-5\mu$; sporophores short, straight, lining the whole of the inside of the loculi. (Fig. 14b.)

On dead leaves of *Ulmus campestris*. Southampton; Quinton, Worcs.; in company with *Dothidella Ulmi*. Oct.

The stromata exactly resemble those of the *Dothidella*, and have for this reason been overlooked. The spores are variable in size. It is a transition form between *Piggotia astroidea* and the Dothidella, whose immature spores may be found in the same loculus as the Placosphaeria.

RABENHORSTIA Fr. Summ. Veg. Scand. 410.

Stroma erumpent, hemispherical-truncate, with a distinct circumscissile often caducous ostiole, dark-brown, paler within, divided into separate loculi or chambers; texture between coriaceous and carbonaceous. Spores oblong-ovoid, continuous, hyaline, on long filiform sporophores. (Fig. 15.)

The non-valsoid erumpent multilocular stroma, combined with the ovoid spores, is the mark of this genus; but in some species all the states may be found between a multilocular and a unilocular stroma according to the stage of development.

Ribes

Rabenhorstia ribesia Cooke & Mass. in Grevill. xvi. 7. Sacc. Syll. x. 233. All. vi. 534.

Stromata scattered, rarely subconfluent, erumpent, discoid or globose-truncate, internally divided into loculi, subcarbonaceous, black. Spores ellipsoid, rounded at the apex, subacute at base, often 1-guttulate, $8-12 \times 3-5\mu$.

On slender twigs of *Ribes aureum*. Kew Gardens (Cooke).

Strongly resembling in habit *Plowrightia ribesia* Sacc., of which it is doubtless the pycnidial stage. The stromata are cake-like in form, more or less similar to the Diatrype on Beech in size and shape. In Grevillea (*l.c.*) the size of the spore is given as $20 \times 10\mu$, but some which I obtained from the type-specimen measured as stated above.

Tilia

Rabenhorstia Tiliae Fr. Summa Veg. Sc. 410. Cooke, Handb. 461. Sacc. Syll. iii. 243. All. vi. 534. Died. p. 309, p. 308, f. 1. Mig. p. 220, pl. 28, f. 1–4. *Sphaeria Tiliae* Fr. Syst. Myc. ii. 485, *p.p.*

Stromata scattered, erumpent, globose-truncate, smooth, black, paler and plurilocular within; disc emerging, unequal, thick, truncate, black. Spores ellipsoid, rather thick-walled, cloudy within or with a large oil-drop, 12–15 × 6–8μ; sporophores filiform, fasciculate, about 60 × 1·5–2μ, but sometimes not half as long and twice as thick. (Fig. 15.)

Fig. 15. *Rabenhorstia Tiliae*: spores, × 600

On dead branches of *Tilia europaea*. Kew; Cheshire; Berwick; etc.

The pycnidial stage of *Hercospora Tiliae* Fr.
Europe (north and south), U.S.A.

Rabenhorstia rudis Fr. Summ. Veg. Scan. 410. (Not *Phomopsis rudis* v. Höhn.)

Petrak and Sydow, having examined a very small specimen of *Rabenhorstia rudis* Fr., from Fries' herbarium, suggest that it is really a Haplosporella, which they name *H. rudis*. They give a long description of it (in Ann. Mycol. 1923, xxi. 356), and say that it is on *Tilia*, and that it is a young state of *Sphaeropsis olivacea* Otth, which they say (and not *Macrodiplodia Curreyi* S. & R.) is the pycnidial stage of *Massariella Curreyi* Sacc. It is said to have hyaline spores, 20–27 × 10–12·5μ, but is a debatable species.

The species on *Laburnum* called by Diedicke and many other authors *R. rudis* Fr. is quite different and is now called *Phomopsis rudis* v. Höhn. (*q.v.*). Cf. also *Rabenh. conica* Sacc. Syll. iii. 243.

FUSICOCCUM Corda, in Sturm's Krypt. Flor. ii. 111.

Stromata arising within the bark, then erumpent, ± valsoid, convex or conical, often somewhat coriaceous, black, divided within into several more or less completely or incompletely separated chambers; wall of several layers, dark-brown. Spores fusoid or elliptic-fusoid, continuous, hyaline, usually nearly straight and rather large: sporophores variable, as long as or longer than the spore. (Figs. 16, 17.)

Distinguished from Dothiorella by having all its loculi in one layer. Myxofusicoccum cannot well be distinguished from Fusicoccum; it is as it were a transitional form between that and Myxosporium.

Many of the species are pycnidial stages of the genus Chorostate, which was once considered a section of Diaporthe; the pycnidial stages of the two other sections of Diaporthe (Euporthe and Tetrastaga) are now mostly ranged in the genus Phomopsis.

The alphabetic order of the hosts is followed, but all the species on CONIFERAE are placed under that name.

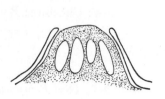 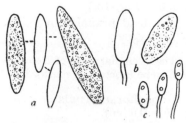

Fig. 16. Vertical section of stroma of *Fusicoccum macrosporum*, × 20.

Fig. 17. Spores of *Fusicoccum*: *a*, of *F. macrosporum*; *b*, of *F. juglandinum*; *c*, of *F. Carpini*; all × 600.

Acer

Fusicoccum obtusulum, comb. nov. *Phoma obtusula* ? Sacc. & Br. Misc. Myc. ii. 24; Syll. x. 151. All. vi. 173. *Myxofusicoccum obtusulum* Died. 316. Mig. 152. *Myxolibertella Aceris* v. Höhn. in Ann. Mycol. 1903, i. 526, *p.p.* *Fusicoccum Aceris* Grove, in Journ. Bot. 1916, p. 189. *Cytodiplospora Aceris* Oud. Contr. Fl. Myc. Pays-Bas, xvii. 266. Sacc. Syll. xvi. 941.

Stromata scattered, conico-depressed, immersed in the bark, at length emerging by a fissure or an irregular opening, dark-cinereous, 0·5 mm. broad, pallid-amber within. Spores very abundant, fusoid, nearly straight, subacute at both ends, at first continuous, at length with a (?) spurious median septum or at least with the protoplasm bipartite, 12–14 × 2–2·5μ; sporophores simple, linear, about as long as the spore, 1·25μ wide.

On branches of *Acer*. Hunt's Cross, Cheshire (Ellis). Apr.

The spores closely resemble those of *F. quercinum*. Does not this belong to *Phomopsis pustulata*, being merely the larger-spored form, as *F. quercinum* is of *Phomopsis quercina*?
Germ. Bosnia.

Betula

Fusicoccum Betulae Cooke, in Grevill. xvi. 48 (1887). Sacc. Syll. x. 241. All. vi. 549. *Cytodiplospora Betulae* Oud. in Hedwig. 1898,

p. 317. *Fusicoccum betulinum* Laub. in Arb. k. Biol. Anst. Land- u. Forstw. v. 208, f. 3 (1906). Sacc. Syll. xxii. 953. Mig. 178.

Stromata verruciform, scattered, erumpent, black; contents of loculi whitish. Spores fusoid, sometimes curved, continuous, hyaline, 10–12 × 2·5–3 (20–25 × 6μ, Cooke, *l.c.*), at length often 1-septate or at least appearing to be so; sporophores long, cylindrical, simple or forked.

On twigs of *Betula papyrifera*. Kew Gardens (Cooke). Apr.

On examining Cooke's specimen, in Herb. Kew, I find the spores to measure as given above; no spores with Cooke's dimensions were seen. Laubert's *betulinum* has spores 7–11 × 2·5–3·5μ, and seems to be the same species; *Myxofusicoccum Betulae* Jaap, in Died. p. 903, is very similar. Cf. also *Myxosporium Lanceola*. The spores as described by Cooke seem to be those of *Dothiorella Betulae* Sacc. in Ann. Mycol. iii. 512, which may be a form of the same species.

Holl. Germ.

Carpinus

Fusicoccum Carpini Sacc. Syll. iii. 250. All. vi. 549. Died. 310 Mig. 178.

Stromata covered, then erumpent, 1–2 mm. broad, opening by an irregular pore, multilocular within. Spores fusoid-lanceolate, biguttulate, hyaline, rather obtuse at both ends, ? at length 1-septate, 9–12 × 3–4μ; sporophores linear, about as long as the spore. (Fig. 17 c.)

On dry branches of *Carpinus Betulus*. Heythrop Park, Oxon. Hadzor Hall, Droitwich.   Jun.–Oct.

The pycnidial stage of *Diaporthe* (*Chor.*) *Carpini* Fckl. Cf. *Phomopsis sordidula* v. Höhn., on *Carpinus*, which has A-spores 8–10 × 2–2·5μ and B-spores 20–26 × 1·5μ, and is assigned to *Diaporthe sordida* Nits. Cf. also *Myxosporium deplanatum* Sacc.

Fr. Belg. Germ. Ital. Swed.

Castanea

Fusicoccum castaneum Sacc. Syll. iii. 249. Died. 420. Mig. 178. *Cytospora castanea* Sacc. in Mich. i. 519. *Diplodina Castaneae* Prill. & Delacr. in Bull. Soc. Myc. Fr. 1893, p. 276, fig. Sacc. Syll. xi. 527. *Cytodiplospora Castaneae* Oud. Contr. Fl. Myc. Pays-Bas, xv. 14, in Ned. Kr. Arch. ser. 2, vi. 292 (1895).

Stromata pulvinate or conical, erumpent, reddish-brown, paler within and divided into several variable loculi. Spores fusoid or sublanceolate, hyaline, straight or faintly curved, continuous and obtuse when young, 6·5–8 × 2–2·5μ, but later

$10-12 \times 2-3\mu$, usually biguttulate, occasionally pluri-micro-guttulate, at length when fully mature 1-septate; sporophores fasciculate, acicular, hyaline, $7-10 \times 1\cdot5\mu$, but ultimately filiform and longer than the spore, rising from a dark-olivaceous stratum; tendrils often flesh-coloured.

On dead twigs and branches of *Castanea vesca*. Ockeridge Wood, Ws. (Rhodes). Piper's Hill Common (Rhodes & Grove). Arundel (E. W. Mason). Oxshott Heath, Surrey.

May–Oct.

The pycnidial stage of *Diaporthe (Chor.) castanea* Sacc., which occurred with it, the pycnospores and asci being sometimes in the same conceptacle.

Most of the pycnospores were eseptate, but as Tulasne correctly observed (Carp. ii. 202) they become longer and 1-septate when ready to germinate. It is this latter state which was named by Oudemans Cytodiplospora; it was figured by Tulasne (*l.c.* pl. 23, f. 8, 9) as well as the earlier state (f. 7), but the mature spores which I have seen are all much more acute at the ends than in Tulasne's figures. The likeness of the Cytodiplospora spores, in shape, to the ascospores of the Diaporthe was so great that it was not until I had seen the former in large numbers seated upon their sporophores that I was satisfied they were not the escaped ascospores devoid of their row of guttules.

Fr. Holl. Germ. Ital.

Fusicoccum cinctum Sacc. & Roum. Rel. Lib. ser. 4, no. 94, pl. 43, f. 23; Syll. iii. 249. All. vi. 549. Mig. 179. Grove, in Journ. Bot. 1922, p. 42, pl. 563, f. 4.

Stromata pulvinate, 0·5–1 mm. wide, scattered or subgre-garious, placed longitudinally on the twigs, only the flat oval disc protruding through the epidermis, blackish-olive, some-times surrounded by an olivaceous zone beneath the epi-dermis, pseudolocellate within. Spores fusoid-oblong, often narrower below, hyaline, eguttulate, $12-18 \times 3-4\mu$; sporo-phores rod-shaped, shorter than the spore.

On bark of dead twigs of *Castanea vesca*. West Kilbride, Ayrshire (Boyd). Piper's Hill Common, Ws.

Sept.–Oct.

The word "teretibus" (? cylindrical), used by Saccardo in his description, suggests an incorrect idea; the spores in his specimen (Roum. Fung. sel. exs. no. 4377!) are exactly like those of Mr Boyd's. The pustule is a flat disc-shaped and olivaceous mass, which at first pierces the epidermis by a minute point; this afterwards expands to

a wide open disc, surrounded by the laciniae of the bark. The shadowy "zone" indicated by Saccardo is caused by this olivaceous mass showing through the periderm, but it is not always visible.

In spite of the differences enumerated above, one cannot help suspecting that this species is only a larger-spored form of the preceding, the two standing to one another exactly as *F. galericulatum* does to *F. macrosporum*.

Fr. (Ardennes).

CONIFERAE

Abies

Fusicoccum abietinum Prill. & Delacr. in Bull. Soc. Myc. Fr. 1890, vi. 98. Died. 310. Mig. p. 181, pl. 23, f. 1. Sacc. Syll. x. 421. All. vi. 550. *Phoma abietina* Hartig, Lehrbuch, 1889, p. 124; and Diseases of Trees, Eng. ed. 1888, p. 138, f. 78, 79. *Phomopsis abietina* Wils. & Hahn, in T.B.M.S. 1928, xiii. 271. Hahn, *ibid.* 1930, xv. 69, pl. 3, f. 1, 2 and text-figs. 25–7 (*non* Grove, in Journ. Bot. 1918, p. 293, and 1921, p. 16). *Dothiorella pitya* Prill. & Delacr. in Bull. Soc. Myc. Fr. 1890, vi. 176, pl. 15, f. 9–11. Sacc. Syll. iii. 241, *p.p.*; Fung. Ital. pl. 1454.

Stromata swollen, convex or conical, subgregarious, black, 400–500μ diam., immersed, often plurilocular with thin pale-olive septa. Spores broadly elliptic-fusoid, acute or subacute at both ends, hyaline, mostly biguttulate, 10–14 × 4–5·5μ; sporophores subulate, stout, persistent, very acute at apex, 7–13 × 1–3μ.

On small branches of *Abies pectinata*. ? Not yet found in Britain; no perfect stage known, but it has been much confused with Phomopses on numerous coniferous hosts. Cf. Lind, Dan. Fungi, p. 421. Migula (*l.c.*) reproduces an excellent figure, by Hartig, of the "Einschnürungsstelle" on a branch of *Abies* which is characteristic of the disease.

Fr. Germ.

Pinus, etc.

Fusicoccum bacillare Sacc. & Penz. in Mich. ii. 627. Sacc. Syll. iii. 248. All. vi. 550. Died. 313. Mig. 182. *Dothiorella pithyophila* Sacc. & Penz. in Mich. ii. 619. Sacc. Syll. iii. 238. All. vi. 524. *Sphaeropsis coniferarum* B. & Br. MS. name (in Herb. Kew).

Stromata gregarious, ± oblong, conical, immersed, then erumpent, somewhat swollen, 0·75–1 mm. broad, black, grey within, spuriously plurilocellate, with a small powdery whitish disc; wall dark-brown without, subhyaline within. Spores cylindrical, nearly always straight, obtuse at both

ends, hyaline, eguttulate, 10–16 × 1·5–2μ; sporophores short, cylindrical, springing from a proliferous stratum which is composed of intricate hyaline hyphae.

On branches, leaves and cone-scales of Coniferae.

Jan.–Apr.

Various forms of this species are known, often occurring in company with one another. The f. *dolosa* Sacc. (Syll. iii. 248), with the stromata more superficial and devoid of the whitish disc, was found on branches of *Larix* at Shere (Cooke), and at Sutton Coldfield with the type; a form between this form and f. *acuum* Fautr. (in Rev. Mycol. 1892, xiv. 9) occurred on twigs of *Pinus silvestris* in Oxshott Woods, Surrey (Bayliss Elliott); the f. *strobilorum* Roum. (in Rev. Mycol. 1890, p. 167) was found on cone-scales of *Picea* at Carlisle; and a rugose, nearly superficial, less compound form, labelled *Sphaeropsis coniferarum* in Herb., was found on bark of *Pinus* at Draycott, Wilts. (Broome). Of these *dolosa* has spores 14–15 × 2μ; *acuum*, 14 16 × 2–2·5μ; and *strobilorum*, 16–18 × 2μ. Von Höhnel places this species in Ceuthospora because of the shape of the spores, perhaps not incorrectly. Cf. *Phoma geniculata, supra*, p. 76.

Fr. Germ.

Fusicoccum Pini Sacc. Syll. iii. 248. All. vi. 551. Died. 313. Mig. 181. *Naemospora Pini* Preuss, Fung. Hoyersw. no. 148.

"Stromata small, gregarious; pycnidia compound, horny, somewhat lens-shaped, black; contents soft, white. Spores oblong, colourless, sharply attenuated at the base; sporophores eseptate."

On cones of *Picea excelsa*, Swaledale, Yorks. (F. A. Mason). *n.v.* June.

The original find of Preuss was on smooth bark of *Pinus*. Germ.

Corylus

Fusicoccum gloeosporoides Sacc. & Roum. Reliq. Libert. iv, no. 97. Sacc. Syll. iii. 249. All. vi. 548. Mig. 178. Grove, in Journ. Bot. 1916, p. 189.

Stromata scattered, immersed in the cortex, then erumpent with a roundish pore, depressed-conical, blackish-brown without, waxy and pallid or greyish within, uni- or plurilocular, 300–500μ wide. Spores oblong or fusoid, rounded above, subacute below, straight, continuous, 8–10 × 2–2·25μ; sporophores lanceolate-linear, 2μ wide, rather longer than the spore.

On twigs of *Corylus*. Hunt's Cross, Cheshire (Ellis).   Apr.

The species, as recorded by Saccardo, is said to have been on the bark of branches of *Betula*(?), in the Ardennes, and I have found a Fusicoccum which seemed to agree with this on *Betula alba* in Earlswood (Clows Wood), near Birmingham.   But cf. *Myxofusicoccum Coryli* Died. with spores $8-12 \times 4 \cdot 5-5\mu$.
Fr. Germ.

Fagus

Fusicoccum galericulatum Sacc. Syll. iii. 250.   All. vi. 552.
Myxofusicoccum galericulatum Died. 318.   Mig. 153.

Stromata loosely aggregated, flatly conico-pulvinate, 1–2 mm. wide, black, covered by the epidermis which is at length pierced by an irregular fissure, seated on the cortex and bordered by a distinct $\pm$ circular line; within multilocellate by irregular partitions.   Spores ellipsoid or oblong-fusoid, obtuse at both ends, rarely inequilateral, hyaline, eguttulate, $10-15 \times 4-6\mu$.

On branches and twigs of *Fagus silvatica*. Oscott College; near Colwich, Staffs. (Rhodes).   Boxhill, Surrey; Quinton, near Birmingham.   Mar.–Jul.

The pycnidial stage of *Diaporthe (Chor.) galericulata* (Tul.) Sacc.
Fr. Germ.

Fusicoccum macrosporum Sacc. & Bri. in Rev. Mycol. 1886, p. 156; see Syll. Addit. p. 439. Sacc. Syll. x. 240. Died. 311. Mig. 179.

Stromata scattered, slightly raised, convex, obtuse, bursting the periderm and surrounded by it, 1–2 mm. diam., plurilocular, colourless within.   Spores oblong-fusoid, hyaline, guttulate and granular within, obtuse at both ends or more tapering below, $30-44 \times 8-10\mu$ ($44-48 \times 12-14\mu$, Sacc.); sporophores short, blunt, colourless, about $8-10 \times 2\mu$. (Figs. 16, 17 a.)

On dead fallen or dying branches of *Fagus silvatica*. Richmond Park; Box Hill, Surrey (E. W. Mason).   Oscott College; Dodderhill Common (Rhodes & Grove). Warley, near Birmingham; Heythrop Park, Oxon.   May.

The spores and the mycelium contain an abundance of oil.   In similar pycnidia, on the same branch, there grew enormous numbers of micro-conidia, rod-like, $3-5 \times 1\mu$. This species is only a form of *F. galericulatum*, standing to it in fact exactly as the large-spored form does to the small-spored form in *F. quercinum*.
Fr.

Juglans
Fusicoccum juglandinum Died. Pilz. Brand. 312. Mig. 181.

Stromata immersed, erumpent, conical, surrounded by laciniae, verruciform, black, paucilocellate, 1–2 mm. broad; peridium of large parenchymatous cells, brown outside, paler within. Spores ellipsoid, obtuse at both ends, somewhat clavulate, thick-walled, granular-cloudy or with a few guttules, 20–40 × 10–14μ; sporophores filiform, up to 25μ long, 1·5–2μ thick. (Fig. 17 b.)

On twigs of *Juglans regia*. Dodderhill Common, Ws. (Rhodes), accompanied by *Cytospora juglandina*.

Similar to *F. Juglandis* Massal. but with different spores.
Germ.

Myrica
Fusicoccum Myricae Grove. *Myxofusicoccum Myricae* Died. p. 318, p. 308, f. 6. Mig. 153.

Stromata scattered, elevating the epidermis in a convex pustule, then flatly pulvinate, oblong, pseudolocellate, 1 mm. long, 300μ broad. Spores 10–12 × 3–4μ.

On small twigs of *Myrica Gale*. Llanberis Castle, Carnarvonshire (Rhodes).   July.

Germ.

Platanus
Fusicoccum hapalocystis Sacc. Syll. iii. 249. All. vi. 554. Mig. 182.

"Stromata very small, causing little elevations of the bark. Spores ovoid-oblong, attenuated towards the base, indistinctly 3-guttulate, pale-yellowish, 28 × 8μ, borne on the apex of filiform sporophores."

On dead branches of *Platanus*. Locality uncertain.

The pycnidium of *Pseudovalsa hapalocystis* Sacc. Syll. ii. 138.
A doubtful *Fusicoccum*; cf. *Phoma hapalocystis* (Fckl.) Sacc., *supra*, p. 97.
Germ.

Quercus
Fusicoccum quercinum Sacc. Syll. iii. 248; Fung. Ital. pl. 1461. All. vi. 555, with fig. Grove, in Journ. Bot. 1916, p. 190, pl. 542, f. 6. *Phomopsis quercina* v. Höhn. Fragm. z. Mykol. 1906, no. 87, p. 33. Died. in Ann. Mycol. 1911, ix. 28, pl. 3, f. 2; Pilz. Brand. 264. Mig. 166.

Stromata transversely elongated or oblong, immersed, then erumpent, divided into several imperfect loculi; contents

pinkish. Spores cylindric-fusoid, gently curved, indistinctly guttulate, $15-18 \times 3-3\cdot5\mu$; sporophores filiform, about as long as the spore or a little shorter.

On bark of *Quercus Robur*, *Q. sessiliflora*. Prenton, Cheshire; Malvern (Ellis). Surrey; Warwicks.; Worcs.; etc. On acorn-cups of *Q. Ilex*, Hadzor Hall, Ws. (Rhodes). Apr. May.

A pycnidial stage of *Diaporthe (Chor.) leiphaemia* Sacc.

All possible intermediate forms of spore may be found, sometimes in the same pycnidium, between that described above and a typical Phomopsis spore measuring $7-10 \times 1\cdot5-2\mu$; many of the larger spores show a tendency to be or to appear 1-septate. Cf. also *Myxosporium Lanceola*, in Vol. II.

Europe, N. America.

Rhamnus

Fusicoccum fibrosum Sacc. Syll. iii. 247. All. vi. 556. *Phomopsis fibrosa* v. Höhn. Frag. z. Mykol. no. 87, p. 33. Died. 265. Mig. 166.

Stromata conical, erumpent, plurilocular, very thick and black; contents of loculi yellowish-fuscous. Spores ellipsoid, acuminate below, biguttulate, $8-11 \times 4-5\mu$; sporophores filiform, $10-16 \times 1\cdot5\mu$.

On dry branches and stems of *Rhamnus catharticus*. No certain British locality known for this stage, but the ascophore is not rare in this country.

The pycnidium of *Chorostate fibrosa* Trav. $=$ *Diaporthe fibrosa* Fckl. Fr. Belg. Germ. Ital. Swed.

Ribes

Fusicoccum viridulum Sacc. Syll. iii. 248. All. vi. 556. Died. 315.

Stromata composed of many erect almost cylindrical loculi, round or ovate. Spores fusoid, curvulous, obtuse at both ends, hyaline "with a faint greenish tinge" (Sacc.), $13-15 \times 5\mu$ (Rhodes); sporophores short, branched.

On branches of *Ribes nigrum*, Blackminster, Offenham, Ws. (Rhodes). Mar.

A doubtful specimen; the spores were not greenish.
Germ.

Sorbus

Fusicoccum Aucupariae Grove. *Myxofusicoccum Aucupariae* Died. Pilz. Brand. 320. Mig. 154.

Stromata loosely gregarious, elevating the epidermis and bursting it, conico-truncate, plurilocellate (? pseudo-). Spores $10-13 \times 4-5\mu$ ("oval, $9-11 \times 3-3\cdot5\mu$", Rhodes).

On small branches of *Sorbus Aucuparia*, Oscott College, Birmingham (Rhodes). June.

Cf. *Rabenhorstia clandestina* (Fr.) Mig. 219; and *Phomopsis sorbicola*, *supra*, p. 220.

Germ.

Ulmus

Fusicoccum depressum Grove. *Phoma depressa* B. & Br. in Ann. Nat. Hist. 1850, v. 370 (*non* Lév. Sacc.). Cooke, Handb. 419. *P. planiuscula* Sacc. Syll. iii. 99 (*non* Karst.). All. vi. 241. Mig. 95, *p.p.*

Stromata rather thick, olivaceous, much depressed above, sometimes plurilocular within and forming scattered pierced pustules, 0·5–1 mm. diam. Spores oblong-ellipsoid, rather acute at both ends, with 2 (or even 3 or 4) guttules, 8–12 × 2–2·5µ; sporophores cylindrical, longer than the spore.

On twigs and branches of *Ulmus campestris* (and ? *Robinia Pseudacacia*). Kew Gardens; Batheaston; King's Cliffe; Highgate; Swanscombe. Feb. Mar.

Possibly the pycnidium of *Chorostate Saccardiana* (Kunze); see Ann. Mycol. xiii. 135. The specimens on *Syringa* in the Kew Herbarium, assigned to this, belong to *Phomopsis depressa* Trav., and most, if not all, of those on *Robinia* are doubtful.

Species of Fusicoccum are mentioned by Saccardo (Syll. i. 466–7), with a ? attached, as belonging to the British pyrenomycetes, *Cryptosporella hypodermia* (on *Ulmus*) and *C. aurea* (on *Carpinus*). The pycnospores of the former are figured by Migula (pl. 82, f. 2) after Brefeld and Engler u. Prantl.

CYTOSPORA Ehrenb. Sylv. Berol. 28.

Stroma covered by the raised epidermis or periderm, sooner or later erumpent, conical or pustular, usually containing a number of chambers (loculi) which are often imperfectly separated and irregular or sinuous in shape, but are often quite separate, circinate, occasionally radiating round a central loculus or a black columella. When the stroma is exposed by the bursting of the covering layer, a disc (often whitish) is seen in which there are one or more black pores; rarely the stroma contains only one loculus. Spores always small (3–10µ in length), cylindrical and more or less curved (sausage-shaped), often very numerous, eseptate, nearly or quite hyaline, issuing from

the pore in damp weather as a globule or tendril according to the humidity; sporophores always evident, simple or not infrequently branched. (Fig. 18.)

The spores are often described as "straight or curved", but this is most frequently an illusion, due to the different postures in which they are seen. If a single spore is watched while rotating in water under the microscope, it may be seen to pass through three phases, straight (face-view), curved (profile-view), and perhaps circular (end-view).

a   b   c   d

Fig. 18. *Cytospora*: spores and sporophores, *a*, of *C. Salicis*; *b*, of *C. Pini*; *c*, of *C. Oxyacanthae*; all × 600; *d*, conical emerging stroma of *C. leucostoma*, on *Prunus Padus* from Wales, showing the white disc and the black central ostiole, × 40.

The members of this form-genus, which can occur on leaves as well as on stems, are probably all pycnidial stages of those Pyrenomycetes which have allantoid (sausage-shaped) spores, such as *Valsa*, *Valsella*, and *Eutypella*. Not infrequently they may be found in company with the ascophorous stage; in that case the Cytospora-stage may be parasitic, and be succeeded by the mature ascophorous stage on the dead host. In some species several hosts are recorded, belonging to different genera or even families; but most of these are doubtless collective species, biologically at least distinct. Many of the older records of this kind are quite unworthy of remembrance.

Von Höhnel divides the genus into two sections:

(1) *Eucytospora* (belonging to *Valsa* proper) without a special basal stroma, so that the pycnidia are immersed in the matrix directly, e.g. *C. ambiens*, *C. Abietis*, *C. carphosperma*, *C. ceratophora*, *C. Curreyi*, *C. germanica*, *C. Pini*, *C. Salicis*, *C. Schweinitzii*, and

(2) *Leucocytospora* (belonging to *Leucostoma* and *Valsella*) with a special "conceptacle", either close to the pycnidia or a millimetre or so away, delimiting the part occupied by them

from the other unchanged matrix; e.g. *C. cincta, C. nivea, C. leucostoma.* Cf. Petrak, in Ann. Mycol. 1921, xix. 128.

In this genus the species on CONIFERAE and ROSACEAE are listed under those family-names; the others in the simple alphabetical order of the hosts, plurivorous species always first.

Plurivorous

Cytospora ambiens Sacc. Syll. iii. 268. All. vi. 567. Died. 332. Mig. 189. Grove, in Kew Bull. 1923, p. 5.

Stromata subgregarious or as it were densely scattered, often extending uniformly along a whole branch or twig, about 1 mm. diam., conico-depressed, covered, then erumpent, blackish-grey, with a roundish flat disc which is paler or brownish but never white; ostiole usually one only, black, scarcely protruding; loculi several, but often confluent into one, the walls composed of dark-brownish or greenish hyphae. Spores sausage-shaped, $5-7 \times 1\mu$, exuding in a white, then yellowish tendril or mass; sporophores often much branched, $20-30\mu$ long, resting on a basal cell; branches acicular, forked or verticillate.

Common on bark of twigs and branches of *Acer, Betula, Castanea, Corylus, Cotoneaster, Fagus, Fraxinus, Malus, Negundo, Populus, Pyrus, Quercus, Rosa, Rubus, Salix, Ulmus,* etc. No doubt a collective species, the pycnidial stage of *Valsa ambiens* Sacc. It is most abundant on *Acer.*

Recorded abroad also on *Alnus, Carpinus, Cornus,* etc., but perhaps incorrectly. The prominent disc is almost always round and varies in colour from grey to black; the spores are very variable, from 4 to 7μ in length, with sporophores from 10μ up to 30μ. The fungus gets its name from the fact that the numerous ostioles of the perithecia of the Valsa stage often constitute a ring just within the periphery of the disc. The most characteristic marks of the forms assigned to this species lie in the dingy disc and the much branched sporophores.

The form on *Betula* may belong to *Valsa betulina* Nits., and other forms, as on *Crataegus* and *Tilia,* have been distinguished, for which *vide infra.*

Europe generally, N. and S. America (incl. Canada).

Cytospora carbonacea Fr. Syst. Myc. ii. 544. Sacc. Syll. iii. 260. All. vi. 610. Died. 366. Mig. 211.

"Stroma proper rather thin; loculi black and becoming

indistinct together with the whitish disc; ostioles black, prominent." (Fr.)

On branches of *Celtis occidentalis*. Kew Gardens (Cooke). These specimens are somewhat doubtful and imperfect, but they are not *C. Celtidis* E. and E. The species is recorded in Germany and Sweden on *Ulmus*, and elsewhere on *Alnus*.

"A species of which little is known, though it is very common; provided with a proper conceptacle; pustules minute, not prominent, immersed in the inner bark; stroma proper carbonaceous, indistinctly locellate, but with a very distinct central columella." (Fr.)

Diedicke's description (on *Ulmus*) is as follows: "Stromata loosely gregarious, at length pushing up the epidermis considerably and erumpent with the whitish disc, depressed-conical, up to 1 mm. broad with very many incomplete radiating chambers arranged round a central columella, with a common ostiole; wall fusco-fuliginous externally, a little paler inwards. Spores $4-5 \times 1-1 \cdot 5\mu$; sporophores simple, filiform, up to 15μ long, 1μ thick, soon disappearing." (*l.c.*)

Belg. Holl. Germ. Swed. N. Amer.

Cytospora ceratophora Sacc. Syll. iii. 268. All. vi. 572. Died. 342. Mig. 196.

Stromata densely scattered, depressed-conical, covered, then erumpent by a very small grey disc, plurilocular; contents dark-olive; pycnidial wall several cells thick, of narrow olivaceous prosenchymatous cells. Spores sausage-shaped, $4-5 \times 1\mu$; sporophores simple or verticillately branched at the base, acicular, $20-50 \times 1\mu$.

On bark of *Quercus* and *Castanea*. Kew; Whitehall; Bartley Green and Earlswood, Warwickshire; Worcestershire; Cheshire; Ayrshire; etc. Sept.–May.

The pycnidial stage of *Valsa ceratophora* Tul.

Recorded abroad also on *Carpinus*, *Fraxinus*, *Sorbus*, *Ulmus*, etc. The Earlswood specimens were in company with a beautiful series of the Valsa, in November, on dead shoots of the previous summer sent up from the stool of a felled Oak.

Europe generally.

Cytospora foliicola Lib. Exs. no. 64. Desm. in Ann. Sci. Nat. 1842, xvii. 117. Cooke, Handb. 754. Sacc. Syll. iii. 275. Died. 332. All. vi. 567. Mig. 189. See Grove, in Kew Bull. 1923, p. 11.

"Stromata gregarious, covered by the epidermis, erumpent, conico-depressed, black, containing few loculi; disc pallid,

with a common central pore. Spores sausage-shaped, 7–10 ×
1μ; issuing in a whitish tendril; sporophores filiform, fasciculate, about 10–15 × 1μ."

Recorded in Britain on leaves of *Hedera, Garrya, Mahonia
Aquifolium,* and *Kalmia,* as well as on cladodes of *Ruscus
Hypoglossum,* etc.

A composite species, which should be distributed among other
names. For instance, var. *Euonymi,* on fading or dead leaves and
small twigs of *Euonymus japonicus* (Eastbourne; Liverpool; Cheshire;
Kew Gardens; etc.) is no doubt *Cytospora Euonymi* Cooke—also var.
Vincae is *Ceuthospora Feurichii* Bub. Some other forms put under this
name are the (A) pycnidia of a Ceuthospora (*q.v.*), and the varieties
recorded by Saccardo and others on leaves of *Acer, Crataegus, Quercus,*
etc. should meet a similar fate to those quoted above.

Cytospora guttifera Fr. Syst. Myc. ii. 545. Cooke, Handb. 462.
Sacc. Syll. iii. 264. All. vi. 578. Died. 339. Mig. 194. *Sphaeria guttifera* DC. Flor. fr. vi. 136.

"Stromata immersed, plurilocular, black, attenuated into
a conical obtuse erumpent neck; gelatinous contents issuing
in a whitish globule. Spores oblong-cylindrical."

On branches of *Quercus.*

Berkeley says "on dead twigs of *Salix*". A confused species, recorded in Germany also on *Corylus* and *Tilia*; but this is a legacy from
the time when it was thought that "issuing in a globule" was different
from "issuing in a tendril". The "species" should be forgotten.
Fr. Germ.

Cytospora leucosperma Fr. Syst. Myc. ii. 543. Cooke, Handb.
462, 826. Sacc. Syll. iii. 268. All. vi. 567. Died. 333. Mig. 190.
Naemospora leucosperma Pers. Syn. 108.

Stromata small, widely scattered, 500–750μ diam., black,
raising the epidermis convexly and at length piercing it by the
round flat whitish disc; loculi several, united in the centre in
a black ostiole; walls rather thick, greyish-green. Spores
sausage-shaped, about 4·5–5·5 × 1·25–1·5μ, issuing in white
tendrils; sporophores filiform, mostly simple, 15–16 × 1μ.

Recorded as common in England (also in Ireland) on twigs
and branches of various rosaceous trees, Plum, Apple, Sorbus,
Hawthorn, Rose, etc. and on *Acer Pseudoplatanus.* But the

records are in most cases meaningless, being a mixture of various species.

Recorded abroad on *Cytisus*, *Carpinus*, *Fagus*, etc., also. It was supposed to be characterised by its *white* tendrils which showed little or no tendency to become yellowish, but most of the specimens seem to be forms of *C. ambiens*. For the form on *Ilex* see *C. Aquifolii* Fr. Europe, N. Amer.

Acer

Cytospora annulata Ell. & Ev. in Proc. Acad. Nat. Sci. Philad. 1893, p. 160. Sacc. Syll. xi. 508.

Stromata immersed, multilocular, about 1 mm. diam., slate-colour within, with a ringed ostiole. Spores oblong, straight or curvulous, $5-6 \times 1-1\cdot25\mu$.

On dead branches of *Acer Negundo*. Kew Gardens (Cooke).

When perfectly developed, as seen in American specimens, this presents a remarkably ringed appearance. The black shining ostiole is surrounded by a narrow ring of whitish stroma; around this is the conspicuous torn margin of the epidermis, and in many cases the whole is surrounded by a wide zone in the form of a dark-brown stain. U.S.A. Canada.

Cytospora hyalosperma Fr. Syst. Myc. ii. 545. Sacc. Syll. iii. 258.

"Stromata immersed, indistinctly cellular, black, as well as the conico-convex erumpent neck. Spores issuing in a colourless tendril."

On bark of *Acer Pseudoplatanus*. Kew Gardens. A very dubious species, which should be dropped and forgotten.

In the Kew specimen the spores are slightly curved, and measure about $6 \times 1\mu$. J. B. Ellis's American specimens, named *hyalosperma*, on *Acer rubrum*, are very different in outward appearance; the spores are smaller, $4-5 \times 1\mu$; "small, without a depressed disc". Swed. U.S.A.

Cytospora macilenta Rob. & Desm. in Ann. Sci. Nat. 1849, xi. 352. Sacc. Syll. iii. 258. All. vi. 565.

Stromata minute, punctiform, numerous, arranged without order, irregularly rounded, ovate, or reniform, convex, brown or black, covered by the epidermis at first, then surrounded by it when ruptured; loculi 5–7, slender, circinate, with fleshy contents. Spores oblong, rather obtuse at the ends,

17-2

straight, 2–4-guttulate, somewhat opaque, 10–$1b \times 2 \cdot 5$–$3 \cdot 5\mu$, issuing in a short thick yellowish-white tendril.

"On dry branches of *Acer obtusatum*, Kew Gardens" (Cooke).

This species, it is said, normally occurs on *Cornus mas*. Desmazières expressly states, on his exsiccatum, that it is not on *Acer Negundo*, as recorded in the *Annales*, but on *Staphylea pinnata*; while Westendorp says that it is not on *Staphylea*, but on *Cornus mas*. The Kew record is therefore untrustworthy.

Fr. Belg. Holl.

Ailanthus

Cytospora Ailanthi B. & C. North Amer. Fungi, no. 3432; see Grevill. ii. 99. Sacc. Syll. iii. 277.

Stromata rather crowded, 250–300μ diam., totally immersed, then bursting the epidermis by a minute pore, and disclosing a blackish disc, but scarcely prominent. Spores sausage-shaped, 5–$6 \times 1\mu$.

On twigs of *Ailanthus glandulosa*. Kew Gardens (Cooke).

Apr.

These specimens are young and somewhat doubtful. Perhaps not the pycnidial stage of *Eutypella Ailanthi* Sacc., for that is said to be *Cytosporina Ailanthi* Sacc., with spores 15μ long, but (?).

U.S.A.

Alnus

Cytospora occulta Sacc. Syll. iii. 258. All. vi. 568. Died. 334. Mig. 191.

"Pycnidia nestling beneath the bark, connate; contents grey. Spores very minute, cylindrical, curved, $6 \times 1 \cdot 5\mu$, expelled in golden tendrils from a common tuberculate black pore."

On dry branches of *Alnus glutinosa*. Regent's Park (Cooke). *n.v.*

Apr.

Said by Fuckel to be the pycnidial stage of *Melanconis occulta* Sacc. Germ. Denm.

Ampelopsis

Cytospora Ampelopsidis Massal. Contr. Mic. Ver. p. 86, pl. 2, f. 12. Sacc. Syll. x. 243. All. vi. 569. Mig. 191.

Stromata scattered, somewhat oval, longitudinally placed, flattened-convex, black, 400–600μ long, nestling in the cortex

and for a long time entirely concealed by it, at length disclosing an oval black disc marked with several minute non-
projecting pores, multilocellate within, the loculi small and
varying much in shape and arrangement, separated by thick
dark-brown walls. Spores very numerous, sausage-shaped,
5–6 × 1·5µ, nearly colourless in mass; sporophores crowded,
parallel, linear, usually very erect and straight, 15–18 × 1µ.

On bark of twigs of *Ampelopsis quinquefolia*, Kirkby,
Lancs. (Ellis). On *A. Veitchii*, Hove (Salmon). Droitwich.
June.

Distinguished from *C. Vitis* Mont. by being all but completely concealed by the periderm. Massalongo says that the tendrils are
"pinkish when moist, reddish-amber when dry".
Germ. Ital.

Baccharis
Cytospora Baccharidis Grove.

Stromata small, scattered, convex-hemispherical, covered,
then bursting the epidermis and emerging by the flat blackish-
brown disc, 200–500µ diam., often surrounded by a distinct
fulvous stain. Spores sausage-shaped, obtuse at both ends,
curvulous, 5–7 × 1–1·5µ; sporophores filiform, acute, straight,
erect, simple or rarely branched, 12–15 × 1µ.

On twigs of *Baccharis halimifolia*. Heythrop Park, Oxon.
(Grove & Rhodes). June.

Betula
Cytospora horrida Sacc. Syll. iii. 259. All. vi. 570. Died. p. 335,
p. 308, f. 12. Mig. p. 192, pl. 24, f. 9, 10.

Stromata loosely gregarious, immersed, elevating the periderm in a conical protuberance, bursting it for the most part
transversely, and raising the pointed almost beak-shaped end
above it, thick-walled, plurilocular within; disc greyish,
pierced by a single black ostiole. Spores sausage-shaped, 5 ×
1µ; sporophores often dichotomously branched, 20–30 × 1µ.

On twigs and small branches of *Betula alba*. Heythrop
Park, Oxon. (Grove & Rhodes). June.

The pycnidial stage of *Valsa horrida* Nits.
Germ.

Carpinus

Cytospora decipiens Sacc. Syll. iii. 263. All. vi. 566. Mig. 193.
Grevill. xiv. 69.

Stromata arising beneath the outermost layer of the bark, usually oblong, spreading at the margin, often arranged in rows, golden, multilocular, the loculi very numerous and arranged without perceptible order. Spores linear-cylindrical, very slender, curved, at length expelled in golden or red tendrils or masses.

On trunks of *Carpinus*. Recorded by Cooke. *n.v.*

Said to be the pycnidial stage of *Anthostoma decipiens* Nits.

Winter, in describing this pycnidial form of the ascomycete, assigns to the spores a length of 10–13μ. It is recorded also (more rarely) on *Acer*, *Betula*, *Fagus*, and *Quercus*. It is apparently not a true Cytospora, but a *Naemospora*.

Fr. Belg. Germ. Ital.

CONIFERAE

Larix, etc.

Cytospora Curreyi Sacc. Syll. iii. 269. All. vi. 573. Lind, in Ann.
Mycol. 1907, v. 275. Died. 330. Mig. 189.

Stromata conico-truncate or almost hemispherical, with a round or rarely oval base, 1–1·5 mm. diam., very protuberant, covered at the sides by the adherent stellately cleft periderm; disc dingy, provided with a single central papilla which is pierced by a very minute pore (sometimes there are two or three papillae); loculi many, radiating or without order. Spores cylindrical, curvulous, 3–6 × 1–1·5μ; sporophores usually simple, sometimes branched, 20–24 or even 32μ long.

On dead branches of *Larix europaea*, Roslin Glen and Forres (Boyd). On branches and cones of *Pinus silvestris*, South Devon (Rhodes); etc. On dead branches and cone-scales of *Picea*, etc., Yorkshire.

The pycnidial stage of *Valsa Curreyi* Nits. Lind says (*l.c.*) that the tendrils are purplish (?).

Fr. Germ. Austr. Denm. Ital.

Cytospora Abietis Sacc. Syll. iii. 269. All. vi. 573. Died. 329.
Mig. 188. *C. Pini* Fckl. *p.p.*

Stromata 500–800μ diam., convex, with a thick roundish or truncate neck, disclosing a grey or yellowish disc that after-

wards becomes brownish and is pierced by a single (rarely more) flat open pore, multilocular within, the loculi very minute and densely crowded without order. Spores cylindrical, curvulous, 5–6 × 1μ (3–4 × 1μ, Sacc.), issuing in dingy-yellow masses; sporophores subulate, 12–16μ long, verticillately branched (sparingly branched, Sacc.).

On small branches of *Larix europaea*. Eastham Wood, Cheshire (Ellis). Shrawley Wood, Ws.   Dec.–Apr.

Said to be the pycnidial stage of *Valsa Abietis* Nits. In other countries it is recorded also on *Picea (Abies) excelsa*, and on *Sequoia*.
Europe.

Picea

Cytospora Friesii Sacc. Syll. iii. 269. All. vi. 574. Died. 330. Mig. 189.

Stromata scattered, small, conico-truncate, bursting through the epidermis with a blackish-grey disc, which is pierced by one or two slightly projecting ostioles; loculi few, circinate. Spores sausage-shaped, 4–5·5 × 1–1·5μ (6–7 × 2μ, Rhodes); sporophores fasciculate, mostly simple, 10–15μ long.

On leaves and twigs of *Picea pectinata*. Hadzor Hall, Droitwich (Grove & Rhodes); etc.   Mar.–May.

The pycnidial stage of *Valsa Friesii* Fckl.
It is found especially on the upper surface of the leaves, but also on the young twigs. The ascophorous stage follows on the main trunk and branches. Sometimes included under *C. Pinastri*.
Fr. Belg. Germ. Austr.

Cytospora Kunzei Sacc. Syll. iii. 270. All. vi. 574. Died. 351. Mig. 201.

Stromata scattered, covered, immersed between the periderm and the cortex, up to 2 mm. broad, multilocular, the loculi labyrinthiform or irregularly arranged, opening by a single pore (rarely by several) in the centre of a minute roundish greyish-yellow disc which alone is visible. Spores sausage-shaped, 4–5 × 1μ, expelled in yellow, then saffron-coloured, tendrils; sporophores linear, sparingly branched or rather fasciculate at base, 20–25μ.

On bark of *Picea excelsa, P. pectinata*. Alnwick; King's Lynn; Kew Gardens.   Aug.–Oct.

The pycnidial stage of *Valsa Kunzei* Nits. Walls of loculi dark brownish-grey; contents dark olive-grey.
Fr. Germ. Switz.

Pinus

Cytospora Pini Desm. in Ann. Sci. Nat. 1843, xix. 362(?). Sacc.
Syll. iii. 270. All. vi. 575. Died. 351. Mig. 201. (*Non* Fckl. Fung.
Rhen. no. 628.) *C. pinicola* Westd.

Stromata scattered, immersed, without any distinct conceptacle, up to 2 mm. diam.; the loculi numerous, black, oblong, irregularly circinate; contents greyish-green; disc flat,
erumpent, smoky-black; ostiole usually one only, prominent,
black, shining; walls of loculi thin, of dark-brown prosenchymatous cells. Spores cylindrical, nearly straight, $4 \times 1\mu$,
issuing in sulphur-coloured, then lemon-coloured tendrils;
sporophores filiform, branched, $20-25 \times 1\mu$. (Fig. 18*b*.)

On bark of *Pinus silvestris*. Twycross (Berk.). Cheshire
(Ellis).   Nov.

The pycnidial stage of *Valsa Pini* Fr.
Westendorp records his form *pinicola* on *Cedrus Libani*, with spores
$6\cdot5\mu$ long. The species is also recorded on *Pinus Strobus* and on
Cupressus, abroad. Desmazières describes his spores as "ovoid, 3μ
long".
Europe (as far east as Dalmatia).

Cytospora Pinastri Fr. Syst. Myc. ii. 544. Cooke, Handb. 462.
Sacc. Syll. iii. 725. All. vi. 575, with fig. Died. 330. Mig. p. 189,
pl. 24, f. 6–8.

Stromata on both sides of the leaves, about 250μ diam.,
globose, immersed, then erumpent, conical, plurilocular;
loculi few, imperfect; pycnidial wall of dark-brown interwoven hyphae; disc roundish, tuberculate, blackish, nearly
obliterated by the shining prominent black ostiole. Spores
sausage-shaped, $4-5 \times 1-1\cdot5\mu$, issuing as a short milk-white
tendril; sporophores fasciculate, branched, acicular or flexuous, $20-25 \times 1\mu$, rising from a greenish-olive parenchymatous
stratum.

On dead leaves of *Pinus silvestris*. England, Scotland. Not
uncommon.

It is recorded abroad also on *Abies, Cryptomeria, Cupressus*,
but probably what has been so-named on leaves of *Abies* is
C. Friesii (*q.v.*).

Europe, N. America.

Taxus

Cytospora Taxi Sacc. Syll. iii. 271. All. vi. 608. Died. 365. Mig. 210. *C. taxifolia* C. & M. in Grevill. xviii. 73. Sacc. Syll. x. 248.

Stromata similar to those of *C. Pinastri*, but occurring more often on the upper side of the leaves, splitting the epidermis by the long black ostiole, which often stands up considerably above it, plurilocular, black, up to 2 mm. diam. Spores cylindrical, curved, 6–$8 \times 1\cdot5\mu$.

On dead twigs and leaves of *Taxus baccata*. Carlisle; Rugby; Worcestershire; Heythrop Park, Oxon.; Glamis; Ireland. Nov. Dec.

The pycnidial stage of *Valsa Taxi* Fckl.
Cooke's specimen from Carlisle (*C. taxifolia*) has spores 5–$6 \times 1\mu$; but Dr Ellis's on leaves and twigs, from Shrawley, Worcs., has spores 7–$9 \times 1\mu$, and mine from Rugby, on leaves, has them 8–$10 \times 1\cdot5\mu$. Germ.

Cornus

Cytospora Corni Westd. 5th Notice, p. 28 in Bull. Acad. Roy. Belg. vol. ii, 1857. Kickx, Flor. Crypt. Flandr. i. 446. Lambotte, Flor. Myc. Belg. ii. 372. Sacc. Syll. x. 246. All. vi. 576. Died. 338. Mig. 193.

Pycnidia black, smooth, compressed, united in groups of 3–5, covered by the raised browned epidermis, at length emerging by a punctiform black shining disc, which is pierced by the united black ostioles of the ± confluent ovoid chambers. Spores cylindrical, straight or curvulous, 5–$6 \times 1\cdot25\mu$, exuding as a yellowish-white tendril; sporophores subulate, 12μ long or more.

On branches of *Cornus sanguinea*. Yarhampton, Hillcot, Glos.; Witley, Ws. (Rhodes). Abberley, Ws. On branches of *Cornus alba*. Hadzor Hall, Ws. (Rhodes & Grove).

The pycnidial stage of *Valsa fallax* Nits.
Belg. Germ.

Corylus

Cytospora Fuckelii Sacc. Syll. iii. 263. All. vi. 577. Died. 338. Mig. 194.

Stromata widely but not densely scattered, obtusely and flatly conical, roundish, 500–700μ broad, long covered by the epidermis, at length piercing it by the greyish disc which is marked by a black pore, multilocular within, the loculi somewhat circinate, with thick walls composed of greenish-grey

prosenchymatous cells. Spores sausage-shaped, $5-6 \times 1.5\mu$; spore-mass greyish; sporophores simple, acicular, curved, $20-26\mu$ long.

On twigs of *Corylus Avellana*. Neston, Cheshire (Ellis).

Dec.

With *Valsa Fuckelii* Nits., of which it is the pycnidial stage. Germ. Ital.

Cytisus

Cytospora Laburni Peyr. in Nuov. Giorn. Bot. Ital. 1918, xxv. 424, f. 22–28.

Stromata subepidermal, then bursting the epidermis and erumpent, showing previously through it as a black dot or ring, conico-truncate. Pycnidia few or one only in each stroma, with a long but hardly projecting ostiole; wall membranaceous, very dark. Spores allantoid, hyaline, $5.5-6.5 \times 1.3-1.5\mu$; sporophores branched, hyaline, $20-40 \times 1-1.5\mu$; ultimate branchlets lageniform.

On dead branches of *Cytisus Laburnum*. Birkenhead (Ellis), "spores oozing out as a red tendril". Oscott College, Birmingham (Rhodes). Apr. May.

The pycnidial stage of *Valsa Laburni* (Allesch.). Ital.

Euonymus

Cytospora Euonymi Cooke, in Grevill. xiv. 4. Sacc. Syll. x. 244. All. vi. 580. Died. 341. Mig. 195.

Stromata densely gregarious, covering large portions of the bark, raising the browned epidermis conically, divided below into several irregularly arranged loculi which converge into a common cavity and emerge as a conical ostiole. Spores cylindrical, bent, $4-7 \times 1-1.5\mu$; sporophores crowded, mostly simple, acicular, $15-25 \times 1\mu$.

On small twigs of *Euonymus americanus*. Kew (Cooke). On dead branches of *E. japonicus*. Hunterston, Ayrshire (Boyd). Wisley, Surrey. Jun.–Sept.

Cooke describes the pycnidia as "rather small, at length blackish and shining; spores $8 \times 2\mu$, issuing in pallid tendrils". He records it only on the twigs, but *C. foliicola*, var. *Euonymi*, is no doubt the same species on the leaves.

Germ. Austr. Moravia.

Fraxinus
Cytospora pruinosa Sacc. Mich. i. 519. *Sphaeria pruinosa* Fr.
Obs. Myc. ii. 328; Syst. Myc. ii. 486, *p.p. Dendrophoma pruinosa*
Sacc. Syll. iii. 179. All. vi. 403. Died. pp. 195, 899, p. 202, f. III, 1.
Mig. 120. *Cytospora melasperma* Fr. var. *Fraxini* All. *Cytophoma*
pruinosa v. Höhn. Fragm. z. Mykol. no. 863 (1914).

Pycnidia gregarious, unilocular (? always), immersed,
black, depressed, adnate to the epidermis, covered with a
greyish pruina, with a black bullate ostiole which in damp
places can be much prolonged; wall rather thick, of several
layers, dark-brown, paler inwards. Spores sausage-shaped,
yellowish or pale-olivaceous in mass, singly hyaline, $5-7 \times 1\mu$,
issuing in a dark-coloured globule or tendril which ultimately
becomes nearly black; sporophores once or twice verticillately
branched, 4–5 times longer than the spore.

On bark of branches of *Fraxinus excelsior*. Twycross (Berk.).
Ham Common, Surrey (E. W. Mason). Mar.

Von Höhnel's *Cytophoma* is supposed to be a *Cytospora* which is
absolutely unilocular. Cf. *Strickeria obducens* Wint.

Var. **Ligustri** Strasser, in Verh. Zool.-Bot. Ges. Wien, 1900, lx. 311.

On small twigs of *Ligustrum vulgare*. Regent's Park
(Cooke). Stevenston and Seamill, Ayrshire (Boyd). West
Kirby (Ellis). Haselor, near Evesham, Worcs. (Rhodes).
Mickleham; etc.

The type species and the variety are both said to be the pycnidial
stage of *Valsa Cypri* Tul. Carp. ii. 194 (Sacc. Syll. i. 133), i.e. of *V.*
Ligustri Schröt. on Oleaceae. The pycnidium on *Ligustrum* does not
always remain unilocular.

Europe, N. Amer.

Hippophaë
Cytospora Hippophaës Thüm. Fung. Austr. no. 282. Sacc. Syll.
iii. 274. All. vi. 583. Died. 345. Mig. 198.

Stromata small, 250–330 mm. diam., scattered, covered by
the blackened epidermis, rather prominent, at length erumpent,
pallid, then black. Spores sausage-shaped, $4-6 \times 1-1\cdot25\mu$;
sporophores fasciculate (4–6 together, Died.), $12-20 \times i\mu$.

On dead twigs and branches of *Hippophaë rhamnoides*.
Ardrossan, Ayrshire (Boyd). Kew Gardens. Apr.–Nov.

In the Ayrshire specimen the loculi were as many as twelve, all
arranged in a circle round a central grey or blackish disc, and each

often piercing it by a separate ostiole. The wall of each loculus was distinct and of a pale-greenish colour. Thümen's specimen is very similar. This is said to be the pycnidium of *Massaria Hippophaës* Jacz. Germ. Austr. Denm.

Hypericum

Cytospora Hyperici Grove, in Journ. Bot. 1922, p. 45.

Stromata densely scattered, pulvinate, oval, up to 2 mm. long, convex, opening by a central pore surrounded by a minute blackish disc, plurilocular within; loculi ± circinate, the walls thin and composed of greenish cells like those of *Cytospora Oxyacanthae* Rab. Spores sausage-shaped, 4–$5 \times 1\mu$; sporophores rod-like, straight, about $10 \times 1\mu$.

On dead branches of *Hypericum*. West Kilbride, Ayrshire (Boyd). Hadzor, Ws. (Rhodes). Jul.–Sept.

Ilex

Cytospora ilicina Sacc. Syll. iii. 274. Mig. 198.

"Stromata immersed, pustular, erumpent, contained in a conceptacle like the Valsa, but smaller, multilocular; locules very minute, numerous, crowded in one layer, opening in the middle of the roundish disc by a central pore. Spores cylindrical, curved or nearly straight, subhyaline, 5–7 (or even 8 or $8 \cdot 5) \times 1\mu$; sporophores subsimple, eseptate, 20–$24 \times 2\mu$."

On dead stems of *Ilex Aquifolium*. Franche, near Kidderminster (Rhodes). *n.v.*

The pycnidial stage of *Valsa Aquifolii* Nits. (Pyr. Germ. p. 231). Germ.

Cytospora Aquifolii Fr. in Duby, Bot. Gall. ii. 725. Sacc. Syll. iii. 274. All. vi. 583. Grove, in Kew Bull. 1923, p. 7.

Stromata subgregarious, conical, up to 500μ diam., black, surrounded by a black stain, covered, then erumpent by a rimose or stellate fissure and disclosing a dark-coloured disc, with a central prominent very black pore which often nearly obliterates the disc, plurilocular within; the loculi rounded, small, and clustered in a circular group; no conceptacle; walls of loculi very thick and blackish-brown. Spores 4–$6 \times 1\mu$; sporophores simple, subulate, about three times as long as the spore, tinged with olivaceous at the base.

On dead bark of *Ilex Aquifolium.* Kew Gardens (Cooke). Harborne and Quinton, near Birmingham. Mar. Apr.

Distinguished from *C. ilicina* by the total absence of a conceptacle, of which the Birmingham specimens showed no trace.

Vosges.

Jasminum

Cytospora Jasmini Cooke, in Grevill. xiv. 4. Sacc. Syll. x. 245. All. vi. 583.

Stromata very loosely gregarious, somewhat conical, sub-epidermal, small, epidermis darkened above. Spores linear, curved, sausage-shaped, $6 \times 1\mu$, oozing forth through a minute orifice.

On thin twigs of *Jasminum officinale,* Kew Gardens. On the same, Hadzor Hall, Droitwich. Apr. May.

Juglans

Cytospora juglandina Sacc. Syll. iii. 267. All. vi. 584. Died. 345. Mig. 198.

Stromata gregarious, covered by the epidermis which is occasionally cleft by the projecting subcylindrical ostiole, black, plurilocular; loculi in a circle round a distinct columella. Spores cylindrical, nearly straight, $6-7 \times 1\mu$; sporophores filiform, $10-15 \times 1\mu$.

On twigs of *Juglans regia.* Kew Gardens; Gloucester. May. Germ. Ital.

Laurus

Cytospora Lauri Grove, in Journ. Bot. 1922, p. 45. *Ceuthospora Lauri* Sacc. Syll. iii. 279, f. *ramulicola.*

No definite conceptacle. Pycnidia scattered, conical, truncate, 0·5–1 mm. diam., with a rather large whitish furfuraceous disc, dark-olive within, composed (when perfect) of many compact narrow ·radiately arranged pseudolocelli or labyrinthiform chambers; walls of locelli (under the microscope) thick and dark-brown, without a trace of olivaceous-green. Spores sausage-shaped, $4-5 \times 0·75-1\mu$, rather more acute at the ends than is usual; sporophores linear, not crowded, $\pm$ curved, $10-12 \times 1\mu$.

On dead twigs of *Laurus nobilis.* West Kilbride, Ayrshire (Boyd). May.

The species here described is quite different from *Ceuthospora Lauri* Grev. (Scot. Crypt. Flor. pl. 254), which was on *Prunus Laurocerasus* and is very common.

Ligustrum, see **Fraxinus**

Lonicera

Cytospora Lonicerae Grove, in Kew Bull. 1923, p. 18.

Stromata somewhat scattered, minute (200–300μ diam.), round, blackish, totally immersed, often surrounded by a brownish-red stain, at last emerging but only by the black pore (disc none), subunilocular within or composed of a few roundish loculi with thick dark walls. Spores sausage-shaped, 5–6 × 1μ, colourless in mass; sporophores subulate, rarely slightly branched, 12–15 × 1μ.

On twigs of *Lonicera*. Bebington, Cheshire (Ellis). May.

Distinguished from the spermogone of *Valsa olivacea* Fckl. (Symb. Myc. Nachtr. 1, 27) by the minuteness of the pycnidia, and the much smaller spores.

Morus

Cytospora atra Sacc. Syll. iii. 257. All. vi. 586. Died. 348. Mig. 200. *Lamyella atra* Bon. Abhandl. ii. 134, pl. 2, f. 15.

"Stromata small, covered, then erumpent, black without, pallid within, distinctly plurilocular, the loculi surmounted by a rather prominent dark disc and each provided with a separate roundish pore. Spores cylindric-oblong, sausage-shaped, very minute; sporophores rather long, branched."

On dry branches of *Morus alba*. Kew Gardens (Cooke). *n.v.*

"Distinguished by its separate ostioles."

Germ. Denm. India.

Myrica

Cytospora Myricae-gales Bres. in Jaap, Verh. Bot. Ver. Prov. Brandenb. 1908, vol. 50, p. 46. Sacc. Syll. xxii. 959. Died. 349. Mig. 200. *C. sororia* Bres. *ibid.* ? *C. Myricae* Jaap, in Ann. Mycol. 1905, iii. 400 (*non* Henn. 1902, which is not truly cytosporoid ?).

Stromata gregarious, immersed in the bark, obtusely conical, about 1 mm. diam., pallid within, at first almost unilocular, then incompletely divided; disc flat, whitish. Spores allantoid, curvulous, hyaline, 4–7 × 1·2–1·5μ; sporophores branched, up to 20μ long and 2μ thick.

On dry branches of *Myrica Gale*. Under Llechwedd and at Ynys Las, Harlech, Mer. (Rhodes). Wheatfen Broad, Surlingham, Norfolk. Aug.

The pycnidial stage of *Valsella Myricae*.

There seems to be no reason whatever for considering Bresadola's two species as distinct. He found them in company with each other;

but says that *C. sororia* has the pycnidium divided into a few completely separate loculi, and has longer spores and sporophores. Such a difference is merely a matter of age, as can be seen in scores of species of Coelomycetes.
Germ.

Palmae

Cytospora Palmarum Cooke, in Grevill. xiii. 95. Sacc. Syll. x. 249. All. vi. 587.

Stromata immersed, then erumpent, loosely gregarious, 0·5–1 mm. diam., at first covered, then cracking the epidermis; loculi few. Spores sausage-shaped, profuse, $6 \times 1\mu$.

On petioles and leaves of Palms. Kew Gardens (Cooke).

Apr.

Platanus

Cytospora Platani Fckl. Enum. Fung. Nass. 52. Sacc. Syll. iii. 267. All. vi. 590. Died. 352. Mig. 202.

Pycnidia numerous, gregarious, roundish, black, up to 500μ diam., raising the epidermis in the form of a tubercle, without a distinct conceptacle or stroma, divided irregularly into incomplete chambers; walls thin, clear-brown, of small indistinct cells. Spores sausage-shaped, $6–8 \times 0·5–1\mu$, issuing in very slender long flexuous pure-white tendrils; sporophores filiform, longer than the spore.

On small dead branches of *Platanus acerifolia*. Kew Gardens.

Apr.

Fr. Holl. Germ. Austr. Ital.

Polygonum

Cytospora Polygoni-Sieboldi Henn. MS. in Mus. Bot. Berol. Died. 353. Mig. 202.

Stromata scattered, immersed, flatly conical, bursting the epidermis by the black disc, multilocular, tHe locules circinate, somewhat irregular, completely separated, with one or more ostioles; texture of walls very dark, prosenchymatous, indistinct. Spores cylindrical or fusoid, straight or curved, inequilateral, $5–8 \times 1·5–2·5\mu$; sporophores filiform, $10–15 \times 1\mu$.

On dead stems of *Polygonum sachalinense*. In a garden, Edgbaston, Birmingham (Rhodes). May.

Probably this species, which was found by Hennings on *Pol. Sieboldi* (i.e. *cuspidatum*), but the specimens are too young for absolute certainty.
Germ.

Populus

Cytospora chrysosperma Fr. Syst. Myc. ii. 542. Cooke, Handb.
462, 822. Sacc. Syll. iii. 260. All. vi. 591. Died. 353. Mig. 203.
Naemospora chrysosperma Pers. Syn. 108.

Stromata somewhat scattered, usually rather flat, but
sometimes very acutely conical, up to 2 mm. wide, covered,
then erumpent with a cinereous-black disc, olivaceous-cinere-
ous within; loculi often irregular; walls thick, very dark, subsclerotial, parenchymatous. Spores sausage-shaped, $4-5 \times 1\mu$,
issuing in very long copious yellow or golden tendrils; sporophores filiform, somewhat branched, $10-15 \times 1\mu$.

On bark of *Populus alba, balsamiferá, nigra, serotina, tremula*, etc. Very common; England, Scotland, Ireland.

May–Sept.

The pycnidial stage of *Valsa sordida* Nits. A serious disease.
Naemospora populina Pers. = *Cytospora populina* Rab. is a similar,
but nevertheless different species, having spores 8μ long; it belongs
to *Valsa populina* Fckl., but has not yet been found in Britain.
Europe, U.S.A., Canada, India.

Cytospora nivea Sacc. Syll. iii. 260 (*non* Fckl.). All. vi. 590.
Died. 354. Mig. 203. *Sphaeria nivea* Hoffm. Veg. Crypt. i. 28, *p.p.*

Stromata gregarious, between conical and discoid, 500–
750μ diam., immersed, then erumpent, black, within dark-
fuscous with many small loculi; disc emerging, roundish,
snow-white, with a black central ostiole. Spores sausage-
shaped, $6-7 \times 1 \cdot 5-2\mu$, issuing in reddish tendrils; sporophores
$10-13 \times 1 \cdot 5\mu$.

On bark of *Populus nigra, P. serotina, P. tremula*, etc. Not
uncommon, in England and the south of Scotland, but not so
abundant as *C. chrysosperma*. The pycnidial stage of *Valsa
nivea* Fr.

Though this has been recorded on many different trees, it will be
better to follow Saccardo, and consider it as confined to *Populus*.
When perfect the white disc, marked with a black eye, is very conspicuous, but, when the Valsa stage supervenes, it may be nearly
obliterated by a ring of perithecial mouths.
Europe, Siberia, U.S.A., Canada.

Cytospora Harioti Briard, in Rev. Mycol. 1889, p. 16. Sacc. Syll.
x. 247. All. vi. 591. Died. 354. Mig. 203.

Stromata scattered or loosely gregarious, not crowded, 0·5–1 mm. diam., conical on a roundish base, or if oval longitudinally elongated, olivaceous-grey, deeply immersed, long covered by the epidermis, then splitting it by a dingy-brown disc, with usually a single blackish pore; loculi several, irregularly arranged, separated by thick brown walls. Spores 4–5 × 1–1·5μ; spore-mass quite colourless; sporophores acicular, 12–15 × 1μ.

On small twigs of *Populus nigra*. Bromborough, Cheshire (Ellis).   Jan.

Fr. Germ.

Quercus
Cytospora intermedia Sacc. Syll. iii. 264. All. vi. 595. Died. 357. Mig. 205.

Stromata gregarious, pustular, multilocular, the loculi arranged radiately or without order round a central columella, opening by a single black pierced papilla (rarely two) in the centre of a very small cinereous disc. Spores sausage-shaped, 5–6 × 1·5μ; sporophores here and there branched below, 20–24 × 1·5 or frequently longer.

On thin twigs of *Quercus Robur*. Kew Gardens (Cooke). Earlswood, Wk.

The pycnidial stage of *Valsa intermedia* Nits.
Germ.

Rhododendron
Cytospora subclypeata Sacc. in Malpigh. 1896, x. 273, pl. 6, f. i; Syll. xiv. 917. Grove, in Journ. Bot. 1922, p. 46.

Stromata pustular, scattered, 500–750μ diam., swollen, covered by the shining dark-brown epidermis, greyish within and unequally plurilocular; disc minute, grey. Spores sausage-shaped, 4–5 × 1μ; sporophores verticillately branched, 25 × 1μ, with acute branches.

On dead branches of *Rhododendron*. Bidston, Cheshire (Ellis). Ayrshire (Boyd). Devon (Rhodes). Edgbaston Botanic Gardens, Birmingham. On leaves of the same, Walton Park Cemetery, Liverpool (Travis).   Feb.–Nov.

The epidermis over the pustules is dark reddish-brown, shining especially at the apex when young. Most of the sporophores seem to

be fasciculate at the base rather than branched; spores vary in length from 3μ to 6μ; the spore-mass is colourless.
Siberia.

Rhus

Cytospora rhoina Fr. Syst. Myc. ii. 546. Sacc. Syll, iii. 257. All. vi. 598. Mig. 206.

Stromata scattered, round, 250–500μ diam., convex, bullate, long covered by the bark, at length bursting it with a slit which afterwards becomes wider and roundish; contents pallid, then blackish. Spores about 5μ long, rarely issuing in pallid tendrils.

On branches of *Rhus glabra, R. radicans*. Kew Gardens (Cooke).   May–Aug.

Forming globose, rather solid tubercles, like a soft sclerotium, composed of indistinct cells. Cf. *C. marchica* Syd. (in Hedwig. 1900, p. (3); Sacc. Syll. xvi. 902; All. vii. 869; Died. 359), on *Rhus* in Botanic gardens, Berlin and Erfurt, which may be identical, or at least a better developed form.
Germ. Hung. Swed. N. Amer.

Ribes

Cytospora Ribis Ehrenb. Sylv. Berol. 28. Fr. Syst. Myc. ii. 545. Roum. in Rev. Mycol. 1891, p. 81. Sacc. Syll. iii. 273. All. vi. 599. Died. p. 359, p. 350, f. 2. Mig. 206.

Stromata scattered or arranged somewhat in lines, covered, then bursting the surface with a greyish brown disc, very sharply conical, divided at the base into numerous narrow complete chambers, radiating round a thick, soon tapering, columella, but forming above a single chamber which opens on the disc by one or two ostioles; walls dark-olive or fuscous-brown, not becoming paler inwards. Spores 3–5 × 1μ; sporophores curved, branched, 25–30 × 1μ.

On branches of *Ribes*. Reported in Britain. *n.v.*

Perhaps, says Saccardo, the pycnidial stage of *Eutypella Brun-audiana.*
Fr. Belg. Germ.

ROSACEAE

Plurivorous

Cytospora rubescens Tul. Fung. Carp. ii. 187. (Fr. Syst. Myc. ii. 542. Cooke, Handb. 462, 821. Berk. in Engl. Flor. v. 281. Sacc. Syll. iii. 253. All. vi. 588. Died. 352. Mig. 202. Mostly *p.p.*)

Stromata not crowded, pustular or subdepressed, covered, then with the disc erumpent (often transversely), rather flat,

dingy, then blackish, 1-2 mm. broad; loculi numerous, circinate. Spores sausage-shaped, curved, $3 \cdot 5$–$4 \times 1\mu$, issuing in deep-red tendrils; sporophores linear, usually straight, 18–24 $\times 1$–$1 \cdot 5\mu$.

The f. *Sorbi* is common on bark of *Sorbus Aucuparia*, and is the pycnidial stage of *Eutypella Sorbi* Sacc.; the f. *Crataegi* has occurred on *Crataegus Oxyacantha* at Birmingham; and it is said also to have forms on *Pyrus*.

The spore-mass, when fresh, is distinctly pinkish under the microscope. This species has been often confused with *C. leucostoma* or *C. Prunorum* (*qq.v.*), which also have reddish tendrils.

Europe, Siberia, N. America.

Crataegus

Cytospora Oxyacanthae Rab. in Bot. Zeit. 1858, p. 503. Sacc. Syll. iii. 255. All. vi. 579. Died. 339. Mig. 195. Grove, in Kew Bull. 1923, p. 20.

Stromata widely gregarious, but not much crowded, covered, when fully developed hemispherical on a rounded base, very convexly swollen, up to 1 mm. diam., bursting irregularly at the summit and showing a whitish disc, then when old blackish, disc marked with 1-3 inconspicuous black ostioles; contents dark-grey, subdivided into numerous loculi, which are ± labyrinthiform, but are frequently arranged in a conspicuously radiating manner; central columella black, often very distinct; outer wall thick and blackish, inner dividing walls of a rather thin greyish-green tissue composed of narrow elongated cells. Spores sausage-shaped, curvulous, 6-7 (rarely 8) $\times 1$–2μ, issuing as a whitish tendril; sporophores subulate, fasciculate at base, sometimes branched above, 15–25 $\times 1$–$1 \cdot 5\mu$ (10–13 $\times 1\mu$, Died.), springing direct from the inner walls. (Fig. 18c.)

On dead twigs, and especially on hedge-cuttings and stakes, of *Crataegus Oxyacantha*. Abundant; England, Scotland. Frequently accompanied by a form of *Valsa ambiens* Sacc.

Often placed by collectors under *C. leucosperma*, and recorded abroad on *Pyrus, Sorbus, Cydonia*, etc., but this is very doubtful; the record on *Quercus* is a mistake. The long grey-green thick-walled cells, about $2 \cdot 5\mu$ wide, composing the partition walls of the loculi, closely resemble the cells of the leaf of *Hypnum cupressiforme*. There are two forms or varieties recorded in Sacc. Syll. xiv. 915—*monogyna* Brun.

with curvulous spores 8–9 × 2–2·5μ, and *crataegicola* Brun, with ovoid
straight spores 7·5–8 × 3μ—on the same host, in France. These are
merely variations on the same theme.
Europe.

Kerria

Cytospora Kerriae Died. 346. Grove, in Journ. Bot. 1922, p. 45.
Mig. 199.

Stromata loosely gregarious, tearing the epidermis into
laciniae, erumpent, conical, with a blackish disc pierced by
one or two pores, irregularly pseudolocular; wall dark-olive,
a little paler within. Spores 6–8 × 1·5–2μ; sporophores fasciculate, mostly simple, 15–25 × 1μ.

On dry dead twigs of *Kerria japonica*. Saltcoats, Ayrshire
(Boyd). July.

Germ.

Prunus

Cytospora cincta Sacc. Syll. iii. 254. All. vi. 593. Died. 356.
Mig. 204.

Stromata aggregated, rather large, pustular, usually transversely erumpent, often with a number of perithecia surrounding the single central pycnidium; disc dingy-white or
even brownish, mostly with a single ostiole; loculi one or few,
rarely more and then somewhat radiating. Spores cylindrical, curved, 6–8 (4–9) × 1·5–2μ, issuing in pale-reddish tendrils; sporophores filiform, slender, usually simple, 10–15 ×
1μ, rising from a thick brown parenchymatous wall.

On stems and leaves of *Prunus* (*Cerasus, domestica, spinosa*).
Studley Castle; Sutton Coldfield; also near Cambridge and at
other places, but specimens less well developed. Spring.

The pycnidial stage of *Valsa cincta* Fr.
This species is common in Germany, and a variety is recorded on
Pyrus. When fully developed it is easily recognised by its ring of protruding perithecial ostioles surrounding that of the pycnidium, all
these within the periphery of the disc and not outside it at a little distance as in *C. germanica*. The mature stroma may measure as much
as 2–3 mm. in diameter. Diedicke records it on *Prunus Padus*, and I
have found a normally developed specimen on a leaf of *Prunus
Laurocerasus*.
Fr. Holl. Germ. Swed.

Cytospora Laurocerasi Fckl. Enum. F. Nass. no. 437; Symb. Myc. 398; Nachtr. I, 27. Tul. Sel. Fung. Carp. ii. 196. Sacc. Syll. iii. 276. All. vi. 593. Mig. 204.

Stromata round at base, conical, obtuse, black, slightly locellate within; disc protruding, round, cinereous-white, with a black central ostiole. Spores sausage-shaped, $5-6 \times 1\mu$, issuing in long slender deep-red tendrils; sporophores acicular or slightly subulate, clustered at the base, granular-guttulate, up to $20 \times 1.5\mu$; spore-mass tinged with red.

On dead leaves and on branches of *Prunus Laurocerasus*. The pycnidial stage of *Valsa Laurocerasi* Tul. England, Wales, Scotland.

The form on the leaves does not differ from that on the branches, except that the former is rarely accompanied by the ascophorous stage, while the latter is so frequently. It has been suggested that this fungus does not really differ from *Valsa cincta* Fr. This idea may be correct; the tendrils of the pycnidial stages of both vary alike in colour, being sometimes almost colourless, or at least pallid. The obstacle to that belief is Tulasne's assertion that the ascospores of his *Valsa Laurocerasi* are "ovate and straight, $6.5 \times 3.5\mu$" (Tul. *l.c.*). Saccardo tries to reconcile the disagreement by assigning to *V. Laurocerasi* spores "allantoid and subovoid in the same ascus".
Fr. Germ. Austr. Ital.

Cytospora leucostoma Sacc. Syll. iii. 254. All. vi. 592. Died. 356. Mig. 204. *Sphaeria leucostoma* Pers. Syn. 39. *C. nivea* "Fckl.", Cooke, Handb. 822. *C. rubescens* Fr., *p.p.*

Stromata often crowded, lenticular or conical, up to 1 mm. wide, multilocular, blackish, immersed, then most often transversely erumpent, the emerging disc flat, snow-white, pierced by one or two black ostioles; loculi (when perfect) narrow, radiating; walls of brown prosenchymatous cells; no columella. Spores sausage-shaped, $5-6 \times 1\mu$; issuing in reddish tendrils; sporophores filiform, simple or rarely branched, $12-20 \times 1\mu$.

On bark of *Prunus* (*Cerasus*, *domestica*, *insititia*, *Laurocerasus*(?), *Padus*, and other species). Evesham; Pershore; Cambridgeshire; Wales; Scotland; etc. (Fig. 18*d*.)

In some districts not uncommon on dead branches of cultivated Plums, and said sometimes to be a weak parasite. The pycnidial stage of *Valsa leucostoma* Fr. (*V. Persoonii* Nits.), which often accompanies it.

In good specimens, such as can be found especially on *P. Padus* in
Wales and Scotland, the round white disc, marked in the centre with
a black "eye", is very conspicuous. The spore-mass, when seen in
water under a microscope, is distinctly pinkish-red; the fresh tendrils
are of the colour called by artists "light-red", not the deep purplish-
red of those of *C. rubescens* and *C. Prunorum*. As the Cytospora-stage
changes into the Valsa, the one or two ostioles increase to several less
prominent ones. *C. cincta* (*q.v.*), also on *Prunus*, resembles this somewhat, but generally has fewer loculi and a dingy-whitish disc.

C. leucostoma is accused by some writers of causing "die back" of
Apple, but this is probably a mistake of identification, though Ader-
hold succeeded in infecting that tree with it from the Plum. See
C. Mali. The Cytosporas on *Prunus* need fresh investigation.

Forma **Cotoneastri**.

A similar fungus has been found on *Cotoneaster bacillaris* by Cooke
at Kew, and on a dead *Cotoneaster* by Rev. H. W. Lett in Ireland, in
each case accompanied by the supposed *V. leucostoma*.

Europe, Siberia.

Cytospora Prunorum Sacc. & Syd. in Ann. Mycol. 1904, ii. 191;
Mycoth. Germ. no. 136! Syll. xviii. 297. Died. 355. Mig. 204.
C. rubescens Kalch. in Bot. Zeit. 1864, p. 174 (*non* Fr. quae *C. leuco-
stoma*, saltem pro parte).

Stromata loosely gregarious, conico-truncate, 1–1·5 mm.
diam., covered, then erumpent by a transverse fissure, greyish-
olive, radially multilocular; disc whitish, marked with a black
pore, then becoming blackish. Spores sausage-shaped, 6–8 ×
1·5–2μ; spore-mass pinkish, issuing in purple or deep-red
tendrils; sporophores linear, crowded, simple or forked, 22–26
× 1·5μ.

On branches of various species of *Prunus* (including
Amygdalus, etc.). Common in England.   Winter and spring.

The pycnidial stage of *Eutypella Prunastri* Sacc.
Differs from *C. rubescens* Fr. in the longer spores. A form of it is
known to cause the death of Cherry trees. Cf. *C. cerasicola* Sacc.,
which has spores 3 × 1μ.
Europe, N. America.

Cytospora microstoma Sacc. Syll. iii. 254. All. vi. 593. Died.
355. Mig. 204.

Stromata convex, more rarely conical, with a roundish or
oval base, 500–650μ diam., multilocular, the loculi arranged
round the circumference, the dingy disc furnished with a

single pore (or rarely more than one). Spores sausage-shaped, proportionately rather thick, 5–6 × 1·5μ; sporophores rather thick, branched, about 28μ long.

On branches of *Prunus domestica*, *P. Laurocerasus*, *P. spinosa*, and other species of *Prunus*. Not uncommon.

The pycnidial stage of *Valsa microstoma* Nits.
The walls of the pycnidial chambers are olivaceous-yellow when young; the spore-mass is nearly colourless. A var. *Cotoneastri* (on *C. frigida*) is assigned to this species by Cooke in Grevill. xiii. 95, possibly without reason.
Fr. Germ. Ital. Swed. Russ. N. America.

Pyrus

Cytospora microspora Rabenh. Deutschl. Kr. Flor. 147. Sacc. Syll. iii. 253. All. vi. 578, with fig. Died. 340. Mig. p. 194, pl. 25, f. 1–5. *Naemospora microspora* Cord. Ic. iii. 26, f. 69, *p.p.*

Stromata gregarious, raising the epidermis conically, bursting it and thrusting the black disc above it, multilocular, the loculi incomplete and arranged round a central columella, with a common ostiole; wall dark fuliginous-brown, olive-brown within, in the upper part of young pustules almost orange-red. Spores 6–8 × 1μ; sporophores linear, 10–20 × 1·5μ; tendrils white.

On twigs of *Pyrus malus*, Cheshire (Ellis). On *Amelanchier*, Kew (Cooke); placed, by error, under *C. microstoma*, in Grev. xiii. 96.

Recorded in Germany on *Crataegus Oxyacantha*, *Sorbus Aucuparia*, and *S. domestica* also. Cf. *C. Mali*.
Fr. Germ. Swed.

Cytospora Mali Grove. *Cytospora* sp. Stevens, in Ill. Agric. Exper. Sta. Bull. no. 217 (1919), with figs.

Stromata small, scattered, immersed, then pustular, erumpent, slightly conical, black, 1 mm. or a little more in diam.; loculi numerous, irregular, circularly arranged, covered by a clypeate stroma; interlocular stroma several cells thick, of firm pseudoparenchyma. Spores sausage-shaped, hyaline, about 7 × 1·6μ; sporophores linear, crowded, simple or rarely branched, 17–20 × 0·5–0·7μ.

On twigs of *Pyrus Malus*, causing a canker. Peterborough;

Kent, etc. Perhaps not yet certainly identified in this
country.

Stevens, who found this in Illinois, transferred it in pure cultures
readily from Apple twigs to Pear, Rose, Plum, Peach, Rubus, on all of
which it grew freely (but not on Cherry or Acer). He wrongly thought
it like *C. leucostoma*, but gives it no name; the title *C. mali* is used
above merely to aid identification.
U.S.A.

Rosa

Cytospora Rosarum "Grev." in Bail. Syst. Pilz. p. 81, pl. 14.
Sacc. Syll. iii. 253. All. vi. 600. Died. 360. Mig. 207. *Cytospora
Rosae* Fckl. Fung. Rhen. no. 624 (*non* Raben.).

Stromata gregarious, rather small, 250–330μ (rarely more)
diam., covered, at length erumpent, conical on a circular base,
sinuously and indistinctly multilocellate within, groyish-
brown, surrounded by the epidermis which is occasionally
reddened or discoloured; disc greyish, small. Spores sausage-
shaped, 4–6 × 1–1·5μ; sporophores ± verticillately branched,
15–25 × 1μ.

On branches of *Rosa canina*, *R. tomentosa*. Scarborough
(Massee). Cheshire (Ellis). Ayrshire (Boyd). Hereford.

Autumn and spring.

The pycnidial stage of *Valsa Rosarum* de Not., which Saccardo calls
a var. of *V. ceratophora* Tul. (Syll. i. 109).
Fr. Germ. Ital. Austr. Poland. U.S.A.

Cytospora rhodophila Sacc. Syll. iii. 253. All. vi. 599. Died. 360.
Mig. 207.

Stromata minute, conico-truncate, with a few spurious
loculi radiately arranged, opening by a single central pore.
Spores cylindrical, curvulous, 5–7 × 1μ; sporophores thin,
12–20μ long, usually simple, bearing the spores only at the
apex.

On dry branches of *Rosa canina*, and cultivated Roses.
Queen's Park, Harborne, near Birmingham (Chesters); etc.

The pycnidial stage of *Valsa rhodophila* B. & Br.
By its attacks it is said to have rendered the growing of certain
Roses, at Harborne, exceedingly difficult.
Holl. Germ.

Cytospora Hendersonii B. & Br. in Ann. Nat. Hist. 1850, v. 379. Cooke, Handb. 462. Sacc. Syll. iii. 252. All. vi. 600.

Pustules small, scattered; cavity subsimple, thin-walled, sometimes lobed at the margin; contents whitish. Spores oblong, gently curved, hyaline, issuing in a formless mass, 7–8 × 2·5–3μ.

On twigs of *Rosa arvensis*. Milton, Norths. (Berk.).

The dimensions of the spores are taken from the original specimen, but it is a doubtful Cytospora.

"Pycnidium nearly regular, but sometimes lobed at the edge, and raised in the centre from the elevation of the subjacent bark. Spores larger than in most *Cytosporae*, oblong, but short, very slightly curved, oozing forth in the form of a dirty-white shapeless jelly" (B. & Br.).

Rubus

Cytospora clypeata Sacc. Syll. iii. 252. All. vi. 600. Died. 360. Mig. 207.

Pycnidia scattered or sometimes in short longitudinal rows, 0·5–1 mm. diam., at first globose, bullate, covered, then splitting the epidermis in a longitudinal slit, at length conical, shining brown outside, emergent and showing a small round dingy disc which finally becomes black and hard by the formation of a little dark mass of dense shining subcarbonaceous tissue around the ostiole of the subunilocular pycnidium; walls of pycnidium firm, rather thick and brownish-olive, of mixed parenchyma and prosenchyma. Spores sausage-shaped, about 6 × 1μ; sporophores filiform, 10–15 × 1μ.

On dead branches of *Rubus fruticosus*. Sherborne, Wk. (Rhodes). Harborne, Lapworth, and Great Barr, near Birmingham. Mar.–Jun.

The pycnidium of *Valsella clypeata* Fckl. These specimens agree with Sydow, Mycoth. Germ. no. 1709.

Holl. Germ.

Salix

Cytospora Capreae Fckl. Symb. Myc. 199 (1869). Sacc. Syll. iii. 262. All. vi. 605. Died. 361. Mig. 208. *C. Schweinitzii* Sacc. Syll. iii. 261 (1884). All. vi. 602.

Stromata gregarious, conico-truncate on a rounded base, 500–700μ diam., somewhat prominent, erumpent through the periderm and surrounded by its torn edges or (if the easily

loosened periderm is thrown off) standing free on the brownish surface of the inner bark, attenuated into a thick neck which is pierced by a rather broad pore, usually 1-chambered or with several spurious loculi which are rather large and radiately disposed. Spores cylindrical, curvulous, 4–5 × 1μ; sporophores simple or branched at the base, 20–25 × 1μ, later dissolving into mucus.

On bark of *Salix* (*Caprea, fragilis, petiolaris*). Kew Gardens, etc. Aug.

The pycnidial stage of *Valsa Schweinitzii* Nits. Germ. Austr. Ital. Alger. Canada.

Cytospora Salicis Rab. Deutsch. Kr. Fung. no. 1340 (1844). Sacc. Syll. iii. 261. All. vi. 603, with fig. Died. 361. Mig. 208. *Naemospora Salicis* Cord. Ic. iii. 26, pl. 4, f. 70, *p.p.* (on *Betula*).

Stromata loosely gregarious, convex, blackish, covered by the browned epidermis, then erumpent, conical, about 500μ diam.; disc greyish, emergent, pierced by one or more ostioles; loculi confluent, forming a star-shaped or labyrinthiform pallid or grey mass. Spores sausage-shaped, rather curved in profile, 4–6 × 1–1·25μ, issuing in a pallid tendril; sporophores densely crowded, linear or subulate, up to 25 × 1μ, occasionally branched. (Fig. 18a.)

On dead twigs of *Salix* (*alba, fragilis, pentandra, purpurea, viminalis, vitellina*, etc.). Very common; England, Wales, Scotland, Ireland. Jan.–Aug.

The pycnidial stage of *Valsa salicina* Fr.
Spores occasionally longer, 7–8μ or even more. Periderm often shining round the disc, which pierces without tearing it. Smaller than *C. fugax*, which has almost no stroma, and has more distinct and well-formed loculi.
Europe, N. & S. Amer. India.

Cytospora fugax Fr. Syst. Myc. ii. 544. Cooke, Handb. 462, 827. Sacc. Syll. iii. 263. All. vi. 576. Mig. 194. *Variolaria fugax* Bull. pl. 432, f. 5.

Stroma little or none. Pustules prominent, 1–1·5 mm. broad, lens-shaped, concrete with the epidermis; loculi black, circling round a central columella; disc flat or somewhat sunken, smoke-brown or black. Spores numerous, sausage-

shaped, not much curved, 6–8 × 1·5μ; tendrils slender, greyish-white.

On bark of *Salix* (*alba, fragilis, nigricans, viminalis*, etc.). Kew Gardens; Kent; Edgbaston and Studley Castle, Wk.; Staffs. Also recorded abroad, but wrongly, on *Corylus*.

I do not believe that this is anything but the final stage of *C. Salicis* (*q.v.*). When perfect, it consists of a circle of 6–20 black loculi, filled with a greyish mass, with almost no stroma, and forming a flattened covered pustule, bursting through in the centre with a ragged opening. Bulliard named it *fugax*, he said, because it seemed to disappear in a short time.

Europe, Asia, N. Amer.

Cytospora fertilis Sacc. Syll. iii. 261. All. vi. 603. Died. 362. Mig. 208.

"Stromata thickly crowded, small, pustular, multilocular, with a central pore; disc whitish; loculi radiating. Spores 5–7 × 2μ, issuing in reddish tendrils; sporophores rather thick, slightly branched, about 20μ long."

On branches of *Salix nigricans*. Kew Gardens (Cooke).

The pycnidial stage of *Valsella fertilis* Sacc.
Germ.

Cytospora germanica Sacc. Syll. iii. 262. All. vi. 604. Died. 355. Mig. 203. Grove, in Journ. Bot. 1922, p. 45.

Stromata scattered or gregarious, conico-truncate or convex, with a roundish base, 0·5–1·25 mm. broad; disc whitish, then cinereous, at length marked with a small black central papilla which is pierced by a pore; loculi numerous, radiately disposed and often imperfectly divided, walls of the chambers of thick brown prosenchymatous cells. Spores sausage-shaped, 5–6 × 1·5μ; sporophores crowded, long, slender, filiform, usually simple, 20–25 × 1–1·25μ.

On dead twigs of *Salix*. Gt. Haywood, Staffs.; Sutton Coldfield, Wk.   Apr.–Aug.

On the same twigs was an abundance of *Valsa germanica* Nits. of which it is the spermogone; when the two occurred together, the 6–9 erect black ostioles of the Valsa formed a ring around the pycnidial disc, piercing the periderm at a distance of 0·5–1 mm. away from it. Occasionally the grey disc of the Cytospora was pierced by two papillae.

Germ. (on *Populus*), Moravia, Finland.

Cytospora translucens Sacc. Syll. iii. 261. All. vi. 602. Died. 362. Mig. 208.

Stromata scattered, very small, blackish, not raising the epidermis much, opening by a single central pore (more rarely by two or three) in a minute whitish dark-margined disc which alone projects, containing within a few radiately arranged loculi or even nearly undivided. Spores sausage-shaped, 4–5 × 1–1·25μ; sporophores filiform, very slender, 40μ or more long (5–12 × 0·5–1μ, soon disappearing, Died.).

On twigs of *Salix babylonica, S. fragilis,* etc. Kew Gardens; Warwickshire; Worcestershire; Staffordshire.   Spring.

The pycnidial stage of *Valsa translucens* C. & de Not.
The disc is at first blackish, but later becomes whitish or grey, beginning in the middle and so leaving the margin dark. The black stromata *shine through* the transparent epidermis.
Europe, N. Amer.

                                                        Sambucus
Cytospora Sambuci Died. in Ann. Mycol. 1906, iv. 414; and Pilz. Brand. 363. Smith, in T.B.M.S. 1910, iii. 222. Mig. 209. *C. Smithiae* Sacc. & Trott. Syll. xxii. 958.

Stromata gregarious, immersed, flat, up to 1 mm. diam., black; chambers numerous, circinate, united upwards to form a single conical ostiole. Spores abundant, sausage-shaped, 5–6 × 1–1·5μ; sporophores filiform, simple, up to 25μ long.

On dead branches of *Sambucus nigra.* Derbyshire (Gibbs).
                                                        Oct.

Diedicke says that the stromata occupy elongated bleached patches of the periderm.
Germ.

                                                        Sarothamnus
Cytospora Sarothamni Sacc. Syll. iii. 272. Ellis, in T.B.M.S. 1916, v. 229. All. vi. 606. Died. 363. Mig. 209.

Stromata densely gregarious, tuberculiform, depressed, black, dark-olivaceous within, multilocular, opening above by a pore or a minute fissure in the epidermis. Spores cylindrical, nearly straight or curved, 7–10 × 1·5–2μ; sporophores densely caespitose, 12–20 × 1μ.

On rather thick branches of *Sarothamnus scoparius.* Darenth (Cooke). Cheshire (Ellis).   Feb.–Apr.

The stroma contains several small loculi, circinate round a central columella. The species has been stated to be the pycnidial stage of *Eutypa macrospora* Sacc., but this seems to be a mistake. Germ. Denm.

Staphylea

Cytospora Staphyleae Cooke, in Grevill. xiv. 4. Sacc. Syll. x. 246. All. vi. 608.

Stromata somewhat convex, with two or three loculi covered by the slightly raised epidermis, which opens by a small elevated often white-margined pore. Spores sausage-shaped, about $6 \times 1\mu$.

On dead branches of *Staphylea pinnata*, *S. colchica*, *S. trifoliata*. Kew Gardens (Cooke). Heythrop Park, Oxon. (Rhodes). Apr. Jul.

Symphoricarpus

Cytospora Symphoricarpi Henn. in Died. Krypt. Fl. Brand. 364 (1912). Mig. 210. Sacc. Syll. xxv. 220. But cf. Grove, in Kew Bull. 1923, p. 26.

Stromata scattered, covered, raising the epidermis slightly, soon erumpent, depressed-conical, with a few completely divided loculi, but having only one ostiole, $500-750\mu$ broad; disc obtuse; walls dark olive-brown. Spores $5-7 \times 1\cdot5-2\mu$; sporophores filiform, $10-25 \times 1\cdot5-2\mu$.

On dead branches of *Symphoricarpus racemosus*. Ayrshire (Boyd); etc. Sept.

Germ.

Syringa

Cytospora Syringae Sacc. Syll. iii. 272. All. vi. 608. Died. 364. Mig. 210.

Stromata minute, bursting through the periderm by small longitudinally placed fissures, multilocular, the loculi crowded without order, opening usually by a single pore in the centre of a grey, then fuscous-brown, disc. Spores sausage-shaped, $5 \times 1\mu$; sporophores densely fasciculate, slightly branched, slender, up to 60μ long.

On branches of *Syringa vulgaris*. Apethorpe (Berk.).

The pycnidial stage of *Valsa Syringae* Nits.

Distinguished by its very minute stromata, which are rather

crowded, and burst through the bark by minute cracks. Berkeley's specimen is exactly like Roumeguère's (Fung. Gall. exs. no. 3970). Belg. Germ. Ital. Russ.

Tamarix

Cytospora Tamaricis Brun. in Act. Soc. Linn. Bord. 1897, p. 143. Sacc. Syll. xiv. 914. All. vi. 620. Died. 365. Mig. 210. *C. tamaricella* Syd. in Ann. Mycol. ii. 192. Sacc. Syll. xviii. 300. Died. 365.

Stromata highly gregarious, hemispherical or subconical, up to 500μ broad, bursting the epidermis above and disclosing a black disc; wall dark-grey and dense, slightly paler within, and giving off thin pale-coloured partitions which at length divide the cavity into several incomplete loculi. Spores sausage-shaped, 4–6 × 1·5–2μ; sporophores filiform-linear, 15–20 1·5–2μ, but often much longer.

On twigs of *Tamarix anglica* (= *gallica*). Ainsdale, Lancs. (Travis). Seaton; Minehead; Cobo, Guernsey (Rhodos). Alum Bay; Ventnor; Ryde; Barmouth. Jun.–Sept.

Is not *Phoma tamaricina* Thüm. merely a small form of this? Phoma-spores occur often in the same pycnidium with the Cytospora-spores. Germ. Austr.

Tilia

Cytospora carphosperma Fr. Syst. Myc. ii. 543. Cooke, Handb. 462, 826. Sacc. Syll. iii. 274. All. vi. 588. Died. 351. Mig. 202.

Pustules gregarious, depressed-conical, about 1 mm. broad; stroma often indistinct, small in quantity; loculi black, circinate; disc round, of a dingy-whitish colour, with usually a single central black ostiole (sometimes two). Spores sausage-shaped, 5–6·5 × 1–1·5μ, issuing in a pale-yellow, then deeper-yellow tendril; sporophores simple or verticillately branched, acicular, 15–20 × 1·5μ.

On bark of *Tilia*. Common; England, Scotland, Ireland. Winter and spring.

Also recorded on *Pyrus communis* and *Aucuparia*, in Scotland, but this seems doubtful; see Scot. Nat. 1886, p. 327, and 1887, p. 127.

If this species is really different from *C. ambiens*, it would be better to consider it as confined to *Tilia*. The specimens distributed on *Pyrus malus* by Westendorp, Rabenhorst, Karsten, and Sydow have more croceous tendrils, and should have a separate name. See Grove, in Kew Bull. 1923, p. 8. Europe.

Vaccinium
Cytospora Vaccinii Died. Pilz. Brand. 366 (1912). Mig. 211.
C. Myrtilli Grove, in Journ. Bot. 1918, p. 294. *C. Petrakii* Zimm. in
Flor. Boh. & Mor. exs. II, no. 858.

Stromata scattered, raising the somewhat blackened epidermis conically and piercing it with the blackish disc, about 600μ diam., lighter coloured within and pseudolocellate, with a single ostiole. Spores sausage-shaped, 4–5·5 × 1μ; sporophores filiform, fasciculate, mostly simple, 30–40 × 1μ (10–15 × 1μ in foreign specimens).

On dead stems of *Vaccinium Myrtillus*. West Kilbride, Ayrshire (Boyd). May.

The slightly convex pustules of the cinereous stroma show dark through the epidermis, which is at length pierced at the centre, it may be by a simple blackish ostiole, it may be by a whitish pruinose disc in which lie 1–5 ostioles.

Germ. Bohem. Morav.

Viburnum
Cytospora Lantanae Bres. in Rev. Mycol. 1891, p. 28, pl. 114, f. 6. Sacc. Syll. x. 245. All. vi. 610. Died. 367. Mig. 211. *C. pruinosa* var. *Lantanae* Sacc. Mich. i. 519. *C. pulveracea* Berk. in Engl. Flor. v. 283. *Dendrophoma pruinosa* var. *β*, Sacc. Syll. iii. 179.

Stromata scattered, 250–300μ diam., multilocular, causing a distinct roundish swelling beneath the epidermis, which finally pushes out at the vertex a grey disc, which is surrounded by the laciniae of the bark and is at length pierced by a black ostiole. Spores curved, 5–7 × 1μ (7–9 × 1·5–2μ, Died.); sporophores verticillately branched, 25–35 × 2–3μ.

On dead twigs of *Viburnum Opulus*, *V. Lantana*. Cheshire (Ellis). Wilmcote, Wk. On leaves of *V. Tinus*, Apethorpe (Berk.). Jan.–May.

The pycnidial stage of *Valsa Viburni* Fckl.
Fr. Hung. Ital.

CEUTHOSPORA Grev. Scot. Cr. Flor. pl. 254.

Conceptacles of two kinds, (A) like those of Macrophoma or a small unilocular Cytospora, and (B) larger, flatter, and more coriaceous; both immersed and then erumpent—the (B) kind by a conico-truncate neck or by several, plurilocular or even

unilocular, mostly surmounted by a dark-brown leathery disc. Spores elongate-oblong or strictly cylindrical, usually quite straight, hyaline, continuous, distinctly pedicellate, often issuing in tendrils. (Fig. 19.)

Allied in part to Cytospora, but differing in having its larger conceptacles covered by a hard flat leathery disc, which is not fragile and reminds one of Phaci-dium, being in fact an anticipation or adumbration of it. In the simpler pycnidia the disc is less conspicuous or altogether absent. The larger con-ceptacles may open by 1–3 (or even 4) ostioles; they are, however, often barren. They occur more frequently upon leaves than upon stems; some of them are the pycnidial stages of species of Phacidium or Trochila. Many of the Ceuthosporae, when showing only the smaller (A) pycnidia, have been placed by authors under

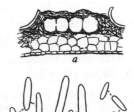

Fig. 19. Ceuthospora: a, verti-cal section of stroma of C. latitans, × 36; b, spores of C. Hederae; c, of C. phacidioides; d, of C. latitans; all × 600.

Macrophoma; the larger (B) pycnidia are presumably only the passage forms to the ascophorous stage, though they may often still produce pycnospores exactly like those in the (A) pycnidia.

Euonymus

Ceuthospora Euonymi Grove, in Journ. Bot. 1916, p. 190; Kew Bull. 1923, p. 354. Macrophoma cylindrospora B. & V. in Atti Soc. Ven.-Trent. 1886, p. 192, pl. 2, f. 12, p.p.

Conceptacles amphigenous, of two kinds, (A) unilocular, (B) plurilocular: (A) small, about 250μ diam., densely crowded or somewhat scattered, prominent, subglobose, black, dehiscing by a conico-truncate opening which is surrounded by the laciniae of the epidermis and exposes the disc; disc furfuraceous, composed of numerous loose cells which may be whitish or often show a pinkish or even reddish tinge: (B) maturing later, larger, scattered, flat, round, discoid, 500μ diam. or even more, black, somewhat shining, for a long time solid and sterile, at length dehiscing by 1–3 (usually one,

rarely four) conico-truncate pore-like openings which are often occupied at first by a similar furfuraceous disc, at length filled with a white mass of the exuded spores. Spores alike in both, quite cylindrical, with rounded ends or slightly pointed at the lower extremity, quite straight, perfectly hyaline and free from guttules, $14-17 \times 2-2 \cdot 5\mu$; sporophores straight, slender, of about the same length.

On leaves (fallen) and twigs of *Euonymus japonicus*. Wallasey, Cheshire (Ellis). Southampton (Rayner). Ayrshire (Boyd). Kew; Eastbourne; Cornwall; Jersey; Gower; etc.

Aug.–Mar.

This species, when found in a less perfect condition, has often been called *Phoma cylindrospora* Desm. The larger conceptacles resemble those of *Ceuthospora phacidioides* Grev., but are distinguished by the usually more slender spores. *Cytospora foliicola* Lib. var. *Euonymi*, found in the U.S.A., is quite different in its sausage-shaped spores. *Cytospora Euonymi* Cooke (*q.v.*) is also different.

Hedera

Ceuthospora Hederae Grove, in Kew Bull. 1923, p. 355. *Macrophoma cylindrospora* B. & V. *l.c.*, *p.p.*

Conceptacles of two kinds: (A) small, resembling those assigned to the Macrophoma: (B) larger, quite flat, hard, leathery, discoid, black or greyish-black, $0 \cdot 75-1$ mm. diam., showing on both sides of the leaf. Spores in both of the same kind, cylindrical, quite straight, obtuse at both ends, colourless, eguttulate, $12-14 \times 2-2 \cdot 5\mu$; sporophores filiform, straight, of about the same length. (Fig. 19 *b*.)

On dead leaves and petioles of *Hedera Helix*. Uncommon. Liverpool (Travis). Shropshire; Edgbaston, Birmingham; Swansea.   Sept.

The larger conceptacles are like those of *C. phacidioides*, and have a similar appearance before the disc emerges; the smaller ones, if occurring by themselves, would be called *Macrophoma*. Could this be, in addition to *Gloeosporium paradoxum* (*q.v.*), a pycnidial stage of *Trochila Craterium*?

Fr. Belg. Ital.

Ilex

Ceuthospora phacidioides Grev. Scot. Cr. Flor. pl. 253. Cooke, Handb. 465, 753. Sacc. Syll. iii. 277. All. vi. 615, with fig. Died. 322. Mig. p. 225, pl. 30, f. 1–3. Grove, in Kew Bull. 1923, p. 357. *Sphaeria*

bifrons Sow. pl. 316. *Cryptosphaeria bifrons* Grev. Flor. Edin. 361.
Phoma Ilicis Desm., *p.p.*

Stromata of two kinds: (A) smaller, Phoma-like in appearance, but with 1–4 loculi (more or less connected) within, texture of wall like that of a Cytospora, splitting the epidermis into 3–4 triangular laciniae: (B) larger, 1–1·5 mm. diam., numerous, immersed, orbicular or nearly so, at first flat, pitch-black, shining, enclosing 3–7 closely combined loculi; ostiole (when perfect) in the centre of a white furfuraceous disc, surrounded by the epidermis which becomes raised in the centre to form a whitish spot, and ultimately splits into 3–5 laciniae. Spores all alike, cylindrical, usually quite straight, obtusely rounded at both ends or sometimes acute below, often granular within, 12–20 × 2–4μ, issuing in a whitish tendril; sporophores papilliform, rather short. (Fig. 19 c.)

On dead fallen leaves of *Ilex Aquifolium*, less often on the dead twigs of the previous year. Very common, but frequently sterile.

The pycnidial stage of *Phacidium multivalve* K. & S. The smaller pycnidia are rarer and are what has sometimes been called *Phoma Ilicis* Desm. (*q.v.*).

It is worthy of note that a variety of *C. phacidioides* is recorded (Sacc. Syll. xxv. 228), on fading leaves of *Laurus nobilis* in France, with cylindric-oblong spores 9·5–10 × 2·5–3μ, on crowded linear sporophores 7 × 1μ. This, it is suggested, is the pycnidial stage of *Diaporthe ceuthosporoides* (Berk.) Sacc. Syll. i. 646. But rather it is allied to or identical with *Ceuthospora Lauri* Cooke, found on dead leaves and on fruits of *Laurus nobilis* in California; the specimen of this is in Herb. Kew, so named by Cooke; it has linear straight spores like those of *Ceuth. phacidioides*. *Sphaeria ceuthosporoides* Berk. was on *Prunus*. Fr. Belg. Holl. Germ. Austr. Ital.

Lycopodium

Ceuthospora Lycopodii Lind, in Ann. Mycol. iii. 429; Dan. Fung. 434. Died. p. 323, p. 308, f. 9.

Stromata scattered, epiphyllous, immersed, and later splitting the epidermis lengthwise, conical, 1 × 0·5 mm., with a few loculi which open into a common mouth. Spores cylindrical, straight, rounded at the ends, eguttulate, 12–16 × 2μ; sporophores unseen.

On dead leaves of *Lycopodium clavatum*. Ness, Wirral, Cheshire (Travis). Sept.

This exceedingly rare species was found by Mr Travis, and communicated to me by Dr P. G. M. Rhodes. I have seen no other record of it except from Jutland, but there is a *Phacidium gracile* Niessl recorded from Laibach on *Lycop. Chamaecyparissus.*

Jutland (on *L. annotinum* and *L. Chamaecyparissus.*)

Mahonia

Ceuthospora Mahoniae Grove, in Journ. Bot. 1918, lvi. 314; Kew Bull. 1923, p. 357.

Conceptacles epiphyllous, gregarious, dimorphic: (A) smaller, 250μ diam., with 1-7 loculi, conico-truncate, then erumpent by a small round whitish furfuraceous disc, which is pierced by a central ostiole: (B) very hard, convex, prominent, solid, round or oblong, 0·5-1 mm. diam., formed from the mesophyll of the leaf, brown within, blackish without, covered by the torn epidermis, then surrounded by it, enclosing 20-40 very minute round crowded loculi with white contents. Spores the same in both, cylindrical, quite straight, obtuse above, continuous, hyaline and eguttulate, 10-14 × 1·5-2μ.

On dead leaves of *Mahonia japonica.* Hadzor Hall, Ws.; Studley Castle, Wk. On dead leaves of *M. Aquifolium.* Hadzor (Grove & Rhodes).

The larger conceptacles are later in development than the smaller, but the spores are exactly the same in both.

Prunus

Ceuthospora Laurocerasi Grove, in Journ. Bot. 1916, p. 191; see also Grove, in Kew Bull. 1923, p. 356 (spores wrongly described). ? *Sphaeria Lauri* Sow. Engl. Fung. pl. 371, f. 4. ? *Ceuthospora Lauri* Grev. Scot. Cr. Flor. pl. 254. Cooke, Handb. p. 465, f. 176. Sacc. Syll. iii. 279, *p.p.* All. vi. 616. Mig. 225.

Conceptacles of two kinds, numerous, amphigenous, obtusely conical, 0·5-1 mm. diam., the smaller ones tending to be unilocular, all brownish-black, surrounded by the elevated brown-black epidermis, which is pierced by the ostiole or sometimes split into 2-4 short erect segments. Spores linear-oblong, straight, obtuse at both ends, eguttulate, colourless, 10-15 × 2-3μ; sporophores crowded, filiform, slender, somewhat branched, longer than the spores.

On dead leaves and small shoots of *Prunus Laurocerasus.* Common everywhere. Aug.-Apr.

Probably the pycnidial stage of *Trochila Laurocerasi* Fr.

Owing to the custom, in Britain, of speaking of *Prunus Laurocerasus*

as "*the* Laurel", great confusion has arisen. It has frequently been erroneously regarded as the true Bay Laurel (*Laurus nobilis*), and its leaves are still sometimes used by our cooks as such. Greville's specimens were on the *Prunus*, not, as he falsely says, on *Laurus*; Saccardo was led astray by this misstatement, and *his* error has been copied frequently. Berkeley knew well of Greville's mistake, and mentioned it in his British Fungi, in Smith's Eng. Flora, vol. v. part 2, p. 283 (1836).

Diedicke, however, states (p. 332) that he had investigated "original material from Scotland, collected by Greville", and found it to be on *Laurus* and places it under *Cytospora foliicola*. Greville's material must have been mixed, or suffered a "sea-change" in crossing the "German Ocean". A Cytospora occurs on *Laurus nobilis* in this country and on the Continent, but no Ceuthospora has ever yet been found on that host in Britain, and Greville's "*Ceuthospora Lauri*" should be forgotten.

The var. *ramulicola* Vize, Fung. Brit. exs. no. 104 (Sacc. Syll. *l.c.*) has the pycnidia usually larger, 1–1·5 mm. broad, but with identical spores; it occurs on small dead shoots of the foregoing summer.

Note that *Cytospora Laurocerasi*, which can be found abundantly upon the leaves and twigs of *Prunus Laurocerasus* and which bears a resemblance externally to *Ceuthospora Laurocerasi*, has no relation to the Ceuthospora, but belongs to *Valsa Laurocerasi* Tul., i.e. to *Valsa Ceuthosporae* Cooke which was so named owing to a confusion of the two Coelomycetes. See Grevill. iv. 113 and vii. 83; also Sacc. Syll. i. 143.

Rhododendron

Ceuthospora Rhododendri Grove. *Cytospora foliicola* Lib., *p.p.*

Pycnidia few, thinly scattered, of the usual two kinds, mostly hypophyllous. Spores strictly cylindrical, rounded at both ends, colourless, 13–18 or longer × 2–3μ; sporophores sometimes branched.

On fallen and long-dead leaves of cultivated *Rhododendron*. Oscott College, Birmingham. Jun.–Oct.

It is conceivable that these pycnidia, which were found in considerable numbers though few on each leaf, were merely as it were strays from the Ceuthospora-infected Holly leaves with which they were lying intermixed on the ground; but it is also possible that they are the pycnidial stage of *Phacidium Falconeri* Henn. on *Rhododendron*.

Vaccinium

Ceuthospora latitans Grove, in Journ. Bot. 1918, p. 314; Kew Bull. 1923, p. 355. *Dothidea latitans* Fr. Syst. Myc. ii. 552. *Dothiorella latitans* Sacc. Syll. iii. 241. All. vi. 531. *Dothiopsis latitans* Karst. in Hedwig. 1884, p. 20. *Phyllachora latitans* Sacc. Syll. ii. 610.

Conceptacles amphigenous, immersed, roundish, then convex, erumpent, splitting the epidermis into four or five

laciniae, black, about 500μ diam.; sometimes unilocular, or loculi several, immersed in a brownish stroma and often imperfectly divided. Spores cylindrical, straight, obtuse at both ends or somewhat tapering below, 8–11 × 1·5–2μ (12–13 × 2μ, Sacc.); sporophores linear, about 12 × 1μ. (Fig. 19 a, d.)

On dry dead blackening leaves and twigs of *Vaccinium vitis-idaea*. Salop; Cheviots; Ayrshire; Cannock Chase; etc.

The pycnidial stage of *Phacidium Vaccinii* Fr. In its sometimes botryose pycnidia it tends outwardly towards *Dothiorella*. In one case similar but more irregular and brownish spores were found mixed with the normal ones: these might be old and decaying spores.

Germ. Switz. Swed. Finland.

Vinca

Ceuthospora Feurichii Bubák, in Ann. Mycol. 1906, iv. 115. Died. p. 324, p. 308, f. 10. Mig. p. 226, pl. 31, f. 1–5. Grove, in Kew Bull. 1923, p. 355. *Cytospora foliicola* Lib., *p.p.*

Conceptacles amphigenous, somewhat uniformly scattered, black, covered by the whitish epidermis or buried deeply in the mesophyll, raising the epidermis and at length piercing it by a roundish pore, divided into several chambers, each oblong and about 220 × 150μ; walls thick, brown. Spores cylindric-fusoid or cylindrical, slightly narrowed below, 12–15 × 2–3μ; sporophores filiform, branched, as long as or longer · than the spore.

On stems and dead or dying leaves of *Vinca minor*. Aberdeen (Trail). Lanarkshire (Boyd). Wyre Forest, Worcs. (Rhodes). Swanscombe. Feb.–Jun.

The pycnidial stage of the rare *Phacidium Vincae* Fckl.

The Aberdeen specimens showed both types of conceptacles exactly like those of *C. Euonymi*, with similar furfuraceous discs.

Fr. Belg. Germ. Austr. Denm. Poland.

The resemblance of the (B) pycnidia of Ceuthospora to a Phacidium suggests the following explanation of the existing state of things. The pycnospores are at first produced in a pycnidium like that of *Macrophoma cylindrospora*; afterwards some of the pycnidia assume the (B) form which ought normally to produce asci and sporidia, but the mycelium of these pycnidia can go on producing in them spores exactly like the pycnospores, although they are frequently sterile. This is the same phenomenon to which I have already called attention by instituting the genus Fusidomus (see Journ. Bot. 1929, pp. 201–3, and *infra*, vol. II, among the Nectrioideae).

HYALODIDYMAE

These Coelomycetes resemble the HYALOSPORAE in all respects except that the spores are provided with a single transverse (usually median) septum.

I. Pycnidia standing singly, without any stroma.
  A. Pycnidia immersed, thin- or thick-walled, cells thin-walled.
    1. Spores without appendages.
      a. Spores hyaline.
        † Pycnidial wall pseudopycnidial or thin.
          α. Spores with not more than 2 cells . *Ascochyta*
          β. Spores occasionally 3-celled · *Stagonosporopsis*
        †† Pycnidial wall thicker. . . . . . *Diplodina*
      b. Spores faintly coloured . . . . . *Ascochytula*
    2. Spores with delicate appendages at end.
      a. Appendages deciduous, bristle-like . . . . *Darluca*
      b. Appendages deciduous, helmet-like. . . *Tiarospora*
  B. Pycnidia superficial, carbonaceous, brittle [*Aposphaeriella*]
  C. Pycnidia sclerotioid, not beaked . . [*Diploplenodomus*]

II. Pycnidia provided with a stroma.
  A. Pycnidia on an erect stroma . . . . . *Fuckelia*
  B. Pycnidia in a flat stroma . . . . . *Placosphaerella*
  C. Pycnidia in a pustular stroma . . . . *Cytodiplospora*
    See also *Amphorula*, placed *ad interim* among the HYALOPHRAG-MIAE.

ASCOCHYTA Lib. emend. Sacc. in Mich. i. 161.

Pycnidia immersed in parts of leaves or stems (which are thereby often more or less changed in colour, especially the leaves), varying from lens-shaped to globose, membranaceous in texture, pierced by a central pore around which the cells are usually darker in colour. Spores ovoid or oblong, 1-septate, hyaline or sometimes very faintly tinged with colour (Fig. 20.)

There has been great confusion between Ascochyta and Diplodina. The former genus was at first considered to occupy well-marked discoloured spots on leaves alone or on leaf-like organs, *A. Pisi* being taken as the type; the latter to grow on

stems without producing distinct spots, *D. Salicis* being the
type. Many species of *Ascochyta*, however, are now known to
infest both leaves and stems of the same plant, nor do all the
species of that genus cause spots. A real
distinction might be found in the nature of
the pycnidial wall: in Ascochyta this is
mainly thin and translucent; the lower part
is sometimes nothing but a proliferous
stratum of mycelium—Diplodina, on the
contrary, should have a more strongly
built wall, surrounding the cavity equally
on all sides, all the cells being fuscous or
brown and ± parenchymatous like those
of a typical Phoma; the wall is therefore
often thick and even nearly opaque. But
the two genera still collide.

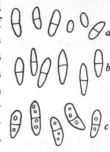

Fig. 20. *Ascochyta*:
a, spores of *A. Matri-
cariae*; *b*, of *A. graminicola* on *Phleum*; *c*, of
A. Kabatiana; ×600.

Species whose spores are tinged with brownish are placed
in Ascochytula; those which tend to have an additional septum are classed as Stagonosporopsis—both these merge into
Hendersonia. At times species of Ramularia have been in-
cautiously mistaken for Ascochyta. The species are arranged
in alphabetical order of their hosts, Dicotyledons first.

Arctium

Ascochyta microspora Trail, in Scot. Nat. 1887, iii. 87. Sacc.
Syll. x. 304.

Spots nearly circular, dark-brown or black. Pycnidia epiphyllous, dotted thickly over the spots, globular, 70μ diam.,
pale-brown under the microscope. Spores subcylindrical, with
rounded ends, straight or curved, 5–$7 \times 1·5$–2μ.

On living leaves of *Arctium Lappa*, near Montrose (Trail).
On leaves of *Petasites vulgaris*, Aberdeen (spores slightly
longer).   Sept. Oct.

Astrantia

[**Ascochyta**(?) **Astrantiae** Roum. in Fung. Gall. no. 33. Sacc.
Syll. iii. 400. All. vi. 671.

On *Astrantia*. Kew Gardens.]   Nov.

There is no probability that this is an Ascochyta, or indeed a
Sphaeropsid at all. No pycnidia can now be found on the Kew speci-

men, and Saccardo could find none on that of Roumeguère; he suggests that the spots belong to a Discomycete, *Fabraea* (*Pseudopeziza*) *Astrantiae.*
Fr.

Atriplex, see **Chenopodium**

Beta
Ascochyta Betae Prill. & Delacr. in Bull. Soc. Myc. Fr. 1891, p. 24, pl. 3, f. 4. Sacc. Syll. x. 306. All. vi. 633.

Pycnidia olivaceous, round, 120–130μ broad, papillate, at length darker. Spores ovoid, continuous, then cylindric-ovoid and 1-septate, not constricted, hyaline, 9–12 × 2·5–3μ.

On the petioles of cultivated *Beta vulgaris* which had been killed by *Phoma Betae* Frank (*q.v.*) in France. Reported on Mangels, Devon, 1928.

Boehmeria
Ascochyta Rheea Grove, in Kew Bull. 1919, p. 439. *Phoma Rheea* Cooke, Fungi of India, in Grevill. viii. 93. Sacc. Syll. iii. 140.

Pycnidia scattered, round, covered by the epidermis, at length emergent in the upper half, blackish, about 300μ diam., in age falling away and leaving a little white pit; texture thin, soft, plectenchymatous, brown. Spores oblong-ellipsoid, somewhat obtuse at both ends, biguttulate, for a long time continuous, at length 1-septate, not constricted, 7–9 × 3–3·5μ; sporophores about as long as the spore.

On dead stems of *Boehmeria nivea.* Kew Gardens. These specimens correspond exactly with those from Assam.

Only a few of the spores were 1-septate, but many showed indications of becoming so. No doubt the fungus was introduced with the plant.
India.

Brassica
Ascochyta Brassicae Thüm. Contr. Myc. Lusit. no. 602. Sacc. Syll. iii. 397. All. vi. 633. Grove, in Journ. Bot. 1913, p. 45, and in Irish Nat. 1912, xxi. 112. T.B.M.S. iv. 175. ? *Asteroma Brassicae* Chev. Fl. par. 449.

Spots dry, round, oblong, or irregular, sometimes confluent, 12–25 mm. diam., whitish-grey, not bordered by a darker line, but sometimes by concentric wrinkles. Pycnidia epiphyllous, very small, black, subglobose, prominent, scattered in a dense crowd all over the spots. Spores fusoid, acute at both ends, straight, 1-septate, 15–16 × 3–4μ.

On leaves of cultivated *Brassica*. Lincolnshire; Kent;
Devon; Shropshire; Cheshire; Montgomeryshire; Co. Antrim;
etc. Sometimes destructive to Cabbages.

The spots are numerous, unusually large, more or less circular, dull-
greyish, less dark-coloured than those of *Phyllosticta brassicicola*.
Diedicke (Ann. Mycol. x. 136) says that this species is merely *Mycosphaerella brassicicola* with the asci overlooked, but this, I think, is
not true of the Irish specimens, at least.
Germ. Port.

Ascochyta oleracea Ellis, in T.B.M.S. 1915, v. 229.

Pycnidia on pallid spots, gregarious, subglobose, membranaceous, yellowish-fuscous, about 160μ diam., opening by a
pore. Spores cylindrical, rounded at both ends, $9-12 \times 2-3\mu$,
finely granular, faintly 1-septate.

On dead stems of *Brassica campestris*. Cheshire (Ellis).

June.

This is a true Ascochyta. It has nothing to do with *A. Brassicae*
Thüm.

Calystegia
Ascochyta Calystegiae Sacc. Syll. iii. 402. All. vi. 635.

Spots vague, irregular, brown when dry, sometimes concentrically zoned, the margin darker. Pycnidia epiphyllous,
scattered, punctiform, lens-shaped, $90-100\mu$ diam., pierced;
texture thin, loosely cellular. Spores oblong or subclavate,
rather obtuse at the ends, not or scarcely constricted, $7-8 \times 3\mu$.

On leaves of *Calystegia sepium*. Near Aberdeen (Trail).

Oct.
Germ. Ital.

Campanula
Ascochyta carpathica, f. *caulicola* Grove in Journ. Bot. 1922,
p. 46, pl. 563, f. 12. *Phyllosticta carpathica* All. & Syd. in Hedwig.
xxxvi, p. (157). All. vi. 109. Sacc. Syll. xiv. 854. Died. 32. Mig. 41.

Caulicolous. No spots. Pycnidia scattered, lens-shaped,
depressed, brownish, covered, then erumpent by the vertex
which is pierced by a minute pore; texture thin, pale-brown,
translucent. Spores at first ovoid, continuous, then oblong
and 1-septate, rounded at the apex, $7-9 \times 2\cdot5-3\mu$.

On dead peduncles of *Campanula Trachelium*, *C. rapun-*

culoides, and *C. rhomboidalis*. Edgbaston, Birmingham; Bidford Churchyard.   Oct.–Mar.

As the spores become 1-septate, they usually grow slightly longer and narrower. But both kinds can be found continually intermixed in the same pycnidium. Allescher's Phyllosticta was found on leaves and was less mature. Also *A. bohemica* Kab. & Bub. is found in Bohemia on the leaves of *C. Trachelium*, with spots, and spores 10–22 × 4–5µ. Germ.

Caryophyllaceae

Ascochyta Dianthi Berk. Outl. 320. Cooke, Handb. 456. Sacc. Syll. iii. 398; x. 301. All. vi. 640. Massee, Dis. Cult. Pl. 432. *Sphaeria* (*Depazea*) *Dianthi* A. & S. Consp. Fung. Lus. p. 47, pl. 6, f. 2. *Phyllosticta Dianthi* Westd.

Spots rather large, subcircular, pallid, with a darker border. Pycnidia irregular, congregated, numerous, minute, blackish. Spores spathulate or ellipsoid, somewhat granular, at length 1-septate, 14–17 × 4–5µ.

On living or fading leaves of *Agrostemma, Dianthus, Lychnis, Saponaria*. Common; England, Scotland.   Summer.

Saccardo afterwards (x. 301) described the spores as "oblong- or clavulate-fusoid, rounded and apiculate at each end, constricted, 14–16 × 3–4·5µ". See *Septoria Dianthi* and *S. Lychnidis, infra*, pp. 380, 391. Europe, U.S.A.

Ascochyta Cookei Mass. in Kew Bull. 1907, p. 241, f. 5, 6. T.B.M.S. 1908, iii. 38. Sacc. Syll. xxii. 1014.

Spots elongated, pale-yellowish, often angular and bordered by the nerves. Pycnidia densely gregarious all over the spots, without order, subepidermal, globose, 70–80µ diam., erumpent by the ostiole, furnished at the base with smoky-brown septate hyphae. Spores cylindric-clavate, more or less curved, septate in the middle, 40 × 4–5µ.

On living leaves of *Dianthus barbatus* and *Lychnis vespertina*. Kew Gardens.

Spots hardly distinguishable from those caused by *A. Dianthi*, but spores cylindrical or faintly clavate, 36–42 × 4–5µ. See *Septoria Dianthi, infra*, p. 380.

Chaerophyllum

Ascochyta Chaerophylli Bres. in Hedwig. 1894, p. 207. Sacc. Syll. xi. 523. All. vi. 637. Grove, in Journ. Bot. 1922, p. 47.

Spots epiphyllous, fuscous, unbordered, at first small, at length spreading over the leaf. Pycnidia epiphyllous, puncti-

form, 60–75μ diam., translucent, very pale brown. Spores
subcylindrical, straight or rarely bent, hardly constricted,
colourless, with two or four guttules, 10–12 × 3–4μ; sporophores very short.

On dead leaves of *Chaerophyllum temulum*. West Kilbride,
Ayrshire (Boyd). Nov.

Germ.

Chenopodium

Ascochyta Chenopodii Rostr. in Bot. Tidsskr. 1905, xxvi. 311.
Died. in Ann. Mycol. 1912, x. 139. Sacc. Syll. xviii. 345. Died. p. 377,
p. 350, f. 5. Mig. p. 266, pl. 35, f. 5–6. *Diplodina Chenopodii* Karst.
in Hedwig. 1885, p. 73. *Ascochyta Atriplicis* Died. in Ann. Mycol.
1904, ii. 180, f. 1. *Diplodina Atriplicis* Vestergr. (1896). *Phyllostįcta
Atriplicis* Cooke, Handb. 452 (*non* Desm.).

Spots roundish (unless bordered by a nerve), sometimes
irregular, 0·5–1 cm. diam., ochraceous, paler in the centre,
with a broad dusky border. Pycnidia epiphyllous, less often
hypophyllous, crowded, amber-coloured, then black, globose-
depressed, 120–150μ diam., pierced by a round pore which just
penetrates the epidermis; texture olivaceous-yellow, thin,
translucent. Spores subcylindric, straight or curved, rounded
at both ends, granular, occasionally irregular or "torulose",
at length 1-septate, often constricted at the septum, very pale
yellowish in mass, 12–20 × 3–4·5μ.

On living leaves of *Atriplex* (*hastata*, etc.) and *Chenopodium*.
Not uncommon around London. On the sea-shore, Ayrshire
(Boyd). On *Atriplex*, Pembrokeshire (Rhodes). Jun.–Aug.

This has been described under many names; no doubt *Ascochyta
nebulosa* Sacc. & Berl. is scarcely different (see Sacc. Syll. x. 305). In
Germany it has been found also on the stems, and has therefore been
placed without reason under *Diplodina*. Moreover, there can be little
doubt that *Septoria Atriplicis* or *S. Chenopodii* is nothing but a more
highly developed stage of the same fungus; see Grove, in Journ. Bot.
1917, p. 346. The curious "torulose," appearance of the immature, not
yet septate, spores was noticed by Cooke.

On *Atriplex portulacoides*, from Kingsmill Lake, Tamar (C. P.
Hurst), the succulent leaves were attacked simultaneously by *Perono-
spora effusa* Rabenh. var. *minor* Casp., with abundant spores in the
mesophyll, and the consequent discoloration profoundly altered the
appearance of the spots, but the spores of the Ascochyta remained
unchanged.

Sometimes the pycnidia are found on a leaf which shows no change of colour; this may be called var. *emaculata.*
Fr. Belg. Germ. Denm. Finland, Siberia.

Cochlearia
Ascochyta Armoraciae Fckl. Symb. Myc. 388. Sacc. Syll. iii.
397. All. vi. 630. Died. 380. Mig. 270.

On living leaves of *Cochlearia Armoracia.* North Wootton; Shrewsbury; King's Lynn; Isleworth; Ayrshire; etc. These are only early states of *Septoria Armoraciae* (*q.v.*); *Ascochyta rusticana* Kab. & Bub. seems to be merely an intermediate stage, on the way to become a Septoria.

Holl. Germ. Denm. Austr.

Cucurbita
Ascochyta Cucumeris Fautr. & Roum. in Rev. Mycol. 1891, p. 79. Sacc. Syll. x. 304.

Spots round, large (up to 4 cm.), ochraceous, then brownish, with a narrow brown border. Pycnidia numerous, crowded, blackish-brown, erumpent, then very prominent, globose, papillate; texture thin, translucent, pale-brown. Spores oblong, 1-septate, $7-10 \times 3\mu$, issuing as a honey-coloured globule.

On leaves and epicarp of *Cucurbita* sp. (Vegetable Marrow, etc.). Kew Gardens. Saltcoats, Ayrshire (Boyd). Sept.–Nov.

The French specimens were on the leaves of Cucumber (*Cucumis sativus*), but those on the fruit appear to be the same species, though differing in certain unimportant particulars. Cf. *A. citrullina,* p. 315. Fr. U.S.A.

Cytisus
Ascochyta Kabatiana Trott. in Sacc. Syll. xxv. 330. *Ascochyta Laburni* Kab. & Bub. in Hedwig. 1912, lii. 347 (*non* Sacc.). Mig. 271. *A. leguminum* Sacc. Syll. iii. 385 (on the legumes).

Spots visible on both sides of the leaf, sinuous, roundish, or oblong, up to 2 cm. wide, 1–3 on each leaf, occasionally confluent, dingy-ochraceous, margined indistinctly by a thin faint brown line. Pycnidia epiphyllous, rather thickly scattered, long covered by the epidermis, subglobose, $100-150\mu$ diam., pale ochraceous or honey-coloured. Spores ellipsoid or sub-cylindrical, broadly rounded at both ends or pointed at the lower end, straight or often bent, long one-celled, at length 1-septate but not always in the middle, not constricted,

often furnished with one or two oil-drops in a loculus, hyaline, $7-15 \times 3-4\mu$. (Fig. 20c.)

On living leaves of *Cytisus Laburnum*. West Kilbride, Ayrshire (Boyd). South Devon (Rilstone). Sept.

Phyllosticta Cytisi Desm. (*q.v.*) without doubt is the early state of this species.
Bohemia.

Deutzia

Ascochyta Deutziae Bresad. in Hedwig. 1900, p. 326. Sacc. Syll. xvi. 927. All. vii. 874. Mig. 272. Sm. & Ramsb. in T.B.M.S. 1913, iv. 175.

Spots indeterminate, alutaceous, becoming pale, not margined. Pycnidia numerous, scattered, punctiform, blackish, globose, thin in texture, somewhat prominent, up to 200μ diam. Spores cylindrical, $7-10 \times 2\cdot5-3\cdot5$, 1-septate, not quite straight.

On fading and fallen leaves (and on other decayed parts as well) of *Deutzia gracilis*. West Kilbride and Saltcoats, Ayrshire (Boyd). Sept.–Nov.

Dicentra

Ascochyta Papaveris Oud. Contr. Fl. Myc. Nov. Seml. 1885, p. 12, pl. 1, f. 10. Sacc. Syll. x. 301. T.B.M.S. vi. 49.

Var. **Dicentrae** Grove.

Pycnidia scattered over the surface of the leaves, about 200μ diam., black; texture membranaceous, formed of rather large fuliginous cells. Spores broadly fusoid or subellipsoid, about $9 \times 3\cdot5\mu$ (Oud.).

On fading or dead leaves of *Dicentra spectabilis*. Saltcoats, Ayrshire (Boyd). Aug.

Agreeing fairly well with the type (which was on leaves of *Papaver nudicaule*), but pycnidia sometimes congregated, $135-170\mu$ diam., and spores $8-12 \times 2-3\mu$.
Nova Zembla.

Doronicum

Ascochyta Doronici All. in Hedwig. 1897, xxxvi. p. (162); Krypt. Flor. vi. 641. Sacc. Syll. xiv. 945. T.B.M.S. iv. 175.

Spots large, ovate, visible on both sides of the leaf, dark-cinereous or slightly yellowish, with a darker border.

Pycnidia immersed, but somewhat prominent, dark-brown. Spores elongate, subcylindrical, obtuse at both ends, straight or rarely somewhat bent, scarcely constricted, 8–12 × 2·5–3·5μ.

On living or fading leaves of *Doronicum*. Perceton, Ayrshire (Boyd). *n.ex.*

Germ.

Faba

Ascochyta Fabae Speg. Fung. Arg. nov. 1899, p. 321. Sacc. Syll. xvi. 928.

Spots amphigenous, orbicular or confluent and irregular, up to 10 mm. broad, dingy-pallid or umber, margined by a distinct fuscous thickened line. Pycnidia generally epiphyllous, immersed, lens-shaped, 100–120μ broad; texture thin, parenchymatous, tinged with ferruginous-brown. Spores cylindrical, rounded at both ends, straight or curvulous, hyaline, 1-septate, subconstricted.

On living or fading leaves of *Faba vulgaris*. Berkshire; Devon; etc. Not common. Feb. Mar.

It is the advanced stage of *Phyllosticta Fabae* (*q.v.*). Argentina.

Fraxinus

Ascochyta metulispora B. & Br. in Ann. Nat. Hist. 1878, i. 30. Sacc. Syll. iii. 386. All. vi. 644.

Spots orbicular, fuscous, with a darker border. Pycnidia epiphyllous, round, lens-shaped, immersed, pallid, about 150μ diam., pierced by a pore; texture thin, darker round the pore. Spores oblong, attenuated at the base or rarely at both ends, faintly guttulate, 8–11 × 2·5–3μ.

On leaflets of *Fraxinus excelsior*. Ballinluig; Glamis (Berk.). Dalry, Ayrshire (Boyd). Autumn.

Spots up to 1 cm. broad, often one only to each leaflet, dark ochraceous, with a rather indefinite broad brown border. "Spores shaped like tip-cats" (B. & Br.), i.e. broadly elliptic-fusoid or biconical. The spores of Mr Boyd's specimen (in which alone spores have been seen) are not more biconical than those of many other Ascochytas. Pycnidia are very rare, but their pallid (not black) colour may distinguish them from those of *Phyllosticta fraxinicola* (*q.v.*); which has similar spots; the two species are probably in part identical.

Galeopsis

Ascochyta Galeopsidis Sm. & Ramsb. in T.B.M.S. 1915, v. 158.
Eliasson, in Svensk Bot. Tidskr. 1915, ix. 408.

Spots varying in form, amphigenous, at first brown, then
growing pale, with a dark-purple or brown border. Pycnidia
epiphyllous, crowded, covered by the epidermis, 100–150μ
diam., pallid-brown, pierced by a pore. Spores cylindrical,
straight or somewhat curved, septate in the middle, 9–11 ×
2–3μ.

On leaves of *Galeopsis Tetrahit*. Irvine, Ayrshire; Arran
(Boyd).   Aug.

Swed.

Galium

Ascochyta caulicola Laub. in Arb. Biol. Abt. Land. u. Forst.
Kais. Gesund. Amt, 1903, iii. 441. Sacc. Syll. xviii. 336. Died. 387.

Spots irregular, visible on both sides of the leaf (on the
stems widely spreading), clear-brown, becoming whitish-grey
in the middle, bordered and crossed by thin dark lines. Pycnidia (on the leaves hypophyllous), subglobose, slightly protruding, clear-brown, 150–180μ diam., darker round the pore.
Spores numerous, cylindrical or tapering somewhat toward
the ends, but still rounded, straight or bent, mostly at length
1-septate, hyaline, 13–18 × 3·5–5·5μ.

On dead stems of *Galium Mollugo*. Polperro (Rhodes).
Salcombe, Devon. Fowey, Cornw.   Apr.

It is recorded by Laubert on leaves and stems of *Melilotus albus*.
A variety (var. nov. *Lupini*) occurred on dead stems of *Lupinus
arboreus* at Talland Bay and Polperro, Cornw., in April. Spores 9–15
× 3–5μ. In some of the pycnidia *all* the spores were still eseptate.
Germ. Moravia?

Glaucium

Ascochyta Glaucii Died. 383. Mig. 275. *Diplodina Glaucii* Cooke
& Mass. in Grevill. xvii. 79. Sacc. Syll. x. 314. All. vi. 688.

Pycnidia loosely gregarious, covering long stretches of the
stem, piercing the epidermis by the convex papilla, clear-
brown, darker round the pore, 150–225μ diam. Spores ellipsoid or subcylindric, rounded at the ends, within microguttulate or cloudy, not constricted at the septum, 10–13 ×
2·5–3μ.

On dead stems of *Glaucium fulvum*, Kew Gardens (Cooke). On dead stems of *G. luteum*, Neston, Cheshire (Travis). Apr. Germ.

Heracleum

Ascochyta Heraclei Grove. *Stagonospora Heraclei* Sm. & Ramsb. in T.B.M.S. 1915, v. 161.

Spots roundish or varying in form, scarcely margined, dingy-brown, becoming paler. Pycnidia immersed, at first covered, then erumpent or free, lens-shaped, black, 75–100μ diam.; texture subtranslucent, plectenchymatous. Spores oblong or subfusoid, straight, at first guttulate, 1 (or very rarely 2) -septate, hardly constricted, 14–20 × 4–5μ.

On fading leaves of *Heracleum Sphondylium*. Ayrshire and Stirlingshire (Boyd).   Aug. Sept.

The original description in T.B.M.S. confuses together the true pycnidia and the beginnings of perithecia (filled with a sclerotioid mass) which are larger, darker, and formed of brown parenchymatous cells.

Humulus

Ascochyta Humuli Kab. & Bub. in Hedwig. 1904, xliii. 419. Sacc. Syll. xviii. 346.

Spots epiphyllous, variable, irregular-roundish, green, then ochraceous-grey with a brown border. Pycnidia epiphyllous, scattered, subglobose, immersed, brownish, slightly papillate, 80–140μ broad; texture yellowish, loosely parenchymatous. Spores copious, ovoid-ellipsoid or shortly cylindric, rounded at both ends, hyaline, straight or slightly bent, 1-septate, sub-constricted, 7–15 × 3–5μ.

On leaves of *Humulus Lupulus*. East Malling (Wormald). *n.v.*

It is a later stage of *Phyllosticta Humuli* Sacc. & Speg. (*q.v.*). The immature spores are smaller and continuous. Bohem.

Ilex

Ascochyta Ilicis Grove.

Pycnidia epiphyllous, few, arising on spots produced by a leaf-miner. Spores cylindric-oblong, 4–5 × 2·5μ, at length 1-septate.

On leaves of *Ilex Aquifolium*. Hereford. Appearing at first to be a Phyllosticta.   Feb.

Juglans

Ascochyta Juglandis Boltshauser, in Zeitschr. f. Pflanzenkr. 1898, viii. 263. Sacc. Syll. xvi. 933. Massee, Dis. Cult. Pl. 432. All. vii. 875. Died. p. 386, p. 350, f. 10. Mig. p. 278, pl. 35, f. 10, 11.

Spots roundish or (if bounded by nerves) irregular, visible on both sides, from 1–10 mm. diam., numerous, greyish-brown, with a darker chestnut-brown border, soon falling out. Pycnidia epiphyllous, globose, almost entirely immersed, 80–120μ diam. Spores oblong, often slightly constricted at the septum, 10–13 × 4–5μ, the loculi often unequal in size.

On leaves of *Juglans regia*. Reported as British. *n.v.*
Germ. Switz.

Lathyrus

Ascochyta Lathyri Trail, in Scot. Nat. 1887, iii. 87. Sacc. Syll. x. 303. All. vi. 648. Died. 387. Mig. 278.

Spots ill-defined, clear greyish-brown, tending to occupy the whole leaflet. Pycnidia numerous, amphigenous, subglobose, depressed, pale-brown, up to 100μ diam. Spores cylindrical, rounded at both ends, 6–10 × 2–2·5μ.

On fading or dead leaves of *Lathyrus silvestris*. Montrose (Trail). Apr.–Oct.

Recorded abroad on other species, e.g. *Lathyrus odoratus*, and on that there is also a variety, *Lathyri-odorati* Bub. & Kab., with 1-septate spores up to 4·5μ wide, which seems to indicate a transition to *A. Pisi* Lib. (*q.v.*). Compare these with the form which occurs on *Erythrina* in Australia in which the spores reach even 19μ in length and 4·5μ in width. Cf. also *A. Viciae* Lib.
Denm. Germ.

Lonicera

Ascochyta vulgaris Kab. & Bub. in Oesterr. Bot. Zeitschr. 1904, liv. 22. Sacc. Syll. xviii. 343. Died. 390. Mig. 279.

α. Var. **Lonicerae.**

Spots visible on both sides, roundish or subangular, often as much as 1 cm. broad, rarely confluent, on the upper side brownish or alutaceous, with a purple border, drying so as to become whitish-yellow beginning at the centre, easily tearing. Pycnidia scattered, seldom two or three together, immersed, somewhat projecting on both sides, compressed-globose, furnished above with a short papilla, rust-coloured, then amber, at length brown, up to 220μ diam.; texture loosely parenchy-

matous, darker round the pore. Spores oblong or cylindrical, rounded at both ends, 1-septate, at times constricted and then biscuit-shaped, with two or more guttules, colourless, 6–14 × 2·5–4·5μ.

On living leaves of *Lonicera*. Very common in Britain. Probably an advanced state of *Phyllosticta vulgaris*. Other forms of this occur on allied plants:

β. Var. **Symphoricarpi** Grove, in Journ. Bot. 1922, p. 48. *Phyllosticta Symphoricarpi* Westd. Sacc. Syll. iii. 19.
On leaves of *Symphoricarpus racemosus*. Arran (Boyd). Kew Gardens, etc. Jun.–Aug.

γ. Var. **Philadelphi** Sacc.
On leaves of *Philadelphus coronarius*. Ayrshire; Lanarkshire (Boyd). Kew Gardens, etc. This may be *A. Philadelphi* Sacc. & Speg. Syll. iii. 386.
There is also Saccardo's var. *Philadelphi* of *Phyllosticta vulgaris* (Syll. iii. 19) to be considered. It may be that all the forms of *Ph. vulgaris* are merely young states of an Ascochyta.
S. & W. Europe.

Malva
Ascochyta malvicola Sacc. Syll. iii. 399. All. vi. 652. Mig. 280.

Spots sinuous or nearly circular, bleached when dry, scarcely bordered. Pycnidia scattered, punctiform, lens-shaped, pierced by a pore. Spores shortly cylindrical, rounded at both ends, gently constricted, with four minute guttules, about 20 × 4μ (18–20 × 3·5–4μ, Trail).

On living leaves of *Malva silvestris*. Aberdeen (Trail). *n.v.*
Sept.

Besides this species there are two others described on *Malva*: *A. Malvae* Zimmerm. with pale dark-bordered spots, and spores 8–9 × 3·5μ; and *A. Malvarum* Mig. (misprinted *malvacum*, p. 281)=*A. Malvae* Died. (p. 391), with large ferruginous spots with a darker border, and spores 7–10 × 3–4μ. Probably these two are the same species. See also *Diplodina Malvae* Togn, p. 335.
Ital.

Matricaria
Ascochyta Matricariae Grove. *Diplodina Matricariae* Moss. & Smar. *ined.*

No spots. Pycnidia scattered, roundish or oblong, immersed, subglobose, scarcely protruding, 130–200μ diam., brownish or honey-coloured; texture thin, pseudopycnidial or

parenchymatous, pale brownish. Spores oblong, very obtuse at both ends, hyaline, eguttulate, 1-septate, not constricted, 9–10 (ranging from 8 to 13 at times) × 3–4μ. (Fig. 20a.) On dead stems of *Matricaria Chamomilla*. Hereford.

Jun. Jul.

I have a specimen, gathered by Smarods in Latvia, on stems of *M. suaveolens* (*discoidea*), which hardly differs, but being caulicolous was of course named Diplodina. Latvia.

Menyanthes

Ascochyta Menyanthis Oud. in Nederl. Kr. Arch. ser. 3, ii. 262, pl. 1, f. 9 (*non* Lasch, quae Septória). All. vii. 876. Sacc. Syll. xvi. 932.

Pycnidia amphigenous, but mostly hypophyllous, scattered irregularly on brown spots of variable size and shape. Spores shortly cylindrical, straight, colourless, rounded at both ends, equally 1-septate, with one or two highly refringent guttules in each loculus, 14–19 × 2·5–3·5μ.

On dead peduncles and capsules of *Menyanthes trifoliata*. Ardrossan, Ayrshire (Boyd). Aug.

It is accompanied on the same spots by *Septoria Menyanthis* (*q.v.*). The septum is very delicate, but can be made clearly visible with iodine. Holl. Germ.

Mercurialis

Ascochyta Mercurialis Bres. in Hedwig. 1906, p. 326. Sacc. Syll. xvi. 933. Grove, in Journ. Bot. 1918, lvi. 316. *Phyllosticta Mercurialis* Desm. in Ann. Sci. Nat. 1849, xi. 371. Sacc. Syll. iii. 53.

Spots roundish, few on each leaf or sometimes more crowded, alutaceous, surrounded by a dark-brown border. Pycnidia gregarious, epiphyllous, immersed, lens-shaped, amber or pale brownish-yellow, 100–150μ diam., pierced by a delicate pore; texture very soft, plectenchymatous, firmer round the pore. Spores oblong, rounded above or at both ends, rarely bent, hyaline, faintly guttulate, at length 1-septate with the loculi frequently unequal, 8–10 × 2·5–3·5μ.

On living leaves of *Mercurialis perennis*. Batheaston; Box-hill, Surrey; Dovedale. Jul.–Sept.

The spores remain continuous for a long time, and may be taken for those of a Phyllosticta, but whether this was, in fact or in part, what Desmazières called *Phyllosticta Mercurialis* is uncertain. See

under that species. The pycnidia are so pale as to be almost invisible except under a lens. The spots resemble the silvery white spots caused by *Cercospora Mercurialis* Passer., but can be distinguished by the absence of the minute black specks which are seen on the underside of the latter.

Var. **autumnalis** Kab, & Bub. in Hedwig. 1909, p. 40. Ayrshire and Arran (Boyd).   Jul. Aug.

In this form there are no especial spots, but the leaves become discoloured irregularly, pale leather-colour and without any distinct brown border. Sometimes the whole leaf is affected, becoming dry and cinereous. But the spores and pycnidia remain the same.

Fr. Germ. Saxony, Moravia, Bohemia.

Mimulus

Ascochyta Mimuli Sm. & Ramsb. in T.B.M.S. 1915, v. 158.

Spots oval, about 1 cm. broad, yellowish, with a darker margin and concentrically zoned. Pycnidia epiphyllous, sub-epidermal, erumpent, globose, brown, 110–120μ diam., pierced by a pore; texture parenchymatous. Spores oblong, rounded at the ends, straight or curvulous, guttulate, 10–14 × 2–3μ.

On leaves of *Mimulus Langsdorfii*. Dalry (Boyd). *n.ex.* Aug.

Nuphar

Ascochyta Nymphaeae Pass. in Hedwig. 1877, p. 120. T.B.M.S. xi. 18. Sacc. Syll. iii. 397.

Spots elliptical, about 8 × 5 mm., dry, brownish, with a darker margin. Pycnidia abundant, occupying the centre of the spot, immersed, subglobose; texture thin, pale-brown, parenchymatous, darker round the ostiole. Spores cylindrical, obtuse at both ends, hyaline, at first continuous, at length 1-septate, 7–10 × 3–3·5μ.

On living leaves of *Nuphar*. Botanic Gardens, Dublin, 1925.   Sept.

Cf. *Phyllosticta Nupharis* All. vi. 133, which has very similar spores, and may be an early stage of this. Some of the specimens under this name are merely Ramularia.

Onobrychis, Orobus

Ascochyta Orobi Sacc. Syll. iii. 398. All. vi. 654. Died. 387. Mig. 281.

Spots visible on both sides, pallid, with a fuscous-brown border, varying in form, 2–3 mm. across. Pycnidia immersed,

raising the epidermis somewhat but only just piercing it, de-pressed-globose, pallid-brown, 80–100μ wide, with a broad pore. Spores ellipsoid or cylindrical, rounded at both ends, guttulate, hardly constricted at the septum, 13–18 × 4–5·5μ.

On *Onobrychis sativa*. Glamorganshire (Rees). *n.v.*

Saccardo's species occurred on *Orobus vernus* and *O. niger*, but the form on *Onobrychis* was considered as a variety of it; see *A. Pisi*, of which it may be merely a form.

Germ. Ital. Siberia.

Phaseolus

Ascochyta Phaseolorum Sacc. Syll. iii. 398. All. vi. 656. Died. 388. Mig. 282.

Spots numerous, indistinct, roundish, variable, somewhat ochraceous when dry. Pycnidia epiphyllous, lens-shaped, about 100μ diam., clear-brown, slightly darker round the pore; texture parenchymatous. Spores oblong-ellipsoid, at length 1-septate, constricted (cells often unequal), often bi-guttulate, 7–10 × 3μ; sporophores not seen.

On leaves of *Phaseolus vulgaris*. Not common. Kilbride, Ayrshire (Boyd). Berkshire; Hampshire; etc.   Oct.

For a long time the spores are eseptate, and the fungus looks like a Phyllosticta.

Germ. Bohem. Denm. Ital.

Philadelphus

Ascochyta Philadelphi Sacc. & Sp. Syll. iii. 386. All. vi. 656. T.B.M.S. 1909, iii. 118. Died. p. 392, p. 350, f. 11. Mig. 282.

Spots almost circular, cinereous, becoming ochraceous when dry, 1 cm. or more broad, with an indistinct darker border. Pycnidia often few, sometimes concentrically arranged, punctiform, 150–200μ diam., opening by a pore. Spores narrow-oblong, attenuated but rounded at both ends, for a long time continuous, then 1-septate, constricted, occasion-ally biguttulate, 8–11 × 4–4·5μ.

On living leaves of *Philadelphus coronarius*. Kew Gardens; Fifeshire; Lanarkshire; Ayrshire.   Aug.–Oct.

At first like a Phyllosticta. Cf. *Ph. vulgaris* var. *Philadelphi* Sacc. *supra.*

Holl. Germ. Denm. Ital.

Pisum

Ascochyta Pisi Lib. Exs. no. 12. Sacc. Syll. iii. 397; xi. 523. Cooke, Handb. 455. All. vi. 658. Died. 388, 905. Mig. p. 275, pl. 35,

f. 1–4. Massee, Dis. Cult. Pl. p. 431, f. 134. Stevens, p. 506. *Ascochyta pisicola* (Berk.) Sacc. iii. 397. *Sphaeria* (*Depazea*) *concava* Berk. in Ann. Nat. Hist. 1841, vi. 363, pl. 11, f. 3.

Spots subrotund, pale-fawn colour, with a distinct brown margin; when on the pods, the spots are sunken or excavated. Pycnidia mostly in the centre of the spot, delicate, brownish, with a small round pore; texture of small parenchymatous cells, 5–7μ diam. Spores oblong, with rounded ends, slightly constricted, guttulate, 14–16 × 4–6μ, extruded to form short thick reddish tendrils which become confluent and paler.

On living leaves, stipules, pods, seeds, and stems of culti-vated Peas. England, Ireland. Widely spread, but not usually common, nor causing serious injury; transmissible by seed.

May–Oct.

This parasite can be destructive in damp seasons; it occurs chiefly on the pods, less often on the leaves, and even occasionally on the veins of the petals. On the pods, the spots are often zoned in a curious manner which is very striking. When the fungus assumes the form of an epidemic, it can possibly spread to other plants of the Pea family, cultivated or wild; e.g. *Cicer, Ervum, Melilotus, Onobrychis,. Phaseolus, Trifolium.* Stone (in Ann. Mycol. x. 564) united with it *A. Lathyri, A. Orobi, A. Viciae*, etc., and stated that forms of *Myco-sphaerella pinodes* (Berk. & Br.) are the respective ascophorous stages and occur on the corresponding dead plants. Among these forms he includes *Mycosph. Viciae*, but his statements are only partially cor-rect; see T.B.M.S. 1934, xviii. 276–9. A form called *A. pinodella* Jones was reported in Yorks. (1931).
Europe, N. Amer. India, Australia.

Plantago
Ascochyta Plantaginis Sacc. & Speg. Syll. iii. 403. All. vi. 659. Scot. Nat. 1887, ix. 188. *Phyllosticta Plantaginis* Sacc. Syll. iii. 53. Died. 78. Mig. 51. *Ph. plantaginella* Sacc. Syll. xi. 481.

Spots circular or various, brown when dried, becoming paler in the middle. Pycnidia gregarious, lens-shaped, um-bilicate, dark-brown, 100–150μ diam., opening by a rather wide pore; texture loose, cellular, smoky-olive. Spores oblong or subellipsoid, obtuse at both ends, often bent or curvulous, not constricted at the septum, biguttulate, 7–12 × 2·5–3μ.

On living leaves of *Plantago major*. Kilwinning, Ayrshire (Boyd). Aberdeen (spores 6–8 × 2–2·5μ, Trail)! Near Ux-

bridge. In the Phyllosticta stage (spores $5 \times 2\mu$) at Kew; Shere; Swanscombe.

Like Diedicke, I find that all the larger and maturer spores become 1-septate. Jun.–Nov.

Germ. Denm. Ital. U.S.A.

Primula

Ascochyta Primulae Trail, in Scot. Nat. 1887, iii. 88. Sacc. Syll. x. 300.

Spots amphigenous, large, whitish, becoming arid, often with a yellowish border. Pycnidia epiphyllous, globose-depressed, papillate, pale-brown, dispersed over the spots, about 100μ diam. Spores cylindrical, obtuse, 5–6×2–$2 \cdot 5\mu$.

On leaves of *Primula vulgaris*. Dunottar (Trail). Shrawley Wood and Brace's Leigh Wood, Ws. Aug.

Phyllosticta primulicola Desm. is probably the early stage of this. U.S.A.

Pyrus

Ascochyta pirina Pegl. Contr. Micol. Avell. p. 23. Sacc. Syll. xi. 523.

"Pycnidia black, minute, 300μ diam. Spores hyaline, 1-septate, gently constricted, 12–14×4–5μ.

On leaves and fruits of *Pyrus communis*."

Kidd & Beaumont (T.B.M.S. 1924, x. 107) record having isolated and cultivated this fungus on two occasions. They found a considerable proportion of non-septate spores. *n.v.*
Ital.

Quercus

Ascochyta Quercus-Ilicis Güssow, in Journ. Bot. 1908, xlvi. 123, pl. 489, f. E, 1–4. Smith, in T.B.M.S. 1909, iii. 118.

Spots numerous, epiphyllous, 1–5 mm. diam., irregular, brownish. Pycnidia hypophyllous below the spots, scattered, ovate, sometimes papillate, punctiform, blackish olive-green, 110–130μ diam. Spores lanceolate, 1-septate, subconstricted at the septum, hyaline to light-green, 12–14×3–4μ.

On leaves of *Quercus Ilex*. No locality given. *n.v.*

The pycnidia are superficial and are hidden by the stellate hairs on the underside of the leaf. Not an Ascochyta.

Ribes

Ascochyta ribesia Sacc. & Fautr. in Bull. Soc. Myc. Fr. 1900, p.
22. Sacc. Syll. xvi. 926. All. vii. 879. Grove, in Journ. Bot. 1922,
p. 15. Died. 394. Mig. 286.

Spots like those of *Phyllosticta Grossulariae*, in fact often
the same spots. Pycnidia epiphyllous, few, lens-shaped, 150μ
diam., blackish, opening by a central pore; texture somewhat
parenchymatous, olive-brown, darker round the pore. Spores
oblong-fusoid, 1-septate, acute at both ends, or somewhat obtuse especially at the upper end, pale-olivaceous, 13–14 ×
2·5–3μ.

On living leaves of *Ribes Grossularia*. Bute; Ayrshire
(Boyd). Aug. Sept.

Pycnidia darker than those of the Phyllosticta. Probably only the
leaf-form of *Hendersonia Grossulariae* Oud., for a few spores were triseptate, and many were 4-guttulate. If it is a distinct species, it should
go to the genus Ascochytula. Cf. *Ascochytula Grossulariae* Died.
Fr.

Rubus

Ascochyta Pallor Berk. Outl. 1860, p. 320. Cooke, Handb. 455.
Sacc. Syll. iii. 399. Journ. Board. Agric. 1912, xix. 125, with fig.
Sphaeria (*Depazea*) *pallor* Berk. in Ann. Nat. Hist. 1841, vi. 362, pl.
11, f. 2. *Diplodina Pallor* All. vi. 694, with fig. *Phyllosticta Pallor*
Oud. Contr. Myc. Pays-Bas, xiii. 34, pl. 9, f. 21. Sacc. Syll. x. 109.

Spots large (up to 12 mm. or more), round or elliptic, pale,
hardly margined, but more often shading off gradually at the
edge, dotted over with the minute pycnidia which are pallid
in the centre with a blackish margin. Pycnidia scattered, immersed, raising the epidermis somewhat prominently above
the indistinct ostiole. Spores linear or subfusoid, curved or
arcuate, at length faintly 1-septate, 13–20 × 2·5–3μ; sporophores simple, filiform, straight, about 15–20μ long.

On living shoots of *Rubus fruticosus*. King's Cliffe, Woodnewton, Northants. (Berk.). On branches of *Rubus idaeus*.
Clyde (Trail). Norfolk. Very rare.

The spores are sometimes curved so as to form a third of a circle;
about one in a hundred shows an indication of a septum. The pycnidial wall is soft and indistinctly parenchymatous.

According to Berkeley, this remarkable species forms subrotund,
sometimes confluent, pale spots, sprinkled with little elevated dark-
bordered dots which indicate the situation of the pycnidia. Pycnidia

extremely delicate, of a pale fawn colour, filled with linear slightly curved spores...some of which contain an obscure row of guttules. Cf. *A. Idaei,* and *Rhabdospora ramealis* which may be the same species. Holl.

Ascochyta Idaei Oud. in Hedwig. 1898, p. 178. *Diplodina Idaei* All. vi. 695. Sacc. Syll. xvi. 937.

Pycnidia aggregated, immersed, then protruding the small papilla, 100–120μ diam., pierced by a pore; texture membranaceous. Spores ellipsoid, rounded at both ends, 1-septate in the middle, scarcely constricted, faintly tinged with colour, 9 × 4·5μ.

On branches of *Rubus idaeus*. Merthyr Tydfil (Rees). Nottingham (Cotton). Feb.–Jun.

Ascochyta argillacea (Bres.), on the leaves of *R. idaeus,* is very similar. Holl.

Scabiosa

Ascochyta Scabiosae Rabenh. in Klotzsch, Herb. Myc. no. 1253. Sacc. Syll. iii. 400. All. vi. 672.

"Tendrils flesh-coloured, hyaline" (Sacc.).

On living leaves of *Scabiosa (Knautia) arvensis*. Ombersley (Rea). *n.v.*

Saccardo considers this to be merely an immature state of *Septoria scabiosicola* Desm. (*q.v.*). Fr. Germ.

Senecio

Ascochyta Senecionis Fckl. Symb. Myc. 386.

No spots. Pycnidia minute, hypophyllous, globose, black, collected into little scattered groups. No spores seen.

On the lower surface of fading leaves of *Senecio sarracenicus,* West Kilbride, Ayrshire (Boyd). On leaves of *Senecio Greyii,* Polperro (Rilstone). Jul. Aug.

Germ.

Solanum

Ascochyta solanicola Oud. Contr. Flor. Myc. Pays-Bas, xvii. 264. Sacc. Syll. xvi. 931. All. vii. 879. Died. 395. Mig. 288. Cf. Brooks & Price, in New Phytol. 1913, xii. 13.

Spots circular or oblong, up to 1·5 cm. long, brown, scarcely showing on the underside, then becoming dry and

greyish, easily falling out. Pycnidia epiphyllous, scattered, subglobose, slightly protruding, clear-brown, up to 200μ diam., not darker round the 20μ wide pore. Spores cylindric, rounded at both ends, straight or slightly bent, hyaline, not constricted at the septum, 8–12 × 2–3μ; sporophores short, conical.

On living leaves of *Solanum Dulcamara, S. nigrum.* Doubtfully distinct.

Germ. Holl.

Ascochyta Lycopersici Brun. in Bull. Soc. Bot. Fr. 1887, xxxiv. 430. Sacc. Syll. x. 304. All. vi. 664. *Phoma Lycopersici* Cooke, in Grevill. 1885, xiii. 94. *Diplodina Lycopersici* Hollós, in Ann. Mus. Nat. Hung. 1907, v. 461. Sacc. Syll. xxii. 1040. T.B.M.S. vii. 192. *Ascochyta socia* Pass. in Bol. Com. Agr. Parm. 1889, p. 2 (extr.). *Phoma destructiva* Plowr. in Gard. Chron. 1881, xvi. 621, f. 123; Trans. Woolhope Club, 1882, p. 110, f. 7. Sacc. Syll. x. 175. All. vi. 303. Massee, Dis. Cult. Pl. ed. II, suppl. p. 7. Jamieson, in Journ Agric. Res. 1915, iv. 1. *Diplodina destructiva* Petr. in Ann. Mycol. 1921, xix. 19. *Sphaeronaema Lycopersici* Plowr. in Gard. Chron. 1881, p. 621, f. 117. See also Gard. Chron. 1915, lviii. 71; Brooks & Searle, in T.B.M.S. 1921, vii. 192; Brooks & Price, in New Phytol. 1913, xii. 13.

Pycnidia scattered or aggregated on swollen spots, subepidermal, then erumpent, subglobose, brown or brownish-black, slightly papillate, pierced by a pore (or two), 100–250μ diam.; texture thin, pa enchymatous, clear pale-brown, cells isodiametric, darker round the ostiole. Spores ovoid, 4–5 × 2–3μ, then subcylindrical, hyaline, continuous, then 1-septate, slightly constricted, with two or no guttules, 4·5–15 × 2·5–5μ (average 9·5 × 3·5μ), issuing in a whitish or flesh-coloured tendril; sporophores short, simple, filiform.

On green and on ripe fruits, also on leaves and stems just above the ground-level, of *Solanum Lycopersicum.* Not common, but occasionally epidemic. May–Jul.

Klebahn (in Zeitschr. f. Pflanzenkr. 1921, xxxi. 1) assigns to it a perithecial stage *Didymella Lycopersici* Kleb.

In the United States it is said to be also parasitic on Potatos. The form on leaves makes scattered brownish spots. The spores are for a long time continuous, but even Cooke's specimens contain many 1-septate spores. In Bohemia and in Britain (Rhodes) it is reported on living leaves of *Lycium barbarum,* under the name *A. destructiva*

(spores 6–10 × 3–4μ). It has been said (T.B.M.S. xvii. 110) to grow on Butter!

Europe, U.S.A., Canada.

Ascochyta citrullina C. O. Smith, in Delaw. Expt. Sta. Bull. 70 (1905). Sacc. Syll. xxii. 1022. Kew Bull. 1909, p. 293, with plate. Gard. Chron. 1913, liv. 167, f. 65. Massee, Dis. Cult. Pl. 218. Smith, in T.B.M.S. 1911, iii. 282. *Diplodina citrullina* Grossenb. Tech. Bull. no. 9, N.Y. Agric. Expt. Sta. p. 226 (1909). Stevens, p. 246, f. 183. See New Phytol. 1913, xii. 13–21.

Pycnidia crowded, subepidermal, then erumpent, globose-depressed, 90–160μ diam., black, pierced by a pore; texture thin, parenchymatous, pale-brown; pore distinct, apical, minute. Spores very numerous, ± cylindric-oblong, becoming 1-septate, occasionally slightly constricted at the septum, 9–16 × 4–6μ (or 7–11 × 3–4μ).

Forming pale patches on the stems of Tomatos (*Solanum Lycopersicum*), near the base, as well as on the fruits. Reported from many counties (Middlesex, Essex, Glos., etc.), but probably incorrectly.

It is recorded also on the stems of Cucumber (Rep. Board. Agric. 1922–4) and more rarely, at Kew, on Vegetable Marrow; in the United States it is said to form grey or whitish patches on the lower portions of the stems of Melon. It has been called "Cucumber and Tomato Canker". The reputed perithecial stage (developed later on friable and broken stems) is *Mycosphaerella citrullina* Gross. *l.c.*, which is stated to have been found in England. But it is possible that the English Tomato-canker is not quite the same as that of the U.S.A. Here the disease shows its presence by an early wilting of the leaves, but is not serious for out-door Tomatos. See also *Ascochyta cucumeris* Fautr. & Roum., and *A. Lycopersici* Brun.

Europe, N. Amer.

Sonchus

Ascochyta Sonchi Grove, in Journ. Bot. 1922, p. 48. *Phyllosticta Sonchi* Sacc. Syll. iii. 44.

Spots roundish, fuscous-brown with a dark-brown border, 8–15 mm. across. Pycnidia rather crowded, about 100μ diam., punctiform, blackish. Spores oblong-ovoid, long 1-celled, straight or curved, with 2–4 guttules, 7–9 × 2·5μ, then 1-septate, 8–10 × 2–3μ, with 1 guttule in each cell.

On leaves of *Sonchus oleraceus*. Ardrossan, Ayrshire (Boyd). Warwickshire. Aug.

Spiraea

Ascochyta Spiraeae Kab. & Bub. in Hedwig. 1908, xlii. 359. Sacc. Syll. xxii. 1018. Mig. 288.

Forma **caulicola** Grove.

No spots. Pycnidia crowded sometimes congested, round, lens-shaped, blackish, 100–200μ diam., immersed, then opening by a very wide pore; texture thin, distinctly parenchymatous with rather large thin-walled cells, pale-brownish, darker round the ostiole. Spores very abundant, oblong, often biscuit-shaped, rounded at both ends, usually straight or rarely bent at the septum, 1-septate, not constricted, hyaline, eguttulate, 8–10 × 2·5–3μ (5–11 × 3–4·5μ, Kab. & Bub.).

On dead stems of *Spiraea Aruncus*. Oscott College, Birmingham (Rhodes). In Bohemia on dead leaves.   Nov.

Stellaria

Ascochyta Stellariae Fautr. in Rev. Mycol. 1896, p. 68. Sacc. Syll. xiv. 943. All. vi. 665. Grove, in Journ. Bot. 1922, p. 47, pl. 563, f. 2.

Spots none or indefinite. Pycnidia more or less aggregated in patches on the dead leaf, immersed, hardly prominent, 150–200μ diam., globose-lens-shaped, honey-fuscous, pierced by a pore; texture very thin, membranaceous, pale except for a narrow dark circle round the pore. Spores irregular, oblong, rounded at both ends, colourless, very clouded and multiguttulate within, eseptate, at times slightly curved and bent as if about to become 1-septate, but not constricted, 23–30 × 6–7μ.

On fading or dead leaves of *Stellaria uliginosa*. West Kilbride, Ayrshire (Boyd).   May.

Possibly a young state of a species of Stagonospora. The texture of the pycnidium is truly Ascochyta-like; the narrow black line around the pore is conspicuous even with a hand-lens.
Fr.

Symphoricarpus, see **Lonicera**

Taraxacum

Ascochyta Taraxaci Grove, in Journ. Bot. 1922, p. 48. *Phyllosticta Taraxaci* Hollós in Ann. Mus. Nat. Hung. 1907, v. 456. Sacc. Syll. xxii. 852.

Spots roundish or somewhat irregular, 4–7 mm. broad, dark brownish-cinereous, often marked with concentric lines,

bordered by a narrow black margin. Pycnidia epiphyllous, few, scattered, lens-shaped, blackish-brown, pierced by a pore. Spores oblong-ellipsoid, rarely tapering below, colourless, 9–10 × 2·5–3μ, mostly 1-septate.

On living leaves of *Taraxacum officinale*. Kilwinning, Ayrshire (Boyd). Aug.

This is the advanced state of the Phyllosticta. In some of the pycnidia large numbers of 1-celled spores were found mixed with the 1-septate spores, and some pycnidia had only the simple spores, differing from Hollós's description merely in being perfectly colourless. *Septoria Taraxaci* Hollós may be a still later stage.

Hung.

Tilia

Ascochyta Tiliae Kab. & Bub. in Hedwig. xlvi. 293. Grove, in Journ. Bot. lvi. 316.

Spots equally visible on both sides, roundish or irregular, variable, 5–15 mm. diam., of a dark smoke-colour, at length becoming thin and translucent-grey, without a border, or darker at the margin. Pycnidia generally epiphyllous, numerous, densely scattered over the spots, immersed, roundish, 100–150μ diam., transparent-brownish with a darker margin; texture truly Ascochyta-like. Spores oblong, rounded at each end or somewhat tapering below, hardly or not at all constricted, without guttules or 2–4-guttulate, 8–10 × 2·5–3μ.

On living and fading leaves of *Tilia grandifolia*. Ayrshire (Boyd). July.

Spots of a uniform dull colour, at length dropping out and leaving "shot-holes".

Bohemia.

Trifolium

Ascochyta Trifolii Bond. & Truss. in the Journal "Bolestni Rasteni", 1913, vii. 215. Siemasko, in Act. Soc. Sci. Vars. 1914, vii. 8 (extr.). Sacc. Syll. xxv. 332. *Phleospora Trifolii* Cav. var. *recedens* Massal. Contr. Mic. Ver. 96. Sacc. Syll. x. 399. Probably also *Stagonospora Meliloti* Petrak; see Ann. Mycol. 1919, xvii. 64.

"Spots amphigenous, at first roundish, elongated, or irregular, then confluent, concentrically zoned, fuscous-brown, paler in the centre. Pycnidia few, usually epiphyllous, immersed, globose, brownish, 100–150μ diam.; ostiole minutely papillate; texture dingy-yellow, indistinctly parenchymatous. Spores ± cylindrical, rounded at both ends, sometimes gently

curved, hyaline, guttulate, rarely 1–3-septate, then constricted, 15–22 × 4·5–6μ."

On leaves of *Trifolium pratense*. Aberystwith (Sampson).
July.

Probably an early state of *Stagonospora compta* (*q.v.* p. 349).
Ital. Russ. Poland.

Urtica
Ascochyta Urticae Sm. & Ramsb. in T.B.M.S. 1915, v. 159.

Spots amphigenous, roundish, ochraceous-brown, becoming
dry from the middle, with a narrow blackish-brown border.
Pycnidia epiphyllous, scattered, immersed, covered by the
epidermis, 120–150μ diam., pierced by a pore about 20μ wide.
Spores irregular in form, ± oblong, constricted at the septum,
10–12 × 2–4μ.

On leaves of *Urtica dioica*. Colintraive (Boyd). *n.ex.* Aug.

Valeriana
Ascochyta Valerianae Sm. & Ramsb. in T.B.M.S. 1913, iv. 176.

Spots conspicuous on both sides, angular, brown, with a
darker margin, about 5–10 mm. diam. or confluent and larger.
Pycnidia epiphyllous, globose-depressed, immersed, 120–180μ
diam., opening by a minute round pore; texture parenchymatous, pallid-brown. Spores elliptic-oblong, septate in the
middle, gently constricted, 8–10 × 2–3μ.

On living leaves of *Valeriana pyrenaica*. Beith, Ayrshire
(Boyd). *n.ex.*   July.

Viburnum
Ascochyta Viburni Sacc. Syll. iii. 387. Grove, in Journ. Bot. lvi.
316. Mig. 290. *Phyllosticta Viburni* Roum. Fung. Gall. no. 2036.

Spots irregularly placed, roundish or sinuous, 3–10 mm.
across, pallid, with a purplish border. Pycnidia epiphyllous,
globose-lens-shaped, immersed, at length erumpent at the
apex, pale-brownish, then darker, about 200μ diam. Spores
oblong or subcylindric-ellipsoid, rounded at both ends or
faintly tapering below, hardly constricted at the septum,
9–12 × 2–3μ.

On living leaves of *Viburnum Opulus*. Beith, Ayrshire (Boyd). Aug.

It is probable that *Phyllosticta Viburni* Pass. (Sacc. Syll. x. 113) is the same species before the septum is developed.
Fr. Germ.

Vicia

Ascochyta Viciae Lib. Crypt. Ard. iii, no. 356 (1837). Sacc. Syll. x. 303. All. vi. 668. Died. 107, 389. Mig. 291. Trail, in Scot. Nat. 1887, iii. 87. *A. viciicola* Sacc. Syll. x. 303. *Phyllosticta Viciae* Cooke, in Seem. Journ. Bot. iv. 97.

Spots roundish, small, reddish, at length paler in the centre, bounded by a prominent dark-sanguineous border. Pycnidia epiphyllous, aggregated, minute, black, 90–100μ diam., opening by a pore; texture thin, dusky round the pore. Spores ovoid-oblong or subcylindric, obtuse at both ends, usually straight, gently constricted at the septum, 12–15 × 4–5μ (13–16 × 2·5–3μ, granular and yellowish, Trail).

On leaves, stems, and pods of *Vicia* (*Cracca, sativa, sepium*). Cheshire; Cornwall; Worcestershire; Renfrewshire; Aberdeen; Stonehaven; etc. Aug. Sept.

This fungus does not seem to be really distinct from *A. Pisi* Lib., and is identical with *A. Orobi* Sacc., and possibly with *A. Lathyri* Trail, and others; *Phyllosticta Viciae* Cooke is its immature stage.
Fr. Belg. Germ. Denm.

Vinca

Ascochyta Vincae Grove, in Journ. Bot. 1916, p. 191. *Phyllosticta Vincae* Thüm. Contr. Fl. Myc. Lusit. ii. 48. Sacc. Syll. iii. 55. See Died. 108; Mig. 57.

Spots large, irregular, fuscous, scarcely becoming paler when dry, bordered by a narrow dark-brown line. Pycnidia mostly epiphyllous, few, often collected in the middle of the spot, immersed, black, punctiform, but slightly prominent. Spores narrowly fusoid, straight or curvulous, tapering more at the base than at the apex, at times slightly unequal, at length delicately 1-septate, not constricted, 11–14 × 2μ.

On leaves of *Vinca major*. Ayrshire (Boyd). Hereford; Ledbury; Churchill, Worcs. Mar.–May.

The spores are for a long time eseptate, oblong, biguttulate, 6–9 × 2–2·5μ, but reaching even 12μ before the septum is formed.
Fr. Germ. Port. Algeria.

Viola

Ascochyta Violae Sacc. & Sp. Syll. iii. 397. All. vi. 668. Massee, Dis. Cult. Pl. p. 431. *Phyllosticta Violae* All. (? *non* Desm.).

Spots of various colours (yellowish, brownish), bleached when dry and easily dropping out. Pycnidia gregarious, globose-depressed, 100–200μ diam., pierced by a pore; texture parenchymatous, pale smoky-brown, thickened round the pore. Spores shortly oblong-fusoid or subcylindric, hyaline, at first continuous, biguttulate, then longer and 2–4-guttulate, at length 1-septate, not constricted, 8–12 × 2·5–3μ (15–18 × 3·5–4μ, Sacc.).

On living leaves of *Viola odorata* and other cultivated species of *Viola*. Not uncommon; England, Scotland. Cf. *Septoria Violae, infra,* p. 416. Spring–autumn.

This can become a very destructive disease, if not quickly checked. Europe, U.S.A.

Vitis

Ascochyta rufo-maculans Berk. Outl. p. 320 (1860). Cooke, Handb. 456. Sacc. Syll. iii. 395; x. 296. Southworth, in Journ. Mycol. vi. 164, pl. 16. *Septoria rufo-maculans* Berk. in Gard. Chron. 1854, p. 676, with fig.

"Spots orbicular, red-brown. Pycnidia emergent, free, of the same colour. Spores oblong, constricted in the middle (? at length 1-septate), 15–20μ long."

On fruit of *Vitis vinifera* (Muscat Grapes). Exeter (specimen in Herb. Kew). *n.ex.*

No doubt this is a Gloeosporium. Berkeley draws the spores on distinct sporophores, and states that there was no septum, and no pycnidial wall. Spaulding and Schrank (1903) in Bull. 44 of the Bureau Pl. Industr. call it *Gloeosporium rufo-maculans*, and place it as the conidial stage of their *Glomerella rufo-maculans*; it has since been found with very distinct spines as a Colletotrichum. It is considered by some to cause the "Bitter-rot" of grapes, apples, cherries, and to be included under *Gloeo. fructigenum*. It is rare in Europe.

MONOCOTYLEDONS

Alisma

Ascochyta Alismatis Trail, in Scot. Nat. 1887, iii. 188. *A. Alismatis* Ell. & Ev. in Journ. Mycol. 1889, p. 148 (Sacc. Syll. x. 307) is probably the same species. *Septoria Alismatis* Oud. in Hedwig. 1876, p. 101; Mat. Myc. Néerl. p. 4. Sacc. Syll. iii. 569. All. vi. 726. Died.

425. Mig. 376. *Rhynchosporium Alismatis* Davis, in Trans. Wisc.
Acad. Sci. 1921, p. 420.

Spots numerous, small, roundish, smoky-black, at length
whitish-grey in the centre, visible on both sides of the leaf.
Pycnidia minute, just visible with a good lens, mostly hypophyllous, black. Spores cylindrical, straight, 1-guttulate at
each end, septate in the middle, 15–18 × 3μ.

On fading leaves of *Alisma Plantago*. Near Aberdeen (Trail).
Solihull, Wk. Recorded in U.S.A. on *Sagittaria* also.   Oct.

The spots were nearly circular, almost black, 1–2 mm. in diam.,
becoming paler in the middle. Pycnidia 80–100μ diam., black, difficult to see. Spores linear, straight, constricted in the middle, 18 × 2–
2·5μ. Diedicke says that the German specimens he had seen seemed
to be nothing but *Ramularia Alismatis* Fautr. misunderstood, and this
is true of the Canadian specimens also.

Belg. Holl. Germ. Denm. Austr. Ital. U.S.A. Canada.

Ascochyta Boydii Grove, in Journ. Bot. 1918, lvi. 315. *Phyllosticta Alismatis* Sacc. & Speg. in Mich. i. 144. Sacc. Syll. iii. 60. All.
vi. 157.

Spots usually few on each leaf, sinuous or irregularly rounded, 5–12 mm. broad, pale-brown or whitish, with a chestnut-
brown or dusky-brown border. Pycnidia epiphyllous, numerous, 50–130μ diam., pale-brown, then darker, pierced by a
pore; texture truly Ascochyta-like. Spores at first obovoid or
ellipsoid, continuous, then oblong and 1-septate, often curved
or bent, rounded at each end or pointed below, often biguttulate, 10–12 × 2–2·5μ.

On living leaves of *Alisma Plantago*. Ayrshire (Boyd).
Cheshire (Ellis).   Jul.–Sept.

The more advanced state of *Phyllosticta Alismatis* S. & S. *Ascochyta
Alismatis* Trail has different spores and smaller and more numerous
spots.

Fr. Germ. Ital. Port. Siber.

Arum

Ascochyta Ari Died. 376 (Nov. 1912). Mig. 265. *Ascochyta aricola*
Sm. & Ramsb. in T.B.M.S. 1913, iv. 175.

Spots amphigenous, conspicuous, up to 3 cm. broad, green,
then brown, not margined. Pycnidia epiphyllous or rarely
amphigenous, densely gregarious, depressed-globose, somewhat prominent, 180–200μ diam., pierced by a round pore;

texture thin, plectenchymatous, pallid-brown. Spores oblong-ellipsoid, straight or sometimes curvulous, hyaline, $8-10 \times 2-3\mu$; no sporophores seen.

On fading leaves of *Arum maculatum*. West Kilbride, Ayr-shire (Boyd). May–Jul.

The spores are for a long time continuous, then they show a faint constriction, where afterwards a septum is formed. *A. arophila* Sacc. in Grevill. xxi. 67, pl. 184, f. 10 (Syll. xi. 525) has greenish spores, 18–21 × 5–6μ, and belongs to Ascochytula(?).
Germ.

Aspidistra

Ascochyta Aspidistrae Massee, in Gard. Chron. 1895, p. 454; Dis. Cult. Pl. p. 431, f. 133.

"Spots various, broad, becoming dry and bleached, scarcely margined. Pycnidia gregarious, rather prominent, lens-shaped, at first covered, 75–100μ diam. Spores cylindric-fusoid, 1-septate, somewhat constricted, hyaline, $9-15 \times 3\mu$ (G.C.), narrowly fusiform, $12-17 \times 2-2\cdot5\mu$ (D.C.P.)."

On living leaves of *Aspidistra lurida*. In various places, no definite locality given (Massee).

The description is that of Massee. On the type specimens in Herb. Kew, I could find no spores, and only a few bodies which might be immature pycnidia, arranged not "on blackish streaks which run across the leaf", but chiefly along the nerves. It is a doubtful species, best forgotten.

Carex

Ascochyta sodalis Grove.

Pycnidia resembling in shape and arrangement those of *Septoria Caricis* (*q.v.*) with which it was growing, but not more than 100μ in diameter, and differing in the texture of the peridial wall, which was composed of thin polyhedral paren-chymatous cells as much as 20μ in breadth. Spores like those of typical *A. graminicola* in shape, very distinctly 1-septate, $12-15 \times 3-4\cdot5\mu$.

On tips of leaves of *Carex arenaria*, on the shore, Broad-haven, Pembrokeshire (Rhodes). July.

Though the pycnidia of the Ascochyta and the Septoria were inter-mingled, each retained its own character, and no forms of spores inter-mediate between the two species could be detected in any of the conceptacles.

Dracaena

Ascochyta dracaenicola All. vi. 641. *Diplodina dracaenicola* Sacc. Syll. iii. 413.

"Pycnidia scattered, minute, black. Spores oblong, slightly constricted in the middle, 15–17·5μ long."

On leaves of cultivated *Dracaena*, accompanied by *Myxosporium dracaenicola* (*q.v. infra*, Vol. II). *n.v.* See Grevill. x. 48, and Ann. Nat. Hist. 1881, vii. 129.

Gramineae

Ascochyta graminicola Sacc. Syll. iii. 407; x. 308; xxv. 327. All. vi. 644. Died. p. 384, p. 350, f. 8. Mig. 266.

Spots various, 5–8 mm. broad, becoming pale or indistinct. Pycnidia gregarious, punctiform, lens-shaped, 100–120μ diam. pierced by a pore; texture distinctly plectenchymatous, pallid, smoky-brown round the ostiole. Spores subfusoid, usually straight, 1-septate, often biguttulate, 10–15 × 3–4μ. (Fig. 20*b*.)

On fading leaves of various Grasses (*Alopecurus*, *Arrhenatherum*, *Dactylis*, *Festuca*, *Holcus*, *Lolium*, *Phleum*, *Poa*, etc.).

England, Scotland, Wales, Ireland. Summer and autumn.

Many varieties have been described, but the species has so many forms that it is hardly possible to distinguish them by words: e.g. on *Brachypodium*, spores 15–17 × 5μ (var. *Brachypodii*); on *Bromus*, *Agropyron*, *Glyceria*, *Psamma*, spores 10–14 × 2–3μ (var. *leptospora*, Trail). Some of these are said to have mucous appendages at each end, but see Tiarospora, and cf. also *Darluca filum*. Diedicke records two vars. on *Triticum*, of which I have found var. *b.* on *T. repens*, var. *littorale*, in September at Sandwich Bay, Kent.

Dr Rhodes has found a form, however, which seems to present a greater difference, and may be called

Var. **Festucae**, var. nov.

Pycnidia scattered, very minute, barely reaching 100μ diam., round, blackish, opening by a rather large pore; texture one cell thick, the cells being large, isodiametric (about 8μ), thin-walled, brownish. Spores fusoid, 1-septate, widest at the middle, acute at both ends, hyaline, eguttulate, 14–17 × 3μ.

On dry leaves of *Festuca ovina*, Broadhaven, Pembr. (Rhodes). July.

The spores broke in two readily at the septum. Europe, U.S.A.

Ascochyta Stipae Died. p. 385, p. 350, f. 12. Mig. 289.

Forma **Agropyri** Grove.

Pycnidia scattered or arranged ± in rows, immersed, piercing the epidermis merely by the minute pore, round or elongated, clear-brown, $200 \times 100\mu$; texture of large cells, yellowish, not darker round the pore. Spores oval-oblong or subcylindric, rounded at both ends, straight or slightly bent, 1-septate, not constricted, nearly colourless, with three or more large guttules, $23–34 \times 8–10\mu$; sporophores not seen.

On dry leaves and stems of *Agropyron junceum*. Sandy seashore, Dale, Pembr. (Rhodes). July.

This is not a true Ascochyta, but probably a young state of a Stagonospora. Germ.

Ascochyta Psammae Oud. in Nederl. Kr. Arch. ser. 3, ii. 263. Sacc. Syll. xvi. 935.

Pycnidia gregarious, crowded, up to 120μ diam., subglobose, immersed, then erumpent by the upper half, black, shining. Spores oval-lanceolate, acute at both ends, broadest at the septum, not at all constricted, nearly colourless, $8–10 \times 2\cdot5–3\mu$ ($12–14 \times 4\cdot5–5\mu$, Oud.).

On dead leaves of *Psamma arenaria*. Cobo, Guernsey (Rhodes). Sept.

A doubtful species.

Helcocharis

Ascochyta decipiens Trail, in Scot. Nat. 1889, iv. 71. Sacc. Syll. x. 307. *Diplodina decipiens* All. vi. 688.

Pycnidia immersed, spherical-depressed, about 120μ diam., thin, dark-brown. Spores abundant, ellipsoid, with a very delicate septum in the middle, but not constricted, $9–11 \times 2\cdot5–3\cdot5\mu$.

On culms of *Heleocharis palustris*. Loch Achray; West Scotland; Forth (Trail). *n.v.* On the same culms was *Coniothyrium Scirpi*.

Allescher appears to have transferred it to Diplodina without having seen it.

Iris
Ascochyta Pseudacori Sm. & Ramsb. in T.B.M.S. 1916, v. 244.

Spots elongated, grey. Pycnidia epiphyllous, very minute, globose, blackish, about 150μ diam. Spores ellipsoid, about 5 × 2·5μ.

On fading leaves of *Iris Pseudacorus*. Colintraive, Argyll; West Kilbride and Saltcoats, Ayrshire (Boyd). Occurring especially on the tips of the leaves.   Aug.

Cf. *Phyllosticta Pseudacori* (Brun.) Allesch.

Luzula
Ascochyta teretiuscula Sacc. & Roum. in Mich. ii. 621; Syll. iii. 405. All. vi. 651. *Diplodina teretiuscula* Died. in Ann. Mycol. 1912, x. 140; Pilz. Brand. 405. Mig. 301.

Spots wanting. Pycnidia immersed, scattered over considerable areas, punctiform, globose, black, 100–180μ diam., opening by a pore. Spores cylindrical, rounded at both ends, 1-septate, scarcely constricted, faintly yellowish, 10–14 × 2·5–3μ.

On leaves of *Luzula silvatica*. Near Aberdeen (Trail). On leaves of *L. pilosa*. Worcestershire; Derbyshire.   Feb.–May.

Specimens gathered by Dr J. W. Ellis, on dead leaves of *L. pilosa*, at Shrawley, Worcs., agree with the description except that the spores have no septum, only a row of minute guttules. Cf. *Hendersonia* (*Stagonospora*) *Luzulae*, which remains uncoloured for a considerable time, and of which the Ascochyta is probably an early state.
Fr. Germ. Denm. U.S.A.

Sparganium
Ascochyta quadriguttulata Kab. & Bub. in Hedwig. 1910, vol. 50, p. 40. Mig. 288. *A. Sparganii* Ellis, in T.B.M.S. 1914, iv. 293.

Spots on both sides, elongated, irregular, confluent and spreading widely, alutaceous or brown, often with a fuscous border, at length dingy-grey. Pycnidia emphigenous, scattered, immersed, long covered by the epidermis and raising it slightly, lens-shaped, ochreous or brown, 120–180μ diam., opening by a pore; texture thin, of large parenchymatous cells. Spores numerous, cylindrical, rounded at both ends or somewhat tapering, 1-septate near the middle, often constricted, each cell biguttulate, 12–26 × 4·5–6μ; sporophores cylindrical, up to 12μ long.

On dead peduncles and leaves of *Sparganium ramosum*. Hartlebury Common, Ws., and Llanstadwell, Pembr. (Rhodes). Rodborough Common (Ellis).

A. quadriguttulata is an advanced state of *A. Sparganii* Ellis, and it reaches its completely developed form in *Stagonospora Sparganii* All. (*q.v.*).

Typha, see under *Stagonospora*

Pteridium
Ascochyta Pteridis Bres. in Hedwig. 1894, p. 208. Sacc. Syll. xi. 525. All. vi. 661. Died. 393. Mig. 285. Grove, in Journ. Bot. 1922, p. 47, pl. 563, f. 6.

Spots scattered, circular or nearly so, very minute, scarcely ¼ mm. diam., pale-ochraceous, thickened at the edge, surrounded by a much broader purple-brown border. Pycnidia epiphyllous, few, rather crowded (but sometimes only one on each spot), about 100μ diam., subglobose, black, piercing the epidermis and at length becoming somewhat superficial; texture thin, pale-brownish. Spores oblong-cylindrical, obtuse at both ends, often bent or flexuose, with a septum which is sometimes median, sometimes above the middle, slightly constricted, 15–20 (or even 30) × 4–6μ, cloudy and furnished with 2, 4, or more guttules.

On dead pinnules and petiolules of *Pteridium aquilinum*, lying in damp places. West Kilbride, Ayrshire (Boyd).

July.

In Germany it is said to occur on the living leaves, and kill the part above the point of attack. Probably a *Stagonospora*. Germ.

Equisetum
Ascochyta Equiseti Grove, in Journ. Bot. 1918, p. 315; Kew Bull. 1921, p. 146. *Phoma Equiseti* Desm. Exs. no. 183. Sacc. Syll. iii. 168; x. 187. All. vi. 341. Lév. in Ann. Sci. Nat. 1846, p. 282. *Sphaeria Equiseti* Sacc. Syll. ii. 442. *Sphaeropsis epitricha* B. & Br. in Ann. Nat. Hist. 1850, v. 375. Cooke, Handb. 427. *Phoma epitricha* Sacc. Syll. iii. 168.

Pycnidia seriate or widely scattered, oval or subglobose, covered by the bleached epidermis, which is then pierced by the minute ostiole and afterwards more widely torn, blackish, 200–800μ diam.; texture soft, pale-brown, pseudopycnidial.

Spores at first ovoid, continuous, biguttulate, 6–7·5 × 3μ, then oblong, 8–10 × 3–3·5μ, then 1-septate, acute at one or both ends, sometimes bent at the septum, 10·5–12 × 3–3·5μ, loculi often unequal; sporophores about 3μ long.

On dry dead stems of *Equisetum limosum, fluviatile, arvense, hyemale* (especially on *limosum*). Ardrossan and Largs (Boyd). Batheaston; Hadzor Hall, Ws.; Harborne, King's Norton, and other places near Birmingham.

Feb.–Apr.

The so-called Phoma is merely the young undeveloped state; both forms of spores may be found in the same pycnidium. But there is a Coniothyrium also found on *Equisetum*, which may easily be mistaken for the Phoma unless closely examined; Bucknall's specimen from Leigh Woods, Bristol, was this.

It is quite credible that *Diplodina Equiseti* Sacc. in Ann. Mycol. 1905, p. 233, and Syll. xviii. 355 (= *Stagonosporopsis Equiseti* Died. 399) is a later stage in the same series. It has cylindrical spores, 16–19 × 4–4·5μ, at length minutely 4-guttulate; Diedicke and others have found the Phoma and the Diplodina growing in company. Nor does there seem to be any reason why *Stagonospora Equiseti* Fautr. in Rev. Myc. 1890, p. 124 (Sacc. Syll. x. 337; All. vi. 973; Died. 555; Mig. 345) should not be considered a still further development. It has similar spores, 20–25 × 4–5μ, but 3-septate and, like the Diplodina, grows on *E. limosum*, which is the favourite host of the Ascochyta. Cf. remarks under *Septoria Chenopodii, infra*, and also p. 362.

Fr. Belg. Germ. Switz. Denm.

STAGONOSPOROPSIS Died. in Ann. Mycol. x. 142.

Pycnidia on leaves and stems, covered, rather thin-walled or pseudopycnidial. Spores hyaline or faintly coloured, at first 1-septate, but forming later a second transverse septum so as to become three-celled. The additional septum is formed in the longer of the two cells, if they were unequal. Very rarely three transverse septa occur. (Fig. 21.)

Equisetum
Stagonosporopsis Equiseti Died. in Ann. Mycol. x. 142; Pilz. Brand. 399. Mig. 293. *Diplodina Equiseti* Sacc. in Ann. Mycol. iii. 233.

Pycnidia loosely gregarious, covered, then piercing the epidermis, but not projecting, globose-lenticular, pseudo-pycnidial, brown, darker round the minute pore, 150–300μ

diam., surrounded by brown hyphae. Spores cylindrical, often somewhat bent, rounded at both ends, with one or two septa, scarcely or not constricted, at length with several oil-guttules, $16-19 \times 4-4 \cdot 5\mu$; sporophores not seen.

On dead sheaths of *Equisetum*. Hartlebury Common, Ws. (Rhodes).

It seems hard to believe that this is anything but a young undeveloped form of *Stagonospora equisetina* Trail (*q.v. infra*), with *Stagonospora Equiseti* Fautr. as an intermediate stage.

Salicornia

Stagonosporopsis Salicorniae Died. in Ann. Mycol. x. 142; Pilz. Brand. 401. Mig. 294. *Ascochyta Salicorniae* Magn. in Schr. Naturw. Ver. Schlesw.-Holst. xii. 30. *Diplodina Salicorniae* Jaap, in Verh. Bot. Prov. Brand. 1907, p. 16. Sacc. Syll. xxii. 1044.

Pycnidia scattered, occupying the lower part of the stems, immersed, $90-150\mu$ diam.; ostiole projecting, with a pore 25μ broad; texture thin, pseudo-pycnidial, darker round the pore. Spores cylindric, rounded at both ends, hyaline or faintly yellowish-olive, with one septum (or rarely two), often 2–4-guttulate, $10-18 \times 3 \cdot 5-5\mu$; sporophores inconspicuous. (Fig. 21.)

Fig. 21. *Stagonosporopsis Salicorniae*: spores of various ages, × 600.

On the lower part of stems of *Salicornia herbacea*. Salt-flats, near Dale, Pembr.; salt marsh, Red Wharf Bay, Anglesey (Rhodes). July.

The Diplodina is on old stems of the same host, has thicker and larger pycnidia, and the spores are wider ($6 \cdot 5-7\mu$), but no longer. Otherwise they are the same.

Germ.

ASCOCHYTULA Potebnia, in Ann. Mycol. 1907, v. 10.

Differs from Ascochyta chiefly in having spores that are not hyaline, but show a clear-brownish or yellowish colour in mass.

There is no real basis for the separation of some of the species of this genus under the name *Ascochytella* Died. on the ground that they have a thinner (pseudopycnidial) peridium.

Similar differences may be found among the species which are placed without hesitation in Ascochyta.

Euonymus

Ascochytula euonymella Grove, nov. comb. *Ascochyta vicina* var. *β, euonymella* Sacc. Syll. iii. 404. *Ascochyta euonymella* All. vi. 642.

No spots. Pycnidia gregarious, globose-depressed, about 200μ wide, pierced by a pore; texture rather thicker than in Ascochyta. Spores narrowly fusoid, acute at both ends, singly pale-olivaceous, rich honey-coloured in mass, 1-septate, not constricted, 9–11 × 2μ (8–10 × 2–2·25μ, Sacc.; 12–14 × 2·5μ, Rhodes).

On twigs of *Euonymus europaeus*. Hadzor, near Droitwich.

Saccardo's variety *β* was on capsules of the Euonymus. This species is similar to *Ascochytula Grossulariae* Died. which it resembles in its pycnidium.

Fr.

Obione

Ascochytula Obiones Died. 410. Mig. p. 305, pl. 37, f. 1–5. *Diplodina Obiones* Jaap, in Verh. Bot. Ver. Prov. Brand. 1905, p. 96.

Pycnidia gregarious, arranged ± in rows, deep-black, somewhat shining, globose-lenticular, immersed, then erumpent by the upper half, with a blunt papilla pierced by a broad pore, 160–200μ diam.; texture truly parenchymatous, rather thin, pale fuscous, much darker round the ostiole. Spores oval-oblong, yellow, somewhat olivaceous in mass, 1-septate, often broadest at the septum, the loculi often unequal and not quite straight, 9–12 × 3–4μ, each cell sometimes with one or more (even three) scattered globules of oil; no sporophores seen.

On dead stems of *Obione portulacoides*. Sandplace, E. Cornw. (Rhodes).   Apr.–Jun.

Accompanied by *Coniothyrium Obiones* Jaap, but larger and more erumpent. No doubt part of the same life-cycle; Jaap, also, found the two species in the same locality. *Leptosphaeria Obiones* Sacc. also occurred with the Ascochytula.

Germ.

Phlomis

Ascochytula Phlomidis Grove.

Pycnidia scattered or arranged in little groups, lens-shaped, brownish-black, 100–120μ diam., papillate, the papilla

emerging through the epidermis as a little turret; texture thin, plectenchymatous. Spores fusoid-oblong, 1-septate, often bent at the septum, yellowish even singly and olivaceous in mass, $7–10 \times 2–3\mu$.

On dead stems of *Phlomis fruticosa*, in a garden at Polperro, Cornw.   Apr.

Ribes

Ascochytula Grossulariae Died. p. 410, p. 350, f. 19. Mig. p. 305, pl. 37, f. 10, 11. *Ascochyta Grossulariae* Oud. Contr. Flor. Myc. Pays-Bas, xvi. 69. Sacc. Syll. xvi. 936. *Diplodina Oudemansii* All. vi. 694.

Pycnidia mostly densely gregarious, immersed, then bursting the epidermis by the projecting summit, depressed-globose, $120–150\mu$ diam.; texture parenchymatous, darker round the pore. Spores cylindrical, rounded at both ends, 1-septate, not constricted, guttulate, pale greenish-yellow, $7–13 \times 2–2 \cdot 5\mu$; sporophores not seen.

On twigs of *Ribes Grossularia*. Ockeridge Wood, Ws. (Rhodes).   Apr.

Ascochytella Grossulariae Died. in Ann. Mycol. x. 141 (Pilz. Brand. 402), differs mainly in having a thinner (pseudopycnidial) peridium but is, I have no doubt, the same species, though it is said to have more fusoid spores.
Germ.

Sambucus

Ascochytula deformis Grove. *Diplodia deformis* Karst. Symb. Myc. Fenn. xv. 156. *Diplodina deformis* Sacc. Syll. iii. 413. All. vi. 696. *Ascochytella deformis* Died. in Ann. Mycol. 1912, x. 141; Pilz. Brand. 402. Mig. 296.

Pycnidia scattered or arranged in groups of 2–6 or more, subglobose, varying form and size, at first mouthless, then pierced by a pore, black, $180–250\mu$ diam.; texture thin or sometimes thicker, darker round the pore. Spores numerous, oblong-fusoid or cylindric, straight, 1-septate, not constricted, hyaline or very pale-yellowish, $8–13 \times 2–3\mu$; sporophores fasciculate, hyaline, about as long as the spore.

On dead twigs of *Sambucus nigra*. East Knoyle, Wilts. (Rhodes). Kew Gardens; Hartlebury Common, Ws.

Apr. May.

I find the spores to be usually 9–10μ long, and sometimes obovoid. Mingled with the Hartlebury fungus was an immature pyrenomycete similar in colour and appearance, and also a Coniothyrium (not *C. fuscidulum*).

Fr. Holl. Germ. Denm. Finland.

Symphoricarpus

Ascochytula Symphoricarpi Died. 411. Mig. 306. *Ascochyta Symphoricarpi* Passer. Diagn. F.N. IV, p. 465. Sacc. Syll. x. 296. *Diplodina Symphoricarpi* All. vi. 699.

Pycnidia loosely gregarious, immersed, lenticular, papillate, raising and piercing the epidermis by the papilla, 100–150μ diam.; texture parenchymatous, amber-brown, darker round the pore, ultimately blackish. Spores cylindric-fusoid, tapering but obtuse at both ends, at length 1-septate, not constricted, hyaline at first, then yellowish or amber-brown, 8–11 × 2–3μ.

On stems of *Symphoricarpus racemosus*. Polperro (Rilstone). June.

Quite different in shape and colour of spores from *Ascochyta vulgaris* var. *Symphoricarpi*, which is found on the leaves. Germ.

Ulex

Ascochytula Ulicis Grove.

Pycnidia gregarious, lenticular, immersed, black, about 200μ diam., rather thick-walled, opening by a pore; texture of minute dark parenchymatous cells. Spores very numerous, fusoid, acute at both ends, 1-septate, not constricted, pale yellowish-olive, 10–14 × 2μ, issuing in a tendril; sporophores not seen.

On dead stems of *Ulex europaeus*. Powick, near Worcester (Rhodes). May.

DIPLODINA Westd. Cinquième Notice, p. 19.

Pycnidia mostly on stems, more rarely on leaves as well, with a complete ± uniform parenchymatous thick brown wall. Spores 1-septate, hyaline; sporophores filiform, but often inconspicuous.

Distinguished from Ascochyta essentially only by its firmer and browner wall, which approaches that of Phoma; its occur-

rence on stems is shared by many (but not all) species of
Ascochyta. It would be more logical to combine the two
genera. Consult also the genus Ascochytula.

Achillea

Diplodina Millefolii All. vi. 676. *Ascochyta Millefolii* Oud. Contr.
Myc. Pays-Bas. xiv. 44. Sacc. Syll. xi. 524.

Pycnidia scattered, 125–200μ diam., subglobose or lens-
shaped, covered by the epidermis, dark-brown, pierced at the
summit by a small pore; texture rather thin, parenchymatous,
fuscous-brown. Spores ovoid-oblong to shortly cylindrical,
obtuse at both ends, hardly at all guttulate, 6–8 × 2–2·5μ, a
few at length 1-septate, but not constricted; sporophores not
perceptible.

On dead stems of *Achillea Millefolium*. Kew Gardens.

Mar.

The spores were all but colourless, even in mass. The pycnidial wall
is similar all round, but occasionally darker at the pore.
Holl. Denm.

Aloysia

Diplodina Aloysiae Grove.

Pycnidia scattered, round, lens-shaped, punctiform, black,
140–150μ diam., pierced by a pore; texture thin, dusky,
parenchymatous, not darker round the pore. Spores oblong,
rounded at both ends, 1-septate, sometimes faintly constricted, colourless, 8–10 × 2·5–3μ.

On thin dead twigs of *Aloysia citriodora*. Polperro, Cornw.
(Rilstone).   Jul.–Mar.

This species might equally well be placed in Ascochyta.

Antirrhinum

Diplodina Passerinii All. vi. 678 (1900). Grove, in Journ. Bot.
1916, p. 191. *Ascochyta decipiens* Pass. Atti. Accad. Linc. (Roma),
Rendic. 1891, vii. 49 (*non* Trail). Sacc. Syll. x. 300.

Spots none. Pycnidia gregarious, oblong, about 200μ diam.,
subepidermal, raising the epidermis in a pustular manner,
fuscous-honey-coloured, pierced by a pore; texture rather
thin, pale-brown, at first darker round the pore. Spores cylindrical, rounded at both ends, at first continuous, then 1-sep-
tate, scarcely or not at all constricted, somewhat guttulate,
7–12 × 2·5–3μ, oozing out in the form of a yellowish globule.

On stems of cultivated *Antirrhinum*, especially at the base, and in the second year. Kew; Hereford; Birmingham; Slough; Ayrshire; etc.   May–Sept.

The oily contents of the spores assume different appearances according to age, and may even look, at first sight, as if there were more than one septum. This species is intermediate between Ascochyta and Diplodina. It is frequently associated with *Phyllosticta Antirrhini* Syd., especially late in the season.

Ital. etc.

Artemisia

Diplodina Artemisiae Bresad. *apud* Jaap, in Ann. Mycol. 1905, p. 400.

Pycnidia scattered, sometimes arranged in lines, covered except for the protruding papilla, thin-walled, 200–300μ diam.; texture parenchymatous, brown, darker and much thickened round the pore. Spores cylindric or narrow-fusoid, straight or rarely somewhat bent, granular within, 1-septate, 8–$12 \times 1 \cdot 5$–$2 \cdot 5\mu$; no sporophores visible.

On dead stems of *Artemisia vulgaris*. Yardley Aqueduct, near Birmingham.   May.

Germ.

Castanea

Diplodina Castaneae Prill. & Delacr. in Bull. Soc. Myc. Fr. 1893, p. 276, with fig. Sacc. Syll. xi. 527. Massee, Dis. Cult. Pl. 429.

Pycnidia subcutaneous, flattened-conical, $300 \times 150\mu$; texture dark-violet, plurilocellate within. Spores 1-septate, not constricted, 6–7×1–$1 \cdot 5\mu$; sporophores 10–12μ long.

On bark of young shoots of *Castanea vesca* (Massee). *n.v.*

This appears to be quite different from the American Chestnut disease (*Diplodina* ?). But probably there is some error; see p. 247.

Fr. Ital.

Cirsium

Diplodina Cirsii Grove, in Journ. Bot. 1918, p. 317, pl. 550, f. 5.

Pycnidia scattered, oval, about 250μ long, black, rather prominent, raising the epidermis and slightly penetrating it by the little papillate pierced ostiole; texture dark-fuscous, parenchymatous. Spores oblong, rounded at both ends, for a long time continuous, then 1-septate, generally constricted at the septum, occasionally curvulous and with two unequal

loculi, perfectly colourless, very rarely 1- or 2-guttulate,7–9 ×
2·5–3μ; sporophores not observed.

On whitish spots of the dead stems of *Cirsium arvense*.
King's Norton.   May, Jun.

Cornus

[**Diplodina Corni** Cooke, in Grevill. xvi. 8. Sacc. Syll. x. 312.
All. vi. 684.

On dead branches of *Cornus sanguinea*, Shotover Planta-
tion (Baxter).]   Mar.

On examination this specimen was found to have its spores in
asci = *Didymella Corni* Sacc. But Dr Rhodes found what appeared to
be a true(?) Diplodina on *Cornus alba* at Hadzor Hall (spores 11–13 ×
3μ), in March, 1930.

Euphorbia

Diplodina Euphorbiae Grove.

Pycnidia somewhat scattered, shining, immersed, then
erumpent, convex above and cleaving the epidermis by a
longitudinal fissure, oval in shape and up to 1 mm. long,
prominent, black; texture thick, soft, formed of minute brown
prosenchymatous cells. Spores oval-fusoid, rounded above,
sometimes pointed below, hyaline, 1-septate, 14–16 × 3·5–
4·5μ; sporophores linear or oblong, 2μ thick, rather shorter
than the spore, rising from a yellowish-olive basal stratum.

On dead stems of *Euphorbia palustris*. Edgbaston Botanic
Gardens, Birmingham.   Mar.

When pieces of the rhizome were transferred to another garden, the
fungus travelled with it.

Galium

Diplodina Galii Sacc. Syll. iii. 412. *Diplodia Galii* Niessl, Pilz.
Mähr. u. Oesterr. p. 33. (Not *Diplodina Kabatiana* Bubák, in Hedwig.
1912, lii. 350.)

Pycnidia scattered, subglobose, black, covered, then erumpent by the papilla, 100–200μ diam. Spores "ovoid, at length
1-septate, constricted at the septum, hyaline, biguttulate,
7–8 × 4–5μ" (Sacc.), ± cylindrical, 9–12 × 3μ (Rhodes).

On *Galium Mollugo*. Polperro (Rhodes). Fowey.   Apr.

Moravia.

Helianthus

Diplodina Helianthi Fautr. in Rev. Mycol. 1895, p. 70. Sacc.
Syll. xi. 527. All. vi. 688. Died. 404. Mig. 300.

Pycnidia gregarious, immersed, at first conical and papillate, then exposed and flattened, black; wall rather thin, darker round the pore. Spores elongated-oblong, rounded at both ends, at length 1-septate, much constricted in the middle at the septum, hyaline, 9–12 × 3–4μ, but only half as long while still eseptate.

On dead stems of *Helianthus tuberosus*, Trearddwr Bay, Holyhead. Of. *H. annuus*, near Birmingham.   Jan.–Apr.

In Fautrey's specimens the pycnidia were mingled with those of *Phoma herbarum*, but were at least twice as large.
Fr. Germ.

Malva

Diplodina Malvae Togn. Contrib. Micol. Tosc. ii, 1895, p. 12.
Sacc. Syll. xiv. 949. All. vi. 691.

Pycnidia scattered or aggregated in oblong patches, covered, globose or depressed, pale-brown, 90–145μ broad, with a papillate ostiole; wall membranaceous, fuscous. Spores oblong, guttulate, at first ellipsoid, 1-celled, then cylindrical, obtuse at apex, 1-septate, gently constricted, 6–10 × 2·5–3μ; sporophores filiform.

On dead stems of *Sidalcea*, Kew Gardens (Cooke). Of *Althaea officinalis*, Sussex (Rhodes).   Apr.–Nov.

In the original fungus (on *Malva moschata*, in Italy) the breadth of the spores was 3–4μ. Probably this species is the stem-form of *Ascochyta Malvae* Died. (p. 391, published 1912). At first it exactly simulates a Phoma and when the septum is first formed the spore is almost dumb-bell-shaped.

Forma **Lavaterae** Grove.

Spores ovoid or oblong, colourless, not often inequilateral, rarely 1-septate, averaging 10 × 3μ, occasionally as large as 15 × 5μ, but also often much smaller.

On dead stems of *Lavatera arborea*, Vazon Bay, Guernsey (Rhodes). On stems of *L. thuringiaca*, Kew Gardens (Cooke).

Mar. Sept.

But see *Ascochyta malvicola* Sacc. (*supra*, p. 306).
Germ. Ital.

Pinus

Diplodina Strobi Grove, comb. nov. *Sphaeropsis Strobi* B. & Br. in Ann. Nat. Hist. 1850, v. 375. Cooke, Handb. 427. *Phoma Strobi* Sacc. Syll. iii. 101. *Macrophoma Strobi* B. & V. in Syll. Addit. 313. All. vi. 371. Sacc. Syll. x. 202.

Pycnidia gregarious, subepidermal, then erumpent and girt by the cleft epidermis, subglobose, with a thick and clumsy papilla, then collapsed, dull black, 250–500μ diam. Spores numerous, subfusoid, acute at both ends, sometimes curved or sigmoid, at length 1-septate, not constricted, hyaline, 10–14 × 2–3μ; sporophores rod-shaped, about as long as the spore.

On scales of cones of *Pinus Strobus*, Glamis (Stevenson); Draycott (Berk.). ? On leaves of *Pinus silvestris*, Cheshire (Ellis). ? On leaves of *Pinus Strobus*, Spye Park, Wilts. (Broome).   Jan.–May.

"Very like *Phoma parca*, but scarcely so much collapsed. It differs in the longer, narrower spores which are never attenuated suddenly" (B. & Br.). See *Macrophoma Strobi, supra.*

The description given above is taken from the original Glamis specimens; those from Draycott are identical, but less developed. The spores much resemble those of *Diplodina Salicis* Westd., but the pycnidial wall is like that of a Phomopsis, being thick, black and many-layered above, thin and paler below, and also in the younger state the upper part is represented by the discoloured epidermis alone, as in *Phomopsis Arctii*. The proliferous stratum at the base of the pycnidium also resembles that of a Phomopsis, and it is probably merely a stage of a Diaporthe. The septum of the spores becomes plain on staining with iodine, and the spores sometimes divide into two parts at that point.

Ribes

Diplodina Grossulariae Sacc. & Bri. in Rev. Mycol. 1886, p. 25. Sacc. Syll. x. 313. All. vi. 693. *Ascochytella Grossulariae* Died. in Ann. Mycol. 1912, x. 141; Pilz. Brand. 402. Mig. 295.

Pycnidia scattered, covered by the epidermis, at length erumpent, rounded or somewhat oblong, black, shining, 160–200μ broad, pierced by a round pore; texture thin, pale-brown. Spores oblong-cylindrical, obtuse or slightly tapering at the ends, 1-septate, not at all constricted, 8–10 × 2–2·5μ, pale brownish in mass.

On dead twigs of *Ribes Grossularia*. Lambourne Hill, Cornw. (Rilstone). Ockeridge Wood, Ws. (?).   Apr.

There is another very similar fungus occurring on the same host, viz. *Ascochytula Grossulariae* Died. (*q.v.*), which differs in hardly any respect, except that the peridium is several layers in thickness, brown outside, hyaline within. They are probably the same fungus in different states, and some of the specimens called *Coniothyrium ribicolum* are still younger states.

Fr. Germ. Denm.

Salix

Diplodina salicicola Sacc. & Trav. Syll. xix. 617; xxii. 1045. *Macrodendrophoma salicicola* Johns. in Sci. Proc. Roy. Soc. Dubl. 1904, x. 158, pl. 13, f. 5, 6.

Pycnidia aggregated here and there, immersed, then erumpent, white within, globose-conical, but without a distinct papilla. Spores ovoid-oblong, 1-septate, scarcely constricted, rounded at both ends, granular within, hyaline, $12 \times 4\cdot5\mu$; sporophores branched (?).

On bark of branches of *Salix triandra*, causing a canker. Connemara, Ireland; Cirencester; etc. *n.v.*

Accompanied by *Physalospora gregaria*, of which it is said to be the pycnidium, and also by *Stagonospora salicicola* (*q.v.* p. 349).

Diplodina Salicis Westd. Cinq. Not. p. 19. Sacc. Syll. iii. 411. All. vi. 695.

Pycnidia scattered, spherical, black, about 600μ diam., covered by the epidermis; ostiole papillate. Spores fusoid, not constricted, $15–18 \times 3\cdot5–4\mu$.

On twigs of *Salix babylonica*, Hampstead; Kew Gardens (Cooke). On twigs of *Salix alba*, Cheshire (Ellis). Sussex; Limerick; Bartley Green, near Birmingham; etc. Dec.–Apr.

I have a twig of *Salix vitellina*, on which are both *Diplodina Salicis* and *Discella carbonacea*, apparently passing gradually the one into the other. As the spores also are practically the same, the two species would seem to be identical, the Diplodina being an early state of the Discella, with a more perfect pycnidium. On the same twig are *Dothiorella Salicis* Karst. and *Diaporthe salicella* Sacc.—all four of them probably stages in the same life-history.

Belg. Holl. Denm. Ital. Canada.

[Diplodina salicina Cooke & Mass. in Herb. Massee, Dis. Cult. Pl. 430.]

This "species" of Cooke and Massee does not exist. Their original specimens at Kew are a mixture of *Diaporthe salicella* Sacc. (with the

asci overlooked) and a Cytospora and *Discella carbonacea*. Yet it has been reported as found at various places, on the faith of Massee's reference above quoted. See *D. salicicola*.

Sonchus

Diplodina Sonchi Henn. in Hedwig. xlv. 32 (1905). Sacc. Syll. xxii. 1042. Smith & Ramsb. in T.B.M.S. v. 159.

Pycnidia caulicolous, piercing the epidermis, subglobose or hemispherical, black, protruding in the centre, 100–120μ diam. Spores oblong-cylindrical, straight or curved, biguttulate, then with a median septum, 8–13 × 3–3·5μ.

On leaves of *Sonchus arvensis*. Colintraive, Argyllshire (Boyd).   Aug.

"The pycnidia sometimes attain a diameter of 180–200μ. The wall of the pycnidium is non-parenchymatous" (Sm. & R.). The original specimens of Hennings were on dry stems of *Sonchus asper*. I find that in Boyd's specimens the pustules are on round fuscous spots, becoming paler, and surrounded by a broad purplish zone, 5–6 mm. diam. I can find no pycnidial wall, merely a cavity in the leaf-tissue, and therefore his fungus is a Marssonina.
Russ.

Carex

Diplodina Caricis Grove.

Pycnidia widely but densely scattered, subglobose, very small (100–160μ diam.) black, covered by the epidermis, then emerging by the papilla alone; texture of angular, rather uniform, pale-brownish cells, each about 10μ wide, scarcely darker around the pore. Spores very numerous, subcylindrical, tapering slightly at each end, but not acute, straight (very rarely bent), distinctly 1-septate, not at all constricted, quite colourless, with one minute central guttule in each loculus, 13–16 × 3–4μ.

On dead leaves of *Carex arenaria*. Cumbrae Is., Buteshire (Boyd).   Aug.

This species might equally well serve in Ascochyta.

Gramineae

Diplodina graminea Sacc. Syll. iii. 413. All. vi. 684. Grove, in Journ. Bot. 1912, p. 51.

Pycnidia ovoid-depressed or oblong, often two or three in a longitudinal row, black, formed beneath the epidermis which is elevated and pierced by the ostiole, and finally in the com-

pound groups is rimose. Spores oblong-ellipsoid or sub-cylindric, somewhat obtuse at both ends or tapering slightly to the base, delicately but clearly 1-septate, faintly constricted, occasionally slightly curved, 14–16 × 3–5μ.

On leaves of *Cynodon Dactylon*, Guernsey (Rhodes). On culms of *Dactylis glomerata*, Selly Oak, Birmingham.

Sept.–Dec.

In some cases the spores had each loculus guttulate, and the guttules were often not round, but oval or irregular and dark-coloured. The texture of the pycnidium is parenchymatous, and clear-olivaceous. Cf. *Tiarospora perforans*.
Ital. (on *Cynodon*).

Laminaria
Diplodina Laminariae Sutherland, in New Phytol. 1916, xv. 39, f. 2. *Phoma Laminariae* Cooke & Mass. in Grevill. xviii. 53. Sacc. Syll. x. 188.

Pycnidia scattered or in groups, globose or slightly flattened, immersed, then erumpent by the papilliform ostiole, 100–200μ diam.; wall parenchymatous, of several layers, darker round the mouth sometimes. Spores continuous when young, then 1-septate, oblong-ellipsoid, straight or curvulous, faintly constricted, 8–12 × 3–4·5μ, issuing as a white shining globule.

On dead or decaying fronds of *Laminaria*, lying dry on the sea-shore. Ayrshire (Boyd). Herm, Channel Is. (Rhodes). Dorset; Orkney; etc.

The spores are often expelled, while still unicellular. The pycnidial wall increases in thickness as it gets older. Phoma-like spores, 6 × 2·5, can be found in the same pycnidium as 1-septate spores, 8 × 3μ.

Lichen
Diplodina lichenoides A. L. Smith, in T.B.M.S. 1911, iii. 283.

Pycnidia crowded, hemispherical or subconical, superficial or with the base very slightly immersed, black, shining. Spores oblong-ellipsoid, about 10 × 3μ; sporophores very short, simple, bearing the spores at the tips.

On bark of Walnut trees (*Juglans*), parasitic on a Lichen thallus. Writtle, Essex, 1849 (H. Piggot). *n.v.* Cf. *Sirothecium lichenicola* Keissl.

DARLUCA Castagne, Cat. Pl. Marseille, suppl. p. 53.

Pycnidia globose, scarcely papillate, membranaceous, pierced by a pore, fuscous tinged with blue, growing parasitically and superficially on the sori of Uredinales, e.g. Uromyces, Puccinia, Melampsora, Aecidium, etc. Spores oblong or fusoid, 1-septate, hyaline, bearing at each end a tuft of mucous appendages.

Differs from Ascochyta (for which it is frequently mistaken) in its parasitic growth on Uredinales, and in its appendages, which however soon fall off.

Darluca Filum Cast. Catal. Pl. Marseill. Suppl. 53. Cooke, Handb. 437. Sacc. Syll. iii. 410; Fung. Ital. pl. 1473. All. vi. 704, with fig. Died. p. 413, p. 350, f. 20. Mig. p. 307, pl. 38, f. 1–6. *Sphaeria Filum* Bivon. Bern. Stirp. rar. Sicil. iii. 12, pl. 3, f. 1. ? *Hendersonia uredinicola* Desm. in Ann. Sci. Nat. 1849, xi. 345. *Ascochyta contubernalis* Oud. Ned. Kr. Arch. ser. 2, v. 170. *A. pucciniophila* Starb. in Bot. Centralbl. 1895, lxiv. 382. Sacc. Syll. xiv. 946. All. vi. 659. *A. graminicola* var. γ, Sacc. Syll. iii. 407, and var. *coerulea* Br. & H.

Pycnidia gregarious, very minute, globose, amber-coloured, then black, somewhat shining, 100–120μ diam., pierced by a minute pore; texture thin, parenchymatous, sometimes with a bluish-fuscous tinge, darker towards the pore. Spores sub-oblong-fusoid, straight, at length 1-septate, but hardly or not at all constricted, 13–18 × 3–4μ, provided at each end with a little tuft of short mucous appendages which readily disappear.

On the sori of many species of Rust Fungi, on the most various kinds of plants. Rather common and world-wide in its distribution.

Darluca genistalis Sacc. Syll. iii. 410. All. vi. 703. Died. p. 412, p. 350, f. 21. Mig. p. 306, pl. 38, f. 7, 8; pl. 41, f. 1–5. Grove, in Journ. Bot. 1913, p. 45; in Irish Nat. 1912, p. 112. *Dothidea genistalis* Fr. Syst. Myc. ii. 551. *Darluca Filum*, β *dothideaeformis* Fckl. Symb. Myc. 379.

Pycnidia about 80μ diam., ovoid, black, slightly and obtusely papillate, collected into little dense tubercular sub-hemispherical erumpent clusters. Spores fusoid, straight,

rather obtuse at the ends, 12–15 × 2·5μ, with at first a tuft of mucous appendages at each end.

On sori of *Uromyces Anthyllidis*, on leaves of *Anthyllis vulneraria*. Co. Dublin (J. Adams)! Sept.

Texture of pycnidium parenchymatous, pale-grey below, dark-brown but still translucent towards the vertex. This species is distinguished from *D. Filum* almost solely by its densely clustered habit. Two varieties, *stromatica*, widely effused, and *hypocreoides*, grey instead of black, are recorded in Germany.

Fr. Belg. Germ.

Darluca Tussilaginis Oud. in Catal. Raison. Champ. des Pays-Bas, 1905, p. 442. Grove, in Journ. Bot. 1922, pp. 48, 49. *Ascochyta Tussilaginis* Oud. Contr. Flor. Mycol. Pays-Bas, xvi, in Nederl. Kruidk. Arch. 3. i. 498 (1899); Hedwig. 1898, p. 178. Sacc. Syll. xvi. 931.

Pycnidia numerous, epiphyllous, agglomerated, membranaceous, black. Spores oblong-fusoid, 1-septate, slightly constricted, often rounded at both ends, and provided with a gelatinous mucro there, pluriguttulate, 11–15 × 3–4μ.

On fading leaves of *Tussilago Farfara*, among the spermogones of *Aecidium Tussilaginis*. Ardrossan, Ayrshire (Boyd). Late autumn or early winter.

Holl.

TIAROSPORA Sacc. & March. in Rev. Mycol. 1885, p. 148.

Differs from Ascochyta in the fact that a helmet-shaped mucoid appendage is to be seen attached to each end of the spore. But these appendages soon fall off and cannot be found when the spores are old.

Psamma
Tiarospora perforans v. Höhn. in Hedwigia, 1918, p. 141. *Sphaeria perforans* Rob. in Ann. Sci. Nat. 1843, xix. 357. *Sphaerella perforans* Sacc. Syll. i. 538. *Ascochyta perforans* Sacc. Syll. iii. 406. *Diplodina Ammophilae* Trail, in Scot. Nat. 1885, viii. 76; ix. 129. Sacc. Syll. x. 316. *Darluca ammophila* Sacc. Syll. x. 311. *Tiarospora Westendorpii* Sacc. & March. in Rev. Mycol. 1885, p. 148. All. vi. 705. ? *A. Psammae* Oud.

Pycnidia on an oval or roundish base, 500 × 250μ, convex, scattered between the veins, subepidermal, black, mem-

branaceous, opening by a papillate ostiole. Spores broadly
ovate-fusoid, somewhat rhomboid, very regular in form, 15–
18 × 4–5μ, 1-septate, hardly or not at all constricted, granular,
hyaline, with a helmet-shaped broad mucous hyaline appendage at each end.

On dead leaves of *Psamma arenaria*. Cheshire; Aberdeen;
Clyde; Harlech; Guernsey; Culbin Sandhills; etc.   Jan. Feb.

This can hardly be distinguished from *A. graminicola*, when it has
lost its appendages. Texture of pycnidium rather thick, dark-olive,
parenchymatous. Robin recorded *S. perforans* on *Calamagrostis
arenaria*, and attributed to it spores 20–25μ long.
Ostend.

APOSPHAERIELLA Died. in Ann. Mycol. x. 140.

[Pycnidia superficial, growing on wood, with a thick firm wall
composed of minute brown cells, becoming at length carbonaceous. Spores hyaline, 1-septate.

Distinguished from Aposphaeria solely by the presence of
the septum. Diedicke (*l.c.*) describes *A. gregaria*, on a rotting
stump of *Corylus*, but this has not yet been found in Britain.]

DIPLOPLENODOMUS Died. in Ann. Mycol. x. 140.

[This genus differs from *Plenodomus Lingam* by having 1-
septate spores. *D. Malvae* Died. *l.c.*, on dry stems of *Malva*,
should be found in Britain, but like the species of Plenodomus
it is merely a subsclerotioid state of some other species, probably in this case of *Ascochyta Malvae* Died. or rather of its
stem-form *Diplodina Malvae* Togn. (*qq.v.*).]

FUCKELIA Bon. Abhandl. 135.

Stromata erumpent, globose-pulvinate, supported on a short
thick stem-like base, solid, brown outside, divided within into
numerous paler angular loculi. Spores ellipsoid, at length
1-septate, hyaline, pedicellate.

Fuckelia conspicua Marchal, in Bull. Soc. Roy. Bot. Belg. 1921, liv. 123.

Pycnidia more or less erumpent, sometimes superficial, very densely clustered, varying in form, subglobose, truncate, ovoid, or subcylindrical, even frequently stipitate, black, covered nearly to the apex with short fuscous-brown hairs, with one or several pores, and with many ± radiating internal loculi. Spores ovoid-elliptic, continuous or when old rarely 1-septate, with one or several guttules, hyaline or faintly smoky, 9·5–12·5 × 6·7–8µ, issuing in a pallid or yellowish tendril; sporophores simple or branched, continuous, slender, nodulose.

On bark of *Pyrus Malus, P. communis*. Herefordshire; Cambs.; etc. The pycnidial stage of *Phacidiella discolor* Potebn., which has been found in Worcestershire on Pear trees. See Zeitsch. f. Pflanzenkr. 1912, xxii. 129. Autumn.

In Belgium it occurred on fruits of Pear and (once) of Apple. Belg.

Fuckelia Ribis Bon. Abhandl. 135. Sacc. Syll. iii. 244. All. vi. 535. Died. p. 417, p. 350, f. 23 a–d. Mig. 220. Massee, Fung. Flor. iv. 121.

Pycnidia either separate or closely associated with the ascophores, subglobose, brown, glabrous, greyish and wrinkled when dry; texture indistinctly parenchymatous. Spores elliptic-subfusoid, usually with two large guttules, for a time continuous, at length 1-septate, rather obtuse at both ends, hyaline, 6–11 × 3·5–4µ; sporophores subulate, rather shorter than the spore.

On twigs of *Ribes nigrum, R. rubrum*. Not common; Forden (Vize); Thame (Plowright); etc.

It is the pycnidial stage of *Scleroderris ribesia* Karst. in company with which it is found.
Fr. Holl. Germ. Finland.

PLACOSPHAERELLA Patouillard, Cat. Raison. Pl. cell. Tunisie, 1897, p. 121.

This genus is similar in all respects to Placosphaeria, except that its spores are 1-septate.

Placosphaerella silvatica Sacc. in Ann. Mycol. viii. 344. Died. 418. Mig. 309. *Cytodiplospora silvatica* Sacc. Syll. xxii. 1050.

Stromata loosely gregarious, often hypophyllous, immersed, black, shining, oblong or lanceolate, 1–2 mm. long; loculi one or several, each with its own ostiole. Spores fusoid, often bent, acute at one or both ends, 1-septate, not constricted 14–15 × 2–2·5μ; sporophores 5–6μ long.

On leaves of *Festuca*. In several localities, accompanying its ascophorous stage *Phyllachora silvatica* Sacc. Syll. ii. 603.

CYTODIPLOSPORA Oud. Contr. Flor. Myc. Pays-Bas, xv. 14.

Stromata erumpent, wart-like, surrounded by the torn periderm, pseudolocellate within. Spores fusoid, hyaline, 1-septate.

Only three species of this genus have been found in Britain, viz. *C. Aceris* Oud., which is now known to be a growth-state of *Fusicoccum obtusulum*, *C. Castaneae* Oud., which is a similar state of *Fusicoccum castaneum*, and *C. Betulae* Oud., which belongs to *Fusicoccum Betulae*. But there are others, e.g. on *Aesculus* and on *Robinia*, which should be found here.

HYALOPHRAGMIAE

Spores ± oblong, or fusoid-oblong, with two or more distinct transverse septa.

I. Pycnidia standing singly, without a stroma.
    A. Spores usually straight, oblong or linear, generally obtuse at the ends . . . . *Stagonospora*
    B. Spores tapering upwards, acuminate.
        1. Acumen an appendage to the upper loculus; 1–4 transverse septa . . . . [*Kellermania*]
        2. Acumen a prolongation of the upper loculus; one septum only (?). . . . . *Amphorula*
II. Pycnidia seated on a stroma.
    A. Texture bluish or bluish-fuscous . . . . *Stagonostroma*
    B. Texture brown . . . . *Cytotriplospora*

See also *Stagonosporopsis* (p. 327).

STAGONOSPORA Sacc. in Mich. ii. 8.

Pycnidia immersed or half-projecting, globose or lens-shaped, usually pierced at the summit by a pore; texture parenchymatous, wall thick or thin, cells usually thin-walled, often darker round the pore. Spores oblong-linear, fusoid, or ellipsoid, hyaline, guttulate, with two or (usually) more distinct septa; guttules often large. (Figs. 22, 23.)

The species are arranged in the usual alphabetic order (Dicotyledons first) of the host-genera, except that all on the GRAMINEAE are placed under that family-name.

Acer

Stagonospora Lophiostoma Sacc. Syll. iii. 449. All. vi. 990. *Hendersonia Lophiostoma* C. & Ellis, in Grevill. vi. 3, pl. 95, f. 10. "*H. mutabilis*" B. & Br. in Ann. Nat. Hist. 1850, v. 373, quoted in Yorkshire Fung. Flor. p. 322.

Pycnidia scattered, erumpent, black, often laterally compressed, ostiole in that case Hysterium-like. Spores oblong-clavate, very obtuse above, sometimes narrowed below, 1–3-septate, perfectly colourless, but filled with highly refractive

contents, 25–28 × 8–10μ when mature; sporophores filiform, about as long as the spore. (Fig. 22.)

On dead twig of Sycamore (*Acer*). Hebden Bridge (J. Needham). Olton, Wk.   May, Oct.

This is recorded in Yorks. Fung. Flor. as *Hendersonia mutabilis* B. & Br., but the specimens preserved in Herb. Kew are not in the least like that species, which is *Dichomera mutabilis* Sacc. They are identical in every respect with the U.S.A. specimens (no. 2540) issued by J. B. Ellis under the name *H. Lophiostoma*, except that those are on *Ulmus* and upon

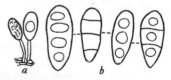

Fig. 22. *Stagonospora Lophiostoma*: *a*, young spores on sporophores, × 300; *b*, spores in various states of development, × 600.

wood not completely decorticated. Cooke, in Grevillea (*l.c.*), represents the spores as somewhat constricted, but in Ellis's specimens there is not the slightest sign of constriction. The spores can be seen to be at first without a septum, afterwards the septa can vary from one to three. The contents of the spores, in both specimens, are very oily and refringent.

U.S.A.

Atriplex

Stagonospora Atriplicis Lind, Dan. Fung. p. 444, pl. 6, f. 79, 80. *Phyllosticta Atriplicis* Westd. in Bull. Acad. Brux. 1851, p. 20. *Ascochyta Atriplicis* Lasch, in Rabenh. Herb. Myc. no. 861. Died. in Ann. Mycol. 1904, p 180. *A. Chenopodii* Rost. 1905, Isl. Svamp. in Bot. Tids. p. 311. *Diplodina Atriplicis* Vestergr. Sacc. Syll. xlv. 952. *D. Chenopodii* Karst. Sacc. Syll. x. 315. *Septoria Atriplicis* Fckl. Sacc. Syll. iii. 556. *S. Westendorpii* Winter, Sacc. Syll. x. 380.

Spots epiphyllous, roundish, pallid when dry, with a yellow margin. Pycnidia numerous, central, at first fuscous, then black, globose, 140μ diam.; texture parenchymatous. Spores cylindric-oblong, often bent, hyaline, granular within, for a long time eseptate, then 1–3-septate, 20–28 × 4–5μ.

On living leaves and stems of *Atriplex* and *Chenopodium* (Lind). On *Atriplex patula*, Worcester.   Sept.

The description given above is that of Lind. My Worcester specimens agreed entirely in most points and the majority of the spores were 1–3-septate; but some of them were more than 30μ long, and a few reached 48μ and were 5-septate though still only 5μ broad. These were the end-spores of a long series of gradual development. See Grove in Journ. Bot. 1917, p. 346, and *Septoria Chenopodii, infra*.

Convolvulus
Stagonospora Calystegiae Grove. *Septoria Calystegiae* Westd. in Bull. Acad. Roy. Belg. 1851, p. 395. Sacc. Syll. iii. 537. All. vi. 765. Died. 446. Mig. 392. *Septoria sepium* Desm. in Ann. Sci. Nat. 1853, xx. 88.

Spots small, crowded, roundish, pale-brown, thickened round the margin like a cushion, almost as if there were a stroma within the mesophyll. Pycnidia few on each spot (1–5), usually hypophyllous, immersed, pallid, opening by a pore; texture extremely thin except around the pore. Spores oblong-cylindrical, curvulous, rounded at both ends, distinctly 3–5-septate (usually 3), often with several (usually 4) guttules, 25–45 × 4–5μ.

On withered spots, on fading leaves of *Convolvulus* (*Calystegia*) *sepium*, Ayrshire; Wigtownshire (Boyd). Cheshire (Ellis). On leaves of *C. Soldanella*, ? Swansea (Cooke). Littlehampton (Gibbs). On leaves of *C. arvensis*, Worthing; Droitwich; Evesham.   Jul.–Sept.

Cf. *Ramularia sepium* Dearn. & Bisby (Fung. Manitoba, p. 130) on leaves of *C. sepium*, accompanied by a Septoria with spores 25–30 × 1μ. Europe, N. Africa, Cyprus, U.S.A.

Ilex
Stagonospora Ilicis Grove, in Journ. Bot. 1886, p. 135, pl. 266, f. 4. Sacc. Syll. Addit. p. 337; x. 330. All. vi. 976, with fig. on p. 964.

Pycnidia hypophyllous, scattered or sometimes two or three together, globose-lenticular, black, veiled by the epidermis which is pierced by a minute pore. Spores cylindric-fusoid, somewhat acute at each end, slender, 3-septate, hyaline but in mass very faintly olive, 14–17 or even 20 × 2–3μ.

On leaves of *Ilex Aquifolium*. Warley Woods, near Birmingham.   Apr.

Oxalis
Stagonospora hygrophila Sacc. in Malpigh. 1899, xiii. 22, f. III, 2; Syll. xvi. 947. All. vii. 913. Grove, in Journ. Bot. 1922, p. 81.

Spots on both sides, mostly marginal, more or less semicircular, whitish, with a rather broad burnt-sienna border. Pycnidia amphigenous, globose-lens-shaped, blackish-brown, 100μ diam., at first covered, then erumpent, opening by a

pore; texture thin, brownish. Spores oblong-fusoid, when young eseptate and biguttulate, $7-9 \times 2\mu$, then 1-septate, with 2, 3, or 4 guttules, $12-16 \times 2 \cdot 5-3\mu$, hardly at all constricted, faintly curved at times, hyaline, occasionally with a mucous appendage at the end; all these forms occurring in the same pycnidium. (Fig. 23b.)

On living leaves of *Oxalis Acetosella*. Dalry, Ayrshire (Boyd). Earlswood, Wk. July.

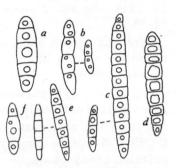

Fig. 23. Spores of *Stagonospora*: a, *St. socia*; b, *St. hygrophila*, var. *vermiformis*; c, *St. vexata*; d, *St. paludosa*; e, *St. Caricis*; f, *St. maritima*; all × 600.

Var. **vermiformis** Grove, in Journ. Bot. 1918, p. 318, pl. 550, f. 7.

Spots amphigenous, small, marginal, roundish, whitish-ochreous, with a distinct fulvous border. Pycnidia generally hypophyllous, scattered, few, lens-shaped, golden-fulvous, becoming blackish, $120-220\mu$ diam., covered by the epidermis, then erumpent by the pore; texture very thin, pallid, darker round the pore. Spores worm-shaped, curvulous, tapering at each end, but rounded at the extreme apex, 3-septate, minutely guttulate, generally constricted, hyaline, then yellowish, $25-32 \times 4-5$, sometimes provided at each end with a little mucous appendage, at length issuing forth and forming honey-coloured globules over the pore.

On living leaves of *Oxalis Acetosella*. Ayrshire (Boyd). Earlswood, Wk.   Aug.

Differing from the type in the strongly constricted and larger spores. Spots not uncommon, pycnidia rare.

Pinus

Stagonospora Pini Grove, in Journ. Bot. 1885, p. 163. Sacc. Syll. x. 332. All. vi. 983.

Pycnidia scattered, epiphyllous, covered, roundish, black. Spores cylindric-fusoid, rather obtuse at the ends, with 1 or at length 3 septa, singly hyaline, but pale yellowish in mass, $16-20 \times 3-4\mu$.

On leaves of *Pinus silvestris*. Ireland (Rev. H. W. Lett)! Aug.

Salix

Stagonospora salicicola Sacc. & Trav. Syll. xx. 879; xxii. 1054;
Tetradia salicicola Johnson, in Sci. Proc. Roy. Soc. Dublin, 1904, x.
157, pl. 13, f. 3, 4.

Pycnidia immersed, then somewhat prominent, depressed-
conical, scarcely erumpent, pallid within. Spores cylindric-
oblong, rather obtuse at the ends, 3-septate, not or hardly
constricted, hyaline, 8–9 × 2–2·5μ; sporophores linear, hyaline
about as long as the spore.

On bark of branches of *Salix triandra*. Connemara, Ireland.

Possibly a pycnidial stage of *Physalospora gregaria*, f. *Salicis*, by
which it was accompanied. With it was also a fungus which may be
another stage, for which see *Diplodina salicicola*, p. 337.

Suaeda

Stagonospora Suaedae Syd. in Ann. Mycol. ix. 557. Mig. 348.

Pycnidia scattered, globose, immersed, emerging by the
summit, 80–100μ diam.; texture thin, pale brownish, darker
round the pore. Spores irregular in shape, straight or variously bent, continuous at first, then 1–3-septate, constricted
or not, obtuse at the ends, loculi often unequal, granular-
guttulate within, but colourless, 12–25 × 3–5μ.

On dry leaves of *Suaeda maritima*. Salt-flats, near Dale,
Pembr. (Rhodes). July.

Germ.

Trifolium

Stagonospora compta Died. in Ann. Mycol. 1912, x. 482; Pilz.
Brand. 559. Mig. 349. *Septoria compta* Sacc. Syll. iii. 508 (1884);
Fung. Ital. pl. 89. All. vi. 869, with fig. *Stagonospora Trifolii* Fautr.
in Rev. Mycol. 1890, p. 167. Sacc. Syll. x. 333. All. vi. 989. T.B.M.S.
iv. 178. *Phleospora Trifolii* Cav. App. Pat. Veg. p. 7, pl. 6, f. 5, 6, and
Rev. Mycol. 1878, pl. 71, f. 5, 6. Sacc. Syll. x. 399. *Stag. Dearnessii*
Sacc. Syll. x. 333. *Ascochyta Trifolii* Auct. *p.p. Gloeosporium Trifolii*
Peck.

Spots amphigenous, roundish or angular, often marginal,
ochraceous-grey, with a broad brown but indefinite border.
Pycnidia amphigenous, immersed, lens-shaped, roundish,
bright blackish-brown, 200–300μ diam., pierced by a pore;
texture soft, darker and parenchymatous around the ostiole.
Spores cylindrical, straight or variously curved or bent, obtuse at both ends, with 2 or 4 large guttules, then 1-septate, at

length 3-septate, constricted at all the septa, 15–22 (or more) × 3–4·5μ, issuing in tendrils.

On living leaves of *Trifolium repens*. West Kilbride, Ayrshire (Boyd). Keswick; Reading (immature); etc. Jun.–Sept. On dead stems of *Trifolium minus*, Cornwall (Rilstone). Nov.

It is recorded abroad on *T. pratense, T. medium*, etc. also, and is said to become ultimately even 4–5-septate. *Septoria Trifolii* and *Ascochyta Trifolii* are merely the younger states of the fungus. See also Petrak in Ann. Mycol. xvii. 64. Cavara's figure is evidently that of a Stagonospora.

Fr. Germ. Ital. Switz. Port. Swed. U.S.A.

Tussilago

Stagonospora Tussilaginis Died. in Ann. Mycol. 1912, x. 482; Pilz. Brand. 560. *Septoria Tussilaginis* Fckl. Symb. Myc. Nachtr. ii, 83 (1873), *non* Westd. *Septoria Fuckelii* Sacc. in Mich. i. 190 (1878); Syll. iii. 545. All. vi. 871, with fig. *Phoma Tussilaginis* C. & M. in Grevill. xv. 108.

Spots epiphyllous, roundish, 0·5–2·5 cm. diam., rusty-brown, with an irregular but broad purple border. Pycnidia epiphyllous, globose, covered by the epidermis, which is afterwards raised considerably and burst at the summit, up to 500μ wide; texture parenchymatous, thick and brown or almost black around the mouth. Spores clavate-fusoid, obtuse at the upper end, acute below, slightly curved, 3-septate, rarely 4–5-septate, hardly constricted, full of oily protoplasm, colourless, then clear pale-olivaceous, 40–70 × 5–7μ, involved for a long time in mucus.

On living leaves of *Tussilago Farfara*. Dalry, Ayrshire (Boyd). Middleton and Earlswood, Wk.; Hereford. Mostly found in the immature (so-called *Phoma*) stage. Jul. Aug.

Holl. Germ. Switz. Ital.

Wood

Stagonospora unica Sacc. Syll. iii. 449. All. vi. 990. *Hendersonia unica* Cooke, Praecurs. Mon. Henders. 24.

Pycnidia scattered, oval, half immersed in the wood, 500μ diam., dull-black; texture thick, carbonaceous. Spores broadly lanceolate or oval-fusoid, slightly constricted in the middle, with 1–6 guttules, at length 1–5-septate, 35–50 × 14–20μ.

On soft rotting wood. Shere.

According to Cooke (*l.c.*) it resembles a Massaria. The guttules are very large; occasionally the spores are provided, both terminally and at the middle septum, with short irregular soft mucous threads, such as Cooke referred to by saying "sometimes crested". It is not allied to the other species of Stagonospora, but rather to the species of Hendersonia of the section Sporocadus, of which many are massarioid.

Acorus

Stagonospora Calami Bres. in Hedwig. 1896, xxxv. 199. Sacc. Syll. xiv. 963. *Ascochyta Acori* Oud. in Hedwig. 1898, p. 177. Ellis, in T.B.M.S. 1913, iv. 125. Sacc. Syll. xvi. 934. All. vi. 627. Died. 374. Mig. 263, pl. 35, f. 7.

"Pycnidia minute, convex, black, scattered sparsely over reddish-brown blotches on the leaves. Spores subcylindrical, rounded at both ends, slightly granular, 25–28 × 7–10μ, the septum often placed so as to make the loculi unequal in size" (Ellis).

On living leaves of *Acorus Calamus*, Canal, Wirral, Cheshire (J. W. Ellis). On the same, Canal, Gt. Haywood, Staffs.

May–Aug.

The pycnidia are scarcely visible without a lens.

Oudemans' description is as follows: Pycnidia membranaceous, loosely collected in clusters, at first covered, then partly exposed, perforated in the centre, about 170μ broad, black, but pale brownish-grey by transmitted light. Spores oblong-cylindrical, straight, rounded at both ends, scarcely constricted at the septum, 4-guttulate.

Diedicke, who considers his species to be the same as that of Oudemans, says (*l.c.*): Pycnidia amphigenous, without especial spots, scattered or loosely gregarious, covered, just piercing the epidermis with the convex summit, fuscous above, subglobose, up to 300μ diam., pore about 24μ wide. Spores oblong-cylindrical, mostly straight, rounded at both ends, 1-septate, not constricted, with 4 oil-drops, later becoming granular, 30–40 × 10–12μ. No sporophores observed.

Both these descriptions read as if they referred to a young Stagonospora, allied to *S. Typhoidearum*, which no doubt the "Ascochyta" is. Bresadola described the spores as "1–3-septate".

Holl. Germ.

Carex

Stagonospora Caricis Sacc. Syll. iii. 452. All. vi. 969. Died. 553. Mig. 344. *Hendersonia Caricis* Oud. in Arch. Néerl. 1873, viii. 361.

Pycnidia scattered, nestling beneath the epidermis and perforating it by the apex which is pierced by a pore, fuscous,

membranaceous. Spores fusoid, acute or obtuse at the ends, straight or a little curved, at length generally 5-septate, often granular within, colourless, eguttulate, 25–40 × 4–6μ, but some spores 7-septate and up to 40–50 × 6–8μ; sporophores not seen. (Fig. 23 e.)

On dead leaves of *Carex acutiformis, arenaria, riparia*, etc. Cheshire (Ellis). Anglesey; Hartlebury Common (Rhodes). Aberdeen (Trail). Besford Court, Ws.; Borth; etc. Feb.–Aug.

This species is so minute that it is not likely to be seen unless specially looked for; spores sometimes 3-septate, often without guttules; it is accompanied by a Leptosphaeria.
Holl. Germ. Denm.

Stagonospora gigaspora Sacc. Syll. iii. 453. All. vi. 970, with fig. Died. p. 554, p. 552, f. 5. Mig. p. 344, pl. 44, f. 3–6. *Hendersonia gigaspora* Niessl, in Hedwig. 1883, p. 181. ? *Stagonospora macrosperma* Sacc. iii. 453. *Hendersonia macrosperma* Sacc. & Roum. in Mich. ii. 629 (1882).

Pycnidia loosely gregarious, covered, piercing the epidermis only by the pore, subglobose, 150–200μ diam. Spores between cylindrical and fusoid, straight, rounded above, more acute below, 6–8-septate, pale-greenish, granular within with many small oil-drops, 60–80 × 11–14μ; sporophores not seen.

On dead leaves of *Carex*. Pembrokeshire; Ockeridge Wood, Worcs. (Rhodes).

Niessl's specimen in Rabenh. Exs. no. 2998 examined. The larger peridia accompanying it were the imperfect perithecia of his *Leptosphaeria gigaspora*. Cf. *St. tetramera* Davis (sp. 55–75 × 10–13μ, triseptate), on *Carex (riparia?)*.
Holl. Germ. Moravia.

Stagonospora macropus Sacc. Syll. iii. 453. All. vi. 970. *Darluca macropus* Cooke, Handb. 437. *D. Typhoidearum* B. & Br. f. *Caricis* Fckl. Symb. Myc. 380. ? *Hendersonia macropus* B. & Br. in Ann. Nat. Hist. 1850, v. 374.

Pycnidia completely covered, depressed, somewhat collapsed, pierced by a minute pore; texture soft, plectenchymatous. Spores elongate-cylindrical, slightly curved, with 3–6 guttules, involved in jelly, faintly coloured by the thick granular protoplasm, 20–22 × 4–5μ; sporophores long(?).

On dead leaves of *Carex*. Spye Park, Wilts. (Berk.). North
Wootton; Scarborough (Plowright).   Jan.–Apr.

The spores, on applying iodine solution, are seen to be in many cases
2- or even 3-septate. Allied to *St. Typhoidearum*. I have not seen
Berkeley's specimen, but believe it to be the same species. The "black
stains" of which he speaks need not mean that the spores were
olivaceous; he ascribes to them long sporophores, cylindrical, but
slightly attenuated at either end, somewhat curved and many times
longer than their diameter.
Germ.

Stagonospora paludosa Sacc. Syll. iii. 453. Trail, in Scot. Nat.
1885, p. 76. All. vi. 970. *Hendersonia paludosa* Sacc. & Speg. in Mich.
i. 353.

Pycnidia amphigenous, scattered or gregarious, immersed
in the parenchyma of the leaf, adhering to the epidermis
round the ostiole, globose, 100–200μ diam., with a minute
papilla, at length scarcely erumpent; texture membranaceous,
fuscous, indistinctly parenchymatous. Spores fusoid, somewhat acute at the ends, straight or curvulous, with 8–10 septa
(7–9, Trail), and 9–11 large guttules, hardly constricted, 50–
60 × 9–10μ. (Fig. 23*d*.)

On dead leaves of *Carex ampullacea*, near Aberdeen (Trail);
Bridge of Don. On *C. riparia*, Cheshire (Ellis). On dead fruits
of *Carex*, South Lancs. (Travis).   Jan.–Aug.

Trail ascribes to the spores a pale yellowish colour, and makes them
42–52 × 8μ. This species is not the same as *St. gigaspora* Sacc.
Ital.

GRAMINEAE

Plurivorous
Stagonospora arenaria Sacc. Syll. iii. 453. All. vi. 972. Also var.
minor Trail, in Scot. Nat. 1886, p. 266.

No spots. Pycnidia in groups, at first subepidermal, dark-
brown, elliptical, about 240 × 200μ, with a very short ostiole.
Spores fusoid or subcylindrical, straight or slightly curved,
obtuse at both ends, often faintly tinged with yellow, guttulate, 3–5-septate, 30–45 × 3·5–4·5μ (22–25 × 3–3·5μ, Trail).

On culms of *Elymus arenarius*, near Montrose (Trail). Of
Phalaris arundinacea, Brecon (Rhodes); Lizard, Cornwall. Of
Psamma arenaria, Guernsey (Rhodes, var. *minor*); Gower

Peninsula, S. Wales. Of *Aira caespitosa*, Baxterley Common,
Wk. May, Jun., Oct.

Trail's var. *minor* is merely a younger triseptate state. The type has
1–5 septa (or even 6 or 7). The species is recorded also abroad on
Phragmites communis and *Hordeum arenarium*.
Denm. Swed. U.S.A.

Stagonospora graminella Sacc. Syll. iii. 454. Grove, in Journ.
Bot. 1912, p. 52.

Pycnidia gregarious, immersed, then piercing the epidermis
by a minute round pore, globose, black, 100–200μ diam.;
texture parenchymatous, rather thick, fuliginous, subtranslucent. Spores subcylindrical, obtuse at both ends, 4–6-
guttulate, 20–21 × 3·5μ.

On dead leaves of *Dactylis* and *Brachypodium*, Cheshire
(Ellis). On leaves and culms of Grasses, Handsworth, Staffs.;
Claverdon, Wk. Oct.–May.

Denm.

Stagonospora subseriata Sacc. Syll. iii. 454. All. vi. 979, with
fig. Died. 556. Mig. 347. *Hendersonia subseriata* Desm. in Ann. Sci.
Nat. 1846, vi. 69. *St. subseriata* var. *Moliniae* Trail, in Scot. Nat.
1889, x. 72. Sacc. Syll. x. 336. All. vi. 979. *St. Moliniae* Died. 557.
Mig. 347.

Pycnidia numerous, scattered or with 2–6 arranged in short
lines, occasionally confluent, 150–180μ diam., erumpent, subglobose or oblong, black, pierced by a minute pore; texture
thin, pale-brown, parenchymatous. Spores oblong-fusoid,
often rounded above, perfectly hyaline, with 6–8 guttules and
at length 3–6 septa, 25–40 × 6–7μ; sporophores filiform,
shorter than the spore.

On dry leaves of Grasses, especially *Molinia*; Wiltshire;
Draycott (Broome). On dead leaves and culms of *Molinia
coerulea* Dalmally, Loch Awe (Trail); Ayrshire (Boyd);
Devon and Pembroke (Rhodes). On leaves of *Aira caespitosa*,
Lyndhurst, Hants. (Cooke). On *Nardus stricta*, Bentley
Common. Also on *Festuca*.

The form on *Molinia* is not worth separating, even as a variety, but
I have found a distinct form, on *Dactylis glomerata* at Carmarthen,

where the pycnidia were arranged in lines on subelongated blackish-brown blotches reminding one somewhat of *Phoma longissima*, but having the spores as described above; this may be called var. *maculata*.
Fr. Belg. Holl. Germ. Denm.

Arrhenatherum
Stagonospora Arrhenatheri Sm. & Ramsb. in T.B.M.S. 1916, v. 245.

"Pycnidia scattered or gregarious, immersed, pallid-brown, globose, pierced by a pore, 170–200μ diam. Spores cylindrical, straight or gently curved, obtuse at both ends or sometimes rather acute, 3-septate, not constricted, 25–35 × 4μ."

On culms of *Arrhenatherum elatius*. Dalry, Ayrshire (Boyd). *n.ex.* Aug.

This would be better considered as a variety of *St. arenaria* Sacc. Dr Ellis found on *Arrhenatherum* in Cheshire (Oct. 1914) a form of it, with spores 40–50 × 6μ and having five or even six septa, which evidently belongs to that species (*St. arenaria*).

Brachypodium
Stagonospora Brachypodii Died. p. 553, p. 552, f. 2. Mig. 344.

Pycnidia scattered, covered by the epidermis, emerging by the vertex, depressed-globose, 100–150μ diam.; texture rather thick, dark-brown, parenchymatous, not darker round the minute pore. Spores cylindric-fusoid, acute or obtuse at the ends, 1- or 2- (rarely 3-) septate, guttulate, hyaline or faintly yellowish, 20–25 × 5–6μ; sporophores up to 10 × 2μ, filiform, fugacious.

On dry leaves of *Brachypodium*, Alfrick and Martley, Worcs. (Rhodes). Apr.

Bromus
Stagonospora Bromi Sm. & Ramsb. in T.B.M.S. 1915, v. 160.

"Spots amphigenous, elongated, often confluent, purple-brown, then becoming pale in the inner portions. Pycnidia black, globose, then horizontally oblong, 150–175μ diam.; texture parenchymatous. Spores fusoid, straight or curvulous, 3-septate, not constricted, 17–24 × 3μ."

On fading leaves of *Bromus ramosus* (= *asper*). Dalry, Ayrshire (Boyd). *n.v.* Aug.

Distinguished from *St. arenaria* by the spots.

Phragmites

Stagonospora vexata Sacc. Syll. iii. 455. All. vi. 980. Died. p.
557, p. 552, f. 8. Mig. 347. *Hendersonia arundinacea* Sacc. Mich. i.
211; ii. 112 (*non* Desm.).

Pycnidia immersed, then erumpent, often arranged in rows,
subglobose, papillate, black, about 500µ diam. Spores subcylindric or linear, straight or faintly curved, rounded at both
ends, with 10–12 septa and 11–13 guttules, colourless, 60–70
× 7µ; sporophores indistinct. (Fig. 23 c.)

On dry culms of *Phragmites communis*. Pembrokeshire
(Rhodes). Scotland (Boyd).

Saccardo records it in company with *Leptosphaeria arundinacea*.
Karsten describes a form, *pauperior*, with 5–7 septa, and 7–8 guttules,
65–75 × 9 10µ. In the same pycnidium, from Pembroke, there were
spores, all looking equally mature, of all sizes from 20 × 3µ, with only
3 septa, up to those described above. A form, *foliicola* Bres., is given
by Allescher on leaves of *Phalaris arundinacea*.
Germ. Denm. Austr. Ital. Finland.

Stagonospora elegans Sacc. & Trav. Syll. **xx.** 878; xxii. 1056.
Hendersonia elegans Berk. in Ann. Nat. Hist. 1841, vi. 430, pl. 11,
f. 9. Cooke, Handb. 434 *St. dolosa* Sacc. & Roum. Syll. iii. 455.
All. vi. 980. Died. 558. Mig. 347. *St. hysterioides* Sacc. Syll. iii. 455,
? *p.p.*

Pycnidia immersed, seated singly in minute grey-brown
spots, rather shining and prominent, erumpent, black, 250–
500µ diam. Spores resting on a ± gelatinous substratum in
which are many oil-drops, broadly fusoid, tapering obtusely
above, ending below in a very short sporophore, 5–8-septate,
loculi thick-walled, each with a large guttule, sometimes
slightly swollen in places so as to make the spore look constricted, 60–70 × 9–10µ.

On dead culms of *Phragmites communis*. Irstead; King's
Lynn; Norths.; Hornsea Mere, Yorks. (*elegans*)—Renfrewshire; Loch Achray; Tay; Galway (*dolosa*). A similar form,
but with only 4 septa, on the leaves of *Phragmites*. Canal,
Droitwich.   Apr.–Aug.

"Pycnidia innate, becoming superficial, globular, dark-brown, 350–
500µ diam. Spores fusiform, with rounded ends, 50–70 × 9–11µ,
hyaline, septa 5–6, guttules 6–7" (Trail, *S. dolosa*).
"Forming little dark-brown spots, in the centre of which is seated

a single shining pycnidium, the upper part of which causes a little pro-
jection above the surface. Spores long, broadly fusiform, pedicellate,
colourless, pellucid, with 6–8 septa, sometimes constricted at the
septa; each of the central cells contains a single large globose guttule"
(Berk. *H. elegans*).

When young the spore has only one septum, then 3, and so on. The
Hornsea specimens were wrongly named *S. hysterioides* (Karst.) Sacc.,
and similar specimens were issued by Magnus from Oranienburg under
the same name; but Karsten's Finland species must be different, since
he gives the size of the spores as 14–16 × 3μ.

There can be but little doubt that *St. dolosa* is the same thing as
St. elegans, though the pycnidia of the former are usually larger (500μ
diam.) than those of the latter. But the spores are identical, as well as
the gelatinous substratum in which they are embedded. Moreover,
St. vexata β pauperior Karst. seems to be closely similar.

Hendersonia elegans was the first Hendersonia described, the genus
being instituted by Berkeley (*l.c.*) to receive it. He named it after his
friend Mr J. Henderson. But it seems likely that his fungus will prove
to belong neither to that genus nor to Stagonospora, since it often has
an incomplete pycnidium like that of a young Phomopsis or (what is
the same thing) like that of one of the Leptostromataceae.

Germ. Denm. Finland ?

Heleocharis

Stagonospora Heleocharidis Trail, in Scot. Nat. 1885, viii. 76.
Sacc. Syll. x. 335. All. vi. 976. Died. p. 555, p. 552, f. 6. Mig. 346.

Pycnidia scattered, subepidermal, nearly spherical, 130–
170μ diam., with a small ostiole. Spores fusoid, pale-yellowish,
5–7-septate, 30–40 × 6–7μ.

On dead leaves and stems of *Heleocharis palustris*. Common
near Aberdeen (Trail). Ayrshire (Boyd).   Jan.–Mar.

Diedicke found the spores, in Saxony, without any tinge of colour.
Germ.

Juncus

Stagonospora innumerosa Sacc. Syll. iii. 451. All. vi. 977.
J. W. Ellis, in T.B.M.S. 1915, v. 135. *Hendersonia innumerosa* Desm.
in Ann. Sci. Nat. 1851, xvi. 305. *Monascostroma innumerosa* v. Höhn.
in Ann. Mycol. 1918, xvi. 160. *St. bufonia* Bres. in Hedwig. 1896, p.
200. Sacc. Syll. xiv. 963. All. vi. 978. Died. p. 556, p. 552, f. 3.
Mig. 347.

Pycnidia very numerous, arranged in parallel longitudinal
series, up to 100μ diam., immersed, then somewhat prominent, globose, rather shining, black, opening by a pore; contents white. Spores oblong or subellipsoid, obtuse, straight or
curvulous, nearly hyaline, with four compressed faintly
coloured guttules, 20–30 × 5–7μ.

On dead culms of *Juncus maritimus*. Alderney (Rhodes). Borth (Bayliss Elliott). St Ives, Cornwall. Of *J. effusus*. Cheshire (Ellis). Hanbury, Ws. (Rhodes). Hartlebury Common, Ws. Nov.–May.

The Cheshire specimens had pycnidia sometimes up to 150μ diam., lying just below the epidermis. Spores at first with four guttules, then with 2, 3, 4, or even 5 septa, rounded at the ends, thin-walled, 22–28 × 4–5μ (5·5–7μ, Ellis).

Stag. trimera (Cooke) Sacc. Syll. iii. 452, on *Juncus maritimus* is possibly the same species, and *Stag. bufonia* on *Juncus bufonius* is an older state. Cf. also *Stag. junciseda* Sacc.

Fr. Germ.

Stagonospora trimera Sacc. Syll. iii. 452. All. vi. 978. *Hendersonia trimera* Cooke, Praecurs. Mon. Henders. 19.

Pycnidia scattered or arranged partly in lines, long covered by the epidermis, then erumpent by a minute pore, black, 200μ diam. Spores elongate-ellipsoid, biseptate, hyaline, granular, 18–25 × 5–6μ.

On *Juncus maritimus*. King's Lynn (Plowright).

Cooke's name was given to the British specimens, which are described above, but others, apparently similar, were issued by Ellis on *Fimbristylis* (New Jersey); in these latter the spores are less granular and each cell has a large guttule. See *St. innumerosa*.

U.S.A.

Stagonospora junciseda Sacc. in Mich. ii. 350; Syll. iii. 452 (as var. of *S. aquatica*, on *Scirpus*, *q.v.*).

Pycnidia like those of *Stag. aquatica*, but larger (200μ) and more prominent. Spores more acute at the ends, 3-septate, hyaline, not constricted, 25–30 × 3–3·5μ.

On stems of *Juncus*. Yarmouth (E. A. Ellis)!

Stag. bufonia Bres. on *Juncus bufonius* differs in having 3–5 septa and obtuse ends; its spores measure 24–27 × 6–8μ; on *J. Gerardi*, Pembroke (Rhodes).

Fr.

Stagonospora socia Grove, in Journ. Bot. 1912, p. 52.

Pycnidia small, black, with a short ostiole. Spores oblong-cylindrical, occasionally narrowed toward one or both ends, obtuse, 5-guttulate, at length 4-septate, 30–35 × 9–10μ. (Fig. 23a.)

On dry culms of *Juncus conglomeratus*, in company with
Dothidea Junci Fr. (*Scirrhia Junci* Rehm). Frankley, near
Birmingham.   Sept.

The pycnidia were not, for the most part, to be distinguished from
the loculi of the Dothidea with which they were mingled, though at
times they stood separately in the leaf-tissue, not immersed in the
stroma, and in that case they were smaller. The guttules were unusually large.

Luzula

Stagonospora Luzulae Sacc. See *Hendersonia.*

Narcissus

Stagonospora Curtisii Sacc. Syll. iii. 451. *Hendersonia Curtisii*
Berk. in Herb. Curtis. Cooke, Praecurs. Mon. Henders. 19 (in Nuov.
Giorn. Bot. Ital. vol. x). *Stagonospora Narcissi* Hollós, in Ann. Mus.
Nat. Hung. 1906, v. 354, pl. 8, f. 16. Sacc. Syll. xxii. 1055. Journ.
Roy. Hort. Soc. 1918, xliii. 57.

Spots large, irregular, brown. Pycnidia amphigenous,
covered, aggregated, globose-depressed, 140–180μ diam.,
pierced by a pore; texture parenchymatous. Spores elongate-
ellipsoid or cylindrical, hyaline, rounded at both ends, 1–3-
septate, constricted, pluriguttulate, 19–27 × 6–8μ.

On leaves (especially at the dead or dying tips) of cultivated
Narcissus (*poeticus*, etc.), and even on the flowers. Cornwall;
Scilly Islands; Devon; Buckinghamshire; Hertfordshire;
Middlesex; Lancashire; Flintshire; etc.

Hungary, ? N. Amer.

Scirpus

Stagonospora aquatica Sacc. Syll. iii. 452. *Hendersonia aquatica*
Sacc. in Mich. ii. 112.

Pycnidia immersed, hardly or not at all erumpent, globular,
100μ diam., with an impressed ostiole; texture minutely
parenchymatous, smoky-brown. Spores cylindric-fusoid,
slightly inequilateral, subobtuse at both ends, at first 4-gut-
tulate, then with about 3 septa, not constricted, 26–28 × 5–6μ.

On *Scirpus* (and *Juncus*). Only the following varieties have
been found in Britain (for the form on *Juncus* see *St. junciseda*).

Var. **sexseptata** Trail, in Scot. Nat. 1887, p. 88. Grevill. xv. 109.
Sacc. Syll. x. 335. All. vi. 988.

Pycnidia larger, 150μ diam. Spores relatively more slender,
32–35 × 5–6μ, and 6-septate.

On dead stems of *Scirpus lacustris*. Corbie Loch, near
Aberdeen.   Sept.

Var. **quinqueseptata** Grove = *St. Scirpi* Tehon, in Mycologia, 1933,
xxv. 247.

Agreeing with the preceding variety, but having at length
only five septa. Spores 33–40 × 5–6μ, faintly curved, perfectly hyaline, often guttulate.

On stems of *Scirpus palustris*, marsh near Aldridge, Staffs.
On *Sc. maritimus*, salt-marsh, Red Wharf Bay, Anglesey
(Rhodes). *St. Scirpi* is described by Tehon as being similar,
but having 3–5 septa, though mostly 4-septate.   July.

Saccardo's species is evidently very variable, but the differences
appear to be mainly, if not entirely, dependent upon age; in different
forms the spores may vary from 25 to 40μ in length, and from 3 to 8μ
in breadth. With it one should compare *Hendersonia longispora* Bub.
& Kab., on the same host (but living), which has spores 45–80 × 4–6μ
with as many as seven septa.

Fr. Denm. Finland, U.S.A.

Stagonospora maritima Syd. in Ann. Mycol. ix. 557. Died. 558.
Mig. 348. Sacc. Syll. xxv. 365.

No spots. Pycnidia hypophyllous, scattered ± in rows between the nerves, immersed, subglobose, papillate, 100–180μ
diam., black, just piercing the epidermis by the papilla, which
is often surrounded by a faint brownish stain; texture rather
thick, parenchymatous. Spores elliptic-oblong, somewhat un-
equal-sided, obtuse though slightly tapering at both ends,
guttulate, 20–24 × 6–6·5μ, continuous, at length 2-septate,
sometimes very slightly constricted at both septa, hyaline,
ultimately with 3 or 4 rather large guttules and the middle
cell wider and longer than the others; sporophores not seen.
(Fig. 23*f*.)

On dry dead leaves, stems, and leaf-sheaths of *Scirpus maritimus*. Often abundant. Llienawg, Beaumaris, Anglesey
(Rhodes). Sandplace, Cornwall (Rilstone & Rhodes). Saltash; Whitstable; Borth (Wales).   Sept. Oct.

Germ.

Sparganium
Stagonospora Sparganii All. vi. 989. Mig. 348. *Darluca Typhoi-*
dearum, α *Sparganii*, Fckl. Symb. Myc. 379. *Stagonospora Typhoi-*
dearum, var. *Sparganii*, Sacc. Syll. iii. 451. *Ascochyta Sparganii* Ellis,
in T.B.M.S. 1914, iv. 293. *Ascochyta quadriguttulata* Kab. & Bub. in
Hedwig. 1910, vol. 50, p. 40. Mig. 288.

Spots elongated, yellow, conspicuous. Pycnidia amphigenous, thinly scattered, immersed, the minute ostiole just
piercing the epidermis, globose, black, 40–150μ diam.; texture soft, clear-olive, parenchymatous. Spores fusoid, tapering often at one or both ends, 1-septate, 12–26 × 4·5–6μ, then
3-septate (the middle septum being formed long before the
others), hardly constricted, furnished with four large globose
guttules, 25–30 × 5–7μ (16–18 × 6–7μ, Ellis); "sporophores
12μ long" (K. & B.).

On dead leaves and stems of *Sparganium ramosum*.
Cheshire, etc. (Ellis). Dumbartonshire (Boyd). Pembroke
(Rhodes). Hampshire; Wiltshire; etc.   Sept.–Feb.

The spores are at first much like those of Ascochyta, and the pycnidia are so small as scarcely to be visible without a lens. The septa
are very delicate. When young the spores have a number of small oil-
drops, which at length coalesce into four large ones. In spite of Kabát
and Bubák's emphatic disclaimer there cannot be the slightest doubt
that their *Asco. quadriguttulata* is the same species as *St. Sparganii*,
but in a younger state. Cf. p. 325.

Holl. Germ. Denm. Bohem. Morav. Poland.

Typha
Stagonospora Typhoidearum Sacc. Syll. iii. 451; xxii. 1056.
All. vi. 989. Died. 560. Mig. 349. *Hendersonia Typhoidearum* Desm.
in Ann. Aci. Nat. 1849, xi. 344. B. & Br. in Ann. Nat. Hist. 1850, v.
374. *Darluca Typhoidearum* B. & Br. Outl. 318. Cooke, Handb. p.
437, f. 160. *Stagonospora Typhae* v. Höhn. Fragm. z. Mykol. nos. 267,
268.

Pycnidia very numerous, but mostly standing singly
though closely together, about 120μ diam., immersed, globose, black; ostiole papilliform, prominent, pierced; texture
parenchymatous, brown, hardly darker round the ostiole.
Spores oblong-fusoid, tapering but obtusely at each end, little
or not at all curved, usually with four large (rarely 3 or 5) globose guttules, at first continuous, then 1-septate, at length
3-septate, 20–25 × 4–6μ, nearly or quite hyaline.

On leaves of *Typha angustifolia*, *T. latifolia*. England and Scotland up to Aberdeen. Common.

Bubák & Kabát record larger spores (30–38 × 8μ) on *T. angustifolia* (see Hedwig. 1910, p. 42), with rarely 4 septa, and perceptible pedicels (5–10μ). The British specimens belong chiefly to Desmazières' f. *minor* (*ibid.* 1853, xx. 223), which has spores 20 × 5μ.

Fr. Holl. Germ. Denm. Austr. U.S.A.

Equisetum

Stagonospora equisetina Trail, in Scot. Nat. 1887, ix. 88. Grevill. xv. 109. Sacc. Syll. x. 337. All. vi. 972. *St. Equiseti* Fautr. in Rev. Mycol. 1890, p. 124. Sacc. Syll. x. 337. Died. p. 555, p. 552, f. 4. Mig. 345. See *Stagonosporopsis Equiseti*, *supra*, p. 327.

"Pycnidia scattered, immersed, globose, brown, 80μ diam. (?). Spores cylindric-fusoid, subacute at the ends, straight, 6–8-guttulate, faintly 5–7-septate, 18–24 × 4–5μ."

On dead sheaths and stems of *Equisetum limosum*, *E. palustre*. Corbie Loch, near Aberdeen (Trail). Earlswood, Wk.; Worcs. On *E. arvense*, Hartlebury Common, Ws. Sept.

Stagonospora Equiseti Fautr. is doubtless a less developed form, having exactly similar spores, but only three septa and four large oil-guttules (on *E. limosum* in Germany), though its pycnidium is described as much larger.

Denm.

AMPHORULA Grove, in Journ. Bot. 1922, p. 82.

Pycnidia immersed, rather solid, carbonaceous. Spores ampulliform, hyaline, septate, and produced upwards into a long beak.

This genus is akin to Kellermania Ell. & Ev., but has a more solid and thicker pycnidium, and the spores have a different form, the beak being, not an appendage to the spore as in *K. yuccigena*, but a prolongation of its upper loculus. Only one transverse septum has so far been distinctly seen in Amphorula, but there were faint indications of two others.

Amphorula sachalinensis Grove, in Journ. Bot. 1922, p. 82, pl. 563, f. 1.

Pycnidia scattered, depressed-globose or placentiform, 300–750μ diam., scarcely papillate, immersed, covered by the epi-

dermis and at first closely adhering to it, afterwards perforating it by a very minute round pore which becomes at
length wider or fissure-like, for a long time
mouthless, black, with a thick dark wall which
becomes paler inwards; at last, when the dead
epidermis scales off, the pycnidia become superficial or peel off with it. Spores elliptic-fusoid,
attenuated upwards into a long filiform beak,
40–60μ long over all, of which the lower elliptic
part measures 15–22 × 2·5–4μ, colourless, often
guttulate, and at last delicately 1-septate;
sporophores short and straight. (Fig. 24.)

On dead stalks of *Polygonum sachalinense*,
in a garden, Sutton Coldfield. Heythrop Park,
Oxon. May–Jul. Accompanied and followed
by *Diaporthe maculosa*, f. *Polygoni* Grove.

Fig. 24. Spores
of *Amphorula
sachalinensis*, in
various stages of
growth, × 600.

At Heythrop Park, the Amphorula once spread from *P. sachalinense* on to *P. cuspidatum*, a clump of which was growing near. If the
Amphorula ultimately becomes 3-septate, as seems likely, *Kellermania
Polygoni* and *K. Rumicis* (which have not yet been found in Britain)
may be congeneric with it, but *K. yuccigena*, the type of the genus,
certainly is not so; see Journ. Bot. *l.c.*

STAGONOSTROMA Died. 561.

Stromata verruciform, formed of parenchymatous thin-walled
cells, bearing one or more pycnidia which are themselves composed of similar, but bluish-tinged, cells. Spores oblong or
fusoid, hyaline, with several septa.

This genus, as has been shown in my article in the Journal
of Botany for 1934, pp. 269–71, is closely akin to *Fusidomus*
and has similar Fusarium-like spores. Presumably, therefore,
it forms a stage in the life-cycle of some species of Gibberella.

Stagonostroma Dulcamarae Died. p. 561, p. 552, f. 10. Mig. p.
351, pl. 45, f. 2, 3. *Stagonospora Dulcamarae* Passer. Diagn. Fung.
nuov. IV, 466. Sacc. Syll. x. 333. All. vi. 988.

Stroma composed of large brown parenchymatous cells.
Pycnidia solitary or a few in botryose groups, about 300μ
diam., composed of cells which are tinged with a pleasant

bluish or fuscous-violaceous colour. Spores elongate-fusoid, curvulous, 3–5-septate, slightly constricted at all the septa, 30–40 × 4–7 μ, sporophores unseen.

On dry dead stems of *Solanum Dulcamara.* Hadzor Hall, near Droitwich.   June.

The spores are exactly of the shape typical of the genus Fusarium; they germinate readily while still within the pycnidium.
Germ.

CYTOTRIPLOSPORA Elliott & Chance, *l.c.*

Stromata erumpent, pustular, surrounded by the torn peri-derm, divided into several often imperfect chambers. Spores numerous, sausage-shaped, hyaline, at first continuous, then biseptate; sporophores longer than the spores.

Cytotriplospora Pini Elliott & Chance, in T.B.M.S. 1921, vii. 47, with fig. *Pestalozzina Rollandi* Fautr. in Rev. Mycol. 1895, p. 71, pl. 153, f. 23. Sacc. Syll. xi. 580. All. vii. 630.

Pycnidia rather crowded, occurring in irregular lines, some-what parallel, following the long axis of the twig, oblong, 1–6-chambered, black, 300–500 μ diam., at length erumpent at the vertex. Spores at first unicellular, curved, rounded at the ends (sausage-shaped), then with one or two septa, about 15 × 4–7 μ; sporophores simple, slender, straight, acute, about 1·5 times as long as the spore which rests obliquely on it.

On dead twigs of *Pinus silvestris,* Oxshott Woods, Surrey. (Bayliss Elliott). On cone-scales of *Picea excelsa,* Swaledale, Yorkshire (F. A. Mason). On branches of *Pinus silvestris,* Sutton Coldfield.   Jan.–May.

When mature, the sporophore breaks away, carrying the spore with it and then looking like a spine or cilium obliquely attached. In this state it exactly resembles Fautrey's figure (*l.c.*) of the Pestalozzina on leaves of *Pinus Strobus*; therefore probably that is a leaf form of the Cytotriplospora; the absence of a pycnidium and the slightly smaller size of its spores (12 × 3 μ) might easily be due to its growing on a thin leaf instead of on a twig. Many other similar cases are to be found among the Coelomycetes. This fungus reminds one, oddly enough, of Berkeley's enigmatic *Sphaeropsis geniculata*, i.e. *Phoma geniculata* Sacc. (*q.v.*, p. 76).
Fr.

SCOLECOSPORAE

Spores elongated, worm-like or fusoid-linear; transverse septa wanting or formed only when the spore is becoming mature.

I. Pycnidia standing singly, without a stroma.
  A. Pycnidia thin- or sometimes thick-walled, cells thin-walled.
    1. Pycnidia not beaked.
      a. Pycnidia immersed in the matrix.
        α. Pycnidia thin-walled, mostly causing spots on leaves . . . . *Septoria*
        β. Pycnidia on leaves, wall almost wanting *Phleospora*
        γ. Pycnidia thicker-walled, mostly on herbaceous stems . . . . *Rhabdospora*
      b. Pycnidia superficial, becoming carbonaceous
                                    Collonema
    2. Pycnidia beaked . . . . . . [*Sphaerographium*]
  B. Pycnidia sclerotioid, cells thick-walled . . . *Micropera*
II. Pycnidia seated in or on a stroma.
  A. Stroma flat; spores penicillate at the ends . *Dilophospora*
  B. Stroma cytosporoid, but with long spores. . *Cytosporina*

SEPTORIA Fr. Syst. Myc. iii. 480 (emend.).

Pycnidia subepidermal, typically on discoloured portions of the leaves (the so-called "spots"), but occasionally on stems, between globose and lens-shaped, pierced at the summit by a pore; texture most often membranaceous, pseudo-pycnidial, darker round the pore. Spores hyaline, filiform or linear, straight or flexuous, often curved or worm-like, mostly provided with guttules or septa, seldom without the one or the other; sporophores very short or imperceptible. (Fig. 25.)

This genus is similar in habit to Phyllosticta and Ascochyta, and in fact only differs from them in its more elongated spores. When these spores are septate, the septa are usually more than two, but they are often very delicate and difficult to see. Septoria may be confused with Cylindrosporium, but the latter can be distinguished by its imperfectly formed pycnidial wall,

which is completely absent above. If the peridium is thick and distinctly pseudo-parenchymatous, the species should be looked for in Rhabdospora, but whatever terms of definition may be used the two genera Septoria and Rhabdospora will still at times collide.

Some of the species which were formerly classed with Septoria are now placed under Phleospora, and others under Septogloeum. The following species are arranged in the alphabetic order of the host-genera—those on Dicotyledons first, on Monocotyledons next (those on GRAMINEAE being placed together under that heading), and lastly on Cryptogams (two only).

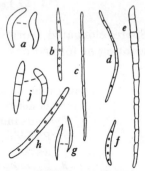

Fig. 25. Spores of *Septoria*: *a, S. oxyspora*, var. *culmorum*; *b, S. polaris*, var. *scotica*; *c, S. scabiosicola*; *d, S. Polygonorum*; *e, S. Alopecuri*, var. *Calamagrostidis*; *f, S. punctoidea*; *g, S. Avellanae*; *h, S. Chrysanthemi*; *j, S. nodorum*; all × 600.

Achillea

Septoria Millefolii Grove. *Rhabdospora Millefolii* Oud. Contr. Flor. Myc. Pays-Bas, xvii. 278.

Pycnidia numerous, crowded, single or confluent, arranged in rows, sometimes semiglobose, at others compressed, glabrous, black, at first covered, then erumpent, 300–500μ diam., pierced by a pore; texture rather thin. Spores linear, straight or gently curved, rounded at both ends, continuous, 2–3-guttulate, hyaline, 9–12 × 2–2·5μ; sporophores as long as the spore, or a little longer.

On dead stems of *Achillea Millefolium*, Henley-in-Arden.

Apr.

Perhaps rather a Rhabdospora.
Holl.

Adoxa

Septoria Adoxae Fckl. Symb. Myc. Nacht. II, 21. Sacc. Syll. iii. 543. All. vi. 723. Died. 423. Mig. 375. Grevill. xiv. 132.

Pycnidia scattered or subgregarious, sometimes on bleached spots, at length free, obtusely conical, flattened at the base, very black; ostiole obtuse, pierced by a pore. Spores cylin-

drical, often straight, hyaline, with one or two septa, 32–36 ×
4µ.

On leaves of *Adoxa Moschatellina*. Forres (Keith).   May.

Germ.

Aesculus
Septoria Hippocastani B. & Br. in Ann. Nat. Hist. 1850, v. 379.
Cooke, Handb. 443. Sacc. Syll. iii. 479. All. vi. 724. Died. 425.
Mig. 376. *S. Aesculi* Westd. in Bull. Acad. Brux. 1851, p. 394. Sacc.
Syll. iii. 479. All. vi. 725. Died. 424. Mig. 375.

Spots numerous, roundish or subangular, scattered over the
whole leaf-surface, often marginal, small, brown or at length
whitish, bordered by a narrow fuscous line. Pycnidia few on
each spot, chiefly epiphyllous, lens-shaped, fuscous, about
180µ diam., pierced by a pore. Spores filiform, curved,
almost falcate, attenuated at both ends but rather obtuse,
faintly 3-septate, 30–57 × 2·5–3·5µ.

On living or dead leaves of *Aesculus Hippocastanum*.
Common; Kew; Warwickshire; Worcestershire; etc.

In the Kew Bulletin, 1907, p. 242, *S. Aesculi* is erroneously reported
to be on leaves of Sweet Chestnut (*Castanea*). It is the pycnidial stage
of *Mycosphaerella maculiformis* Schröt. var. *Hippocastani* Jaap, Fung.
sel. exs. no. 423. *Ascochyta Aesculi* Lib. is an early state of the same
fungus, and there seems to be little reason why *S. aesculina* Thüm.
should not be considered also to form part of the same life-cycle though
it has smaller spots, each usually with one pycnidium. *S. aesculicola*
(Fr.) Sacc. is said to be distinguished by its shorter and much narrower
spores (20–30 × 1µ).
Europe, U.S.A.

Alnus
Septoria alnicola Cooke, in Seem. Journ. Bot. iv. 97, f. 23;
Handb. 451. Sacc. Syll. iii. 506.

Spots pallid, brown, or tawny, roundish, 5–7 mm. diam.
Pycnidia epiphyllous, scattered, semi-immersed, minute,
black, pierced at the summit. Spores oblong-fusoid, tapering
at one or both ends, compressed, occasionally faintly biguttulate, 8–10 × 2–2·5µ.

On living leaves of *Alnus glutinosa*. Shere (Cooke).   Oct.

The description is amended according to a specimen issued by
Cooke, Exs. no. 203. The species is not a *Septoria*; the spores are
formed as if a fusiform shape were cut out of thin wood, as may be

seen by causing them to roll over in water; they are straight in face view, ± curved in profile. There is no distinct pycnidium. It is an early state of *Leptothyrium alneum (q.v.)*.
Germ. Ital. U.S.A.

Anemone

Septoria Anemones Desm. Exs. no. 940. Sacc. Syll. iii. 521. All. vi. 730. Died. 426. Mig. 377.

Spots dry, at length brown. Pycnidia epiphyllous, gregarious, distinct, immersed, nearly spherical, about 100μ diam., dark-brown, rather thin, opening by a very short ostiole. Spores filiform, not or faintly septate, 20–22 × 1–1·25μ (with 6–8 indistinct guttules, Sacc.), exuding at the pore.

On *Anemone nemorosa*. Highgate; Darenth; Surrey; Botley; Rednal, Ws.; Aberdeen; Aboyne; etc.   June.

Spots not bordered, sometimes hardly different in colour from the rest of the leaf, greenish or brown, paler in the centre.
Europe, U.S.A.

Antirrhinum

Septoria Antirrhini Rob. & Desm. in Ann. Sci. Nat. 1853, xx. 87. Sacc. Syll. iii. 535. All. vi. 731. Died. 427. Mig. p. 377, pl. 49, f. 5–7, pl. 51, f. 3. T.B.M.S. iii. 222. Chittenden, in Journ. Roy. Hort. Soc. 1909, xxxv. 216, f. 82.

Spots small, nearly circular, yellowish, then earthy-brown, with a definite purplish-brown border. Pycnidia amphigenous, minute, numerous, scattered or crowded, rather prominent, blackish, 50–70μ diam., pierced by a pore. Spores cylindrical, obtuse at both ends, straight or curved, with 4–7 guttules, 15–20 × 2–2·5μ, issuing in white tendrils.

On dead stems and half-rotting leaves of *Antirrhinum majus*. Kew; Kent; Devon; Essex; Suffolk; Staffordshire; Warwickshire; etc.; Dublin.   May–Sept.

The spores seem at length to be very delicately septate.
Fr. Germ. Ital. Port.

Apium

Septoria Apii Chester, in Bull. Torr. Bot. Club, 1891, p. 372. Rostr. Plantepatologi, 1902, p. 575. Died. 427. Mig. 378. *S. Petroselini* Desm. var. *Apii* Br. & Cav. Fungh. Paras. 144. Sacc. Syll. xiv. 972. *Phlyctaena Magnusiana* Bres. in Ber. Bot. Ver. Landshut, xii, 62. Sacc. Syll. xi. 551. All. vi. 938. *S. Apii-graveolentis* Dorogin; see Sacc. Syll. xxv. 454.

Spots visible on both sides, brown, then whitish, round or angular, surrounded by a definite border, at times confluent

and larger. Pycnidia amphigenous, somewhat prominent, clear-brown, 90–150μ diam., darker round the pore. Spores filiform, straight, hardly curving, indistinctly guttulate, at length 3–4-septate, 30–50 × 1·5–2μ.

On living leaves, stems, and fruits of wild *Apium graveolens*, in the Tamar, Cornw. (Hurst) and in the canal, Droitwich; also on cultivated Celery everywhere in the British Isles. June to October, even lasting till December, and causing a serious disease, which is propagated chiefly by sowing infected seed.

Europe, N. America.

Arbutus

Septoria Unedonis Rob. & Desm. in Ann. Sci. Nat. 1847, viii. 20. Cooke, Handb. 446. Sacc. Syll. iii. 493. All. vi. 732. Mig. 378.

Spots small, numerous, irregular, whitish and dry in the centre, with a very broad purplish border. Pycnidia epiphyllous, few, scarcely prominent, convex, blackish, then collapsing and becoming concave. Spores elongated, very slender, curvulous, without apparent septa, 25–30 × 1·5–2μ.

On fading leaves of *Arbutus Unedo*. Highgate; Dereham; Shrewsbury; Perranzabuloe; Glamis; Glasgow. Sept.–Nov.

Briosi and Cavara record a form on the same host with spores as much as 80μ long. In a specimen, on the same from Cyprus, I found the spores to measure 25–63 × 2–3μ.

Fr. Germ. Austr. Ital. Port. Cyprus.

Aristolochia

Septoria Aristolochiae Sacc. Syll. iii. 558. All. vi. 733.

Spots none. Pycnidia hypophyllous, gregarious, punctiform, lens-shaped, 40μ diam., pierced by a small pore. Spores rod-shaped, somewhat clavulate, without guttules, curvulous, 15–20 × 1·75–2μ.

On leaves of *Aristolochia Clematitis*. Kew Gardens. *n.v.*

In France, Brunaud records a variety (*maculicola*) which differs in having the pycnidia epiphyllous, on roundish or subangular, whitish, brown-bordered spots.

Fr. Ital.

Asperula

Septoria Asperulae Bäuml. Fung. Schemn. p. 4. Sacc. Syll. x. 373. All. vi. 736. Died. 429. Mig. 380. T.B.M.S. iv. 176.

Spots at first irregular, then extending over the whole leaf, becoming grey, with a fuscous margin. Pycnidia gregarious,

globose, 60–200μ diam., pierced by a minute pore; texture membranaceous, rusty-ochre in colour. Spores elongate-filiform, curvulous, tapering toward the lower end, provided with several guttules, 30–50 × 2μ, at length delicately 3-septate.

On living or fading leaves of *Asperula odorata*. Ayrshire (Boyd).   Feb.–Jun.

Germ. Hung. Denm.

Astragalus

Septoria Astragali Rob. & Desm. in Ann. Sci. Nat. 1843, xix. 345. Cooke, Handb. 451. Sacc. Syll. iii. 508. All. vi. 737. Died. 430. Mig. 380. Potebnia, in Ann. Mycol. viii. 66, f. 16.

Spots irregular, greenish-grey, then reddish-fuscous, paler in the centre, 1–3 mm. broad, longer on the stems. Pycnidia few, epiphyllous, globose, somewhat prominent, black, pierced by a wide opening. Spores filiform, tortuous, very long, 60–100 (or even 120) × 3μ, not quite colourless, at length 9–10-septate.

On leaves and stems of *Astragalus glycyphyllos*. Darenth (Cooke).   Autumn.

This has been described as *Phleospora Astragali* Potebn. (and in America as *Phleosp. reticulata* E. & E.), for the pycnidia are at first imperfect, but develop later into a true Septoria. The var. *santonensis* Brun., with shorter spores and 3–5 septa or guttules, occurs on the leaves in France, possibly a younger state.

Europe, U.S.A. Canada.

Atriplex

Septoria Atriplicis Fckl. Symb. Myc. 390. Sacc. Syll. iii. 556. All. vi. 737. Died. 430. Mig. 380. *Phyllosticta Atriplicis* Westd. in Bull. Acad. Brux. 1851, p. 397.

Spots greenish-olivaceous, then becoming paler, ochreous or whitish, ± circular. Pycnidia amphigenous, but mostly epiphyllous, immersed, piercing the epidermis by the pore which projects slightly, 100–150μ diam., clear-brown, darker round the pore. Spores cylindrical, obtuse at both ends, pluriguttulate, then with 1–5 septa, even slightly constricted, 22–35 × 4–5μ.

On living leaves of species of *Atriplex*. Common.

A var. *emaculata*, with the spots almost absent, is found on maritime species of *Atriplex*. The two so-called species *S. Atriplicis* and *S. Chenopodii* (*q.v.*) are probably identical.

Fr. Belg. Germ. Ital. Siberia, S. Amer.

Azalea

Septoria Azaleae Voglino, in Malpigh. 1899, xiii. 73–86. Sacc.
Syll. xiv. 976. Gard. Chron. 1927, lxxxi. 286, f. 139–143.

Spots beginning usually at the tip of the leaf, but at length
occupying the whole leaf, reddish-yellow, then rusty-brown.
Pycnidia amphigenous, immersed, subglobose, black, 100–
145μ diam., pierced by a pore. Spores oblong-linear or subcylindric, obtuse at both ends, ± curved, granular, colourless,
15–20 × 2·5μ (11–34 × 1·5–2·5μ, Salmon), afterwards 1–4-sep-
tate, slightly constricted, at length expelled in tendrils or
masses.

On leaves of *Azalea indica*, forming the disease called
"Leaf-scorch". Kent, 1927 (on imported Azaleas); Surrey;
Oxfordshire; etc.   Mar.–Sept.

"On the damp leaves, the spores give rise to secondary conidia
7–11 × 2–3μ, by which the disease is spread." *n.v.*
Belg. Germ. Ital.

Bellis

Septoria Bellidis Desm. & Rob. in Ann. Sci. Nat. 1853, xx. 90.
Sacc. Syll. iii. 548. All. vi. 740. Died. 431. T.B.M.S. v. 160.

Spots olivaceous, then becoming dry and yellowish-brown,
roundish or irregular. Pycnidia amphigenous, remaining
covered by the epidermis which is pierced only by the ostiole,
brown, not darker àt the pore, 50–70μ diam. Spores filiform,
straight or slightly flexuous, becoming somewhat pointed at
the ends, indistinctly guttulate, 30–40 × 1–1·5μ.

On fading leaves of *Bellis perennis*. Blackpool (Sm. & R.).
West Kilbride and Dalry (Boyd). Richmond, etc., Surrey.

Jun.–Aug.

Fr. Holl. Germ.

Berberis

Septoria Berberidis Niessl, in Raben. Fung. Eur. no. 1080. Sacc.
Syll. iii. 475. All. vi. 741. Died. 433. Mig. 381.

Spots roundish, 3–4 mm. diam., brownish when dry,
bordered by a dark purple zone. Pycnidia epiphyllous, aggregated, globose, then lens-shaped, up to 150μ diam.,
pierced by a pore; texture pale, thin. Spores filiform, flexuous
or sinuous, somewhat thickened and obtuse above, acute below, with many small guttules, at length faintly 4–5-septate,
42–58 × 2–2·5μ.

On living leaves of *Berberis vulgaris*. Darenth (Cooke).
Pembrokeshire (Rhodes).　　　　　　　　　　Apr. Aug.

Fr. Germ. Austr. Switz. Ital. Russ.

Beta

Septoria Betae Westd. Exs. no. 296, and in Kickx, Flor. Crypt.
Flandr. i. 425. Sacc. Syll. iii. 556. All. vi. 741. Mig. 382. Died. 433.

Pycnidia very crowded, on blanched elongated oval spots
on the stems, very minute, 60–65μ diam., globose, blackish;
texture extremely thin, elongate-prosenchymatous, with
hardly a darker zone around the ostiole. Spores cylindrical,
nearly always straight, very rarely curvulous, subacute at
both ends, eguttulate, hyaline, 13–18 × 1–1·5μ.

On dead stems of *Beta maritima*. Vazon Bay, Guernsey
(Rhodes).　　　　　　　　　　　　　　　　　Sept.

All the other records seem to be on leaves of cultivated Beet; the
size of the spores cannot be compared, as the authorities are silent on
that point.
Belg. Germ.

Campanula

Septoria obscura Trail, in Scot. Nat. 1889, x. 73. Sacc. Syll. x.
377.

Spots round or irregular, dingy-brown when dry, with a
narrow and indistinct dark border. Pycnidia amphigenous,
scattered, immersed, minute, black, with a short ostiole.
Spores cylindric-filiform, obtuse at the ends, curvulous, 3-
septate, yellowish, 22–35 × 1·5μ.

On living leaves of *Campanula rotundifolia*. Hell's Glen,
Clyde. *n.v.*

Castanea

Septoria castaneicola Desm. in Ann. Sci. Nat. 1847, viii. 26.
Cooke, Handb. 450, 913. Sacc. Syll. iii. 504. All. vi. 752. Died. 438.
Mig. 386.

Spots small, unbordered, spread over nearly the whole leaf,
tawny-brown. Pycnidia hypophyllous, numerous, 60–90μ
diam., partly immersed, brownish-black, pierced by a pore.
Spores cylindrical, rather obtuse at both ends, curvulous, 3-
septate, 30–40 × 3–4·5μ, issuing in dingy-white tendrils.

On living or fading leaves of *Castanea vesca*. Common
wherever Castanea is grown.　　　　　　　　Sept. Oct.

The early stage of *Mycosphaerella castaneicola* or (according to Cooke) of *M. maculiformis*, var. *oblivia*. The "spots" are due to the fact that the parts of the leaf occupied by the pycnidia do not lose so much colour in the autumn, as the rest of the leaf does. The fungus has been placed in herbaria as *Cylindrosporium castaneicolum*.

Europe.

Centaurea

Septoria Centaureae Sacc. Syll. iii. 551. All. vi. 753. *Phyllosticta Centaureae* Roum. Fung. Gall. no. 1633. Died. 438. Mig. 386.

Spots amphigenous, small, oval, pallid, with a distinct brownish border, at length dropping out and leaving a shot-hole. Pycnidia punctiform. Spores linear, curvulous, rather obtuse at both ends, delicately 2–4-septate, not constricted, 55–60 × 1·5–2μ.

On fading leaves of *Centaurea nigra*. Kew Gardens (Cooke). Ayrshire (Boyd). Aug. Sept.

Cerastium

Septoria Cerastii Rob. & Desm. in Ann. Sci. Nat. 1849, xi. 347. Sacc. Syll. iii. 518. All. vi. 754. Died. 439. Mig. 387.

Spots abundant, pallid-yellowish, then greyish. Pycnidia amphigenous and on the stems, situated in the centre of the spots, globose-depressed, fuscous, pierced by a pore, 80–150μ diam: Spores linear, straight or very slightly curved, indistinctly guttulate, 30–50 × 1μ (at length 4–5-septate, Fragoso).

On stems, fading leaves, and calyces of *Cerastium triviale*. Lancashire; Scotland (Ayrshire, Tay, etc.). Jul.–Oct.

The pycnidial stage of *Fabraea cerastiorum* Rehm. Europe, U.S.A.

Cheiranthus

Septoria Cheiranthi Rob. & Desm. in Ann. Sci. Nat. 1847, xi. 20. Sacc. Syll. iii. 521.

Spots amphigenous, roundish or irregular, pallid-buff or yellowish. Pycnidia mostly epiphyllous, few, black, sub-globose, rather prominent, about 60μ diam., pierced by a pore, then concave and collapsing. Spores very delicate, curvulous, faintly guttulate, 20–25 × 1μ, colourless, subacute at ends.

On fading leaves of *Cheiranthus Allionii*, Lambourne Hill, W. Cornwall (Rilstone). June.

Fr. Ital.

Chelidonium

Septoria Chelidonii Desm. in Ann. Sci. Nat. 1842,xvii. 110. Cooke, Handb. 449. Sacc. Syll. iii. 521. All. vi. 756. Died. 441. Mig. 388.

Spots angular or roundish, greenish-olive or brownish, sometimes dry and whitish in the centre. Pycnidia amphigenous, covered by the epidermis, slightly flattened, nearly black, 75–120μ diam., pierced by a large apical pore. Spores elongated, linear, straight or curved, with several guttules, 20–30 × 1·5μ, issuing in yellowish tendrils.

On fading leaves of *Chelidonium majus*. Albury; Shere; Irstead; Kew; North Wales.   Aug.–Oct.

The spots are not distinctly bordered, although with a very definite outline which is determined by the veins and venules.

Europe, Siberia.

Chenopodium

Septoria Chenopodii Westd. in Bull. Acad. Brux. 1851, p. 396. Sacc. Syll. iii. 556. All. vi. 756. Died. 442. Mig. 388.

Spots amphigenous, scattered, greyish-brown, with a distinct margin, mostly circular, but often confluent. Pycnidia crowded, epiphyllous, immersed, black, about 125μ diam.; texture thin, pale in colour, darker round the wide pore. Spores cylindrical, obtuse at both ends, mostly straight, pluriguttulate, later with one or two septa, hyaline, 13–18 × 2·5–3μ, issuing in white masses.

On living leaves of *Chenopodium*. Common around London, but local. Cf. *S. Atriplicis, supra*, p. 370.

There can be no doubt that this is merely a more highly developed state of *Ascochyta Chenopodii*. See Journ. Bot. 1917, p. 346, "*Septoria Chenopodii*", where it is suggested that *Stagonospora Atriplicis* Lind, Dan. Fungi, p. 444, pl. 6, f. 79, 80 is a still later stage.

Belg. Germ. Ital. Port.

Chrysanthemum

Septoria Chrysanthemi Allesch. Verz. Süd. Bay. Pilz. iii. 57 (1891). Rostr. in Bot. Tidsskr. xviii. 48 (1897). Cav. Atti Ist. Bot. Pavia, ii, ii. 266; Fung. Long. exs. no. 40. Sacc. Syll. xi. 542. Mig. 408. *S. chrysanthemella* Sacc. Syll. xi. 542. All. vi. 804. Died. 442. T.B.M.S. iv. 177. *S. Chrysanthemi-indici* Kab. & Bub. in Hedwig. 1907, xlvi. 294. *S. Rostrupii* Sacc. & Syd. Syll. xiv. 973. *S. socia* Passer. Sacc. Syll. iii. 549 (a young state).

Spots round, ochraceous or brownish-red, margined with brown, 10–15 mm. diam. (smaller on *C. Leucanthemum*).

Pycnidia epiphyllous, subglobose, 100–120μ diam., with an ostiole; texture pallid, thin. Spores filiform, narrow, rather obtuse at the ends or subclavulate, straight or curved, with several minute guttules and/or 4 or 5 faint septa, 40–60 × 2–2·5μ. (Fig. 25h.)

On living leaves of *Chrysanthemum Leucanthemum, C. maximum, C. indicum*. Rather common; England, Scotland, Guernsey.   Jun.–Nov.

It causes a disease of Chrysanthemum cuttings; the attacked leaves become crumpled at the edges. See Magnus, in Ber. Deutsch. Bot. Gesell. 1907, xxv. 299, for the synonyms given above, and cf. *S. Leucanthemi* and *S. cercosporoides*.

Europe, U.S.A. Canada, Australia.

Septoria cercosporoides Trail, in Scot. Nat. 1887, ix. 89. Sacc. Syll. x. 370. Died. 479. Mig. 408.

Spots roundish or irregular, ill-defined, dark-brown, most conspicuous on the upper face of the leaf. Pycnidia collected in groups, elliptic, rather pale-brown, 90–200μ diam. Spores obclavulate, with the lower end obtuse and broader, thus resembling the conidia of *Cercospora*, nearly hyaline, 5–8-septate, 50–100 × 2–3μ (mostly 60–70 × 3μ).

On fading leaves of *Chrysanthemum Leucanthemum*; Montrose; near Aberdeen (Trail). On leaves of *Chrys. maximum*, cult. Ayrshire (Boyd). Polperro (Rilstone).   Jul.–Oct.

Cf. *S. Leucanthemi* and *S. Chrysanthemi*, which are probably all the same species.

Germ.

Septoria Leucanthemi Sacc. & Speg. in Mich. i. 191 (1878). Syll. iii. 549. All. vi. 803. Died. 478. Mig. 409. Gard. Chron. 1925, lxxviii. 353.

Spots rather large, roundish or sinuous, often becoming confluent into large patches, fuscous-ochraceous with a darker border, at length paler in the centre. Pycnidia mostly epiphyllous, scattered or in little groups, lens-shaped, black, 100–160μ diam., at length pierced by a pore; texture thin, pallid-brownish, subpellucid, darker brown around the periphery. Spores straight or bent, linear, tapering slightly at one or both

ends, grossly pluriguttulate, scarcely septate, hyaline, 60–110 × 4–4·5μ (100–130 × 4–5μ, Sacc.), oozing out to form a globule.

On leaves of *Chrysanthemum maximum*, Maidstone; Bearsted, Kent; Hampshire (Wormald). Rednal, Ws.; Somerset; Wales. May–Sept.

Ital. Port.

Chrysosplenium

Septoria posoniensis Bäuml. in Hedwig. 1885, p. 75. Sacc. Syll. x. 367. All. vi. 757. Died. 443. Mig. 389. Grove, in Journ. Bot. 1922, p. 84.

Spots roundish, 3–6 mm. diam., greyish-green or dark-cinereous, without any distinct border, very inconspicuous. Pycnidia epiphyllous, closely gregarious, globose, 60–130μ diam., immersed, penetrating the epidermis with a rather prominent widely pierced papilla; texture thin, pale-fuscous, darker round the ostiole. Spores numerous, filiform, flexuose or bent, faintly and minutely guttulate, 25–56 × 1·3–1·5μ.

On living leaves of *Chrysosplenium oppositifolium*. West Kilbride, Ayrshire (Boyd). Aug.

Germ.

Clematis

Septoria Clematidis Rob. & Desm. in Ann. Sci. Nat. 1853, xx. 93. Sacc. Syll. iii. 524. Cooke, Handb. 447. All. vi. 761. Died. 444. Mig. 390.

Spots roundish, angular or irregular, greyish, with a dark fuscous border. Pycnidia amphigenous, very minute, immersed, scarcely prominent, pallid-brown, pierced by a pore. Spores elongated, rod-like, curved or flexuous, obtuse at both ends, sometimes rather clavate, occasionally guttulate, 4–6-septate, 50–80 × 4μ, issuing in a whitish tendril.

On living leaves of *Clematis Vitalba*. Dartford; Darenth; Tay. Summer and autumn.

Fr. Germ. Austr. Ital. Siber. Canada.

Clinopodium

Septoria Clinopodii Grove, comb. nov. *Rhabdospora Clinopodii* All. vi. 898. Mig. 444.

Pycnidia widely scattered, covered by the epidermis, round, lens-shaped, black, 400–500μ diam.; texture pseudopycnidial,

pale-brown, translucent, much darker round the pore. Spores copious, acicular, very acuminate at both ends, straight or curvulous, eseptate, faintly guttulate, colourless, 40–50 × 1–1·5μ.

On the upper part of old stems of *Calamintha Clinopodium*. Banks of the Usk, Brecon; Shelsey Kings, Ws. (Grové and Rhodes). Feb. May.

By the texture of the pycnidium this is a true Septoria, although it occurs on the stems and not on the leaves. The spores closely resemble in shape those of *Rhabdospora Galii* Died. If wetted again, after being dried, they show faint traces of having three or four septa.

Austria.

Cochlearia

Septoria Armoraciae Sacc. Syll. iii. 519. Oud. Aan. Myc. Nederl. p. 5 (1875). All. vi. 733. Died. 444. Mig. 391. *Ascochyta Armoraciae* Fckl. Symb. Myc. 388. Sacc. Syll. iii. 397. All. vi. 630. Died. 380. Mig. 270. *Phyllosticta Armoraciae* Cooke, in Fung. Brit. no. 32.

Spots rather small, roundish, irregular, ochraceous when dry, with a narrow darker border and occurring in plenty all over the leaf. Pycnidia punctiform, pallid, collected ± in the middle of the spot, 60–100μ diam., pierced by a pore. Spores cylindrical, curvulous, rather obtuse at the ends, continuous when young, then 1–3-septate, minutely guttulate, 15–20 × 2–3μ when mature.

On living leaves of *Cochlearia Armoracia*. Upwell (Vize). Ayrshire (Boyd). Jul.–Oct.

This species can be found in the Phyllosticta stage, as at King's Norton, Worcs., with spores measuring 9–13 × 2·5–3μ, and in the Ascochyta stage, as at Isleworth, King's Lynn, and Shrewsbury, etc., with spores 13–17 × 4μ. It is this stage that is most commonly met with, but on further search 3-septate spores can almost always be found. *Phyllosticta Orbicula* E. & E. in Proc. Acad. Nat. Sci. Philad. 1893, p. 455 (Sacc. Syll. xi. 477) is probably the same species.

Ramularia Armoraciae Fckl. produces similar spots and has similar spores, but of course has no pycnidium; it is a mistake to place this hyphomycete in Ovularia, as in Massee's Fungus Flora, iii. 321, for its spores are often 1-septate.

Holl. Germ. Ital.

Convolvulus

Septoria Convolvuli Desm. in Ann. Sci. Nat. 1842, xvii. 108. Cooke, Handb. 444. Sacc. Syll. iii. 536. All. vi. 764. Died. 446. Mig.

392. *S. flagellaris* E. & E.; Sacc. Syll. x. 377. *Sphaeria fuscella* Berk. in Currey, Simpl. Sphaer. no. 396. *Depazea convolvulicola* DC. Flor. fr. vi. 148. *Ascochyta Convolvuli* Lib. *p.p.*

Spots orbicular, then large, confluent and irregular, reddish or greenish-brown, at length pale in the centre, at first scarcely bordered. Pycnidia epiphyllous, immersed, up to 125μ diam., brown, pierced by a wide pore; texture parenchymatous, very thin. Spores linear, curvulous, somewhat tapering at the ends, with 5, 6, or more guttules, at length faintly 5-septate, 35–55 × 1–1·5μ.

On fading leaves of *Convolvulus arvensis, Calystegia sepium*. Rather common; England, Scotland (less so), Ireland.

Jul. Aug.

Saccardo records a var. *dolichospora*, on *C. sepium*, in Dakota, with spores 80–95μ long; see Ann. Mycol. 1915, xiii. 122. The absence or presence of septa cannot be used as a criterion; on *C. arvensis* the spores may often be found without any signs of septation or with five or fewer distinct septa, all within the same pycnidium. See *Sept. septulata* and *S. Soldanellae*.
Europe, N. & S. America, Cyprus.

Septoria septulata Beach, in Amer. Journ. Bot. 1919, vi. 19. Sacc. Syll. xxv. 419.

Spots orbicular, then confluent and irregular, light- to dark-brown. Pycnidia mostly epiphyllous, immersed, globose, 60–90μ diam., with a wide prominent ostiole. Spores curved or flexuous, one end narrowed and more acute, 3–5-septate, 30–50 × 1–2μ.

On fading leaves of *Convolvulus arvensis*. Dumfriesshire (Boyd). Sept.

Said to be distinguished from *S. Convolvuli*, by being more distinctly septate. But this depends upon the state of development; spores on *C. arvensis* can be perfectly eseptate, as in some of Mr Boyd's specimens, or fully septate, at the same apparent stage of growth.
Europe, U.S.A.

[**Septoria Soldanellae** Speg. Dec. Mycol. 115. Sacc. Syll. iii. 532. "On *Soldanella*. Swansea" (Cooke, in Grevill. xiv. 103).]

This seems to be a misunderstanding. Spegazzini's fungus is purely alpine. The Swansea specimen (which I have not seen) may have been

S. Convolvuli var. *Soldanellae* Brun. (Sacc. Syll. x. 377) or more likely *Stagonospora Calystegiae* Grove, which is not uncommon along our coasts on *Convolvulus Soldanella.*

Cornus

Septoria cornicola Desm. Exs. no. 342. Cooke, Handb. 444. Sacc. Syll. iii. 492. All. vi. 766. Died. 447. Mig. p. 392, pl. 51, f. 4, pl. 53, f. 6, 7.

Spots orbicular, about 10 mm. across, at first olivaceous, then greyish, with a narrow dark-purple border. Pycnidia few, epiphyllous, scattered, subglobose, somewhat depressed, black, 50–80μ diam. Spores cylindrical, slightly curved, indistinctly 2–4-septate, 30–40 × 2–3μ, issuing as a whitish tendril.

On living or fading leaves of *Cornus sanguinea.* Rather common; Kew; Highgate; Darenth; Dorset; etc.

Aug.–Oct.

Often accompanied by *Phyllosticta cornicola.*
Europe, U.S.A. Canada.

Corylus

Septoria Avellanae B. & Br. in Ann. Nat. Hist. 1876, xvii. 141. Cooke, in Grevill. v. 56. Sacc. Syll. iii. 503. All. vi. 766. Died. 447. Mig. 392.

Spots large, indistinct, brown, indeterminate or with a darker border. Pycnidia hypophyllous, 80–100μ diam., convex, black, growing mostly in large irregular groups. Spores filiform-fusoid, curved, 14–20 × 1·5μ (10μ long, B. & Br.).

On living or fading leaves of *Corylus Avellana.* Bathford (Broome). Clyde (Trail). Goosehill Woods (Rhodes). Randan Woods; Hanbury, Ws. (Fig. 25g.) Sept.–Nov.

It occurs as often on the green, as on the brown, parts of the fading leaves.
Germ. Austr. Ital.

Crepis

Septoria Crepidis Vestergr. Bidr. Känned. Gotl. Swampfl. p. 24, in K. Svensk. Vet. Akad. Handl. 1896, p. 24. Sacc. Syll. xiv. 974. All. vi. 767. Died. 448. Mig. 393. T.B.M.S. iv. 177.

Spots amphigenous, rather large, almost circular, irregularly confluent, dark-brown, becoming paler in the centre, with an indistinct border. Pycnidia numerous, mostly epiphyllous, slightly projecting, with a papillate ostiole which gradually opens in a wide pore. Spores filiform, straight or

curvulous, acute at both ends, usually with several guttules
or faint septa, 25–40 × 1–1·5μ.

On living or fading leaves of *Crepis paludosa*, Ayrshire
(Boyd). Probably also on leaves of *C. virens* (= *C. capillaris*)
and other species of the genus.

Germ. Swed.

Cytisus

Septoria Cytisi Desm. in Ann. Sci. Nat. 1847, viii. 24. Sacc. Syll.
iii. 485. All. vi. 770. Died. 449. Mig. 394. Grove, in Journ. Bot.
1885, p. 163.

Spots amphigenous, numerous, minute, angular or roundish, but becoming confluent and therefore tortuous or
irregular, when dry nearly white, with a brown border. Pycnidia epiphyllous, few (1–3) on each spot, about 125μ diam.;
brownish-black, opening by a pore. Spores filiform-clavate,
curved or flexuous, with many (up to 10) septa, 90–100 ×
2·5–3·5μ.

On living and fading leaves of *Cytisus Laburnum*, often on
the epidermis above places eaten out by a leaf-miner. Ayrshire (Boyd). Kew; Highgate; Hampton-in-Arden.

Aug. Sept.

Accompanied by *Phyllosticta Cytisi* and *Leptosphaeria Lucina*,
which are doubtless stages of the same species. It is possible that
Ascochyta Laburni Lib. and *Septoria Laburni* Pass. are also stages of
the same life-cycle.
Fr. Germ. Austr. Hung. Ital. Russia.

Dianthus

Septoria Dianthi Desm. in Ann. Sci. Nat. 1849, xi. 346. Sacc.
Syll. iii. 516. Grove, in Journ. Bot. 1884, p. 195; 1885, p. 163. All. vi.
772. Died. 450. Mig. 395. Journ. Roy. Micr. Soc. 1903, p. 337.
Journ. Roy. Hort. Soc. 1903, p. 428, f. 114–16. *Ascochyta Dianthi*
Berk. Outl. 320. *Ascochyta Cookei* Mass. in Kew Bull. 1907, p. 241.

Spots roundish or oval, about 5 mm. diam., ochraceous,
with a broad purple border. Pycnidia numerous, epiphyllous,
round, black, the epidermis forming a raised white dot in the
centre of each, at length broadly perforate, about 125μ diam.
Spores cylindrical, flexuous, slender, 30–40 × 3–4μ (1-septate,
Massee).

On leaves, etc., of *Dianthus barbatus*, *D. Caryophyllus*, and
other cultivated species of *Dianthus*. Reading; Sibbertoft;

Warwicks.; Worcs.; Hants.; Cheshire; Northumberland; Scotland; Ireland; etc. A common pest.   Jul.–Sept.

This is not the same as *S. Dianthi* Cooke, Exs. i, 429, and Grevill. v. 70; they are on *Saponaria*. It is certain that *A. Dianthi* Auct. is merely the early state of this species.

Europe, U.S.A., S. Africa, Australia, New Zealand.

Septoria Sinarum Speg. Nov. Add. p. 165. Sacc. Syll. iii. 517. All. vi. 773. Died. 451. Mig. 395.

Spots whitish, circular, rather large, often spread over nearly the whole leaf. Pycnidia amphigenous, gregarious, covering the whole spot, globose-lens-shaped, 80–110µ diam., pierced by a minute pore; texture parenchymatous, membranaceous, dark-olive. Spores acicular, straight or curvulous, somewhat tapering but rounded at both ends, with 1 or 2 septa, ± constricted at the septa, 20–25 × 2–2·5µ.

On living or fading leaves of *Dianthus barbatus*. Aberdeen (Trail). *n.v.*   July.

Germ. Ital.

Digitalis

Septoria Digitalis Pass. Fungh. Parm. Sept. no. 94. Sacc. Syll. iii. 534. All. vi. 774. Ellis, in T.B.M.S. iv. 125.

Spots fuscous, irregular, large, at length withered and dry. Pycnidia minute, scattered. Spores filiform, multiguttulate, 25–30 × 1·5µ (Sacc.).

On dying leaves of *Digitalis purpurea*. Cheshire (Ellis).

                                                          July.

"In my specimens the pycnidia are convex, black, shining and perforated by a minute pore, and each stands within a darker, circular, slightly elevated area of the general macula which occupies one-third of the leaf. The spores vary from elongated-cylindrical with rounded ends, straight or slightly curved, 15 × 4·5µ to filiform and flexuous, 28 × 1·5µ" (Ellis, *in litt.*). But in some of these specimens from Dr Ellis I could find only what looked like the spores of an Ascochyta, oblong, curvulous, 1-septate, 15–20 × 2·5–3µ, i.e. *A. Digitalis* Fckl. Symb. Myc. p. 388 (Sacc. Syll. iii. 403).

Ital.

Doronicum

Septoria Doronici Pass. Fungh. Parm. Sept. no. 75. Sacc. Syll. iii. 548. All. vi. 775.

Spots fuscous, effused, becoming larger by confluence, showing chiefly on the upper side. Pycnidia epiphyllous,

densely scattered, punctiform. Spores slender, straight,
eseptate, 18–20µ long.

On leaves of *Doronicum Pardalianches*. Kew Gardens. Aug.

Ital.

Epilobium

Septoria Epilobii Westd. in Bull. Acad. Brux. 1852, xix. 120.
Cooke, Handb. 448. Sacc. Syll. iii. 513. All. vi. 776. Died. 453. Mig.
396. G. Martin, in Journ. Mycol. iii. 81.

Spots small, irregular or angular, limited by the veins,
crowded or confluent, olivaceous, then pale in the centre.
Pycnidia amphigenous, minute, brown, pierced by a pore.
Spores filiform, straight or curved, multiguttulate or with a
few indistinct septa, about 50 × 1·5µ, issuing in white tendrils.

On living leaves of many species of *Epilobium*. Common;
England, Scotland, Ireland.   Jul. Aug.

There is the American species of the same name on *Epilobium
coloratum* with orbicular spots and faintly yellowish spores, 20–35 ×
1·25µ (see Journ. Mycol. *l.c.*). A Ramularia on *Epilobium* has sometimes been confused with the Septoria.

Europe, Siberia, U.S.A.

Eryngium

Septoria Eryngii Pass. Fungh. Parm. Sept. no. 57 (*non* Westd.).
Sacc. Syll. iii. 532.

Pycnidia scattered or aggregated, hypophyllous, Sphaeria-
like, carbonaceous, black. Spores very slender, straight or
curved, eseptate, 20–25 × 1–1·5µ.

On leaves of *Eryngium*. Near Liverpool (Cooke).

There can be no doubt that Cooke's fungus is the B-spores of
Phomopsis eryngiicola Trav. *S. Eryngii* Westd. is different, and is
probably a species of Phleospora. Cf. Sacc. Syll. x. 367.

Euonymus

Septoria Euonymi Rabenh. in Flora, 1848, p. 506. Sacc. Syll. iii.
482. All. vi. 781. Died. 455. Mig. 397. T.B.M.S. iv. 294.

Spots usually epiphyllous, rather broad, pale when dry,
scarcely margined. Pycnidia few, punctiform, lens-shaped,
pierced by a pore. Spores filiform, very slightly curved, with
few and indistinct septa, 20–25 × 1·5µ (20–40 × 2–3µ, with
sometimes as many as 5 septa, Ellis).

On leaves of *Euonymus japonicus.* Liverpool (Ellis). Kew Gardens (Cooke). Apr.

Often on the same spots was *Cytospora foliicola,* var. *Euonymi.*

"Pycnidia minute, rather convex, black, sparingly scattered over pale brownish-grey spots that usually occupy the apical half of both surfaces of the leaves" (Ellis).
Germ. Ital.

Fragaria
Septoria Fragariae Desm. in Ann. Sci. Nat. 1842, xvii. 111. Sacc. Syll. iii. 511. All. vi. 783. Died. 456. Mig. p. 398, pl. 55, f. 4–6. Massee, Dis. Cult. Pl. 424. Stevens, Pl. Dis. 519. *Ascochyta Fragariae* Lib.

Spots roundish or confluent, fuscous, with a brownish-red border. Pycnidia epiphyllous, very minute, immersed, but somewhat prominent, smoky-fuscous, opening by a wide round pore. Spores oblong or cylindrical, obtuse at both ends, 3-septate, 20–30 × 3–4μ, issuing in whitish tendrils.

On living or fading leaves of *Fragaria vesca,* also on the sepals and even on the fruit. England; common. Jul. Aug.

Distinguished from *Marssonina Fragariae* by the pycnidial wall.
Cf. also *Sept. Tormentillae.*
Europe, Siberia.

Fraxinus
Septoria Fraxini Desm. Exs. no. 1086. Cooke, Handb. 449. Sacc. Syll. iii. 495. All. vi. 784. Died. 457.

Spots roundish, brown. Pycnidia hypophyllous, numerous, aggregated, minute, semi-immersed, black. "Spores cylindrical, truncate at both ends, multiguttulate" (Sacc.).

On living leaflets of *Fraxinus excelsior.* Rather common England, Wales, Scotland. Spots usually few on each leaflet.

But the peridia seem never to contain spores, and the name probably designates nothing but an early state of a Mycosphaerella, the so-called spores being the beginnings of asci. *Septoria Fraxini* Fr. Elench. ii. 119 is a Cercospora = *C. Fraxini* Sacc.
Europe, U.S.A. (without spores).

Galeopsis
Septoria Galeopsidis Westd. in Bull. Acad. Roy. Belg. ser. II, vol. ii, no. 7. Sacc. Syll. iii. 539. All. vi. 785. Died. p. 458, p. 432, f. 3. Mig. 399. *S. cotylea* Pat. & Har. in Bull. Soc. Myc. Fr. 1905, p. 85.

"Spots hypophyllous, greenish or brown, irregular, angular, bounded by the veins. Pycnidia scattered, brown, puncti-

form, up to 80μ diam. Spores cylindrical, straight or flexuous, 30–40 × 1–1·5μ."

On leaves of *Galeopsis*. Abridge (Cooke). *n.v.*

The form, *S. cotylea*, is said to occur on the cotyledons, but does not seem to differ from the typical form. *Ascochyta Galeopsidis* can be found in company with the Septoria, on the same spots, abroad.

Europe, U.S.A. Canada.

Galium

Septoria Galiorum Ellis, in Bull. Torr. Bot. Club, 1882, p. 74. Sacc. Syll. iii. 543.

Pycnidia globose or ellipsoid, minute, punctiform, black, scattered, slightly prominent, seated on a thin mycelium of brown, creeping, jointed, torulose hyphae; texture parenchymatous, dark olivaceous-brown. Spores filiform, often somewhat curved, apparently continuous, 20–23 × 1–1·5μ; sporophores acicular-subulate, a little shorter than the spore.

On dead stems of *Galium Aparine*, *G. Mollugo*, Polperro, Cornwall (Rilstone). On *Rubia peregrina*, near the Lizard (Rhodes), f. *Rubiae* S. & S., in Sacc. Syll. xviii. 385 (spores faintly 3-septate). June.

In the same or similar pycnidia were found young asci (? of *Ophiobolus*).

Port. N. Amer.

Geranium

Septoria Geranii Rob. & Desm. in Ann. Sci. Nat. 1853, xx. 93. Sacc. Syll. iii. 514. All. vi. 788. Died. 459. Mig. 401.

Spots small, roundish, but confluent and irregular, olivaceous-brown, with a broad purple border. Pycnidia epiphyllous, rarely hypophyllous, immersed, very minute, pallid, pierced by a simple pore. Spores filiform, straight or slightly flexuous, indistinctly 3-septate, 35–52 × 1–1·5μ, issuing in yellow tendrils.

On leaves of *Geranium pyrenaicum, G. dissectum, G. lucidum*. Hackney; Chirk; Symond's Yat; Montgomeryshire, etc. May.

Fr. Germ. Ital. Spain (on *G. Robertianum*).

Geum

Septoria Gei Rob. & Desm. in Ann. Sci. Nat. 1843, xix. 343. Cooke, Handb. 450. Sacc. Syll. iii. 510. All. vi. 788. Died. 460. Mig. 401.

Spots orbicular or irregular, 4–5 mm. broad, brownish-ochraceous, then dry and cinereous in the centre, with a

purplish-brown border. Pycnidia epiphyllous, numerous, 80–100μ diam., brownish-black, hemispherical, then collapsed and concave. Spores filiform, acute at both ends, somewhat flexuous, clouded, continuous or guttulate, 30–50 × 1–1·5μ.

On living or fading leaves of *Geum urbanum*, *G. rivale*, *G. intermedium*. England, Scotland.   Autumn.

Cooke says that the pycnidia are sometimes arranged along the veins of the leaves.
Europe, U.S.A.

Hedera

Septoria Hederae Desm. in Ann. Sci. Nat. 1843, xix. 340. Cooke, Handb. 445. Sacc. Syll. iii. 490. All. vi. 790. Died. p. 469, p. 432, f. 19. Mig. 402. *Sept. insularis* B. & Br. in Ann. Nat. Hist. 1854, xiii. 460, pl. 15, f. 8. Cooke, Handb. 443. Sacc. Syll. iii. 491.

Spots roundish, 3–12 mm. wide, dry, brownish, at length whitish, with a broad brown border. Pycnidia epiphyllous, gregarious, about 100μ diam., globose, opaque, at length black, covered by the epidermis which is pierced by the ostiole, opening by a pore. Spores linear, straight or flexuous, indistinctly guttulate, 30–40 × 1–2μ.

On living leaves of *Hedera Helix*. England, Wales; very common everywhere.   Apr.–Nov.

Without microscopical examination this can hardly be distinguished with certainty from *Phyllosticta hedericola*, which is its forerunner. It is said to be the pycnidial stage of *Mycosphaerella hedericola* Lindau. *S. insularis* is a state in which the brown border is not so distinctly marked; the relation of *S. insularis* to *S. Hederae* is the same as that of *Phyllosticta Hederae* (spots uniform) to *Phyllo. hedericola* (spots bordered).
Europe generally.

Helleborus

Septoria Hellebori Sacc. Syll. iii. 524; xvi. 956 (*non* Thüm.). ? All. vii. 894. *Septoria helleborina* v. Höhn. in Ann. Mycol. 1905, iii. 333. *Rhabdospora helleborina* Sacc. Syll. iii. 588. All. vi. 907.

Spots greyish-ochraceous, bounded by the veins. Pycnidia very numerous, hypophyllous, densely aggregated, globose to lens-shaped, 70–100μ diam., opening by a wide pore, each usually situated under a stoma. Spores linear, straight or curved, guttulate, 18–22 × 1·5μ (Syll. xvi. 956).

On leaves of *Helleborus*. Doubtfully British, since the Kew

specimens, like Thümen's, under this name are *Coniothyrium Hellebori*.

It is by no means certain that all the three names given above refer to the same fungus. Cooke (Journ. Roy. Hort. Soc. 1902, p. 10, pl. 1, f. 2) describes a fungus as *Sept. Hellebori*, with spores 40–50μ long, but I have seen nothing corresponding to this description.
S. Europe.

Hepatica
Septoria Hepaticae Desm. in Ann. Sci. Nat. 1843, xix. 340. Sacc. Syll. iii. 522. All. vi. 792. Died. p. 470, p. 432, f. 4. Mig. 403.

Spots orbicular or confluent and irregular, blackish-brown, at length whitish, with a distinct dark border. Pycnidia epiphyllous, covered by the epidermis, 100–120μ diam., black, opening by a pore which is papillate and somewhat prominent. Spores filiform, straight or flexuous, guttulate, not distinctly septate, 25–30 × 0·7–1μ.

On leaves of *Hepatica triloba*. Forden (Vize).   April.

Spots large, roundish, dark in colour, concentrically zoned, becoming black.
Fr. Belg. Germ. Austr. Switz. Ital. Swed.

Hieracium
Septoria Mougeotii Sacc. & Roum. Rel. Lib. iv. no. 151. Sacc. Syll. iii. 553. All. vi. 793, with fig. Died. 470. Mig. p. 403, pl. 50, f. 5–7.

Spots large, yellowish, somewhat olivaceous in the centre. Pycnidia epiphyllous, numerous, covered, between punctiform and lens-shaped, 80–100μ diam., fuscous, piercing the epidermis with the pore. Spores filiform, without guttules, 20–40 × 1μ, or sometimes shorter.

On leaves of *Hieracium stoloniferum*. Kew Gardens (Cooke).

Forms of this with spores as short as 13–15μ have been recorded in Germany.
Fr. Germ.

Humulus
Septoria Humuli Westd. in Kickx, Flor. Crypt. Flandr. i. 433. Sacc. Syll. iii. 557. All. vi. 795. Died. 471. Mig. 404.

Spots small, irregular, smoky-pallid, indistinctly bordered. Pycnidia epiphyllous, scattered in the centre of the spots, lens-shaped, 50–100μ diam. Spores filiform, gently flexuous, rather obtuse at the ends, not guttulate, 25–35 × 1–1·5μ, sometimes showing a septum.

On fading leaves of *Humulus Lupulus*. Highgate; Dartford (Cooke).

Europe, Siberia.

Hydrangea

Septoria Hydrangeae Bizz. Fung. Ven. Nov. p. 6. Sacc. Syll. x. 349. All. vi. 795. Died. 471. Mig. 404.

Spots ferruginous-brown, with a blood-red border, irregular, at length confluent. Pycnidia immersed, of indistinct brown parenchymatous cells. Spores cylindric, straight or bent, hyaline, eseptate, $16-22 \times 1 \cdot 5 \mu$.

On leaves of *Hydrangea hortensis*, often causing great harm. Lincolnshire, 1929. *n.v.*

Germ. Ital.

Hydrocotyle

Septoria Hydrocotyles Desm. in Ann. Sci. Nat. 1842, xvii. 109. Sacc. Syll. iii. 531. Cooke, Handb. 447. All. vi. 795. Died. p. 471, p. 432, f. 21. Mig. 104.

Spots irregular or angular, sometimes bordered by the veins, rufous or brownish, then pallid. Pycnidia epiphyllous, blackish, very minute, immersed, $60-100\mu$ diam., pierced by a pore. Spores linear, curvulous, microguttulate, rarely with 3 indistinct septa, $16-25 \times 1-2\mu$, issuing in a whitish tendril.

On fading leaves of *Hydrocotyle vulgaris*. Epping; Irstead; Aboyne; Rannoch; Ayrshire, etc.   Aug.–Oct.

Fr. Belg. Holl. Germ. Denm. Austr. U.S.A.

Hypericum

Septoria Hyperici Rob. & Desm. in Ann. Sci. Nat. 1842, xvii. 110. Sacc. Syll. iii. 515. All. vi. 796. Died. 472. Mig. 405.

Spots round, oblong or indeterminate, reddish-brown, with a yellow border. Pycnidia chiefly epiphyllous, somewhat prominent, about 75μ diam., brown. Spores linear, straight or curvulous, minutely 8–16-guttulate, occasionally 3- or 4-septate, $30-50\mu$ long, issuing in yellowish or whitish tendrils.

On fading leaves of *Hypericum perforatum*, *H. quadrangulum*, *H. hirsutum*, *H. montanum*, *H. pulchrum*, *H. elodes*, etc. Lyndhurst; Norwich; Dinmore; Scotland generally.

Aug.–Oct.

The form on *H. elodes* differs slightly from the type.
Fr. Belg. Holl. Germ. Ital. Denm. Swed.

Jasione
Septoria Jasiones Died. 474. Grove, in Journ. Bot. 1922, p. 83,
pl. 563, f. 8. Mig. 405. *Phlyctaena Jasiones* Bres. in Hedwig. 1897,
p. 381. Sacc. Syll. xiv. 987. All. vi. 939.

Pycnidia hypophyllous, scattered or aggregated, subglobose or lens-shaped, blackish, 60–100μ diam.; texture
parenchymatous in the centre, paler and more prosenchymatous towards the margin, darkest round the ostiole. Spores
elongated, filiform, straight or more often arcuate, scarcely
guttulate, 20–35 × 1–1·25μ.

On living and dead leaves, stems, and involucral bracts of
Jasione montana. Stevenston and West Kilbride, Ayrshire
(Boyd).   Aug.

The pycnidium, in the Ayrshire specimens, is complete all round,
and exactly that of a typical Septoria, not of a Phlyctaena.
Germ. Spain.

Lamium
Septoria Lamii Sacc. Syll. iii. 538. All. vi. 800. Died. p. 476,
p. 432, f. 7. Mig. 406. Passer. in Thüm. Myc. Univ. no. 1183. *S.
lamiicola* Sacc. Syll. iii. 538. *S. heterochroa* Cooke, Handb. 445, *p.p.*

Spots small, roundish or irregular, often limited by the
veins, brown, at length whitish, with a rufous border. Pycnidia epiphyllous, few, punctiform, brown, 70–90μ diam.
Spores filiform, tortuous, hyaline, distinctly 3–5-septate, 40–
50 × 1–1·5μ.

On living leaves of *Lamium album*, *L. purpureum*. Swanscombe; Oundle; Forden; Glamis, etc.

This species differs from *S. heterochroa* in its longer and more distinctly septate spores. *S. Lamii* is the younger and *S. lamiicola* the
older state of the same fungus; *S. intermedia* Massal. is the intermediate state. Cf. *S. balloticola* All. vi. 739, which is *S. Lamii* var.
Ballotae Massal. (Sacc. Syll. xvi. 966), on *Ballota nigra*.
Fr. Ital.

Lavandula
Septoria Lavandulae Desm. in Ann. Sci. Nat. 1853, xx. 86.
Cooke, Handb. 451. Sacc. Syll. iii. 537. All. vi. 802. Died. 478. Mig.
408.

Spots amphigenous, numerous, rounded or irregular, dry,
bleached, with an elevated purplish border. Pycnidia usually
epiphyllous, few, globose, somewhat prominent, black, pierced

by a pore, collapsed and cup-shaped when dry, 50–75μ diam.
Spores linear, straight or curved, 20–35 × 1–2μ.

On fading leaves of *Lavandula*. Swanscombe; Hertfordshire; Yorkshire; Ayrshire; etc.; often with *Phoma Lavandulae*.
Jul.–Sept.

Fr. Belg. Germ. Denm. Swed. Ital. Madeira.

Leontodon
Septoria Leontodontis Sm. & Ramsb. in T.B.M.S. 1916, v. 246.

Spots amphigenous, whitish and dried, about 1 mm. wide,
roundish, with a thick rufous-brown border. Pycnidia scattered, globose, brown, about 80μ diam., pierced by a pore.
Spores needle-shaped, 1–several-septate, about 25 × 1μ.

On leaves of *Leontodon autumnalis*. Arran (Boyd). Aug.

Rhabdospora Leontodontis Henn. (Hedwig. 1904, p. 73) is probably
the same species, but grows on dried stalks of *Leontodon*, apparently
without forming spots, as indeed is usual in such cases.

Lepidium
Septoria Lepidii Desm. in Ann. Sci. Nat. 1842, xvii. 110. Cooke,
Handb. 442. Sacc. Syll. iii. 519. All. vi. 803. Died. 478. Mig. 408.

Spots none. Pycnidia amphigenous, but especially hypophyllous, scattered or approximate, immersed, but slightly
prominent, convex, black, at length pierced by a broad round
opening. Spores elongate, linear, flexuous, 50–60μ long,
issuing in white tendrils.

On living leaves of *Lepidium Smithii*. England, Wales,
Scotland, Ireland, but not common. Occurs abroad on other
species of *Lepidium*. Autumn.

"After the spores are discharged, the mouths of the pycnidia en-
large, and they collapse so as to have the appearance of a small black
Peziza" (Cooke).

Fr. Belg. Germ. Denm. Austr. Ital. Spain, Port. Siberia.

Ligustrum
Septoria Ligustri Kickx, Flor. Crypt. Flandr. i. 354. Sacc. Syll.
iii. 497. All. vi. 805. Died. 479. Mig. 409. *Depazea Ligustri* Desm.
Exs. no. 776.

Spots amphigenous, broad, irregular, pale-ochraceous, with
a rufous border. Pycnidia epiphyllous, scattered, numerous,
punctiform, globular. Spores cylindrical, curvulous or
flexuose, obtuse at both ends, guttulate, about 15 × 1μ.

On fading leaves of *Ligustrum vulgare*. Kew Gardens;
Highgate. Sept. Oct.

Spots very irregular with a purple-brown margin. Sometimes found
in company with *Phyllosticta Ligustri* (*q.v.*); both are probably pycnidial stages of *Mycosphaerella Ligustri* Fckl.
Fr. Belg. Germ. Austr.

Linnaea
Septoria Linnaeae Sacc. in Bull. Soc. Myc. Fr. 1889, v. 121; Syll.
x. 358. Lind, Dan. Fung. pl. 7, f. 81–2. All. vi. 806. Died. 480. Mig.
410. *Sphaeria* (*Depazea*) *Linnaeae* Ehrenb. in Klotzsch, Herb. Myc.
viv. no. 363. *Sept. borealis* Rostr. Ascom. Dovre, p. 12. Sacc. Syll.
xi. 544. All. vi. 807.

Spots one or two on each leaf, small, round, ochraceous,
with a scarcely distinct border. Pycnidia epiphyllous, rather
large, prominent, black, shining, opening by a large torn pore.
Spores very long, vermiform, multiguttulate, $30–40 \times 1\mu$ (50–
76μ, Lind; $40–50 \times 1–1\cdot5\mu$, with 6 or 7 septa, Died.).
On living leaves of *Linnaea borealis*. Aberdeen (Dickie).

The description is founded on these specimens; they are no doubt
rather undeveloped and have shorter spores than the Continental
forms. Briard and Hariot record (Journ. de Botan. 1891, p. 171) a
form with spores $40–70 \times 2–3\mu$.
Germ. Denm. Austr. Norw.

Lunaria
Septoria Lunariae Ellis & Dearn. in Canad. Record Sci. 1893, p.
269. J. W. Ellis, in T.B.M.S. 1912, iv. 126.

Spots cloudy, black and subopaque. Pycnidia scattered,
subglobose, black, shining, opening by a minute pore, 100–
150μ diam. Spores elongated, curvulous, subacute at both
ends, at first elliptical and pluriguttulate, then 1- or 2-septate,
finally cylindrical and 4- or 5-septate, hyaline or faintly
coloured, $25–30 \times 3\mu$.
On outer surface of silicules of *Lunaria biennis*. Cheshire
(Ellis). July.

It is curious that the same name was given, at nineteen years apart,
by each of the Ellises. "The pycnidia were not developed on the discoloured pods until after they had been kept for some weeks in a moist
condition" (J. W. Ellis).
N. America.

Lychnis

Septoria Lychnidis Desm. in Ann. Sci. Nat. 1849, xi. 347. Sacc. Syll. iii. 517. All. vi. 810. Died. 483. Mig. 411. *S. lychnidicola* Brun. Sphaerops. Char. 1889, p. 77. Sacc. Syll. xiv. 969.

Spots visible on both sides, roundish or irregular, reddish-brown, or pallid with a rufous border. Pycnidia mostly epi-phyllous, scattered, somewhat protruding, brown, opening with a wide pore, 70–80μ diam. Spores linear, straight or bent or curved, when young pluriguttulate or faintly 1-septate, then with more septa (2–7), 30–50 × 2–3μ (up to 70μ long, Died.).

On living leaves of *Lychnis dioica*. Cheshire (Ellis). Ayrshire (Boyd). Aberdeen and Dunottar (Trail, var. *pusilla*). Hopwood, Ws. On *L. chalcedonica*, Lostwithiel (Rhodes).

May–Sept.

A very variable species, according to age. Trail's variety *pusilla* (in Scot. Nat. 1887, p. 89. Sacc. Syll. x. 364) is the commonest form, which is 1·5–2μ wide, with 1–4 septa, and is called *Sept. pusilla* by Bubák (Beitr. Pilzfl. Ung. 1907, p. 35 extr.). Cf. *S. Jaapii* Bres. in Ann. Mycol. 1905, iii. 400, with spores 33–60 × 3–4μ, and sometimes two septa.

Fr. Holl. Germ. Ital. Latvia.

Lycopus

Septoria Lycopi Pass. in Hedwig. 1878, p. 60. Sacc. Syll. iii. 540. All. vi. 811. Died. 484. Mig. 411. *S. palustris* Sacc. Mich. ii. 103 (1880).

Spots irregularly scattered, amphigenous, angular, bordered by the nerves, dingy-fuscous. Pycnidia scattered, scarcely visible, 60μ diam., lens-shaped, pierced. Spores rod-shaped, curved, faintly or spuriously septate, about 50 × 2μ.

On leaves of *Lycopus europaeus*. Kew Gardens; Arran.

Aug. Sept.

Fr. Germ. Denm. Ital.

Lysimachia

Septoria Lysimachiae Westd. in Bull. Acad. Brux. 1852, iii. 120. Cooke, Handb. 450. Sacc. Syll. iii. 533. All. vi. 811. Died. 484. Mig. 411.

Spots roundish or indeterminate, brown, scattered over the whole leaf. Pycnidia epiphyllous, scattered, blackish, 100–120μ diam., pierced by a pore. Spores linear, straight or

gently curved, multiguttulate, then 2–3-septate, 60–75 ×
2·5–3µ (4–6-septate, 40–50 × 1·5µ, Sacc.).

On leaves of *Lysimachia nemorum, L. Nummularia, L.
thyrsiflora, L. vulgaris.* Darenth; Lyndhurst; Marston Green;
Scotland.   Aug.–Oct.

Saccardo records (Syll. xvi. 968) a form in Italy on *L. Nummularia,*
viz. f. *raphidospora* Tassi, with spores 20–22 × 0·33–0·5µ; no doubt
merely a young state.
Europe generally.

Lythrum

Septoria Brissaceana Sacc. & Let. in Mich. ii. 625 (1882). Sacc.
Syll. iii. 512. All. vi. 811. Sm. & Ramsb. in T.B.M.S. v. 246. Died.
484. Mig. 411.

Spots small, irregular, up to 1 cm. across, ochraceous, with
a darker or purplish border. Pycnidia epiphyllous, puncti
form, about 100µ diam., with a wide ostiole (25–40µ) which
is surrounded by dark-brown cells. Spores filiform, slightly
bent, narrowed at the ends, with a few guttules or obscurely
2-septate, 25–35 × 1–1·5µ.

On leaves of *Lythrum Salicaria.* Arran and Ayrshire (Boyd).
                                                      Jul.–Sept.
Fr. Germ. Denm. Thuringia.

Malva

Septoria heterochroa Desm. in Ann. Sci. Nat. 1847, viii. 22.
Cooke, Handb. 445. Sacc. Syll. iii. 538. All. vi. 813.

Spots amphigenous, scattered, minute, roundish, greyish-
brown, then whitish or becoming indistinct, often with a
brown border. Pycnidia few, epiphyllous or rarely hypophyllous, rather thin, tawny-brown, at length black, opening
by a pore, concave when dry. Spores linear, very slender,
straight or curved, 25–30µ long.

On leaves of *Malva silvestris.* Neatishead; Shere; Find-
haven.

This has shorter spores than *S. malvicola* Ell. & Mart., and differs
in other respects.
Fr. Belg. Holl. Ital. Denm. Switz. Canada.

Mentha

Septoria Menthae Oud. in Mat. Flor. Myc. Néerl. p. 4. Sacc.
Syll. iii. 538. All. vi. 815. Died. 486. Mig. 413. *Depazea Menthae*

Thüm. Fung. Austr. no. 1275. *Septoria menthicola* Sacc. & Let. Syll. iii. 539. All. vi. 815. T.B.M.S. 1909, iii. 118. Died. 487. Mig. 413.

Spots small, subrotund, visible on both sides, somewhat ochraceous with a purple-brown border. Pycnidia lens-shaped, punctiform, pierced at the summit. Spores filiform, bent or flexuous, eseptate, 30–45 × 1μ (epiphyllous; spores 3-septate, 35–48 × 1μ, Lind; indistinctly 3-septate, 45–60 × 1–2μ, Died.). On fading leaves of *Mentha arvensis*. Ayrshire (Boyd). Goosehill Woods, Ws. (Rhodes). Aug.

The spots on these specimens have a purple-brown border when dry; I think *menthicola* is merely a younger state of *Menthae*.
Fr. Holl. Germ. Denm. Austr. Ital. U.S.A. Canada.

Menyanthes
Septoria Menyanthis Desm. in Ann. Sci. Nat. 1853, xx. 89. Cooke, Handb. 447. Sacc. Syll. iii. 532. All. vi. 816. Died. 487. Mig. 414. *Ascochyta Menyanthis* Lasch.

Spots rufous-brown, irregular, not bordered. Pycnidia amphigenous, very minute, of the same colour, pierced by a pore. Spores elongated, linear, straight or curved, scarcely guttulate, 30–40 × 1·5μ, issuing in a white tendril.

On fading leaves of *Menyanthes trifoliata*. Bungay; Ayrshire; Lanarkshire; Aberdeen; Peterhead. Aug.–Sept.

Fr. Belg. Holl. Germ. Denm. Bohem. Austr. Siber. U.S.A.

Myrica
Septoria Myricae Trail, in Scot. Nat. 1888, iii. 229. Ellis & Ev. in Bull. Torr. Bot. Club, 1897, p. 290. Sacc. Syll. xiv. 977.

Spots ill-defined, greenish, becoming tinged with brown, 1–3 mm. across, visible on both sides of the leaf. Pycnidia few, difficult to distinguish, epiphyllous, immersed, brown, about 50–60μ broad. Spores filiform, obtuse at the ends, with 4–6 septa, 15–20 × 1·5–2μ.

On fading leaves of *Myrica Gale*. Near Aberdeen (Trail). Ayrshire; Arran (Boyd). Aug. Sept.

The American specimens were described and named without a knowledge of Trail's discovery; they had spores 8–10 × 1·25μ, but are probably only a younger state.
U.S.A.

Oenanthe
Septoria Oenanthes Ell. & Ev. in Proc. Acad. Nat. Sci. Philad. 1894, p. 367. Sacc. Syll. xi. 542.

Spots on the leaves scattered, irregular, 1–3 mm. wide, definite, subangular, whitish or ochraceous. Pycnidia few (3–6) on each spot on the leaves, crowded on silvery patches on the stems, small, black, almost mouthless, about 75µ diam. Spores fusoid-cylindrical, slightly curved, hyaline, guttulate, subacute at the ends, 20–35 × 1·5–2µ.

On fading leaves and stems of *Oenanthe crocata*. Isles of Cumbrae, Bute; Ardrossan and West Kilbride, Ayrshire (Boyd). Aug.

The form on the stems has spores up to 48µ long, but seems to be the same species.
Latvia, U.S.A.

Oenothera
Septoria Oenotherae Westd. in Bull. Acad. Roy. Belg. ser. 2, vol. ii, no. 7. Sacc. Syll. iii. 513. All. vi. 819. Died. 488. Mig. 415.

Spots epiphyllous, roundish, 2–3 mm. diam., at first greenish, then brown, with a vinous-red border. Pycnidia punctiform, aggregated in the centre of the spots, blackish-brown, 75–100µ diam. Spores filiform, curvulous, with several minute guttules or at length 3-septate, 30–55 × 1·5–2µ.

On leaves of *Oenothera* in gardens. Not common.

Europe, N. Amer. (incl. Canada).

Paeonia
Septoria Paeoniae Westd. in Bull. Acad. Roy. Belg. vol. 19, no. 9 (1852). Sacc. Syll. iii. 526. All. vi. 822. Died. 490. Mig. 417.

Var. **berolinensis** All. in Hedwigia, 1896, p. (34). Sacc. Syll. xiv. 967. T.B.M.S. iv. 177.

Spots scattered, rounded, then irregular, 2–8 mm. wide, ochraceous-brown, with concentric markings, becoming whitish in the centre, with a broad dark-purplish border. Pycnidia few, epiphyllous, gregarious, immersed, brown, piercing the epidermis only by the pore. Spores elongate-fusoid, lunate or curvulous, slightly pointed at both ends, with several indistinct guttules, 20–30 × 1·5–2µ.

On leaves of cultivated spp. of *Paeonia*. Wisley; Wisbech; Forden; Somerset; Swansea; Ayrshire.   May–Sept.

The early stage is *Phyllosticta Paeoniae* Vize. The variety seems to differ from the type only in having concentric foldings in the leaf-spot.

Fr. Belg. Holl. Germ. Denm. Canada.

Petroselinum
Septoria Petroselini Desm. Exs. no. 1174, and Mém. Soc. Sci. Lille, 1842. Kickx, Flor. Flandr. i. 424. Sacc. Syll. iii. 530. All. vi. 824. Died. 492. Mig. 418. *Phleospora Petroselini* Westd. *Ascochyta Petroselini* Lib.

Spots amphigenous, varying, brownish, then whitish, sometimes with a definite brown border. Pycnidia amphigenous, lens-shaped, about 100μ diam., membranaceous, pierced by a pore; texture thin, plectenchymatous, olivaceous. Spores filiform, straight or flexuous, with 6–10 guttules or faintly and indistinctly septate, 30–40 × 1–2μ.

On living or fading leaves and on seeds and stems of *Petroselinum sativum*. Surrey; Reading; Wallington; Worcs.; Staffs.; Shropshire; Warwick; Ayrshire; Glamis; Aberdeen; Ireland. See also *Rhabdospora nebulosa, infra,* p. 438. Jul. Aug.

Var. **Torilis** Trail, in Scot. Nat. 1890, x. 281.

On stems of *Torilis Anthriscus*. Near Inverurie.   Oct.

Europe, U.S.A., Canada, S. Amer.

Phlox
Septoria Phlogis Sacc. & Speg. in Mich. i. 184; Syll. iii. 533. All. vi. 826. Died. 493. Mig. 418.

Spots amphigenous, orbicular or angular, at first clear-brown, then whitish, often becoming confluent. Pycnidia epiphyllous, covered, clear-brown, not darker round the wide pore, 100–200μ diam. Spores filiform, mostly bent or flexuous, 1–3-septate, 40–60 × 1–2μ.

On leaves of *Phlox* (*alba, decussata, repens, virginica*). In gardens; doubtfully British, but see next species.
          Aug.–Oct.

Said to have an ascophorous stage *Leptosphaeria Phlogis* Bos. Germ. Holl.

Septoria divaricatae Ell. & Ev. in Journ. Mycol. 1889, v. 151.
S. Phlogis Ell. & Ev. *ibid.* 1887, iii. 85 (*non* Sacc. & Speg.). *S. Drummondi* Ell. & Ev. ?

Spots amphigenous, round, olivaceous below, whitish above, 1–3 mm. broad or becoming confluent and larger, with a purplish border. Pycnidia epiphyllous, rather numerous, immersed, then bursting the epidermis, subglobose, dull-black, 100–120μ diam. Spores filiform, nearly straight, hyaline, faintly guttulate, eseptate, 18–30 × 0·75–1μ, but variable in length, mostly 20–25μ, issuing in whitish tendrils.

On leaves of *Phlox* spp. cult. Wisley (Dowson). June.

Sept. Phlogis E. & F. is doubtless nothing more than an advanced state of this fungus. It is said to differ by having "white spots and flexuose, 1–3-septate spores, 40–60 × 1–2μ", but this difference is no greater than can often be found between mature and immature specimens on the same plant. Moreover, the British specimens on *Phlox Drummondi*, labelled "*Sept. Drummondi*" (*q.v.*), seem to me to belong also to the present species.
Germ. U.S.A.

Septoria Drummondi Ell. & Ev. in Journ. Mycol. vii. 133. Sacc. Syll. xi. 544. All. vi. 826. Died. 493. Mig. 418.

Spots amphigenous, at first olivaceous-green, then whitish or bright-ochraceous, variable in form, often confluent, and then occupying the greater part of the leaf. Pycnidia epiphyllous, densely gregarious, covered, clear-brown, not darker round the wide pore, 75–150μ diam. Spores acicular, straight or slightly bent, with a few indistinct guttules or septa, 35–50 × 1·5–2μ (25–50 × 1·5–2μ, Died.).

On fading leaves of *Phlox Drummondi*. Reading (Buddin). Also Buckinghamshire, Durham, Cumberland, etc.

The original species, in Canada, was described as having no definite "spots", but since it has been found in Germany in an earlier stage on the same host *with* spots the distinction seems to have disappeared.
Germ. Canada.

Pimpinella

Septoria aegopodina Sacc. Syll. iii. 529. All. vi. 723. Trail, in Scot. Nat. 1888, ix. 227.

Var. **Trailii** Grove.

Spots small, indeterminate in form, purple, becoming fuscous in the centre. Pycnidia immersed, 60–80μ diam.,

pale-brown, with a rather wide pore. Spores very slender, filiform, straight or curved, not septate, $20–25 \times 0.8–1.2\mu$.
On leaves of *Pimpinella Saxifraga*. Near Aberdeen.

"A variety or new species" (Trail). This does not seem to differ much from *S. inconspicua* Massal. (Sacc. Syll. xvi. 964) on *P. magna*, which, however, must have a new name, being antedated by *S. inconspicua* B. & C. (Sacc. Syll. iii. 554).
Ital.

Pinus

Septoria acuum Oud. in Nederl. Kruid. Arch. 1885, iv. 234. Sacc. Syll. x. 360. All. vi. 829. Smith & Ramsb. in T.B.M.S. v. 245.

Pycnidia on both surfaces of the leaf, punctiform, immersed under the epidermis, convex, about $230–270 \times 150–200\mu$. Spores abundant, cylindrical, simple, $16–18 \times 2–2.5\mu$; sporophores about $8 \times 3\mu$.
On leaves of *Pinus silvestris*. Swansea. Sept.

This species seems to me to be merely a leaf-form of *Fusicoccum bacillare*, viz. f. *acuum* Fautr. (in Rev. Mycol. 1892, xiv. 9); see p. 250. Holl. Denm.

Pisum

Septoria Pisi Westd. in Bull. Acad. Roy. Belg. ser. II, vol. xii, no. 7. Sacc. Syll. iii. 509. Died. 494. Mig. 420.

Spots amphigenous, broad, irregular, elongated and limited by the veins of the leaves, whitish or pallid-brownish. Pycnidia brownish-yellow, then black, scattered. Spores cylindrical, straight, $30–40 \times 3–3.5\mu$, issuing as yellowish tendrils.
On fading leaves of *Pisum sativum*. No certain British locality known.

Belg. Germ.

Plantago

Septoria Plantaginis Sacc. Syll. iii. 554. All. vi. 831. Died. 495. Mig. 421. Ellis, in T.B.M.S. iv. 126. ?*Ascochyta Plantaginis* Ces.

Spots grey, at first round, with a distinct margin. Pycnidia minute, covered by the epidermis which is slightly raised over each and finally pierced by a small pore, from which the spores protrude as a grey tuft. Spores filiform, curvulous, continuous or with faint and distinct septa, $30–60 \times 2.5–3.5\mu$.
On fading leaves of *Plantago lanceolata*. "Not uncommon

in the Wirral district of Cheshire during the summer of 1911" (J. W. Ellis). Glamis and Fern, Scotland, in Herb. Kew.

All the specimens I have examined under this name seem to me to be *Ramularia plantaginea* Sacc. & Berl. Germ. Ital.

Septoria plantaginea Pass. Fungh. Parm. Sept. no. 105. Sacc. Syll. iii. 554. All. vi. 831. Died. 495. Mig. 420.

Spots visible on both sides, round, greyish-brown, with a darker border, often confluent and occupying the whole leaf. Pycnidia epiphyllous, covered, then erumpent by the broad ostiole, up to 150μ diam. Spores filiform-clavate, straight or faintly arcuate, 3–4-septate, 45–55×2–3μ (5-septate, 75–100 × 5μ, Lind).

On dying leaves of *Plantago lanceolata*. Near Aberdeen (Trail). Ayrshire (Boyd). Oct.

A variety with shorter spores is recorded in Italy and Canada on *Plantago major*. Holl. Germ. Denm. Ital.

Polygonum

Septoria Polygonorum Desm. in Ann. Sci. Nat. 1842, xvii. 108. Cooke, Handb. 444. Sacc. Syll. iii. 555. All. vi. 833. Died. 496. Mig. 422. *S. polygonicola* Sacc. in Bull. Soc. Myc. Fr. v. 121; Syll. x. 380.

Spots numerous, roundish, tawny with a broad purplish border, 2–6 mm. diam. Pycnidia epiphyllous, immersed, pale-brown, pierced by a broad pore, at length concave, 100–150μ wide; texture thin, subtranslucent. Spores filiform, gently flexuous, often with four or five minute guttules, 25–50 × 1–$1\cdot5\mu$. (Fig. 25 d.)

On living leaves of *Polygonum Bistorta*, *P. Convolvulus*, *P. Hydropiper*, etc., and especially of *P. Persicaria*. Common: England, Wales, Scotland, Ireland. Jul.–Oct.

On *P. Persicaria* the spores are often up to 70μ long, and become very indistinctly septate = var. *Persicariae* Trail (in Scot. Nat. 1889, x. 73). *Sept. polygonicola* seems to me merely a state in which the purplish border of the spots is less marked; it is common in Cornwall on *P. lapathifolium*, but many intermediate states can be seen there. Europe, Siberia, U.S.A. Canada.

Populus

Septoria Populi Desm. in Ann. Sci. Nat. 1843, xix. 345. Cooke, Handb. 445. Sacc. Syll. iii. 502. All. vi. 834. Died. p. 497, p. 432, f. 10. Mig. 422.

Spots orbicular, 1–2 mm. diam., scattered or confluent, dry whitish in the centre, greyish towards the margin, with a fuscous border. Pycnidia epiphyllous or amphigenous, few, when moist convex, pallid, when dry rather concave, blackish, opening by a wide round pore, about 225μ diam. Spores vermiform, obtuse at both ends, curved, 1-septate, $30–45 \times 3–3\cdot5\mu$.

On leaves of *Populus* (especially *P. nigra*, *P. serotina*). Swanscombe; Kew; Highgate; etc.

Probably not uncommon. The pycnidial stage of *Mycosphaerella Populi* Schröt.
Europe generally.

Potentilla
Septoria Tormentillae Rob. & Desm. in Ann. Sci. Nat. 1847, viii. 22. Sacc. Syll. iii. 511. All. vi. 868. Died. p. 498, p. 432, f. 20.

Spots irregular, usually oblong, 1–4 mm. long, dingy or ochraceous-whitish, with a rosy border which is at length very indistinct. Pycnidia numerous on each spot, lens-shaped, dark-brown, $50–110\mu$ diam. Spores filiform, curved or flexuous, faintly yellowish, sometimes (not often) with 7–8 septa, $40–55 \times 1–1\cdot5\mu$.

On leaves and stipules of *Potentilla Tormentilla* (*P. erecta*) and its var. *procumbens*. Highgate (Cooke). Scotland (Trail). Ayrshire; Buteshire (Boyd). Earlswood, Wk.   Jul.–Sept.

Western Europe.

Primula
Septoria Primulae Bucknall, in Grevill. xiv. 40. Sacc. Syll. x. 376. All. vi. 836.

"Spots scattered, orbicular, pallid, with a brown margin. Pycnidia epiphyllous, few, punctiform, semi-immersed, seated in the centre of the spots, black. Spores linear, straight, 47μ long."

On leaves of *Primula vulgaris*, Leigh Woods, near Bristol (Bucknall). On *P. polyanthus*, *P. veris*; Malvern; Wyre Forest; Somerset; Cheshire; etc.   Aug. Sept.

I have never seen a Septoria answering to this description, and believe that all those so called are nothing but *Ramularia Primulae* Thüm. misunderstood. See Journ. Bot. 1912, pp. 14, 15.

Prunella

Septoria Prunellae (as "Brunellae") Ell. & Harkn. in Journ.
Mycol. 1885, i. 6. Sacc. Addit. p. 346; Syll. x. 376. *S. Prunellae* Trail,
in Scot. Nat. 1887, pp. 89, 228. *S. Trailiana* Sacc. Syll. x. 375. All. vi.
744. Died. p. 434, p. 432, f. 15. Mig. 383.

Spots irregular, brown, bordered by the larger veins of the
leaf. Pycnidia numerous, immersed, 80–100μ diam. Spores
filiform, multiseptate, nearly hyaline, 40–70 × 1–1·5μ.

On living leaves of *Prunella vulgaris*. Dinnet, near Ballater,
and other places in Scotland (Trail). Ayrshire (Boyd).

Aug.–Oct.

There can be no doubt that *S. Prunellae* of Trail is the same as
S. Brunellae of Ellis and Harkness, and therefore Saccardo's name for
it, *S. Trailiana*, is superfluous. Diedicke says that the spores have
several septa.

Germ. Swed. Ital. U.S.A.

Prunus

Septoria staganosporoides Massal. Nuov. Contr. Mic. Veron. in
Malpigh. 1894, viii. 200.

Spots almost none. Pycnidia hypophyllous, densely scattered, lens-shaped, black, 140–200μ diam. Spores guttulate,
greenish-yellow, 15–20μ long.

On fallen leaves of *Prunus Laurocerasus*. Torquay (Gepp.).
n.ex.   July.

Pyrus

Septoria pyricola Desm. in Ann. Sci. Nat. 1850, xiv. 114. Cooke,
Handb. 446. Sacc. Syll. iii. 487. All. vi. 829. Died. p. 493, p. 432, f. 9.
Mig. p. 420, pl. 55, f. 1–3. Duggar, p. 358, f. 176–9. *Depazea pyrina*
Fr. *Septoria Pyri* Westd. in Bull. Acad. Roy. Belg. xviii. 15. *Septoria
nigerrima* Fckl. Symb. Myc. 104. Sacc. Syll. iii. 487. All. vi. 829.

Spots small, scattered or somewhat crowded, roundish,
subangular or irregular, dry, greyish-white, shining, with a
narrow brown border. Pycnidia epiphyllous, few, minute,
thin-walled, rather prominent, black, pierced by a pore.
Spores elongate-filiform, curvulous, multiguttulate, often 2-
septate, pale-olivaceous, 48–60 × 3–4μ, issuing in olivaceous
viscid tendrils.

On leaves of *Pyrus communis* (not on the fruit). In several
English counties, but does little harm here.   Jul.–Oct.

The pycnidial stage of *Mycosphaerella sentina* Schröt.
For the life-cycle see Klebahn in Zeitschr. f. Pflanzenkr. 1908, xviii.

5–17. The ascophores appear on the fallen leaves during the winter. In my Hereford specimens the spores are obtuse at the apex, attenuated at the base.
Europe, U.S.A.

Septoria Ralfsii B. & Br. in Ann. Nat. Hist. 1854, xiii. 459, pl. 15, f. 6. Cooke, Handb. 443. Sacc. Syll. iii. 558.

Pycnidia subepidermal, elevating the surface into a pustule, the centre of the pustule white. Spores oblong, straight, with about 6 guttules, 30μ long.

On decayed fruits of *Pyrus Malus*. Penzance (Ralfs.).

The only British specimen is in Herb. Kew. "Forming black irregular patches, dotted with minute pustules, the centre of which is white" (B. & Br.).
Holl.

Quercus

Septoria quercicola Sacc. Syll. iii. 505. All. vi. 840. See Roum. in Rev. Myc. 1891, p. 80. *S. dubia* Sacc. & Syd. Syll. xiv. 978. All. vi. 841. Died. 499. Mig. 425. *S. quercina* Fautr. in Rev. Myc. 1895, p. 170.

Spots amphigenous, variable, 1–2 mm. broad, reddish-brown, paler when dry. Pycnidia hypophyllous, brown, 100–125μ diam. Spores cylindrical, curvulous, rounded at both ends, guttulate, at length 3-septate, not constricted, 25–30 × 3–4μ (40–50μ long, Died.).

On leaves of *Quercus pedunculata*. Darenth (Cooke).

The spots are small and scattered, becoming dry and pallid, but without any definite border. Probably the pycnidial stage of a Mycosphaerella, being allied to *S. castaneicola* Desm. which has very similar spores.
Fr. Germ. Holl. Ital. Port. U.S.A.

Septoria quercina Desm. in Ann. Sci. Nat. 1847, viii. 25. Cooke, Handb. 912. Sacc. Syll. iii. 504. All. vi. 840. Died. 500. Mig. 425.

Spots amphigenous, minute, few, rounded, whitish, dry, with a broad brown border. Pycnidia 1–3 on each spot, very minute, immersed, but subprominent, black, pierced by a pore. Spores elongated, filiform, curvulous, pluriguttulate, 40 × 1·5–2μ.

On fallen leaves of *Quercus pedunculata*. Kew (Cooke).

The spots in Cooke's specimens are only about 1 mm. in diameter, scattered, round or angular, bleached-white, with a much thickened

purplish-brown border; one, rarely two pycnidia, on each spot, visible on both sides of the leaf. He regarded it as a pycnidial stage of *Mycosphaerella maculiformis*, but this is improbable.

Fr. Belg. Holl. Germ. Denm. Austr. Ital.

Ranunculus

Septoria Ranunculacearum Lév. in Demid. Voy. p. 114, pl. 5, f. 4. Sacc. Syll. iii. 523. All. vi. 841. Died. 500. Mig. 425. *Septoriella* All. vi. 949.

Spots brown. Pycnidia usually epiphyllous, punctiform, brownish-black, irregular. Spores filiform, straight or curvulous, acute at both ends, pluriguttulate or pluriseptate, 50–70 × 3–4μ.

On leaves of *Ranunculus repens*. Ayrshire (Boyd). Bidston, Cheshire (Ellis). Aug.

A doubtful Septoria. Diedicke says that it belongs rather to Cytosporina; it might possibly find a better place in Septoriella. In Dr Ellis's specimens the spores are septate, and occasionally measure 40 × 5μ. The width 1·5μ, given by Saccardo, is probably an error in transcription.

Fr. Ital. Siberia, Crimea.

Septoria polaris Karst. in Hedwig. 1884, p. 38. Sacc. Syll. iii. 523.

Var. **scotica** Grove, in Journ. Bot. 1922, p. 83, pl. 563, f. 7.

Spots indistinct, brownish-black or fuliginous, without any distinct border. Pycnidia here and there densely aggregated, mostly epiphyllous, immersed, then emergent, globose-conical, black, up to 100μ diam., at length pierced by a pore; texture very thin, pale-brown, of loose parenchymatous cells. Spores linear-fusoid, tapering at both ends, straight or somewhat curved, furnished with a row of guttules, 33–35 × 1·5μ. (Fig. 25 b.)

On fading leaves of *Ranunculus Flammula*. Kilwinning, Ayrshire (Boyd). July.

The spores of Karsten's species, on *R. lapponicus*, measured 16–20 × 2–3μ.

Septoria Ficariae Desm. Exs. no. 1087; and in Ann. Sci. Nat. 1841, xv. 135. Cooke, Handb. 447. Sacc. Syll. iii. 522. All. vi. 782. Died. 456. Mig. 425.

Spots small, roundish or confluent, pallid, then cinereous in the centre, with an irregular brownish border. Pycnidia

epiphyllous or amphigenous, immersed, lens-shaped, 70–80μ diam., black, somewhat shining, pierced by a pore; texture parenchymatous, ochraceous-brown. Spores filiform, straight or curvulous, without guttules, 25–35 × 1–1·5μ.

On fading leaves of *Ranunculus Ficaria*. Common: England, Scotland.   May–July.

Trail records (Scot. Nat. 1885, p. 187) a form of this on *R. Flammula*, on the links near Aberdeen, having larger pycnidia (110–120μ diam.) and longer spores (35–45μ), but otherwise alike. Cf. *S. polaris*, var. *scotica*.

Europe.

Rhododendron

Septoria Rhododendri Cooke, North American Fungi, in Grevill. v. 151. Sacc. Syll. iii. 494.

Spots orbicular or various, pallid, with a dark-purple margin. Pycnidia epiphyllous, punctiform, aggregated or circinate. Spores filiform, 30–40 × 0·8μ, curved or hooked.

On leaves of *Rhododendron ponticum*. Looe, Cornw. (Rilstone).   May.

The spots become confluent, and occupy a large area of the leaf which is thereby killed. The Septoria is accompanied by an immature ascomycete. Is it the B-spores of a Phomopsis?

Maine (U.S.A.).

Ribes

Septoria Ribis Desm. in Ann. Sci. Nat. 1842, xvii. 111. Cooke, Handb. 450. Sacc. Syll. iii. 491. All. vi. 845. Died. 502. Mig. 426. Duggar, Fung. Dis. Pl. p. 363, f. 181. Stevens, Pl. Dis. 519. Lind, Dan. Fung. pl. 4, f. 51, 53. *Ascochyta Ribis* Lib. Exs. no. 53. *Phlaeospora Ribis* Westd. in Bull. Acad. Roy. Belg. 1850, xii. no. 9 (1845).

Spots numerous, 1–4 mm. diam., irregular and angular, often bounded by the veins, purplish-brown, paler in the centre. Pycnidia hypophyllous or a few epiphyllous, immersed, very small, convex, blackish-brown, at length pierced by a wide apical pore. Spores elongate-linear, curved, multi-guttulate, 40–50 × 1·5–2μ, issuing in rose-coloured tendrils, finally 3–4-septate.

On fading leaves of *Ribes nigrum*, *R. rubrum*, and other species of *Ribes*. Rather common, but not doing much injury. England, Scotland.   Jul.–Oct.

The pycnidium of *Mycosphaerella Ribis* Feltg. *Phyllosticta Grossulariae* is placed, with hesitation, by Klebahn in the same life-cycle;

see his Haupt- und Nebenfruchtformen der Askomyzeten (1918), p. 66. Cf. also *Sept. Grossulariae*. The "spots" of the Septoria can be easily distinguished from those of *Gloeosporium Ribis* by their paler centre and their well-defined outline; the two fungi often occur together on the same leaf.

Europe, U.S.A., Canada.

Septoria Grossulariae Westd. Crypt. Belg. no. 944. Sacc. Syll. iii. 491. All. vi. 845. Died. 501. Mig. 426. *Ascochyta Grossulariae* Lib. Exs. no. 250.

Spots 1–4 mm. diam., at first brown, then whitish, dry in the centre, with a fuscous border. Pycnidia few, epiphyllous, scattered, immersed, subglobose, about 150μ diam., black, pierced by a wide pore. Spores linear, curvulous, with six or seven minute guttules, $12–16 \times 1–1·5\mu$, issuing in a whitish tendril.

On living leaves of *Ribes alpinum*. Aberdeen (Trail), but not quite typical. Kickx describes the spores as having 10–12 guttules.

It usually occurs on *Ribes Grossularia*. Sometimes there is only one pycnidium on a spot. It is questionable whether *Sept. Grossulariae* is really distinct from *Sept. Ribis*.

Belg. Holl. Germ. Austr. Ital. U.S.A.

Rosa

Septoria Rosae Desm. Exs. no. 535. Sacc. Syll. iii. 485. All. vi. 846. Died. 502. Mig. 427. *S. Rosarum* Westd. in Bull. Acad. Brux. 1851, p. 396. Sacc. Syll. iii. 486. Cooke, Handb. 448. All. vi. 846. *S. Rosae-arvensis* Sacc. Syll. iii. 486. See Trail, in Scot. Nat. 1888, p. 224.

Spots small, roundish, scattered, at first fuscous, then pallid or grey, with a reddish or purplish border. Pycnidia epiphyllous, sometimes rather few, semi-emergent, black, about 100μ diam. Spores cylindrical, flexuous, obtuse at one or both ends, 25–55 (or more) $\times 2·5–3\mu$, 3–6-guttulate, and at length 4–5-septate $(70–90 \times 3·5–4\mu$, Sacc.; $45–75 \times 2·5–3\mu$, 3–7-septate, Trail).

On living leaves of wild and cultivated Roses. England, Wales, Scotland; occasionally met with.   Jun.–Nov.

Said to be the pycnidial stage of *Sphaerulina Rehmiana*, which has not yet been recorded for Britain. Trail says the spores "are effused as a white crust on the leaf".

Europe, N. Africa.

Rubus

Septoria Rubi Westd. Exs. no. 938. Sacc. Syll. iii. 486. All. vi.
847. Died. p. 503, p. 432, f. 11. Mig. 427. Duggar, Fung. Dis.
Pl. 363. *Rhabdospora Rubi* Ellis, in Journ. Mycol. 1887, p. 90. Sacc.
Syll. x. 388.

Spots amphigenous, numerous, angular or roundish, 1–
3 mm. diam., rufous-brown or pale ochraceous, then whitish
in the centre, bordered by a purple zone. Pycnidia epiphyllous, few or only one in the centre of each spot, somewhat
flattened, brownish-black, 80–100μ diam., opening by a wide
pore. Spores filiform, curvulous, indistinctly guttulate or
with 1, 2, 3 or more very faint or even distinct septa, 35–60 ×
1·5–2μ (20–25μ, Ellis).

On living or fading (especially over-wintering) leaves and
stems of *Rubus fruticosus*, *R. idaeus*, etc. Very common everywhere.

This is one of the most widely distributed species, like *S. scabiosicola*
and *S. Polygonorum*. Possibly belongs to *Mycosphaerella Ligea*.
Europe, U.S.A., Canada.

Rumex

Septoria Acetosae Oud. Contr. Flor. Myc. Pays-Bas, 1894, xv. 16.
Sacc. Syll. xi. 545. All. vi. 848. Died. 504. Mig. 427. T.B.M.S. iv. 176.

Spots rose-coloured, up to 1 cm. broad, often with a purplish margin. Pycnidia numerous, crowded, blackish, up to
1 mm. broad, emerging on both sides of the leaf, but especially on the upper side. Spores subcylindrical, curved or bent,
1–3-septate, 32–43 × 3–3·5μ (40–50 × 3–4·5 or even 5μ), emerging as long curving whitish tendrils.

On living leaves of *Rumex Acetosa*. Rothesay, Bute; Perthshire; Dumfriesshire, etc. (Boyd).   Jul.–Sept.

Said to be distinguished from the Siberian *S. Rumicum* Sacc. &
Paol. (1889) by its usually epiphyllous pycnidia and its shorter and
broader spores, and from *S. Rumicis* Trail, Fung. Hardanger (1889) by
its longer and broader spores. Spores of the former 50–68 × 3μ, of the
latter 24–32 × 2·5μ (Sacc. Syll. x. 380). *Phyllosticta Acetosae* can occur
on the same leaf; probably all are stages or forms of a single species.
Holl.

Salix

Septoria salicicola Sacc. Syll. iii. 502. All. vi. 849. Died. 505.
Mig. p. 427, pl. 53, f. 1–5. *Depazea salicicola* Fr. Syst. Myc. ii. 530.

Sept. Capreae Westd. in Bull. Acad. Roy. Belg. ser. ii, vol. xi, no. 6.
Sacc. Syll. iii. 501. All. vi. 849.

Spots epiphyllous, angular or roundish, scarcely 1 mm.
diam., shining ivory-white, with a red-brown or fuscous border. Pycnidia epiphyllous, scattered, punctiform, convex,
black, shining, piercing the epidermis by the ostiole, about
100μ diam. Spores cylindrical, curvulous, faintly 2–4-septate,
20–50 × 2·5–3·5μ.

On leaves of *Salix*. Audley End (Cooke); Aberdeen (Trail);
etc.   Autumn.

On the same host are found *Rhabdospora salicella* Sacc. (*q.v.*), and,
on the Continent, *S. Salicis* Westd. (spores not septate, 22–25 × 1·7μ)
and *S. didyma* Fckl. (spots fuscous; spores vermiform, 1-septate, 30–
40 × 2·5–3μ). *S. salicina* Peck has small dark-coloured spots.
Europe, Siberia.

Saponaria
Septoria Saponariae Savi & Bccc. Erb. Critt. Ital. no. 882. Sacc.
Syll. iii. 516. All. vi. 850. Died. 507. Mig. 428. *Depazea Saponariae*
DC. Flor. fr. vi. 147.

Spots round or irregular, ochraceous, without a distinct
border. Pycnidia chiefly epiphyllous, very numerous, fuscous,
globose-depressed, about 120μ diam. Spores cylindrical, curvulous, obtuse at both ends, 4–5-guttulate or 1–3-septate, 40–
50 × 3·5–4·5μ, occasionally shorter.

On leaves of *Saponaria officinalis*. Eastbourne (Muller);
Leatherhead. Also reported on *Silene inflata*.

This species is closely allied to *S. Dianthi*, and was considered by
Desmazières (Ann. Sci. Nat. 1849, xi. 346) to be merely a variety of it.
Europe generally.

Scabiosa
Septoria scabiosicola Desm. in Ann. Sci. Nat. 1853, xx. 96.
Cooke, Handb. 449. Sacc. Syll. iii. 553. All. vi. 851. Died. p. 475,
p. 432, f. 12. Mig. 406. *Ascochyta Scabiosae* Rab. Herb. Mycol. no.
1253.

Spots orbicular, purple, with a pallid surrounding zone, at
length dry and whitish in the centre. Pycnidia 1–3 in each
central white spot, minute, black. Spores filiform, nearly
straight, with 5 or 6 guttules or a few indistinct septa, 40–
60 × 1–2μ. (Figs. 25c, 26.)

On leaves of *Scabiosa succisa* and *Knautia arvensis*. Very common; England, Wales, Scotland, Ireland.   Autumn.

A variety of this has been found on *Cephalaria* in Germany. In the young state, this species, on the first-mentioned host, has sometimes been mistaken for *S. succisicola*. It is recorded abroad on *Scabiosa columbaria*. When perfect, the spots show three zones of colour. Europe, Siberia, Africa.

Septoria succisicola Sacc. Syll. iii. 553. All. vi. 866.

Spots indistinct or absent. Pycnidia clustered in little groups 2–3 mm. wide, amphigenous, punctiform, black, up to 80μ diam. Spores acicular-filiform, straight or rarely bent, sometimes minutely guttulate, 15–20 × 0·5μ.

Fig. 26. Leaf of *Scabiosa succisa*, with a number of "spots" caused by *Septoria scabiosicola*; reduced.

On dead leaves of *Scabiosa succisa* (*Succisa pratensis*). West Kilbride, Ayrshire (Boyd).   Aug.

"As wide as the heavens" (as Saccardo puts it) apart from that form of *Septoria scabiosicola* which occurs on *Succisa*. It looks much like a Mycosphaerella at first sight.
    Ital.

Scleranthus
Septoria Scleranthi Desm. in Bull. Soc. Bot. Fr. 1857, iv. 861. Cooke, Handb. 449. Sacc. Syll. iii. 518. All. vi. 852. Died. 507. Mig. 429.

Spots scarcely visible. Pycnidia densely scattered, half-immersed, convex, black, somewhat shining, with a minute conical ostiole, 80–100μ diam. Spores linear, tending to be arcuate, tapering but obtuse at the ends, indistinctly guttulate, 30–40 × 2·5–3μ.

On calyces, leaves, and stems of living or dead *Scleranthus annuus*. Bungay (Stock).   Jun.–Sept.

Found in Germany also on *Scler. perennis*.
Fr. Holl. Germ. Denm. Swed. U.S.A.

Scutellaria
Septoria Scutellariae Thüm. Pilzfl. Sibir. nos. 630, 631. Sacc. Syll. iii. 539. T.B.M.S. v. 159. Died. 508. Mig. 429.

Spots on both sides of the leaf, small, round or sinuous, brown, soon withering and becoming whitish, surrounded by

a well-marked dark reddish-brown border. Pycnidia epiphyllous, covered, light-brown, 100–150μ diam., piercing the
epidermis only by the pore, which is 25μ wide and scarcely
darker coloured. Spores filiform, usually bent or flexuose,
subacute at the ends, occasionally with 3 indistinct septa,
45–60 × 1–1·5μ.

On leaves of *Scutellaria galericulata.* Argyllshire (Boyd).
Cleeve Prior; Cornwall (Rhodes). Aug.

In the original the spores were 1–2-septate, 40–46 × 2μ; the spots
soon dropping out of the leaf; the pycnidia subgregarious.
Germ. Siber. Canada.

Sedum

Septoria Sedi Westd. Exs. no. 943. Cooke, Handb. 448; and in
Seem. Journ. Bot. iv. 112, pl. 45, f. 29. Sacc. Syll. iii. 527. All. vi.
854. Died. 508. Mig. 430.

Spots visible on both sides of the leaf, about 1 cm. diam.,
circular, grey, then greyish-brown. Pycnidia epiphyllous or
amphigenous, numerous, about 120–150μ diam., scattered,
erumpent, dark-brown, pierced by a pore. Spores linear,
cylindrical, usually straight or slightly curved, with none or
several guttules, 20–32 × 1μ, issuing in white tendrils.

On leaves of *Sedum Telephium,* and (?) stems of *S. reflexum.*
Bungay; near Aberdeen. Sept.

Fr. Belg. Germ. Denm.

Senecio

Septoria Senecionis-silvatici Syd. in Hedwig. 1899, xxxviii.
(139). Sacc. Syll. xvi. 964. T.B.M.S. 1915, v. 160. All. vi. 854. Died.
509. Mig. 430.

Spots amphigenous, roundish-oblong, pale-brownish, without a distinct border. Pycnidia numerous, epiphyllous, immersed, subglobose, pale-brown, 70–90μ diam., perforating
the epidermis only by the pore, which is of the same colour
and 20–25μ wide. Spores filiform, somewhat narrowed at both
ends, straight or flexuous, with a few indistinct septa, 30–50 ×
1·5μ, issuing as tendrils.

On leaves of *Senecio aquaticus, S. Jacobaea.* Ayrshire
(Boyd). Jul.–Oct.

The original German specimens were on *Sen. silvaticus;* on *S.
aquaticus* the spots have a more distinct dark border.
Germ. Denm.

Sium

Septoria Sii Rob. & Desm. in Ann. Sci. Nat. 1853, xx. 92. Sacc. Syll. iii. 529. All. vi. 857. Died. 511. Mig. 431. Grove, in Journ. Bot. 1922, p. 84.

Spots epiphyllous, scattered or confluent, irregular, roundish-angular, up to 4 mm. broad, brownish-yellow, with an indistinct border, afterwards becoming pallid in the centre. Pycnidia epiphyllous, scattered, somewhat prominent, brown, 70–120μ diam. Spores abundant, filiform or somewhat fusoid, flexuous or curved, with numerous (7–8) guttules, 30–45 × 1·5–2μ, emerging in copious tendrils.

On living leaves of *Sium angustifolium*. West Kilbride, Ayrshire (Boyd).   Sept.

According to Diedecke the spores become at length 1–3-septate. Saccardo says it can infest the stems (var. *caulicola*) and then has more highly developed pycnidia; his statement that the spores of the stem-form alone are guttulate is not correct.

Fr. Belg. Holl. Germ. Ital. Latvia, Canada.

Solanum

Septoria Dulcamarae Desm. in Ann. Sci. Nat. 1841, xv. 135. Sacc. Syll. iii. 535. All. vi. 858. Died. 511. Mig. 432.

Spots visible on both sides, first olivaceous, then turning brown or pallid on the upper side, round or oblong, with a darker border. Pycnidia epiphyllous, crowded, pierced by a pore, 90–120μ diam., clear-brown, darker round the wide pore. Spores filiform, straight or curved, "at length indistinctly 3–4-septate" (Died.), 50–60 × 1·5–2·5μ.

On fading leaves of *Solanum Dulcamara*. Dodderhill Common, Ws. (Grove and Rhodes).   Oct. Nov.

Spots 3–4 mm. in diameter, sometimes confluent. Texture of pycnidium very thin and translucent. No septa were seen, but the spores were furnished with several oil-guttules or granules.

Fr. Belg. Germ. Bohem. Ital. Port.

Septoria solanicola Grove.

Pycnidia ± gregarious, but not crowded, immersed, globose, blackish, about 300μ diam.; texture pseudopycnidial (truly Septoria-like), pale-olivaceous, darker round the pore. Spores numerous, linear, occasionally slightly curved, but mostly straight, obtuse at both ends, singly hyaline, but in

mass faintly olivaceous, eseptate or faintly 1-septate, 15–25 × 1·7–2μ, with 2–5 guttules.

On stems of *Solanum Dulcamara*. Polperro (Rilstone). Near Oakham, Rutland. July.

This cannot well be a caulicolous form of *S. Dulcamarae* Desm. for that has spores 50–60μ long.

Septoria Lycopersici Speg. Fung. Argent. pug. iv, no. 289. Sacc. Syll. iii. 535. All. vi. 858. Gard. Chron. 1908, xliv. 121, f. 46; 1913, liv. 417, f. 145; 1916, lx. 208. Journ. Board Agric. 1908, xv. 111, f. A–E. Duggar, Fung. Dis. 362. Stevens, Pl. Dis. 521.

Spots numerous, small at first, then increasing to about 1 cm., often scattered over the whole leaf and also on all other green parts, roundish or indefinite in outline, dingy-greyish-brown or blackish-green. Pycnidia amphigenous, scattered, subglobose, rather prominent, black; texture membranaceous, plectenchymatous, olivaceous. Spores numerous, linear, cylindrical or slightly thickened at one end, curvulous, pluriguttulate, then with 3–11 septa, somewhat tapering but still rounded at each end, 70–110 × 3μ (40–120 × 2–3μ).

On fading leaves and stems, etc. of *Solanum Lycopersicum*. Not common. Aug.–Nov.

This disease, "Tomato Leaf-spot", was first noticed in Argentina in 1882, and in the U.S.A. in 1893; since then it has spread wherever the Tomato is cultivated.

Europe, America, Australia.

Solidago
Septoria Virgaureae Desm. in Ann. Sci. Nat. 1842, xvii. 109. Cooke, Handb. 451. Sacc. Syll. iii. 546. All. vi. 859. Died. 512. Mig. 432.

Spots amphigenous, roundish or irregular, dry, variegated with whitish and brown. Pycnidia epiphyllous, immersed, convex, 100–120μ diam., blackish, with a wide pore. Spores filiform, obtuse at both ends, curvulous, indistinctly multiguttulate, but not septate, 80–100 × 1·5μ, issuing in a white tendril.

On fading leaves of *Solidago Virgaurea*. Darenth; Scarborough; Scotland (several places). Aug.

Diedicke describes the spores as straight or curvulous with indistinct guttules, 30–60 × 1–1·5μ, and possibly at length 3-septate.

Fr. Belg. Germ. Denm. Austr. Ital. Switz. Finland, U.S.A.

Sorbus

Septoria Sorbi Lasch, in Klotzsch, Herb. Myc. no. 459. Sacc.
Syll. x. 351. All. vi. 861. Died. 513. Mig. 433. (*Non* Cooke.) *S.
Aucupariae* Bres. in Hedwig. 1892, p. 40. Rabenh. Fung. Eur. no.
1265.

Spots minute, irregular, brownish, without a distinct border. Pycnidia mostly hypophyllous, blackish, about 180μ
diam., densely aggregated round the margins of the leaves or
in scattered clusters, forming dark spots. Spores filiform,
curved or arcuate, with a faint yellowish tinge, occasionally
with two delicate septa, 60–70 × 3·5–4μ; sporophores very
short.

On fading leaves of *Sorbus Aucuparia*. Highgate; Shere;
Lancashire; Tay; Ross-shire; Aberdeen. Rather common.

Jun. Jul.

Some of the British specimens are placed under *Phoma Sorbi*, but
on examination the spores are seen to be those of a Septoria. The
spots look blackish from the crowded pycnidia. Probably the pycnidial stage of *Leptosphaeria Sorbi* Jacz.; see Ann. Mycol. i. 30. Cf.
also *Phoma Sorbi*.
Fr. Holl. Germ. Ital. Switz.

Spiraea

Septoria quevillensis Sacc. Syll. iii. 512. All. vi. 864. T.B.M.S.
iv. 177.

Spots visible on both sides, blackish-red above, becoming
pale in the centre, brownish below, 1–2 mm. diam. Pycnidia
few on each spot, lens-shaped, 60–80μ diam., opening widely
and appearing like punctate holes in the leaf; texture parenchymatous, yellowish. Spores not numerous, linear, curvulous, with several guttules, 30–40 × 1–1·5μ.

On leaves of *Spiraea Ulmaria*. Ayrshire (Boyd). Cornwall
(Rilstone & Rhodes). Jun.–Aug.

Said to have less definite spots than *S. Ulmariae*; the spores also
are narrower, 1·5 instead of 2·5μ. But they may be identical species.
Fr. Holl. Swed.

Stachys

Septoria Stachydis Rob. & Desm. in Ann. Sci. Nat. 1847, viii. 19.
Sacc. Syll. iii. 539. All. vi. 865. Died. 515. Mig. 434.

Spots amphigenous, roundish, scattered or confluent, sometimes angular, greenish-brown, then brownish, rather dry,

bounded by the veins, 5–10 mm. diam. Pycnidia gregarious, epiphyllous, brownish-black, opening by a pore, 80–100μ diam. Spores linear, curvulous, bent, or flexuous, indistinctly septate, 25–40 × 1–2μ.

On living or fading leaves of *Stachys silvatica.* Surrey; Gloucestershire; Worcestershire; Cheshire; Yorkshire; Forfarshire; Ayrshire; Renfrewshire; Argyllshire; etc. Jun.–Nov.

The spots of this species are unusually dark-coloured and distinct. It has been found in Germany on other species of *Stachys*; e.g. on *S. palustris* with three distinct septa.

Europe, U.S.A., Canada.

Stellaria

Septoria Stellariae Rob. & Desm. in Ann. Sci. Nat. 1847, viii. 22. Cooke, Handb. 918. Phill. & Plowr. in Grevill. xiii. 50. Sacc. Syll. iii. 518. All. vi. 865. Diod. 516. Mig. 435.

Spots amphigenous, whitish, with a very distinct border, at length widely confluent. Pycnidia epiphyllous, thickly scattered over the spots, ovoid, 50–80μ diam., fuscous, opening by a pore. Spores linear or subclavate, curvulous, indistinctly septate, 50–70 × 1·5–2μ.

On living and dying stems and leaves of *Stellaria media*, *S. graminea.* Surrey; Arundel; Gloucestershire; Worcestershire; Montgomeryshire; Ayrshire; Clyde; Fife; Forres; Aberdeen.   May–Sept.

Fuckel (Symb. Myc. 101) says that it is the pycnidial stage of *Mycosphaerella isariphora* Johans.

Europe, Siberia, Canada, Australia.

Tanacetum

Septoria Tanaceti Niessl, in Mähr. Krypt. Flor. ii. 36. Sacc. Syll. iii. 546. All. vi. 867. Mig. 435.

Spots epiphyllous, indefinite, irregular, often confluent, fuscous. Pycnidia very minute, immersed, then slightly protruding, fuscous-black, with a conical ostiole, 100μ diam. Spores filiform-fusoid, straight or flexuous, obtuse at both ends, pale yellowish-brown, 5–7-guttulate, then often 3-septate, 20–30 × 1·5–2μ.

On fading leaves of *Tanacetum vulgare.* Montrose; near Aberdeen.   Sept. Oct.

Migula gives the spores as up to 90μ long, and having 3–5 septa. Fr. Germ. Austr. Bohem.

Taraxacum

[**Septoria Taraxaci** J. W. Ellis, in T.B.M.S. 1914, iv. 294.

"On leaves of *Taraxacum officinale*. Cheshire."]

On examination these specimens are seen to be *Ramularia Taraxaci* Karst.

Teucrium

Septoria Scorodoniae Pass. *in litt. apud* Sacc. Miscell. Myc. no. 2243; Syll. iii. 540. All. vi. 867. Died. 516. Mig. 435.

Spots minute, rufous-ochraceous, irregular in shape, 1–1·5 mm. diam. Pycnidia few, epiphyllous, punctiform, brownish, 80μ diam. Spores linear, continuous, hyaline, about $30 \times 1·5\mu$, somewhat obtuse at both ends.

On fading leaves of *Teucrium Scorodonia*. Loch Ard, Perthshire (Boyd). Near Hampton-in-Arden. Jul. Aug.

Fr. Holl. Germ. Ital. Russ.

Tilia

Septoria Tiliae Westd. Exs. no. 956. Sacc. Syll. iii. 476. All. vi. 868. Died. 517. Mig. 436.

Spots thickly or loosely scattered, roundish, brown, at length pale in the centre with a rather broad dark-brown border, 2–3 mm. diam. Pycnidia few, amphigenous(?), scattered or circinate. Spores linear, straight or gently curved, 3–4-septate, for the most part $35–40 \times 2–2·5\mu$, but sometimes much longer.

On living or fading leaves of species of *Tilia*. Ascot (Cooke). Sept.

I have seen no certain British specimens of this fungus; it seems to be often confused with other fungi, e.g. Cercospora.

Belg. Holl. Germ. Denm. Austr. Ital. Switz.

Torilis, see Petroselinum

Urtica

Septoria Urticae Rob. & Desm. in Ann. Sci. Nat. 1847, viii. 24. Cooke, Handb. 451. Sacc. Syll. iii. 557. All. vi. 873. Died. 519. Mig. 437.

Spots visible on both surfaces, rounded or angular, 1–3 mm. diam., ochraceous- or smoky-brown, at first surrounded by a yellow zone. Pycnidia epiphyllous, numerous, 60–80μ diam., greyish-brown, translucent under the microscope, pierced by

a pore. Spores very numerous, elongated, slender, acicular, pointed below, curved or flexuous, occasionally indistinctly guttulate, $30-50 \times 1-2\mu$; sporophores very short, linear.

On leaves of *Urtica dioica*. Cheshire (Ellis). Scotland (Boyd). West Hills, Worcs.; etc. On leaves of *U. urens*, West Kilbride, Ayrshire (Boyd). Not uncommon.   May–Aug.

The spots at length fall out and leave a round shot-hole.
Europe, U.S.A., Canada.

Vaccinium

Septoria stemmatea Sacc. Syll. iii. 493. Cooke, Handb. 445. Ellis, in T.B.M.S. 1912, p. 126. *Sphaeria (Depazea) stemmatea* Fr. Syst. Myc. ii. 528. Berk. in Ann. Nat. Hist. 1841, vi. 362.

Pycnidia epiphyllous, gregarious, minute, globose, seated on spots which are round, 4–6 mm. broad, dry, dingy greyish-brown, with a darker border line. Spores elongate-cylindrical or filiform, indistinctly septate or multiguttulate, $18-22 \times 2\mu$.

On leaves and stems of *Vaccinium Myrtillus*, Helvellyn; on leaves of *V. vitis-idaea*, Forres (Ellis).   Sept.

The spores seem to have been quite unknown until discovered on Helvellyn by Dr Ellis in Sept. 1911, and therefore the identity of his species with that of Fries must remain doubtful. Since Diedicke assigns to the same name a species with different spores, this is here kept provisionally distinct; see *Rhabdospora stemmatea*, *infra*, p. 445.
Belg. Holl. Germ. Denm. Austr. Ital. Swed. Russ.

Verbena

Septoria Verbenae Rob. & Desm. in Ann. Sci. Nat. 1847, viii. 19. Sacc. Syll. iii. 537. All. vi. 873. Died. 520. Mig. 437.

Spots roundish, definite, white, with a violet-purple border. Pycnidia minute (80–120μ diam.), membranaceous; texture densely parenchymatous, smoky-brown. Spores cylindrical, straight or flexuous, pluriguttulate, $40-50 \times 1-1 \cdot 5\mu$.

On leaves and stems of *Verbena officinalis*. Abinger (Cooke).

Spots surrounded by a broad purple border; on the stem they may reach a length of several centimetres.
Europe, N. Amer. Fiji.

Veronica

Septoria Veronicae Rob. & Desm. in Ann. Sci. Nat. 1849, xi. 348. Sacc. Syll. iii. 534. All. vi. 874. Died. 520. Mig. 438. Stevens, Pl. Dis. 524. *Phyllosticta Veronicae* Cooke, Fung. Brit. no. 615.

Spots amphigenous, small, roundish, indistinct, fuscous or grey, at length when dry whitish with an umber margin.

Pycnidia epiphyllous, often few, subglobose, rather prominent, pallid, then fuscous-black, 80–100μ diam., opening
by a pore. Spores numerous, filiform, straight or flexuous,
indistinctly guttulate, 25–40 × 1–1·5μ, Died. (13–15 × 2·5μ,
Boyd; 15–18 × 2·5μ, Ellis), sometimes appearing as if septate.
On living or fading leaves of *Veronica Chamaedrys*, *V.
hybrida*, *V. officinalis*. Surrey; Worcestershire; Cheshire;
Denbighshire; Ayrshire; Leinster. Aug.

Recorded abroad on *V. hederifolia*, etc. also. The spores seem to
differ very widely according to the host on which they grow. Diedicke
gives a var. *major*, with spores 45–60 × 1–1·5μ, on *V. triphyllos*.
Septoria exotica, which grows on all our cultivated shrubby Veronicas,
differs in the character of the spots.
Europe, U.S.A., Canada.

Septoria exotica Speg. Fung. Argent. ii, no. 107. Sacc. Syll. iii.
533. All. vi. 873. Died. 521. Mig. 438.

Spots round, 3–5 mm. diam. (some even up to 10 mm.),
visible on both sides of the leaf, numerous, often confluent,
above pallid or grey, surrounded by a definite purple zone,
below brownish and girt by a darker brown zone. Pycnidia
scattered, at first covered, then protruding at the vertex,
brown, darker round the pore, 80–125μ diam. Spores filiform,
rather obtuse at the apex, sometimes tapering below, i.e. subclavate, straight or curvulous, eguttulate, for a long time continuous, at length distinctly but faintly 3-septate, pale-
olivaceous, 25–35 × 2–3μ (20–35 × 1μ, Died.).

On living leaves of cultivated shrubby Veronicas (*V. spe-
ciosa*, *decussata*, etc. and hybrids). Lambourne Hill, West
Cornwall (Rilstone). Polperro (Rilstone & Rhodes). Saltash
(Hurst). Ireland (Armitage). Barmouth; Criccieth; etc.

May–Nov.

The spores described by Diedicke were eseptate, probably immature.
Germ. Argentina.

Viburnum
Septoria Viburni Westd. in Bull. Acad. Roy. Belg. 1852, xix. 121.
Cooke, Handb. 446. Sacc. Syll. iii. 493. All. vi. 874. Mig. 438.

Spots roundish or irregular, occasionally rather large,
whitish in the centre, with a brown border. Pycnidia epi-

phyllous, minute, semi-emergent, black, pierced by a pore.
Spores cylindrical, obtuse at the ends, 5–7-guttulate, 20–25
× 3μ.

On leaves of *Viburnum Lantana, V. Opulus.* Highgate;
Hampstead; Darenth; Surrey; Glamis.   Sept. Oct.

Diedicke says this is probably *Cercospora tinea* Sacc. and no
Sphaeropsid at all. It is true that most of the specimens I have examined (including all the British ones) either showed "spots" alone,
or if they yielded any spores they were not those of a Septoria, but
either *Phyllosticta Opuli* or doubtful. But some French specimens of
Roumeguère were an exception and represented the species as described above.

Fr. Belg. Germ. Denm. Austr. Ital.

Villarsia

Septoria Villarsiae Desm. in Ann. Sci. Nat. 1842, xvii. 108. Sacc.
Syll. iii. 541. All. vi. 806. Died. 480. Mig. p. 409, pl. 54, f. 1, 2, pl.
56, f. 6–8. *S. Limnanthemi* Thüm. Fung. Kirgh. no. 13.

Spots roundish, scattered or confluent, greyish- or reddish-
brown, without any distinct border, 3–5 mm. diam. Pycnidia
numerous, epiphyllous, very minute, covered, black. Spores
elongated, linear, straight or somewhat flexuous, multiseptate
and guttulate, 30–50 × 1·5μ, issuing in whitish tendrils.

On living or dying leaves of *Limnanthemum (Villarsia)
nymphaeoides.* Ely (Plowright). Old Bedford River, Earith,
Hunts. (Rhodes).   Aug.

Diedicke states that he was unable to find more than three septa.
Fr. Belg. Holl. Germ. Ital.

Viola

Septoria Violae Westd. Exs. ii, no. 91. Sacc. Syll. iii. 518. All.
vi. 876. Died. 521. Mig. 438.

Spots ± orbicular, 5–10 mm. across, pallid, zoned, with a
broad reddish-brown border. Pycnidia epiphyllous, numerous,
scattered, 80–100μ diam., prominent, membranaceous, brownish. Spores filiform, straight or flexuous, indistinctly guttulate, ends subacute, 17–20 × 1–1·25μ (faintly 3–4-septate,
40–50 × 1·5μ, Ellis; 25–30 × 2·5–3 or more, Trail).

On fading leaves (and stipules) of species of *Viola,* e.g.
V. canina, V. Riviniana, V. silvatica, V. tricolor, etc. and the
cultivated hybrids. England, Scotland, Ireland; not uncommon.   Aug. Sept.

Phyllosticta Violae has large white spots without a broad border, by which it can be easily distinguished. *Ramularia lactea* often occupies the same spots as the Septoria.

Europe, U.S.A. Canada.

Var. **palustris** Grove. *Septoria Violae-palustris* Died. 522. Mig. 438.

On *Viola palustris*. Ardrossan, Ayrshire (Boyd).

This variety differs chiefly in the much smaller spots; the spores are exactly the same.

Diedicke assigns to his species spores 25–40 × 1–1·2μ, but fully developed forms of *S. Violae* have spores as long as this. Allescher gives a form on *Viola biflora* with spores 20–30 × 1μ.

Vitis

Septoria Badhami B. & Br. in Ann. Nat. Hist. 1854, xiii. 460, pl. 15, f. 9 (*non* Thüm.). Cooke, Handb. 444. Sacc. Syll. iii. 480.

"Pycnidia amphigenous, fuscous, collected here and there into little groups which are not surrounded by a border. Spores variable, elongate, clavate, rather thick, 50μ long, with a few minute granules, rarely with one or two septa."

On leaves of *Vitis vinifera*. Highgate; Shere; Twycross; East Bergholt. Oct. Nov.

"Forming little brownish specks on either side of the leaf, consisting of a few subconglomerate pycnidia. Endochrome of spores sometimes retracted to one end" (B. & Br.). *n.ex.* It has not been recognised in this country since Berkeley's time.

Holl.

Wistaria

Septoria Wistariae Brun. Espèc. nouv. Sphérops. p. 3. Sacc. Syll. x. 351. All. vi. 878.

Spots hypophyllous, irregular, variable in form, clear-brown, without a distinct border. Pycnidia scattered or aggregated, numerous, punctiform, brownish-black, pierced by a pore. Spores rod-like, obtuse, straight or curvulous, for a long time without septa, 20–25 × 1–1·5μ.

On fading leaves of *Wistaria sinensis*. Kew Gardens; Besford Court, Ws.

Fr.

MONOCOTYLEDONS

Alisma

Septoria Alismatis Oud. Mat. Myc. Néerl. p. 4. Sacc. Syll. iii. 569. All. vi. 726. Died. 425. Mig. 376.

Spots smoke-coloured, roundish, at length greyish-white in the centre, visible on both sides. Pycnidia very small, mostly hypophyllous, black, scarcely visible even with a lens. Spores cylindrical, straight, with a guttule at each end, at length septate in the middle, 15–20 × 3μ.

On fading leaves of *Alisma Plantago*. Haverfordwest (Rhodes). Kingcausie (Trail). Solihull, Warwicks.   Oct.

"Rather an Ascochyta than a Septoria" (Trail). This is considered by some to be *S. heterochroa*, f. *Alismatis*, but von Höhnel and Diedicke both assert that it is only misunderstood *Ramularia Alismatis* Fautr. In part at least that statement is true of the British records, but probably both species exist.

Holl. Germ. Austr. Denm. U.S.A.

Carex

Septoria Caricis Passer. Fungh. Parm. Sept. no. 135. Sacc. Syll. iii. 566. All. vi. 750. Died. 437. Mig. 386.

Spots occupying the dead tips of still living leaves, greyish-brown, unbordered. Pycnidia very numerous, crowded, 250–280μ diam., lens-shaped, black, pierced by a pore; texture pseudopycnidial, almost transparent, darker round the pore. Spores cylindrical or slightly elliptic-fusoid, obtuse at both ends, 20–35 × 2·5–3μ, occasionally curved, with one or a row of several guttules, continuous, colourless, later apparently 1-septate, but the septum is very delicate.

On leaves of *Carex arenaria*, on the shore, Pembrokeshire (Rhodes). Goosehill Woods, Ws., on *C. pendula* (Rhodes).

July.

It was accompanied in Pembrokeshire by crowds of pycnidia of an Ascochyta (*A. sodalis* Grove, *q.v.*), densely intermingled with it, but the spores remained always distinct.

Germ. Ital. Canada.

Septoria caricicola Sacc. Syll. iii. 566. All. vi. 749. Died. 437 ?

Spots subcircular, whitish when dry, with a rather broad brown border. Pycnidia punctiform, scattered singly or

arranged in lines, chiefly epiphyllous, black, covered by the epidermis which is at length pierced, about 150μ diam. Spores elongate-cylindrical, curved or flexuous, obtuse at both ends, with 7 (rarely 6 or 8) very distinct septa, slightly constricted, very pale yellow, 35–55 × 4μ.

On dead leaves of *Carex riparia*, Cheshire (Ellis). On *Carex* sp., Pembroke (Rhodes). Apr.

When the leaves are completely withered, the spots are not discernible. Diedicke's *S. caricicola* seems rather to be *S. riparia* Pass. Holl. Germ. Ital. Latvia (on *C. vesicaria*).

Septoria gracillima Sacc. Syll. iii. 566. Grevill. xiv. 104. *Darluca gracillima* Cooke, Praec. Mon. Henders. 26.

Pycnidia very numerous and densely scattered, black, subglobose, 100–150μ diam., just perforating the epidermis by the ostiole which is pierced by a round pore; texture very thin and translucent, dark around the pore. Spores numerous, collected into a dense cluster, acicular, very acute at one or both ends, straight or faintly curvulous, singly hyaline, but olivaceous in mass, multiguttulate, 20–28 × 1–1·5μ.

On leaves of *Carex*. Near Edinburgh (Cooke).

The description is amended from the original specimens. Round each solitary ostiole there is a little blackish area. The pycnidium is quite Septoria-like.

Septoria lineolata Sacc. Syll. iii. 567. All. vi. 750.

Spots none. Pycnidia arranged ± in lines, globose, then depressed, blackish, at first covered, then semi-erumpent, 125–170μ diam., pierced by a pore; texture yellowish-fuscous, of loose, thin-walled cells, Septoria-like. Spores linear, faintly curvulous, rounded at both ends, seldom tapering, yellowish in mass, "60–70 × 1·75–2μ"; no sporophores visible.

On dead leaves of *Carex arenaria*, and doubtless of other Carices. Pembrokeshire; Ayrshire; Aberdeen. Oct.–Mar.

Scarcely visible without a lens. Distinguished from other species on *Carex* by the linear arrangement of the pycnidia and the absence of spots. Sometimes, in these specimens, the spores measured only 34–45 × 0·75–1μ; at others as much as 80 × 2·75μ.

The form of the spores is not as Saccardo described, but more like his figure of *S. caricinella*; they ultimately became 6–8-septate.

Fr. Holl. Ital.

Septoria punctoidea Karst. in Hedwig. 1884, p. 38. Sacc. Syll. iii. 566.

No distinct spots. Pycnidia scattered, subepidermal, very minute (up to 50–60μ diam.), subglobose, blackish, at length erumpent by the vertex. Spores fusoid-acicular, tapering acuminately at each end, appearing sometimes straight or nearly so, but always bent or curved or even exactly lunate (crescentic) in profile, pluri-microguttulate, hyaline, 15–20 × 1·5–2μ (20–24 × 2μ, Rhodes). (Fig. 25f.)

On small dead leaves of *Carex arenaria*. Formby, Lancs. (Travis).

It seems most likely that this is nothing but an early (or at least not fully developed) state of *Septoria Caricis*, which has been found on the same host in Pembrokeshire. Karsten's specimen was from Lapland. But cf. *Sept. lunata* Grove, on *Molinia*.

Septoria riparia Pass. Fungh. Parm. Sept. no. 134. Sacc. Syll. iii. 567. All. vi. 750.

Pycnidia scattered, at first covered, then erumpent and surrounded by the ruptured epidermis, subglobose, black. Spores filiform, scarcely curved, very minutely guttulate, not septate, 37–57 × 2μ (60–65 × 2·5–3μ, Ellis).

On dead leaves of *Carex* (? *vulpina*). Cheshire (Ellis).

Doubtfully correct; the spores of the Cheshire specimens are pale-greenish in colour, and they probably belong to *S. caricicola*.
Ital. (on *C. riparia*).

Septoria Epipactidis Sacc. in Mich. i. 107; Syll. iii. 575. All. vi. 777. Died. 453. Mig. 396.

Spots oblong, brown, becoming whitish when dry. Pycnidia lens-shaped, black, pierced by a pore. Spores linear-cylindrical, attenuated but obtuse at both ends, curvulous, hyaline, with 4–6 minute guttules, 25–30 × 1·5–2μ (20–22 × 0·8μ, Boyd).

Forma **subsparsa** Grove.

Pycnidia not confined to the spots, but scattered over the leaf.

On dead leaves of *Epipactis latifolia*, Kilwinning, Ayrshire (Boyd).

It is possible that this should be considered rather as a var. of *S. Orchidearum* on account of the narrowness of the spores.

Germ. Ital.

Gladiolus

Septoria Gladioli Pass. in Raben. Fung. Eur. no. 1956; Fungh. Parm. Sept. no. 127. Sacc. Syll. iii. 574. Grove, in Journ. Bot. 1934, p. 267.

Spots roundish, dry, whitish, about 3 or 4 mm. across, surrounded by a broad bright-brown margin. Pycnidia black, clustered in the centre of the spot, 100–120μ diam. Spores cylindrical or somewhat clavate at the upper end, hyaline, pluriguttulate, continuous (or at length 3-septate, Massey), straight or curving, 20–55 × 2·5–4μ (40–60 × 2–3·5μ).

On stems, leaves, and corms of cultivated *Gladiolus*. Devon and Cornwall, 1925. Scilly Isles, 1926–7. Lancashire, etc. Ireland (Armagh), 1927.

It has been imported on the corms, in a subsclerotial stage called "Hard Rot". In its younger state, it simulates an Ascochyta; see Massey, in Cornell Univ. Agr. Exp. Sta. Bull. 380 (1916), pp. 149–181; also Journ. Bot. *l.c.*

Germ. Port. Ital. Cyprus, U.S.A.

GRAMINEAE

Plurivorous

Septoria graminum Desm. in Ann. Sci. Nat. 1843, xix. 339. Cooke, Handb. 445. Sacc. Syll. iii. 565. All. vi. 789. Died. 462. Mig. 401. Stevens, Pl. Dis. 520. See Phytopathology, 1923, xiii. 1–23.

Spots ± elongated, narrow, yellowish, becoming pale or grey, usually with a narrow fuscous border, often limited by the veins. Pycnidia crowded or arranged in rows on the spots or sometimes scattered without distinct spots, immersed, fuscous, minute, scarcely perceptible without a lens. Spores very slender, linear or subclavulate, straight or flexuous, minutely guttulate, 45–75 × 1–1·5μ, rarely with a few indistinct septa; sporophores imperceptible.

On living leaves of many Grasses, e.g. Wheat, Barley, Oat, Brome, Poa, etc. Common: England, Scotland, Wales.

Summer.

Usually does little harm, but may become injurious under certain conditions.

Var. **Moliniae** Trail.

On *Molinia coerulea.* Clyde (Trail).

Var. **crassipes** Grove, in Gard. Chron. 1916, lx. 210, f. 82. ? *Septoria macropoda* Pass. Fungh. Parm. Sept. no. 141.

Spores as in the type; sporophores short, ampulliform, cuspidate, 10–13 × 2·5–3μ.

On leaves of Wheat (*Triticum*). Carmarthenshire.   July.

This variety was first discovered on leaves of Wheat from Australia. Europe, N. America, Australia.

Septoria nodorum Berk. in Gard. Chron. 1845, p. 601. Cooke, Handb. 442. Sacc. Syll. iii. 561. Grove, in Gard. Chron. 1916, lx. 194, f. 1–3. *S. glumarum* Passer. Fungh. Parm. Sept. no. 147. Sacc. Syll. iii. 561. All. vi. 870. Died. 468. Mig. 100. *Phoma Hennebergii* Kühn, in Hedwig. 1877, p. 121. Sacc. Syll. iii. 167. *Macrophoma Hennebergii* Berl. & Vogl. in Atti Soc. Ven.-Trent. 1886, p. 197. Sacc. Syll. Addit. 315. Mig. 112.

No distinct spots, except on the glumes where it makes a roundish spot with a brown border. Pycnidia epiphyllous on the leaves, or on the nodes or glumes, scattered or crowded in short lines, globose, 70–100μ diam., slightly prominent, pierced by a pore, reddish-ochraceous, but ultimately blackish; texture soft, sinuously prosenchymatous, ochraceous-brown, semipellucid. Spores oblong-cylindrical, straight or gently curved or bent, obtuse at the ends or tapering below, 3-septate when mature, singly colourless, but remaining long clustered together, of a pinkish-isabelline tinge in mass, 20–25 × 2–2·5 or even 3μ. (Fig. 25j.)

On leaves, nodes, and glumes of *Triticum vulgare* and its varieties. King's Cliffe (Berkeley). Cheshire (Ellis). Northumberland; Wiltshire; etc. Also on nodes of *Dactylis.* On *Lepturus incurvatus*, Lelant, Cornwall. On *Psamma*, Merioneth (Rhodes).

First observed by Berkeley in 1845, on the nodes of Wheat, just before the ears were ripe. As shown in Gard. Chron. 1916, *l.c.* the forms on various parts of the Wheat are all alike; the spores are at first continuous, then 1-septate and measuring 15–17μ, but ultimately larger and 3-septate.

It does little injury, unless in abundance. Said to be the pycnidial

stage of *Mycosphaerella exitialis* Morini, but Davis, Trans. Wiscons. Acad. Sci. 1919, p. 685, says "sometimes accompanied by perithecia which seem referable to Sphaerulina". Most likely the ascophorous stage is a Leptosphaeria; see Phytopathology, 1922, xii. 543.

Europe, U.S.A., Canada, Kenya, Australia.

Septoria Tritici Rob. & Desm. in Ann. Sci. Nat. 1842, xvii. 107. Sacc. Syll. iii. 561. All. vi. 870. Died. 465. Massee, Dis. Cult. Pl. 424.

Amphigenous. Spots ± linear, longitudinally placed, rusty-yellow, at length whitish, often with a dark-purple border. Pycnidia immersed, minute, subglobose, opening by a round pore. Spores cylindric-fusoid, gently curved, pluriguttulate, 3–5-septate, $60-65 \times 3 \cdot 5-5 \mu$, issuing in flesh-coloured tendrils.

On fading leaves of *Glyceria fluitans*, Lyndhurst. Aug. On *Triticum*, Devon; Belfast; etc. May. Also recorded abroad on leaves of *Brachypodium* and *Festuca*, and on the grains of Wheat.

It may belong to *Leptosphaeria Tritici* Pass. Distinguished from *Sept. graminum* by its larger pycnidia, and its much broader spores; on *Triticum* both these forms can occur together.

Experiments seem to suggest that *S. Tritici* R. & D. is confined to *Triticum*. Cavara (see Amer. Journ. Bot. 1919, p. 12) gives the typical spores of *S. Tritici* as $50-60 \times 1 \cdot 5-2 \mu$. *Septoria cerealis* Pass., in Thüm. Herb. Myc. Oec. no. 602, lies exactly between *S. Tritici* and *S. graminum*, having spores $40-65 \times 2-2 \cdot 5 \mu$. Further experience is evidently required. See Zeitschr. f. Pflanzenkr. 1893, iii. 19.

Europe, U.S.A., Canada.

Septoria oxyspora Penz. & Sacc. Fung. Mortol. p. 14, pl. 4, f. 13 (1884). Sacc. Syll. iii. 505; Fung. Ital. pl. 1487. All. vi. 715, 735, with fig. Grove, in Journ. Bot. 1916, p. 192, pl. 542, f. 9. *S. culmifida* Lind, in Gartner Tidende, 1907, p. 112; Danish Fung. p. 451, pl. 7, f. 90, 91; and in Ann. Mycol. 1907, v. 276. Sacc. Syll. xxii. 1120.

Spots (on the leaves) evident, aggregated or scattered, oval, 2–5 mm. long, bleached or pallid, surrounded by a narrow purple border. Pycnidia separate, but often densely congregated, very minute, up to 100μ diam., round, depressed, black, scarcely visible without a lens, immersed, piercing the epidermis by the minute ostiole alone, but showing faintly black through it; texture of loose, round or oval, brownish cells, translucent under the microscope. Spores fusoid, but always more or less bent like a sickle, often with a double

curve, ends acutely cuspidate, hyaline, eseptate, eguttulate, 13–22 × 3–4μ. (Fig. 25 a.)

On leaves, sheaths, and culms of many Grasses. Aberystwith; Cardiff; near Bromsgrove, Worcs. (var. *culmorum*); etc.

May–Jul.

The original specimen was on *Arundo Donax*. Many of the spores have the shape (in outline) of a boomerang. In Latvia it has been found on culms and sheaths of *Phragmites communis*. At Aberystwith Miss K. Sampson has found it on leaves of *Alopecurus, Arrhenatherum, Dactylis, Phleum,* and *Poa*. I have myself found it in S. Wales, and at Burcot, near Bromsgrove, on culms of *Dactylis*; the spores of these fungi exactly resemble those of Saccardo's pl. 1487. Lind says that it is the pycnidial stage of *Metasphaeria culmifida* Sacc. with which it regularly occurs in Denmark on *Phleum*.

Denm. Ital. Latvia, Finland, Cyprus.

Septoria lunata Grove.

Pycnidia ± loosely aggregated, black, round or oblong, up to 160μ long, sometimes in rows, depressed-convex, pierced by a pore; texture thick, parenchymatous, blackish-olive. Spores narrowly fusoid, lunate, acute at both ends, colourless, 10–18 × 1·5μ (25–30 × 2μ, Rhodes), sometimes with an indistinct row of guttules, but mostly hyaline.

On the peduncles of *Molinia*, Devon, and near Dreenhill, Haverfordwest, Pembr. (Rhodes). On haulm and glumes of a Grass (? *Festuca*), the cliffs, Polperro, Cornw. (Rhodes & Rilstone). Jul. Aug.

Allied to *S. Stipae* Died. p. 467, but the spores are not bent irregularly, but strictly and beautifully lunate. They are much narrower than in *Rhabdospora curva* and its allies.

Septoria Alopecuri Syd. in Hedwig. 1899, p. (138). Sacc. Syll. xvi. 974. All. vi. 728. Died. 461. Mig. 377. *S. Bromi,* var. *Alopecuri* Karst. Symb. Myc. xv. 151. Trail, in Scot. Nat. 1888, ix. 231.

Spots indistinct or none. Pycnidia numerous, black, 80–100μ diam. Spores linear, straight or bent, obtuse at both ends, hyaline or faintly yellowish, 45–75 × 2·5μ, with numerous indistinct septa.

On a dead culm of *Alopecurus geniculatus*. Near Aberdeen (Trail). July.

Var. **Airae** Grove.

No spots. Pycnidia up to 200μ diam., scattered, black. Spores fusoid-cylindrical, tapering equally at both ends, flexuous, pale-yellowish, minutely guttulate or even faintly (pseudo)septate, 60–75 × 2·5–3μ.

On dead culms of *Aira caespitosa*. Sneyd's Coppice, Ws.
March.

Var. **Phalaridis.** *Septoria Bromi*, var. *Phalaridis* Trail, in Scot. Nat. 1887, ix. 40, 231.

Spores 53–65 × 3·5–4μ, with 8–15 septa.

On dead leaves of *Phalaris arundinacea*. Near Aberdeen (Trail).   Sept.

Var. **Calamagrostidis** Grove.

Spores linear, obtuse above, acute below, yellowish, 40–100 × 3–4μ, faintly curved, with 3–13 distinct septa. (Fig. 25e.)

On dead leaves of *Calamagrostis Epigejos*. Goosehill Woods, Worcs. (Rhodes). Cf. *S. epigejos*, in Lind, Dan. Fung. pl. 7, f. 88.   Jan.

Germ. Finland.

Septoria affinis Sacc. Syll. iii. 563. All. vi. 743. Scot. Nat. ix. 231.

Spots linear or oval, longitudinal, bleached when dry, bordered with red. Pycnidia scattered, immersed, punctiform, lens-shaped, 200μ diam., blackish, pierced by a rather wide opening. Spores rod-shaped, somewhat flexuose, rather obtuse at the ends, 4–5-septate, not constricted, hyaline, then very pale yellowish-green, 25–30 × 2–2·5μ.

On leaves of *Avena* and *Agropyron repens*. Aberdeen (Trail).   Sept.

Dr Rhodes found a form on dead leaves of *Brachypodium* (at Broadhaven, Pembr.) with spores up to 80 × 3μ, but otherwise as described.

Ital. (on Bromus).

Septoria Bromi Sacc. Syll. iii. 562. All. vi. 744. Died. 463. Mig. 382. See Phytopathology, 1923, xiii. 8.

Spots elongated or indefinite, indistinct, becoming pale-brown or greyish. Pycnidia amphigenous, numerous, globose

or lens-shaped, black, up to 125µ diam., pierced by a pore; texture thin, translucent. Spores filiform or occasionally obclavate, i.e. obtuse at one end, acute at the other, gently curved, with several minute guttules, 45–60 × 1·2–2µ.

On fading leaves of *Bromus* and *Holcus*. Not uncommon.

Jun.–Sept.

Var. **Brachypodii** Sacc. *l.c.* Died. 463. Mig. 382.

Spores smaller, 30–40 × 1–1·5µ. On leaves of *Agrostis alba* and *Lolium perenne*. Ayrshire (Boyd).

Var. **Arrhenatheri** Grove. On *Arrhenatherum*, Ayrshire (Boyd).

It is also recorded abroad on *Festuca gigantea*.
Fr. Germ. Denm. Austr. Ital. Spain, U.S.A. Canada, Australia.

Avena
Septoria Avenae Frank, in Ber. Deutsch. Bot. Gesell. 1895, p. 64. Sacc. Syll. xi. 547. All. vi. 738. Died. 461. Phytopathology, 1922, xii. 454.

Spots numerous, round, pale, with a brownish border. Pycnidia epiphyllous, more often crowded on the edge of the spot, immersed, round, pale-brown, 130–150µ diam. Spores cylindrical, straight or slightly bent, 3-septate or even 4-septate, not constricted, 30–40 × 3–4µ.

On leaves of *Avena sativa* (only). Warwickshire; Worcestershire; etc.

The pycnidial stage of *Leptosphaeria avenaria* Weber, for which see Phytopathology, *l.c.* Cf. *Sept. affinis.*
Germ. U.S.A. Canada, Australia.

Bromus
Septoria bromicola Speg. Fung. Chil. 1910, p. 168. Sacc. Syll. xxii. 1118. *S. bromicola* Sm. & Ramsb. in T.B.M.S. 1916, v. 246, seems hardly different.

Spots indistinct. Pycnidia amphigenous, rather gregarious, minute, up to 80µ diam., brown, pierced by a pore 20µ broad. Spores filiform, gently flexuose, acute at both ends, continuous, 50–60 × 1µ.

On fading leaves of *Bromus mollis*. Arran (Boyd). Aug.

This species is said to differ from *S. Bromi* Sacc. (*q.v.* p. 425) in the absence of spots, the smaller pycnidia, and the constantly narrower spores which are not wider at the base.

Holcus

Septoria Holci Pass. Fungh. Parm. Sept. no. 139. Sacc. Syll. iii. 562. All. vi. 794.

Spots small, roundish, grey. Pycnidia deeply immersed, hardly visible on the surface, very minute, globose, black. Spores vermiform, 3-septate, contents opaque, $20-25 \times 3\mu$.

On fading leaves of *Holcus mollis*. Lyndhurst. Aug.

Spores similar to those of *S. affinis* Sacc., but the spots and pycnidia are different. Distinguished from *S. Bromi* by its much shorter spores. Ital.

Phragmites

Septoria arundinacea Sacc. Syll. iii. 564. All. vi. 827.

Spots oblong, amphigenous, dingy-ochraceous, with a fuscous border. Pycnidia gregarious, immersed, globose, then lens-shaped, about 140μ diam.; texture delicately and loosely parenchymatous, smoky-brown. Spores linear, curvulous, scarcely attenuated but rounded at each end, 6–7-septate, not or very slightly constricted, provided with minute guttules near the septa, hyaline, then pale-olive, "$60-70 \times 5-6\mu$" (Sacc.).

On dead leaves of *Phragmites communis*. Cheshire (Ellis, spores $35-45 \times 2.5\mu$). Dublin (var. *major* Sacc. *l.c.*, spores $50-55 \times 4-7\mu$). Summer.

This is an ill-understood or very variable species, especially in width of spore. It is recorded, perhaps in error, on other grasses. Fr. Ital.

Psamma

Septoria Ammophilae Syd. in Hedwig. 1900, p. (127). Sacc. Syll. xvi. 974. All. vii. 887. Died. 461. Mig. 377.

Spots visible on both sides, up to 1.5 cm. long, but only 1 mm. broad, bounded by the veins, sometimes confluent, whitish above. Pycnidia hypophyllous, arranged in rows, globose, 180μ diam., covered, piercing the epidermis only by the wide ostiole; texture clear-brown, thicker and darker round the pore. Spores very numerous, filiform, variously bent or flexuose, eguttulate, but ultimately provided with (at times) several septa, rather acute at both ends, $48-60 \times 2\mu$ (Died.).

On dead leaves and on the underground parts of *Am-*

SCOLECOSPORAE

mophila (*Psamma*) *arenaria*. Norfolk? St Davids, etc., Pembr.; Pwllheli; Carnarvon (Rhodes). Aug.

Sydow found his specimens in Germany, on living leaves. The description given above is that of the German specimens; those of Dr Rhodes were on *dead* leaves. In them there were no visible spots; the spores were very often thickened and obtuse at one end, and measured about 35 × 3μ. A very similar fungus was found on living leaves of *Glyceria fluitans* in a ditch at Dale, Pembr. (Rhodes), with distinctly 5-septate spores, 45 × 3μ.

No doubt these Septorias on Grasses could be reduced in number by further study, and it seems probable that *Ascochyta graminicola* is an early state of some of them.

Juncus

Septoria Junci Desm. in Ann. Sci. Nat. 1853, xx. 85. Sacc. Syll. iii. 569. *Rhabdospora Junci* All. vi. 910. Died. 530. Mig. 447.

Pycnidia immersed in the culms, very numerous, arranged more or less in lines, globose-conical, then depressed, 80–200μ diam., fuscous, covered by the greyish epidermis; ostiole very short, rather prominent, pierced by a pore; contents whitish or yellowish. Spores very long, filiform or wormlike, straight or bent, even flexuose, 10–20-guttulate, 50–80 (or even 100) × 2·5–3μ, at length distinctly septate (7 septa on *J. maritimus*).

On dead culms of *Juncus effusus, J. conglomeratus*; on culms and leaves of *J. maritimus*; (in Belgium on the tips of the leaves of *J. articulatus*). Worcestershire; Norfolk; Cheshire; Borth; Dumbartonshire; Aberdeen; Anglesey; etc.

Feb.–Oct.

The guttules are large and yellowish, giving a colour to the spore-mass.
Fr. Belg. Germ.

Luzula

Septoria minuta Schröt. Pilz. Labrad. p. 19, in Jahresber. Schles. Ges. 1887, p. 284. Sacc. Syll. x. 383.

Pycnidia very minute (usually 40–60μ diam.), black, immersed in the leaf, and congregated to form irregular cloudy patches. Spores fusoid, curved or falcate, acute at both ends, hyaline, 10–20 × 1–2μ.

On leaves of *Luzula maxima*, Llanspyddid, Brecon (Rhodes).

July.

The pycnidia are hardly visible singly, but lie in lines, forming cloudy spots. The original specimens were found on leaves of *Luzula spicata* in Greenland. The spores in the Welsh specimens were sometimes quite straight, though often curved.
Greenland.

Maianthemum

Septoria Maianthemi Westd. Exs. no. 940. Sacc. Syll. iii. 573. All. vi. 812. Mig. 412.

Spots numerous, broad, unbordered, greyish. Pycnidia hypophyllous, scattered, brownish-black, at length flattened. Spores cylindrical, sometimes thickened at one end, obtuse, 6–9-guttulate, $50–70 \times 3\mu$, issuing in whitish tendrils.

On leaves of *Maianthemum bifolium*. Ken Wood; Hampstead (Cooke). Spots large or small, at first roundish and brown, then greyish-black and indeterminate.

Belg. Germ. Austr.

Scilla

Septoria Scillae Westd. in Kickx, Flor. Crypt. Flandr. 1867, i. 423. Sacc. Syll. iii. 571. All. vi. 852. Mig. 429.

Spots pale-brown, without any distinct border. Pycnidia semi-immersed, flat, brownish, becoming darker, about 200μ diam. Spores cylindrical, straight or slightly bent, $50–75 \times 2\cdot5–3\mu$, with 5–7 faint irregular septa.

On living leaves of *Scilla nutans*. West Kilbride, Ayrshire (Boyd). May.

Recorded abroad on other species of *Scilla* and on *Muscari*; usually occupying the tips of the leaves.

Fr. Belg. Germ. Hung. Ital. Port.

Scirpus

Septoria dolichospora Trail, in Scot. Nat. 1885, p. 188 (*non* E. & E., 1891). Sacc. Syll. x. 384. *S. Trailii* Cooke, in Grevill. xiv. 104 (1886). *Rhabdospora dolichospora* All. vi. 923.

Pycnidia scattered, subepidermal, oval-lens-shaped, $280 \times 240\mu$, opening by a prominent pore, pale-brown, the pore in a darker ring. Spores very long, filiform-fusoid, $120–130 \times 2–3\mu$, flexuous or much curved, faintly yellowish, pluri-guttulate or with 9–12 (6–8, Cooke) very faint septa.

On dead drifted stems of *Scirpus lacustris*. Near Aberdeen (Trail). May.

Remarkable for the length and thinness of the spores. *S. lacustris* Sacc. & Thüm. (Syll. iii. 567) comes nearest to it; that has spores 75–

85×3–$3 \cdot 5\mu$, and will probably be merely a younger state of the same species, since it occurred on the same host in exactly similar circumstances.

Fr.

Sparganium

Septoria Sparganii Pass. Fungh. Parm. Sept. no. 124. Sacc. Syll. iii. 569. T.B.M.S. v. 136.

Spots none or indistinct. Pycnidia very minute, about 50μ diam., immersed, arranged somewhat in rows and seated on a rather blackened area (the epidermis around each discoloured), globose, black, slightly prominent. Spores elongate-linear, straight or curved or bent at an obtuse angle, bluntly rounded at the ends, pluriseptate (invariably 7-septate, with a small guttule in each cell, Ellis), very pale transparent yellow, 35–$45 \times 2 \cdot 5\mu$.

On dead leaves of *Sparganium ramosum*. Leasowe, etc., Cheshire (Ellis). Llanstadwell, Pembr. (Rhodes). Aug.

Holl. Ital.

Typha

Septoria menispora Sacc. Syll. iii. 569. All. vi. 872. *Sphaeropsis menispora* B. & Br. in Ann. Nat. Hist. 1850, v. 376. Cooke, Handb. 428.

Pycnidia elliptic, covered by the epidermis, black, at length pierced by a round pore which just emerges. Spores very long, curved, very acute at both ends, multiguttulate, with the guttules pellucid, globose, and scattered here and there.

On dead leaves of *Typha latifolia*, Spye Park, Wilts. (Broome). On leaves of *T. angustifolia*, Cheshire (Ellis) with *Stagonospora Typhoidearum*. Mar. Apr.

In Dr Ellis's specimens, the pycnidia are about 170μ diam., the spores between lunate and spiral, 100–$130 \times 2 \cdot 5\mu$, tapering a little at each end, with numerous inequidistant guttules, and appearing at last to be very delicately multiseptate, with one or more guttules on each side of a septum. The shape of the spores may be compared with that of *Spirillum Undula*, with one turn of a very open spiral.

Belg.

Equisetum, see under *Septogloeum*

Polypodium

Septoria Polypodii Grove, in Journ. Bot. 1922, p. 84.

Spots none. Pycnidia scattered, separate, but sometimes arranged in short rows or groups, orbicular, lens-shaped,

somewhat prominent, shining, black, 100–150μ diam., pierced by a minute pore; texture parenchymatous, thin, membranaceous, but not pellucid, fuliginous-brown, darker round the pore. Spores abundant, very narrow, filiform, usually straight, not guttulate, 35–45 × 0·5μ; sporophores linear, colourless, septate, erect, 3–4 times wider than the spore, 9–10 × 1·5μ.

On dead leaves of *Polypodium Phegopteris*. Glen Falloch, Perthshire (Boyd). May.

The pycnidia chiefly occupy the rachis, and the petiolules and nerves of the leaflets.

Polytrichum
Septoria thecicola B. & Br. in Intell. Observer, 1863, p. 9, f. 1. Cooke, Handb. 446. Sacc. Syll. iii. 577. All. vi. 833. *Sphaeropsis thecicola* B. & Br. in Ann. Nat. Hist. 1850, v. 376.

Pycnidia scattered or in groups, immersed, convex, black, rugose, opening by a pore which just pierces the epidermis, at length collapsing. Spores very delicate, linear, straight, about 18–22 × 1–1·5μ, on short sporophores.

On setae, apophysis, and capsules of old *Polytrichum commune*, *P. piliferum*, and other species of *Polytrichum*. Aberdeen (Dickie). West Kilbride and Kilwinning, Ayrshire (Boyd). Minehead. Aug.–Oct.

Karsten found this species, in Finland, on setae of *P. juniperinum*. Boyd's Kilbride specimens, on *P. commune*(?), are much more conspicuous than the ordinary scattered form, and may be called var. *congesta*, being in little groups.
Denm. Finland.

PHLEOSPORA Wallr. Fl. Crypt. Germ. ii. 176.

Pycnidia immersed, imperfectly developed, often very thin, when full-grown more or less broadly open. Spores elongated, linear or somewhat fusoid, often curvulous, rather broad, hyaline, frequently at length septate. (Fig. 27.)

Very similar to Septoria on the one hand, and to Cylindrosporium on the other. Diedicke considers that this genus cannot be maintained (Ann. Mycol. x. 484). He places some of the species in Septoria and others in Cylindrosporium. But

there *is*, in those here mentioned at any rate, an imperfect peridium, though its form is rather that of an open cup or saucer than of a globose pycnidium. Phleospora inclines to the Excipulaceae.

Most of the species listed here begin as a Phyllosticta, and only gradually assume the form of a Phleospora, e.g. *P. Aceris,P. Oxyacanthae, P. Aegopodii.* Others should be looked for in Septogloeum or Septomyxa.

Acer

Phleospora Aceris Sacc. Syll. iii. 577. All. vi. 933. *Ascochyta Aceris* Lib. Exs. no. 54. *Septoria Aceris* B. & Br. in Ann. Nat. Hist. 1850, v. 379. Cooke, Handb. 442. *Gloeosporium acerinum* West.

Spots none or small, roundish, brown, crowded in groups. Pycnidia generally in little clusters, imperfectly developed, sometimes without any visible wall; pustules of spores amphigenous, 150–200μ broad, brown or reddish, concealed below the epidermis. Spores subcylindrical or clavate-fusoid, distinctly 3-septate when mature, often constricted at the septa, 20–30 × 4–5μ, issuing through a little pore in whitish tendrils or small rounded masses.

On living or fading leaves (especially of seedlings, including the cotyledons) of *Acer campestre* and (more often) of *Acer Pseudoplatanus.* All the British Isles, common.

Summer, autumn.

Verging toward Septogloeum; even when the pseudopycnidia are developed, they often contain no spores. The dimensions of the spores are variable, being often up to 40–45μ (or even more) in length, and in breadth as little as 2–3·5μ; they can also be flexuose or irregular in form, and frequently more or less guttulate. The Phleospora is sometimes preceded and accompanied by a Phyllosticta.

Europe, U.S.A. ?, Canada.

Phleospora Pseudoplatani Bubák, Pilz. Montenegro, 16. Sacc. Syll. xviii. 489. *Septoria Pseudoplatani* Rob. & Desm. in Ann. Sci. Nat. 1847, viii. 21. Sacc. Syll. iii. 478. All. vi. 719.

Spots visible on both sides of the leaf, roundish, very small, at length confluent, red- or earthy-brown, with no distinct border or with a faint yellow one. Pycnidia epiphyllous, very minute, numerous, reddish-olive, then dark-brown, immersed, but somewhat prominent, opening by a pore, at length nearly

flat. Spores elongated, very narrow, straight or curved, often obtuse at the ends, 4-guttulate or guttules irregular, ultimately 3-septate, $30–50 \times 2–3\mu$, issuing in whitish or pallid tendrils.

On living or fading leaves of young seedlings or older plants of species of *Acer*, and apparently on the cotyledons and the fruits also. Common in the British Isles.　　　Jun. Jul.

The descriptions supposed to distinguish the two preceding forms have been transcribed, but there is little reason to believe that the distinction can be maintained. The many names given by authors to these fungi upon *Acer* are made to depend upon the host, or the epiphyllous or hypophyllous position of the pustules, etc.; see Mig. 602. Other reasons for the tortuous synonymy are: (1) the peridium is very indefinite at best and ultimately vanishes; (2) the septa of the spores are not always to be seen, although at other times they are quite distinct; (3) the guttules vary in appearance, being often, not the normal spherical oil-drops, but formless refringent masses. As a curiosity there will now be given a list of these other names which come into consideration on this point:

Septoria incondita Desm. in Ann. Sci. Nat. 1853, xx. 95 (f. *acericola*). Sacc. Syll. iii. 479. *S. epicotylea* Sacc. in Malpigh. xi. 314. *S. acerina* Peck, in 25th Rep. p. 87. Sacc. Syll. iii. 478. *Cylindrosporium Pseudoplatani* Died. in Ann. Mycol. x. 486; Pilz. Brand. 840. *C. saccharinum* Ell. & Ev. in Journ. Mycol. 1889, p. 155. *C. pseudoplatanicola* Mig. 602. *Septogloeum acerinum* Sacc. Syll. iii. 802. *S. hercynicum* Syd. in Ann. Mycol. iii. 234.

But *Septoria acerella* Sacc. Syll. iii. 479, having much narrower spores, $20–25 \times 1·5–2\mu$, must perhaps be considered to be in a different class. See *Phleospora Platanoidis* also.

Europe, N. Amer. (including Canada).

Phleospora Platanoidis Petr. in Ann. Mycol. xvii. 71. *Septoria seminalis* Sacc. var. *Platanoidis* All. in Hedwig. 1896, p. (34). Sacc. Syll. xiv. 971. All. vi. 720. *? S. apatela* All. vi. 721. *S. samarigena* Bub. & Krieg. in Ann. Mycol. x. 49. *Cylindrosporium Platanoidis* Died. in Ann. Mycol. x. 486; Pilz. Brand. 840.

Spots small, roundish, ochreous, without a distinct border, about 2 mm. wide. Pycnidia epiphyllous, covered, then open, about 100μ diam. Spores filiform, curved or falcate, with several guttules, at length 3-septate, $60–70 \times 1·5–2·5\mu$.

On leaves of *Acer platanoides*. Heythrop Park (on young plants only).

Germ. Austr. Swed.

Aegopodium

Phleospora Aegopodii Grove. *Cryptosporium Aegopodii* Preuss, Fung. Hoyersw. no. 322. *Septoria Aegopodii* Desm. Crypt. Fr. no. 616. Sacc. Syll. iii. 529. *S. Podagrariae* Lasch, in Klotzsch, Herb. Myc. no. 458. Sacc. Syll. iii. 529. All. vi. 724. Died. 423. Mig. p. 375, pl. 50, f. 8–10, pl. 51, f. 1.

Spots amphigenous, pale-yellowish above, becoming pale-brown or whitish, about 1–3 mm. wide, angular because bounded more or less by the veins, sometimes with an indistinct border. Pycnidia amphigenous, up to 250μ diam., covered by the raised epidermis, opening chiefly on the upper face. Spores vermiform, linear or subclavate, obtusely tapering at both ends, pluriguttulate, at length often 1-septate in the middle, then (pseudo)triseptate, 50–80 × 2·5–4μ; sporophores short, straight, about 8 × 2μ. (Fig. 27 a.)

On living leaves of *Aegopodium Podagraria*. Not uncommon: England, Scotland, Ireland.   Jul.–Sept.

It is frequently accompanied by *Phyllosticta Aegopodii* All. and, like that, is considered to form a part of the life-cycle of *Mycosphaerella Aegopodii* Potebn. See Ann. Mycol. viii. 49, 65.

It exactly resembles *Phleospora Heraclei* in general features, only the curving spores are more worm-like than arcuate. The middle septum is quite definite, the other two seem often to be illusory. Just as in *Ph. Heraclei* the spores ooze out in large quantities and form little whitish heaps on the surface (chiefly, but not solely, the upper). There is often a kind of pycnidium to be seen, very thin, pellucid or pale-brownish, but distinct and darker (almost black) around the pore.

Europe, U.S.A., Canada.

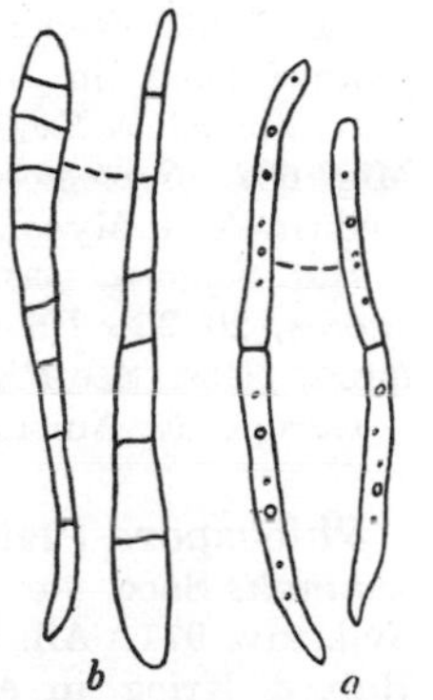

Crataegus

Phleospora Oxyacanthae Wallr. Flor. Crypt. Germ. 177. Sacc. Syll. iii. 578. All. vi. 935. Massee, Dis. Cult. Pl. 456. *Septoria Oxyacanthae* K. & S. Mykol. Hefte, ii. 108 (1823). Cooke, Handb. 442. *Cylindrosporium Oxyacanthae* Died. in Ann. Mycol. x. 486; Pilz. Brand. p. 842, p. 823, f. 12. Mig. 604.

Fig. 27. Spores of *Phleospora*: a, *Phl. Aegopodii*; b, *Phl. Oxyacanthae*; both × 600.

Spots variable in size, becoming yellow or purple-brown, sometimes wanting. Pycnidia aggregated, generally hypophyllous, cup-shaped, 100–150μ diam., frequently imperfect;

texture loosely parenchymatous, smoky-brown. Spores obclavate, slightly curved, at first guttulate and granular, then
with 6–8 septa (rarely more), 50–80 × 6–8μ, issuing in pale-
yellowish masses, which arc surrounded by a dark margin.
(Fig. 27b.)

On living leaves of *Crataegus Oxyacantha*. Albury; Bungay;
Worcestershire; Glamis; Appin; etc.

At times a harmful pest. The spots may be present, and yet few or
no spores be developed.

Jaap proved (Abhandl. Bot. Ver. Brand. 1907, li. 15) that it is the
pycnidial stage of his *Mycosphaerella Oxyacanthae*. Intimately mixed
up on the same spots with the Phleospora-pycnidia (often actually in
contact with them) can be found a number of the pycnidia of *Phyllosticta monogyna* Allesch., which is in fact only the early state of the
Phleospora. The transition from the one to the other is gradual, the
Phleospora-spores arising from the same proliferous stratum which
had previously produced the Phyllosticta spores, and thereby bursting
open the subglobose peridium and making it cup-shaped.

Europe, N. Amer.

Heracleum

Phleospora Heraclei Petr. in Ann. Mycol. xvii. 71. *Ascochyta
Heraclei* Lib. Exs. no. 51. *Septoria Heraclei* Desm. Pl. Crypt. no. 534.
Cooke, Handb. 441. Sacc. Syll. iii. 528. All. vi. 792. *Cylindrosporium
Heraclei* Ell. & Ev. Fung. Columb. no. 784, and in Journ. Mycol. 1888,
p. 52 (*non* Oud.). Von Höhn. Fragm. z. Mykol. no. 84 (1906). Sacc.
Syll. x. 502. Died. 843. *C. hamatum* Bres. *apud* Voss, Myc. Carn. iv.
256. Sacc. Syll. xi. 582. All. vii. 726. Mig. 604.

Amphigenous, but more conspicuous on the lower surface.
Spots none or indistinctly yellowish. Pycnidia scattered or
aggregated in little clusters, often immersed deep in the leaf
tissue, subglobose, brown-black, pierced at the summit.
Spores cylindrical, arcuate, obtuse at both ends, pluriguttulate or 1–4-septate, 45–60 × 3·5–4μ, issuing in a whitish
tendril.

On living or fading leaves of *Heracleum Sphondylium*.
Common: England, Wales, Scotland.   Summer–autumn.

The spores are very abundant; after they are expelled, they lie in
white patches upon the leaves. This fungus is said to be the pycnidial
stage of *Phyllachora Heraclei* Fckl. There has been great dispute
whether a pycnidium exists or not. But, on careful examination of
fresh specimens, a thin Septoria-like peridial wall can easily be seen,
exactly as can be found in *Phleospora Aegopodii*. The middle septum

28-2

of the spore is often alone conspicuous, the others are exceedingly delicate, if present at all.

A form similar to this has also been found on cultivated *Pastinaca sativa*, Mickleton, Glos. (Cotton). This may be compared with *Cylindrosporium Pimpinellae*, var. *Pastinacae* Sacc. Syll. xi. 583; Died. 844. Cf. also *Ramularia Pastinacae* Bubák and *Cercosporella Pastinacae* Karst.

Europe.

Robinia

Phleospora Robiniae v. Höhn. Fragm. z. Mykol. 1905, no. 90, and Annal. Myc. iii. 334. *Ascochyta Robiniae* Lib. Exs. no. 357. *Septoria Robiniae* Desm. in Ann. Sci. Nat. 1849, xi. 349. Sacc. Syll. iii. 484. All. vi. 845. *Cylindrosporium Robiniae* Died. 846. *Septosporium curvatum* Rabenh. & Br. Krankh. d. Pflanz. p. 14, pl. 1 A. *Septoria curvata* Sacc. Syll. iii. 484. *Fusarium Vogelii* Henn. in Zeitschr. f. Pflanzenkr. 1902, p. 15.

Spots irregular, yellowish, at length brown, sometimes with a faint darker margin. Pycnidia amphigenous, numerous, very small, scattered, immersed, pallid, opening by a wide pore. Spores linear, straight or gently curved, continuous or indistinctly 1-septate, $25–28 \times 2 \cdot 5\mu$, issuing in a little whitish mass like a Gloeosporium.

On living, but fading, leaflets of *Robinia Pseudacacia*. Kew (Cooke). Autumn.

The pycnidial wall, if not absent, is at any rate very thin. The habit is that of a Septogloeum. This fungus has been known at times to cause an epidemic disease. There is a f. *major* Brun. in Act. Soc. Linn. Bord. 1888, p. 101 (see Sacc. Syll. xiv. 973), with spores measuring $35–45 \times 1–1 \cdot 5\mu$.

Oudemans (Nederl. Kr. Arch. 1903, ser. 3, ii. 271) attributes to *Septoria curvata* spores $40–60 \times 5–6\mu$, with 1–3 septa, and no trace of constriction. It reminds one of Septogloeum.

Fr. Belg. Holl. Germ. Austr. Hung. Ital. U.S.A.

Ulmus, see under *Septogloeum*

RHABDOSPORA Mont. Flor. Algér. Bot. pp. 589, 592.

Pycnidia usually on stems, rather firm-walled, formed of distinct brown parenchymatous cells in one or several layers; cells rather thin-walled. Spores more or less like those of Septoria. (Fig. 28.)

The distinction of this genus from Septoria is exactly like that of Diplodina from Ascochyta. The firmer pycnidial wall is associated with the habit of growing upon the more solid parts of the host. "Spots" are usually absent or indefinite, but the two genera will always collide. Many species that have been referred to Rhabdospora have little or no pycnidial wall, and should be rather called Crypto-sporium; others belong to Phomopsis, e.g. *R. pachyderma* K. & B. on *Plantago*, and *R. Lebretoniana* Sacc. & Roum. on *Genista*.

Fig. 28. Spores of *Rhabdospora*: a, *R. Scrophulariae*, var. *Hesperidis*; b, *R. Cervariae* on *Peucedanum*; c, *R. inaequalis*; d, *R. ramealis*; all × 600.

The species are all arranged in the alphabetic order of their host-genera except that the plurivorous species are placed first.

Plurivorous

Rhabdospora Cervariae Syd. Bot. Notis. 1899, p. 170; and in Hedwig. 1900, p. 128. Sacc. Syll. xvi. 978. All. vii. 907. Died. 530. Mig. 447.

Pycnidia scattered or gregarious, black, globose-depressed, covered by the epidermis which is blackened above them, variable in size, 180–330μ diam. (usually 200–300μ), shining; texture of minute roundish cells. Spores linear or fusoid, curved, somewhat falcate, rather obtuse at both ends, eseptate, hyaline, 20–28 × 2·5–3μ; sporophores short, rather thick, eseptate, hyaline, 8–10 × 3–4μ. (Fig. 28 b.)

On dry stems of *Peucedanum officinale, Oenanthe peucedanifolia*, and (?) *Oenanthe crocata*. Anglesey (Rhodes). Brecon (Grove & Rhodes). Whitstable.   May–Aug.

The spores sometimes contain a row of guttules. They are like those of *R. Scrophulariae*.

Germ.

Rhabdospora Cirsii Karst. Symb. Myc. xv. 151. Sacc. Syll. iii. 592. All. vi. 897. Died. 525. Mig. 443. *Septoria pleosporoides* Sacc. var. *Cirsii* Karst. in Hedwig. 1884, p. 4. Sacc. Syll. x. 391.

No spots. Pycnidia numerous, scattered or gregarious, almost superficial, rounded or depressed, often saucer-shaped,

about 400μ diam., brown-black, often sunken round the base of the prominent ostiole, which ultimately becomes half as long as the pycnidium; base of pycnidium surrounded by short fuscous hyphae. Spores filiform, straight or rarely curvulous, attenuated at each end, pluriguttulate, with faint or no septa, 40–45 × 1–1·5μ (35–52 × 1–2μ, Karst.).

On dead stems of *Cirsium palustre*, near Aberdeen (Trail). On an old stem of *C. arvense*, Ballycastle, Antrim. Spring.

This is variously regarded as the spermogone of *Leptosphaeria dolioloides* var. *Cirsii* or of *Ophiobolus Cirsii*. The species is recorded abroad on other plants: *C. lanceolatum, C. oleraceum, Gnaphalium silvaticum, Trifolium medium,* and *Solanum tuberosum.*

Var. **Rumicis** Grove.

Spores 30–50 × 1μ, often quite straight and acicular, but occasionally also gently curved and lunulate, sometimes pluriguttulate, never seen septate.

On dead stems of *Rumex obtusifolius*. King's Norton, near Birmingham. Mar.

Fr. Germ. Holl. Finland.

Rhabdospora Hypochoeridis Allesch. in Hedwig. 1897, p. (163); Krypt. Flor. vi. 909. Sacc. Syll. xiv. 984. Died. 529. Mig. 446.

Pycnidia small, scattered or gregarious, covered by the epidermis, then erumpent, subconical, black. Spores filiform, straight or curvulous, hyaline, 16–30 × 0·6–1μ.

On dead stems of *Hypochoeris radicata*. On the cliffs, Polperro, Cornw. (Rhodes & Rilstone). July.

Referred to Allescher's species with doubt, for the spores of the Cornish specimens are better described as fusoid and arcuate, acutely pointed at both ends, eguttulate, 16–25 × 1–2·5μ. They resemble those which I have illustrated for *R. inaequalis*. A very similar form on *Cochlearia officinalis*, near the same place, with spores 26–28 × 2–3μ. Germ.

Rhabdospora nebulosa Sacc. Syll. iii. 589. All. vi. 889. Died. 524. Mig. 442. *Septoria nebulosa* Desm. in Ann. Sci. Nat. 1843, xix. 341.

Spots grey, elongated in the direction of the stem. Pycnidia at first covered, then piercing the epidermis with the sub-

conical black thickened ostiole, 60–100μ diam.; texture thin, brown, parenchymatous. The pycnidia are often arranged in long parallel rows. Spores filiform or acicular, mostly straight, with 10–15 minute guttules, 30–40 × 1μ, issuing in thin white tendrils.

On dead stems of *Petroselinum sativum*. Blackminster, near Evesham (Rhodes). This seems to me to be the stem-form of *Septoria Petroselini*. Dec.

Dr Rhodes records var. *minor* Desm. on dark spots of dead stems of *Aster Tripolium* in Anglesey, but I have not seen the spores.
Fr. Germ.

Rhabdospora phomatoides Sacc. Syll. iii. 579. All. vi. 906. Died. 528. Mig. 446. *Septoria phomatoides* Sacc. in Mich. i. 175.

Pycnidia here and there gregarious on areas of the stem which are distinctly paler than the surrounding parts but are not bordered by a definite margin, partly immersed, black, globose-depressed, 100–200μ diam., pierced by a pore. Spores linear, straight or faintly curvulous, ± obtuse at one or both ends, pluriguttulate, hyaline, 15–20 × 1–1·5μ.

On dead stems of *Reseda Luteola*. Near Alfrick, Worcestershire (Rhodes). Sept.

Var. **brachyspora** Sacc. in Mich. ii. 626; Syll. *ibid*

Spores shorter than in the type, biguttulate, 10–12 × 1·5–2μ; otherwise similar, but smaller and not on pallid spots.

On *Phlomis fruticosa*, Polperro. Apr.

Rhabdospora pleosporoides Sacc. Syll. iii. 588. Grove, in Journ. Bot. 1886, p. 137; 1912, p. 52. All. vi. 895.

Spots none. Pycnidia scattered, veiled by the epidermis, depressed-globose, black, 500μ diam.; texture rather dense; ostiole short, papillate. Spores filiform, straight or curvulous, indistinctly guttulate, 30–50 × 1–1·5μ.

On old stems of the larger herbaceous plants, e.g. *Rumex, Urtica, Heracleum, Chaerophyllum temulum, Oenanthe crocata*, etc. Earlswood Lakes, Wk.; Worcestershire; Suffolk; Cheshire; Farne Islands; Antrim; etc. Jan.–Mar.

The pycnidia resemble in size and habit the perithecia of *Pleospora herbarum*. It has been found abroad on the stems of many other similar plants, and even on the fruits of *Heracleum*.

Var. **rubescens** Karst. Symb. Myc. xv. 151. Sacc. Syll. iii. 589. All. vi. 896. Trail, in Scot. Nat. 1885, p. 188.

Pycnidia on dull reddish spots on the dead stems, sub-epidermal, globose-depressed, with a short ostiole. Spores fusoid, slender, usually curved, pluriguttulate, $25-30 \times 1 \cdot 5-2\mu$. On dead stems of *Angelica silvestris*. Near Aberdeen (Trail).

Europe generally, the var. in Finland. May.

Rhabdospora Scrophulariae Grove.

Pycnidia scattered, covered by the epidermis, then erumpent, black, $300-400\mu$ diam.; texture thin, brownish, darker round the pore. Spores filiform, mostly curved or arcuate, rarely straight, acute at both ends, containing a row of minute guttules, $25-36 \times 1 \cdot 5-2\mu$; sporophores linear, narrow, shorter than the spore.

On dead stems of *Scrophularia nodosa*. King's Norton. Apr.

There is an all-round true pycnidial wall, though it is very thin and like that of a Septoria. This fungus might well be the stem-form of *Septoria Scrophulariae* Peck, but that species has not yet been found in Britain, nor so far as I know in Europe. No sign of a septum was perceived, and the breadth of the spore was uniform except at the extreme ends. The spores resemble those of *R. Cervariae* on *Oenanthe*.

Var. **Hesperidis** Grove (Fig. 28a).

On *Hesperis matronalis*. Landeviddy, Polperro (Rilstone).

The spores of this fungus resemble those of *R. Cervariae* in being fusoid-falcate, very acute at the ends, and having a row of guttules (5-8) down the centre; they measured $25-30 \times 1 \cdot 5-2\mu$.

Artemisia
[**Rhabdospora Artemisiae** Trail, Fung. Hardanger, in Trans. Bot. Soc. Edin. xvii. 494. Sacc. Syll. x. 395.

"Pycnidia scattered uniformly, but very profusely, over the stems, globular, $130-140\mu$ diam.; ostiole prominent, piercing the epidermis. Spores fusoid-filiform, straight or slightly curved, pluriguttulate, hyaline, $8-15 \times 1\mu$."

"On dead stems of *Artemisia vulgaris*, at Graven, Scotiae" (Sacc.).]

This is an error of Saccardo's. Graven is in Norway, not in Scotland, as he thought, but the fungus may well be found in this country.

Betula

Rhabdospora fibriseda Sacc. Syll. iii. 586. *Hendersonia fibriseda*
Berk. in Hook. Journ. Bot. Kew, 1853, p. 43, pl. 3, f. 10. Cooke,
Handb. 436.

"Pycnidia minute, subglobose, very delicate, blackish-blue.
Spores elongated, flexuous, obtuse at both ends, faintly guttulate, about 37 × 5μ; sporophores short, obtuse."

On wood of *Betula*. King's Cliffe. *n.v.* Dec.

"Pycnidia punctiform, seated on definite white spots, following the
direction of the fibres. Very delicate pale blackish-blue, especially at
the edge which consists of interwoven fibres" (Berk. *l.c.*). The spores
are figured as containing a row of six or seven guttules.

Centaurea

Rhabdospora coriacea Bubák, in Ann. Mycol. 1904, p. 398. Sacc.
Syll. xviii. 401. Died. 525. Mig. 443.

Spots small, silvery-grey, often confluent. Pycnidia gregarious, depressed-globose, roundish or oblong, black, 80–
130μ diam.; texture parenchymatous, firm, somewhat coriaceous. Spores acicular, straight or curved, hyaline, faintly
guttulate, 20–30 × 1μ.

On dead stems of *Centaurea nigra*. Ayrshire (Boyd).
Spernal, Wk.; and Ockeridge Wood, Ws. (Rhodes). Ribbes-
ford, by the Severn. On *C. Scabiosa*, Tilshead, S. Wilts.
(Rhodes).

The spots are often very shining and silvery, especially on *C.
Scabiosa*.
Bohemia.

Equisetum

Rhabdospora detospora All. vi. 901. Proc. Roy. Irish Acad.
1931, p. 54. *Septoria detospora* Sacc. Syll. iii. 576.

Pycnidia loosely gregarious, lens-shaped, covered by the
epidermis which is not elevated, up to 500μ diam. Spores
cylindrical, flexuose, pluriguttulate, hyaline, 60 × 3μ, joined
to one another at the base by a short lateral process.

On stems of *Equisetum limosum*. Co. Down, Ireland. Apr.

But see *Septogloeum Equiseti* Died. (in Vol. ii), which is the same
species.
Fr. Germ.

Euphorbia
Rhabdospora Euphorbiae Brun. Liste Sphaerops. p. 52. Sacc.
Syll. x. 396. All. vi. 903. Grove, in Journ. Bot. 1922, p. 84. ? *Phoma*
Euphorbiae f. *amplior* Brun. in Bull. Soc. Sci. Nat. Nantes, 1894, iv.
34. Sacc. Syll. xiv. 884. All. vii. 801.

Pycnidia crowded, gregarious, subepidermal, then erumpent by a slit, 120–200μ diam., shining, black; texture thick,
dark olive-brown. Spores cylindrical, usually quite straight,
obtuse at the ends, sometimes with a faint guttule at each
end, 10·5–18 × 2–2·5μ; sporophores very short.

On dead stems of *Euphorbia palustris*. Edgbaston Botanic
Gardens. Feb. Mar.

Cf. *R. nicaeensis* Sacc. Syll. iii. 587, which is similar.

Fagus
Rhabdospora princeps Sacc. Syll. iii. 584. *Septoria princeps* B.
& Br. in Ann. Nat. Hist. 1861, vii. 380, pl. 15, f. 11. Cooke, Handb.
446. Tul. Carp. Fung. ii. 227, pl. 25, f. 7.

Pycnidia rather large, depressed, papillate, covered by the
epidermis. Spores oblong-cylindrical, obtusely rounded at
both ends, 5–7 septate, 50–60 × 9·5–15μ, oozing out in an irregular mass; sporophores straight, simple, 13–20μ long.

On dead sticks of *Fagus silvatica*. Batheaston (Broome).
n.v.

Said by Tulasne to belong to *Massaria eburnea* Sacc. Syll. ii. 153,
which accompanies it. Tulasne states that the pycnospores which are
not extruded become fuscous-black when old. Not really congeneric
with the other Rhabdosporas.
Denm.

Phragmites
Rhabdospora curva All. vi. 916. Died. p. 531, p. 432, f. 27. Mig.
p. 447, pl. 57, f. 18. *Septoria curva* Karst. Symb. Myc. xxi. 103. Sacc.
Syll. x. 385.

Pycnidia scattered, at first covered, then piercing the epidermis by a pore, black, globose or elliptic, depressed, up to
400μ or more long, at length vanishing in the upper part and
leaving an open black cup; texture thick, of rather small-
celled parenchyma, almost carbonaceous. Spores inequi-
laterally fusoid, tapering at both ends and even subacute below, sharply curved, falcate, hyaline, 14–25 × 3–4μ, with
many minute guttules, at length with a median septum.

On dry culms of *Phragmites communis*. Herm, Channel Islands (Rhodes). Sept.

The spores are said by Diedicke to give indications of becoming at length unequally 3-celled. It is not a good Rhabdospora, and but for its septum (or septa) might be considered the stem-form of *Septoria oxyspora*.

Germ. Finland.

Plantago

Rhabdospora pachyderma Kab. & Bub. in Hedwig. 1904, p. 420. Sacc. Syll. xviii. 400. Mig. 448.

"Pycnidia scattered, black, immersed, lens-shaped, 100–130μ diam., raising the epidermis, colouring it cinereous, and piercing it with the pore; wall parenchymatous, firm, thick, brown. Spores acicular, tapering at both ends, almost acute; straight or slightly bent, 1-septate, hyaline, 15–25 × 1–1·75" (Kab. & Bub.).

On dry stems of *Plantago lanceolata*. Tilshead, Wilts. (Rhodes). Near Earlswood Lakes, Birmingham.

This fungus constitutes simply the C-spores of *Phomopsis subordinaria*, by which it was accompanied at both localities.

Moravia, Bohemia.

Rubus

Rhabdospora ramealis Sacc. Syll. iii. 580. All. vi. 919. *Septoria ramealis* Rob. & Desm. in Ann. Sci. Nat. 1853, xx. 94. *Septocyta ramealis* Petrak, in Ann. Mycol. 1927, xxv. 330. *Cytosporina ramealis* Petr. in Ann. Mycol. 1920, xvii. 81. *C. Rubi* Died. p. 549, p. 432, f. 37 (on living *R. plicatus*). Mig. 460.

Spots purple or rufous-brown, at length dry and pallid-white and then bordered with purple, elongated or oval, 3–8 mm. long or more, covered with black dots. Pycnidia oblong, convex, usually arranged more or less in lines, 250–500μ diam., immersed, then somewhat prominent when the epidermis splits, pierced by a minute pore. Spores linear, straight or rarely curved, faintly 5–7-guttulate, at length pseudo-triseptate, 20–27 × 1·5–2μ (15–25 × 1μ, Sacc.; 25–42 × 1–1·5μ, Boyd; 18–28 × 1–1·5μ, Died.), issuing as a white tendril; sporophores slender shorter. (Fig. 28d.)

On living stems of *Rubus* (*fruticosus*, etc.). Barnet (Cooke). Wirral (Ellis). West Kilbride (Boyd). Oxford (Cotton), var.

macrospora. Osterley; Kent; Barmouth; etc. Occasionally doing serious damage. Mar.–May.

There is a var. *crassiuscula* Berl. (Sacc. Syll. x. 388) on dead or dying stems of *Rubus*, in Italy, in which the spores are 3μ thick, and the spots indistinct or none. The var. *macrospora* Appel & Laub., is described in Arb. Biol. Anst. f. Land. u. Forstw. 1905, v. 150, with spores up to 60 × 2·5μ. Petrak's genus Septocyta is founded on the idea of there being a kind of plurilocular stroma in this fungus. W. Europe.

Salix

Rhabdospora salicella Sacc. Syll. iii. 585. All. vi. 920, with fig. Died. 532. Mig. p. 449, pl. 57, f. 15. *Septoria salicella* B. & Br. in Ann. Nat. Hist. 1854, xiii. 459, pl. 15, f. 7. Cooke, Handb. 442.

Pycnidia subglobose, concealed by the epidermis, which is elevated in little pustules. Spores fusoid, 3-septate, 30μ long, issuing in irregular pale-pink tendrils.

On branches of *Salix*. Penzance (Ralfs). No doubt this is *Septomyxa Salicis* Grove (*q.v.* Vol. II) in a more developed state.

"Concealed by the cuticle, which is obscurely pustulate in consequence of the pressure of the subglobose pycnidia" (B. & Br.). Rabenhorst found what he regarded as the same species, at Dresden, on leaves of *Salix*. Belg. Germ. Denm.

Sorbus

Rhabdospora inaequalis Sacc. Syll. iii. 580. Grove, in Journ. Bot. 1886, p. 137. All. vi. 925, with fig. Died. p. 534, p. 432, f. 29. Mig. p. 450, pl. 57, f. 9–11. *Septoria inaequalis* Sacc. & Roum. in Rev. Mycol. 1884, p. 35, pl. 44, f. 30.

Pycnidia densely gregarious, immersed, raising the epidermis, then erumpent and subsuperficial, depressed-globose, extremely unequal, scarcely papillate, black, up to 250μ diam. Spores fusoid, acute at both ends but more so at one end, curved, continuous or (seldom) 1-septate, 15–18 × 2·5–3μ; sporophores filiform, hyaline, variable, 20–40 × 2·5μ. (Fig. 28c.)

On smooth bark of *Sorbus Aucuparia*. Harvington, Ws. (Rhodes). Harborne, Birmingham. Mar.

My specimens (Harborne) had the pycnidia somewhat shining, varying much in size and form, slightly papillate or not at all. Sporophores fasciculate or subramose at base, often swollen in the middle, averaging double the length of the spores or more. Ardennes, Germ. Denm. Holl.

Tanacetum

Rhabdospora tanaceticola Bub. & Kab. in Hedwig. 1909, vol.
50, p. 42. Sacc. Syll. xxii. 1132. Mig. 451.

Pycnidia often scattered, sometimes crowded or arranged
in lines, 100–150μ broad, lens-shaped, depressed, black, subepidermal, dehiscing by an excentric black pore; texture
parenchymatous, brownish-black. Spores abundant, filiform,
curvulous or arcuate, rarely straight, attenuated towards
each end, but rounded, hyaline or faintly greenish, 3-septate
(but at first continuous), 20–42 × 2·5–3μ.

On dead stems of *Tanacetum vulgare*. Hanbury and Ribbesford, Ws. (Rhodes). Gt. Haywood, Staffs.   Apr.–Aug.

So far as the Worcestershire specimens go they have no real pycnidium, and should be classed under Cryptosporium, as *C. tanaceticola*.
Their spores are usually straight, 20–28 × 1·5–2·5μ, sometimes
thickened at one end, colourless, and showing no sign of septation.
The two genera seem to merge into one another, when growing on
herbaceous stems. *R. Tanaceti* Oud. has spores 50–60 × 2μ.
Bohemia.

Vaccinium

Rhabdospora stemmatea Died. 536. Mig. 451. *Asteromella
stemmatea* Petr. in Ann. Mycol. 1924, xxii. 40.

Spots scattered, mostly round, fuscous, surrounded by a
darker brown border. Pycnidia epiphyllous, gregarious, often
confluent, thick-walled, with the vertex slightly projecting
through a torn opening. Spores filiform, somewhat acute at
the ends, hyaline, 6–10 × 1–1·5μ; no spurophores visible.

On leaves of *Vaccinium Vitis-idaea*. Aboyne, Scotland
(Babington). Recorded on the same also at Forres; Tay; and
Ross-shire.

Cf. *Septoria stemmatea, supra*. Both species have been referred to
the same Friesian name *Depazea stemmatea*; the older mycologists
seem never to have met with any spores in the pycnidia.
Germ. Austr. Swed.

Vitis

Rhabdospora Müggenburgii Sacc. Syll. iii. 581. All. vi. 929.
Septoria Müggenburgii Pirott. Fung. Parass. Vit. p. 66.

Pycnidia minute, spherical, black, immersed in the bark, at
length erumpent. Spores fusoid, curvulous, hyaline, with
several (about 9) guttules, 25–35 × 4–5μ.

On branches of *Vitis vinifera*. Kew Gardens (Cooke). Apr.

In the original description the spores are stated to be "pale-brownish, 46–63 × 3μ". I find the spores of the Kew specimens to be perfectly hyaline, and to measure as given above; their shape is rather clavate-fusoid, and not at all rod-shaped as stated by Pirotta of his. Slavonia.

COLLONEMA Grove, in Journ. Bot. 1886, p. 136.

Pycnidia subglobose, somewhat carbonaceous, glabrous, superficial, pierced with a pore, sometimes papillate. Spores long, cylindrical or fusoid, one-celled or pseudoseptate, hyaline, expelled in tendrils or as a globose. (Fig. 29.)

Distinguished from Aposphaeria by its elongated spores.

Collonema papillatum Grove, in Journ. Bot. 1886, p. 136, pl. 266, f. 5. All. vi. 931, with fig. Sacc. Syll. x. 397.

Pycnidia gregarious, minute, globose or subovoid, the base immersed in the wood, then free, attenuated above into a well-formed conical papilla which is pierced by a delicate pore, rugose, black, 80–130μ diam.; contents white, firmly glued together. Spores fusoid, acuminate at each end, very pointed, somewhat curved, eguttulate, 18–19 × 2·5μ.

Fig. 29.   *Collonema papillatum*: pycnidium with tendril,   × 90; spores, × 600.

On the inside of the loose bark of a fallen tree, *Acer Pseudoplatanus*. Sutton Coldfield.   Dec. Jan.

It was accompanied by *Graphium penicilloides* Corda. Even after lying for a long time in water, the spores separate from one another with difficulty; they ooze out from the pycnidium in a very long slender filiform tendril.

[SPHAEROGRAPHIUM Sacc. Syll. iii. 596.

No species of this genus, which resembles Sphaeronaema in shape but differs in its elongated spores (30μ long or more), have yet been found in Britain. Two, one on *Lonicera* and another on *Viburnum*, are likely to occur here.]

MICROPERA Lév. in Ann. Sci. Nat. 1846, v. 283.

Pycnidia fasciculate or caespitose, more or less conical or oblong, of a corky or leathery texture, composed of thick-walled prosenchymatous cells; there is a little stroma at the base in which the pycnidia are somewhat sunken, the ostioles are imperfectly developed. Spores filiform-fusoid, bent or flexuous, hyaline, pluriguttulate; sporophores short. (Fig. 30.)

Most of the species are pycnidial stages of the genus Cenangium or Dermatea.

Micropera Drupacearum Lév. in Ann. Sci. Nat. 1846, v. 283.
Cooke, Handb. 462. Sacc. Syll. iii. 605. All. vi. 961, with fig. Died. p. 542, p. 432, f. 32. Mig. p. 456, pl. 59, f. 7–10. Massee, Fung. Flor. iv. 117. Tul. Carp. iii. 157, pl. 19, f. 15.

Pycnidia leathery, forming pustules or groups, covered by the periderm, immersed in the cortex, then emerging by a transverse fissure, obovoid or sub-cylindrical, varying in shape through mutual pressure, reddish-black, clad with a whitish floccose or scurfy covering except around the ostiole, about 250μ diam. Spores narrowly cylindric-fusoid, acuminate at both ends, curved or undulated, pluriguttulate, at length 1-septate, 40–50×2–3μ; sporophores branched or fasciculate, subulate, up to 20μ long.

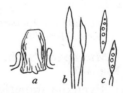

Fig. 30. *Micropera padina*: a, *pycnidium*, × 12; b, young spores on sporophores, and c, mature spores, × 600.

In bark of dead branches of species of *Prunus* (Plum, Cherry, Gean, etc.). King's Cliffe, Northants.; Forden; Birmingham; Roxburgh; Ayrshire; etc.   Autumn.

The pycnidial stage of *Dermatea Cerasi* de Not., with which it often grows intermixed. Phillips (Discom. 341) describes the spores as being 3–5 septate, and they may ultimately become so; he also (following Tulasne) assigns to this species "spermogonia", smaller than the pycnidia, with filiform curved spores 13–16μ, on very short sporophores.

Europe, U.S.A., Canada.

Micropera padina Sacc. Syll. iii. 605. All. vi. 961. Died. p. 543, p. 432, f. 33. Mig. p. 457, pl. 59, f. 11, 12. *Sphaeronaema brunneoviride* Auersw.; Mig. p. 126, pl. 12, f. 1, 2!

Pycnidia loosely gregarious, very prominent, separate or rarely connate, oblong-conical, up to 1 mm. high, umbilicate at apex, ferruginous-brown; texture very thick, paler within. Spores fusoid or lanceolate-obclavate, straight or faintly curved, hyaline, with a few guttules or eguttulate, 20–25 (or more) $\times$ 3·5–4μ, issuing in pinkish tendrils or globules; pedicels subulate, forked at base, hyaline, as long as or longer than the spore (45–60 $\times$ 2·5μ, Petr.). (Fig. 30.)

On the smaller dry branches of *Prunus Padus*, in abundance, Cwm Llwch, and by the roadside under Cerrig Gleisiau, Brecknock (Rhodes & Grove). A very similar form occurred on the cultivated (Pershore) Plum, at Blackminster near Evesham, with arcuate spores, 20–22 $\times$ 2–3μ (Rhodes).

Mar.–Jul.

Altitude (on *Padus*) up to 1000 ft. Belongs to *Dermatea Padi* Fr. Germ. Moravia.

Micropera Sorbi Sacc. Syll. iii. 605. All. vi. 962. Died. 543. Mig. 457.

Pycnidia imperfect, loosely gregarious, up to 400μ diam., erumpent but not prominent, globose-depressed; texture of very small dense cells. Spores fusoid, acute at both ends, curvulous, eseptate, 15–16 $\times$ 0·75–2μ; sporophores verticillately branched, 20–25 $\times$ 2·5μ, rising from a fuscous-violet basal stratum.

On bark of twigs of *Sorbus Aucuparia*. Bidston Hill, Cheshire (Ellis). June.

Fuckel stated that this is the pycnidial stage of *Cenangium inconstans* (Fr.).
Fr. Germ. Ital.

DILOPHOSPORA Desm. in Ann. Sci. Nat. 1840, xiv. 6.

Pycnidia globose, pierced by a pore, usually covered with a black stroma-like crust. Spores cylindrical, continuous, hyaline, furnished at each end with a tuft of simple or forked setae. (Fig. 31.)

Gramineae

Dilophospora Alopecuri Fr. Summ. Veg. Scand. p. 419 (1849).
Bessey, in Journ. Mycol. 1906, p. 57. *Sphaeria Alopecuri* Fr. Elench.
Fung., part 2, p. 90 (1828). *D. graminis* Desm. in Ann. Sci. Nat.
1840, xiv. 6, pl. 1, f. 2. Berk. in Gard. Chron. 1862, p. 1009, with fig.
Berk. & Br. in Ann. Nat. Hist. 1865, xv. 401. Cooke, Handb. p. 436,
f. 159. Sacc. Syll. iii. 600. All. vi. 948, with fig. Died. p. 544, p. 432,
f. 34. Mig. p. 457, pl. 58, f. 9–11. Massee, Dis. Cult. Pl. 427. Stevens,
525.

Pycnidia very minute, covered with a blackened crust,
seriate, crowded, subconnate, globose, immersed in a colourless stroma; ostioles punctiform, black, in wet weather surrounded by a whitish disc. Spores cylindric-
fusoid, straight or curvulous, with a row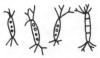
of two or more small guttules, at length
even 3-septate, $10–15 \times 1 \cdot 5–2\mu$ ($15–20 \times 2–$
$2 \cdot 3\mu$, Bessey), producing at each $\pm$ truncate   Fig. 31. *Dilophospora*
end 2–6 delicate filiform sometimes forked   *Alopecuri*: spores (one,
divergent setae, which are about $4–6\mu$ long   on the right, mature),
and $0 \cdot 5–0 \cdot 75\mu$ broad. $\times 600$.

On cultivated Wheat and wild grasses (*Poa, Festuca, Agrostis, Alopecurus, Dactylis, Holcus*, etc.), attacking both the
leaves and sheaths and the spikelets, which may become much
distorted. All Great Britain, as far north as Aberdeen, and
also in Ireland; occasionally ruining a crop.   May–Oct.

It is said to have a perfect ascigerous form, *Dilophia graminis* Sacc.
(Syll. ii. 357), but this seems to have not yet been found in Britain.
On the leaves the pycnidia are less perfectly formed, and are immersed
in a colourless stroma which causes swelling and distortion of the
parenchyma.
Fr. Belg. Holl. Germ. Hung. Denm. U.S.A.

CYTOSPORINA Sacc. in Mich. ii. 263.

Stroma valsiform, verruciform, or effused, on bark or wood,
hard, brown-black without, paler within. Pycnidia more or
less immersed, emerging even completely, plurilocular or
pseudolocellate, opening by one or more ostioles. Spores filiform, curved, continuous, over 12μ long.

Differs from Cytospora in its more elongated spores. But

most of the forms that have been assigned to it are the B-spores of Phomopsis. What true species there are seem to belong to Cryptosphaeria or Eutypa.

Cytosporina Acharii Grove, in Kew Bull. 1923, p. 358. *Cytospora Acharii* Sacc. Syll. iii. 267. All. vi. 566. Died. 369. Mig. 212.

Stroma widely effused, thin, black outside, paler within. Pycnidia partly immersed, seated on the wood, convex on a roundish or elliptic base, unilocular, black, usually densely aggregated, with thick walls, opening by a narrow pore or slit. Spores filiform, curved or lunate, about 13–15μ long, at length issuing in whitish tendrils; sporophores about as long, fasciculate (or, rather, branched at the base), each with a single apical spore.

On decorticated branches, especially of *Acer*. Not uncommon.

The pycnidial stage of *Eutypa Acharii* Tul.
Recorded in other countries also on *Carpinus*, *Fagus*, *Populus*, *Prunus*, etc. The pycnidia usually appear before the perithecia.
Europe, N. America.

Cytosporina flavovirens Grove, in Kew Bull. 1923, p. 358. *Cytospora flavovirens* Sacc. Syll. iii. 268. All. vi. 566. Died. 331. Mig. 189.

Stroma thick, more or less effused, of a greenish-yellow colour within, but nearly black outside. Loculi totally immersed, very crowded, oblong, about 500μ diam., with thick fleshy indefinite greenish yellow walls, at length opening by an inconspicuous pore or slit. Spores copious, linear-filiform, curved or lunate, 30μ long or more, nearly sessile, agglutinated, expelled during wet weather in whitish tendrils which become darker with age.

On bark or wood of *Acer*, etc. Not uncommon.

The pycnidial stage of *Eutypa flavovirens* Tul.
It has been recorded on many hosts, *Fagus*, *Quercus*, etc., but can be recognised at once, on sectioning, by the peculiar colour of its stroma, which is that of flour of sulphur mixed with a little powdered charcoal. The pycnidia are not abundant; they are usually formed before the perithecia.
Europe, N. America.

Cytosporina ludibunda Sacc. Syll. iii. 601. All. vi. 955. Died. 548. Mig. 460.

"Stromata immersed, variable, surrounded by a black line, plurilocular; contents golden-yellow. Spores filiform-hamate, hyaline, 25–30 × 1μ, issuing in yellowish-rose-coloured tendrils; sporophores acicular, once verticillate, hyaline, 15–20 × 2μ" (Sacc.).

"On branches of *Prunus, Robinia*, and *Ulmus.*"

Kidd & Beaumont obtained this fungus on Apple twenty times in cultures, from the stalk or at the calyx, rarely at a lenticel. It had been found once before on Apple. See T.B.M.S. 1924, x. 107. Some at least of the specimens published under this name belong to Phomopsis, and the description given above reminds one strongly of the B-spores of that genus, so that it is conceivable that *C. ludibunda* on *Ulmus* is a pycnidial stage of *Cryptosporella hypodermia* Sacc., while the forms on *Prunus, Robinia*, etc. belong to the corresponding *Diaporthae*.

Fr. Ital.

Cytosporina milliaria Sacc. Syll. iii. 602. All. vi. 953. Died. 546. Mig. 458.

Stromata small, punctiform, subglobose, pallid, unilocular, just sunken at the base in the wood, at length opening by a pore or slit. Spores filiform, variously curved, about 24 × 1μ.

On branch of *Quercus*. Prenton, Cheshire (Ellis).

The pycnidial stage of *Valsa milliaria* Nits. = *Eutypa milliaria* Sacc.

It is recorded abroad also on *Fagus* and *Staphylea*.

Germ. Swed. Ital. U.S.A.

Cytosporina notha Died. p. 545, p. 432, f. 36. Mig. 458. *Rhabdospora notha* Sacc. Syll. iii. 583. All. vi. 886. *Phomopsis notha* Lind, Dan. Fungi, 422.

Stromata cortical, bursting the outer layers and surrounded by the laciniae of the bark, free above, for the most part multilocular, each loculus having a separate ostiole, 250–300μ diam.; texture dark-brown without, paler within, indistinctly parenchymatous. Spores arcuate-filiform, tapering towards both ends and subacute, hyaline, continuous, 30 × 1–1·5μ; sporophores cylindrical, straight, 9–11 × 1μ.

On dry bark of *Acer Pseudoplatanus, A. platanoides.*
Cheshire, several places (Ellis).

This is suggested by Saccardo to be a pycnidial stage of *Diaporthe
Hystrix* Sacc. It seems to be a form of a Phomopsis, in any case, but
Wehmeyer does not place it under his *Cryptodiaporthe hystrix.*
Fr. Germ. Denm.

Cytosporina hysterioides Cooke, in Grevill. xvi. 48 (1887). Sacc.
Syll. x. 403. All. vi. 951.

"Stromata gregarious, elongated, elliptical, black, breaking
through the bark in the form of a Hysterium. Spores cylindrical, obtuse, curved, $20-4\mu$; sporophores short."
"On slender twigs of *Celtis.*" Kew Gardens (Cooke). Apr.

" Resembling very closely an erumpent Hysterium."
It is a doubtful member of the genus, and had better be suppressed.
Cooke's description is incorrect in several particulars; see Kew Bull.
1923, p. 359.

Cytosporina millepunctata Sacc. Syll. iii. 602. All. vi. 953. Died.
547. Mig. 459.

Stromata scattered, immersed, minute, subglobose, pallid,
mostly unilocular. Spores filiform-cylindric, variously curved,
hyaline, 40–48 (or even 60) $\times 1\mu$, at length issuing in pink or
yellowish tendrils; sporophores obsolete or very short.
On dead fallen branches of *Fraxinus excelsior.* Rather
common, but easily overlooked. Nov.

The pycnidial stage of *Cryptosphaeria millepunctata* Sacc. = *Valsa
eunomia* Nits., which is equally common. The two stages occur
intermixed.

Cytosporina Ribis Magn. in Ann. Mycol. 1903, i. 508, pl. 11, f.
1–6. Sacc. Syll. xviii. 406.

Stromata small, blackish, hairy without, loculi tortuous,
opening by one or more mouths. Spores in mass yellowish,
filiform, bent or lunate, about $33 \times 1\cdot5\mu$, issuing in long tendrils; sporophores filiform, straight, about as long as the
spore.

Reported as "Collar Fungus" on collar and roots of *Ribes Grossularia*. Middlesex; Kent; Hereford; Hampshire; Cambridgeshire; etc.

No true specimens seen. See Ann. Mycol. 1903, i. 503, and 1910, viii. 174, pl. 3, f. 8–10; also Journ. Board Agric. 1909, April, p. 34. *Libertella Ribis* A. L. Smith is very similar, if not identical; both of them seem to be the B-spores of *Phomopsis pungens* (*q.v.*, p. 212).
Belg. Holl. Germ.

Cytosporina Staphyleae Cooke, in Grevill. xvi. 48. Sacc. Syll. x. 403. All. vi. 956.

Stromata scattered, erumpent, minute, convex, blackish. Spores cylindrical, obtuse, curved, guttulate, 20–25 × 3–4μ; sporophores simple, very short.

On twigs of *Staphylea trifoliata*. Kew Gardens. A doubtful species. June.

Cf. *C. milliaria*, which has narrower spores.

Cytosporina stellulata Sacc. Syll. iii. 602. All. vi. 956.

Stromata small, very crowded, erumpent, depressed-conical, with several loculi immersed irregularly in a dark-grey mass. Spores abundant, filiform, bent, curved, flexuous, or hooked at the end, 25–30 × 1μ, emerging in golden tendrils.

On branches of *Ulmus campestris*. Droitwich; Sutton Coldfield; etc.

These specimens seem to agree with the fungus which Saccardo (*l.c.*) assigned to *Eutypella stellulata*. It is evidently not that which Fuckel (Symb. Myc. p. 196) assigned to his *Valsa stellulata*, for the spores of that measure 16 × 3–4μ. It is probable, however, that Saccardo was mistaken, and that the *Cytosporina stellulata* which he described as above was really the spores of a Phomopsis; for in the same pycnidium with these I have often found the ordinary A-spores of that genus. Das Gupta (*Annals of Botany*, 1930, xliv. 350) observed the same phenomenon in his cultures of a fungus which he had received under the name of *Cytosporina ludibunda*. Therefore that name ceases to have any meaning, and the same may be said of the names *Cytosporina Ribis* and *C. stellulata*; these three "species" are merely states of the *Phomopses* on each host (*Prunus, Robinia, Ribes* and *Ulmus*) respectively. Saccardo's *C. stellulata* on *Ulmus* was no doubt the same as his *C. ludibunda* on that host.
Fr. Germ. Swed.

ADDENDUM

Closely similar to these three Cytosporinas just mentioned are the members of the discredited genus *Phlyctaena*. All the British species previously ranged under *Phlyctaena* are now known to be merely the B-spores of the genus *Phomopsis*. But, for the sake of completeness, they will be enumerated here in alphabetical order:

PHLYCTAENA Desm. in Ann. Sci. Nat. 1847, viii. 16 (as Phlyctema).

Pycnidia immersed, usually simple, at length erumpent, globose or oblong, frequently dehiscing by a slit; peridium for the most part only slightly developed or at times almost wanting except above. Spores filiform or elongate-fusoid, very narrow, curved or hooked at the upper end.

Phlyctaena arcuata Berk. North Amer. Fungi, in Grevill. ii. 100. Sacc. Syll. iii. 595. On *Solidago*, Polperro (Rilstone). To *Phomopsis linearis*, p. 178.

Phlyctaena Coryli Lamb. & Fautr. in Bull. Soc. Myc. Fr. 1899, p. 155. On twigs of *Corylus*, Doncaster (Ellis). To *Phomopsis revellens*, p. 182.

Phlyctaena Fraxini Ellis, in T.B.M.S. 1913, iv. 126. On *Fraxinus*, Malvern (Ellis), accompanied by the A-spores. To *Phomopsis scobina*, p. 188.

Phlyctaena Johnstonii B. & Br. in Ann. Nat. Hist. 1852, ix. 328 (note). Cooke, Handb. 464. On *Senecio Jacobaea*, Berwick (Johnston). To *Phomopsis Achilleae*, p. 174.

Phlyctaena Lituus Grove. *Septoria Lituus* B. & Br. in Ann. Nat. Hist. 1854, xiii. 459, pl. 15, f. 5. Cooke, Handb. 443. *Rhabdospora Lituus* Sacc. Syll. iii. 586. On smooth twigs (unnamed), Highgate; Penzance (Berk.).

Phlyctaena maculans Fautr. in Rev. Mycol. 1896, p. 70. On *Solanum tuberosum* (Cotton). To *Phomopsis Tulasnei*, p. 226.

Phlyctaena phomatella Sacc. Syll. iii. 594. On twigs of *Ulmus campestris*, Hampstead (Cooke). To *Phomopsis oblonga*, p. 232.

Var. on *Aesculus*, Swansea (Ellis). To *Phomopsis coneglanensis*, p. 167.

Phlyctaena Pseudophoma Sacc. Syll. iii. 595. *Septoria Pseudophoma* Sacc. Fung. Ital. pl. 1176. On branches of *Populus*, Derbyshire (Smith). To *Phomopsis putator* (?), p. 208.

Phlyctaena vagabunda Desm. in Ann. Sci. Nat. 1847, viii. 16. Cooke, Handb. 464. A composite species, occurring e.g. on *Dipsacus* and *Tamus*. Often recorded, especially on the latter host; see *Phomopsis Dipsaci* and *P. tamicola*, pp. 184, 230.

A fortunate discovery by Mr Rilstone at Polperro has enabled me to supplement the account given of *Phomopsis Coronillae* on p. 182:

Phomopsis Coronillae Trav.

Pycnidia very imperfect, forming little lanceolate or linear deep-black flecks, arranged in longitudinal series on the decorticated stem, immersed in the wood. Spores narrow-lanceolate or simply fusoid, very acute especially at the lower end, faintly and irregularly guttulate, $8\text{--}10 \times 2\text{--}2\cdot5\mu$; sporophores acicular, a little longer than the spore, 1μ broad. No B-spores seen.

On dead stems of *Coronilla glauca*, Polperro (Rilstone), April. Diaporthe-like stains were visible here and there on the stems, but no ascophores.

DIAGNOSES NOVARUM SPECIERUM

IN HOC VOLUMINE DESCRIPTARUM

Phyllosticta aquifolina Grove. Maculae parvae, rotundae, dein irregulares, 1–3 mm. diam., cinereo-fuscae, margine atro-brunneo. Pycnidia gregaria, 300–400 μ diam., atra. Sporulae oblongo-ellipsoideae, acutae, biguttulatae, $6\text{--}7 \times 2\text{--}2\cdot5\mu$; sporophoris filiformibus.

Hab. in foliis *Ilicis Aquifolii*. (Page 23.)

Asteroma euphorbiaceum Grove. Maculae rotundatae, parvae, 2–3 mm. diam., atro-brunneae, centro paulo dilutiores, plures in foliis singulis, in facie superiore magis conspicuae. Fibrillae obscurae, atrobrunneae, ramosae, subter epidermidem radiantes. Pycnidia minuta.

Hab. in foliis *Euphorbiae amygdaloidis*. (Page 145.)

Asteroma Ilicis Grove. Maculae plurimae in foliis singulis, indeterminatae, irregulares, confluentes, olivaceo-brunneae, fibris non visis.

Hab. in foliis *Ilicis Aquifolii*. (Page 145.)

Sphaeronaema floccosum Grove. Pycnidia cortici immersa, ± seriata, atra, nitida, ventre perfecte glabro; rostrum rectum, cylindricum, poro obtusissimo praeditum qui epidermidem nonnihil superat, floccis numerosis brunneis flexuosis patentibus instructum. Sporulae oblongae, utrinque obtusae, biguttulatae, $4\text{--}5 \times 1\text{--}1\cdot5\mu$.

Hab. in stipitibus emortuis *Cirsii arvensis*. (Page 158.)

Sphaeronaema mirabile Grove. Pycnidia subglobosa, basi ligno infossa, aterrima, subrugulosa, 140–160 μ diam., sursum subito in rostrum longissimum atrum cylindricum leniter curvatum attenuata; rostro vix basi 20 μ crasso, apicem versus non ciliatum 10 μ crasso,

800–1000 μ longo. Sporulae elliptico-fusoideae, obscure guttulatae, achroae, 5–7 × 2 μ.

Hab. in ligno emortuo friabili. Rostrum octogies longius quam crassum. (Page 162.)

Phomopsis Araucariae Grove. Pycnidia imperfecte evoluta, sparsa, globosa, 200–300 μ diam., atra, immersa, prominula, dein poro aut rima emergentia. A-sporulae lanceolato-fusoideae, deorsum magis acutatae, biguttulatae, 7–9 × 2–2·5 μ: B-sporulae filiformes, curvulae, interdum hamatae, 22–25 × 1·5 μ, A-sporulis immixtae.

Hab. in faciebus ambabus foliorum *Araucariae imbricatae* humi jacentium, socia Diaporthe immatura. (Page 181.)

Phomopsis brachyceras Grove. Pycnidia late sparsa, diu velata, globosa, circum circa haud denigrata, 300 μ diam. A-sporulae acute lanceolato-fusoideae, ferme biconicae, curvulae, 7–9 × 1·5–2 μ, sporophoris 15–20 × 1·5 μ: B-sporulae copiosae, filiformes, flexae, 20–24 × 1 μ.

Hab. in ramulis emortuis *Ligustri*. (Page 196.)

Phomopsis Choisyae Grove. Pycnidia dense sparsa, globosa, 400 μ diam., nigra, epidermide denigrata. A-sporulae fusoideae, biguttulatae, 9–10 × 1·5–2·5 μ: B-sporulae hamatae, 20–25 × 1 μ, immixtae.

Hab. in stipitibus vetustis emortuis *Choisyae ternatae*. (Page 172.)

Phomopsis Cirsii Grove. Pycnidia sparsa v. in stipitum striis seriata, oblonga, usque ad 500 μ longa, nigrescentia, mollia et imperfecte evoluta. A-sporulae paucissimae (et praecipue in foliis nidulantes), ellipsoideae, biguttulatae, 12–14 × 3–4 μ: B-sporulae stipatae, copiosissimae, filiformes, curvae, flexuosae v. plurimae hamatae, 20–30 × 0·7–1 μ, sporophoris brevissimis suffultae.

Hab. in stipitibus foliisque emortuis *Cirsiorum*. (Page 177.)

Phomopsis Escalloniae Grove. Pycnidia sparsa, velata, tarde emergentia. A-sporulae ovali-fusoideae, biguttulatae, 6–9 × 1·5–2 μ; sporophoris 14–16 × 2 μ: B-sporulae filiformes, curvatae, 28–30 × 1 μ.

Hab. in ramulis emortuis *Escalloniae macranthae*. (Page 184.)

Phomopsis ligulata Grove. Pycnidia magna, pulvinata, matricis aterrimâ epidermide circumfusa, loculis irregularibus praedita. A-sporulae ± oblongae, obscure biguttulatae, 6–8 × 1·7–2·5 μ, sporophoris linearibus, rectis, 10–15 × 1 μ: B-sporulae curvatae, 10–21 × 1 μ.

Hab. in ramis emortuis *Ulicis europaei*. (Page 231.)

Cytospora Baccharidis Grove. Stromata parva, sparsa, convexa, immersa, disco plano, atro-brunneo, saepe maculâ distinctâ fulvâ circumdata. Sporulae allantoideae, 5–7 × 1–1·5 μ, sporophoris filiformibus acutis rectis 12–15 × 1 μ suffultae.

Hab. in ramulis *Baccharidis halimifoliae*. (Page 261.)

Ceuthospora Rhododendri Grove. Pycnidia pauca, sparsissima, biformia. Sporulae stricte cylindricae, 13–18 v. longiores × 2–3 μ.
Hab. in foliis jacentibus diuque emortuis *Rhododendrorum* cultorum. (Page 292.)

Ascochyta Ilicis Grove. Pycnidia epiphylla, pauca, atra. Sporulae cylindrico-oblongae, diu continuae, denique uniseptatae, 4–5 × 2·5 μ.
Hab. in foliis *Ilicis Aquifolii*. (Page 304.)

Ascochyta Matricariae Grove. Maculae nullae. Pycnidia sparsa, rotunda v. oblonga, immersa, subglobosa, vix prominula, 130–200 μ diam., brunneola v. mellea, contextu tenui, pseudopycnidiali v. parenchymatico, dilute brunneolo. Sporulae oblongae, utrinque obtusissimae, hyalinae, eguttulatae, 1-septatae, haud constrictae, 9–10 × 3–4 μ.
Hab. in stipitibus emortuis *Matricariae Chamomillae*. (Page 306.)

Ascochyta sodalis Grove. Pycnidia iis *Septoriae Caricis* (quibuscum vigebant) forma atque digestione simillima, at multo minora, et contextu peridii parenchymatico e cellulis maximis (usque ad 20 μ latis) conflato. Sporulae ut in *Ascochyta graminicola*, evidentissime 1-septatae, 12–15 × 3–4·5 μ.
Hab. in apicibus foliorum *Caricis arenariae*. (Page 322.)

Ascochytula Phlomidis Grove. Pycnidia sparsa v. congregata, lenticularia, atro-brunnea, 100–120 μ diam., papillata, papilla epidermidem turriculae instar perforante, contextu plectenchymatico. Sporulae oblongo-fusoideae, 1-septatae, saepe ad septum flexae, etiam singulae luteolae ac coacervatae olivaceae, 7–10 × 2–3 μ.
Hab. in stipitibus emortuis *Phlomidis fruticosae*. (Page 329.)

Ascochytula Ulicis Grove. Pycnidia gregaria, lenticularia, immersa, atra, ca. 200 μ diam., contextu crassiusculo e cellulis obscuris minutis parenchymaticis conflato, poro pertusa. Sporulae fusoideae, utrinque acutae, 1-septatae, non constrictae, dilute olivaceo-flavae, 10–14 × 2 μ, sporophoris non visis.
Hab. in stipitibus emortuis *Ulicis europaei*. (Page 331.)

Diplodina Aloysiae Grove. Pycnidia sparsa, punctiformia, nigra, ca. 150 μ diam., contextu tenui, obscurato, parenchymatico, circa porum non obscuriore. Sporulae oblongae, utrinque rotundatae, 1-septatae, aliquando leniter constrictae, achroae, 8–10 × 2·5–3 μ.
Hab. in ramulis *Aloysiae citriodorae*. (Page 332.)

Diplodina Caricis Grove. Pycnidia late at dense sparsa, subglobosa, minima, ˙nigra, velata, dein papilla emergentia, contextu e cellulis dilute brunneis conflato, circa porum vix obscuriore. Sporulae copiosissimae, subcylindricae, utrinque leniter attenuatae, subrectae, distincte 1-septatae, haud constrictae, achroae, 13–16 × 3–4 μ.
Hab. in foliis emortuis *Caricis arenariae*. (Page 338.)

Diplodina Euphorbiae Grove. Pycnidia subsparsa, nitidula, immersa, dein erumpentia, ovalia, usque ad 1 mm. longa, nigra, epidermide fissâ; contextu crasso, molli, minute prosenchymatico. Sporulae ovali-fusoideae, hyalinae, 1-septatae, $14–16 \times 2·5–4·5 \mu$; sporophoris linearibus, 2μ crassis, quam spora paulo brevioribus.

Hab. in stipitibus emortuis *Euphorbiae palustris*. (Page 334.)

Septoria lunata Grove. Pycnidia laxe aggregata, atra, rotunda vel oblonga, depresso-convexa, interdum seriata, usque ad 160μ longa; contextu crasso, parenchymatico, atro-olivaceo. Sporulae anguste fusoideae, lunatae, utrinque acutatae, aliquando obscure seriato-guttulatae, sed plerumque hyalinae, $10–18 \times 1·5 \mu$.

Hab. in culmis *Moliniae*. (Page 424.)

Septoria solanicola Grove. Pycnidia subgregaria, immersa, globosa, atra, ca. 300μ diam.; contextu pseudopycnidiali, dilute olivaceo, circa porum obscuriore. Sporulae copiosae, lineares, raro curvatae, utrinque obtusatae, singulae hyalinae, acervatae dilute olivaceae, eseptatae vel obsolete uniseptatae, 2–5-guttulatae, $15–25 \times 1·7–2 \mu$.

Hab. in stipitibus *Solani Dulcamarae*. (Page 409.)

Rhabdospora Scrophulariae Grove. Pycnidia sparsa, epidermide velata, dein erumpentia, atra, $300–400 \mu$ diam., contextu tenui, fuscescente, circa porum obscuriore. Sporulae filiformes, plerumque curvatae vel arcuatae, raro rectae, utrinque acutae, guttulis minutis seriatis praeditae, $25–36 \times 1·5–2 \mu$, sporophoris linearibus, angustis, brevioribus suffultae.

Hab. in stipitibus emortuis *Scrophulariae nodosae*. (Page 440.)

INDEX OF HOSTS

INDEX OF BINOMIAL NAMES

In this Index no distinction is made between the specific names adopted
in the text and those regarded as synonyms.

CAMBRIDGE: PRINTED BY WALTER LEWIS, M.A., AT THE UNIVERSITY PRESS

REPRINTED 1967

BY PERMISSION
OF THE ORIGINAL PUBLISHER
BY
VERLAG VON J. CRAMER · 3301 LEHRE

PRINTED IN GERMANY

BIBLIOTHECA MYCOLOGICA

HERAUSGEGEBEN VON

 CRAMER

BAND 7

THE
TAXONOMY OF THE GENUS PHYTOPHTHORA DE BARY

by

C. M. TUCKER

REPRINT 1967

3301 LEHRE
VERLAG VON J. CRAMER

WHELDON & WESLEY, LTD. AND STECHERT-HAFNER SERVICE AGENCY, INC.
CODICOTE, HERTS.

NEW YORK, N.Y.